Neurotransmitters in Action

NEUROTRANSMITTERS

IN

ACTION

Edited by

David Bousfield

1985

ELSEVIER BIOMEDICAL PRESS
Amsterdam – New York – Oxford

ISBN: 0 444 80671 7

Published by
Elsevier Biomedical Press BV
P.O. Box 1527
1000 BM Amsterdam
The Netherlands

Sole distributors worldwide except for the U.S.A. and Canada
Elsevier Publications (Cambridge)
68 Hills Road
Cambridge CB2 1LA
United Kingdom

Sole distributors for the U.S.A. and Canada
Elsevier Science Publishing Company Inc.
52 Vanderbilt Avenue
New York, NY 10017, U.S.A.

Preface

This book surveys some of the most exciting recent advances in our understanding of chemical communication in the nervous system. The 44 articles republished here from *Trends in NeuroSciences* were chosen to highlight seven major themes: namely, mechanisms of action, neurotransmitter systems, the peptide 'explosion' and the impact of molecular genetics, substance P, opioid peptides and their receptors, dopamine and disease, and, finally, neurotransmitter actions on behaviour. Each of these areas is introduced by a specially commissioned review relating all the articles chosen to illustrate a particular theme. Because many of the reprinted articles are relevant to more than one theme the contents of the book have not been divided up.

Early work on transmitters focused on the relatively accessible neuromuscular junction, and in particular on fast-acting excitatory and inhibitory mechanisms. However neurotransmitters can say more than just 'yes' and 'no', and may not always act via conventional synapses. Roger Nicoll introduces these latest findings and reconsiders the criteria that must be satisfied in order for a substance to qualify as a neurotransmitter. The rate of discovery of new transmitters seemingly outstrips their possible functional usefulness. Jean Rossier introduces this complex topic and the articles themselves provide a primer on the molecular techniques which have made this progress possible; many hormones, including the hypothalamic releasing factors postulated by Geoffrey Harris, are found in neurons projecting throughout the CNS. These and many of the newer peptides have been found to coexist inside neurons which contain 'classical' transmitters such as acetylcholine and noradrenaline. Given this diversity, what use does the term 'neurotransmitter system' have – Piers Emson explains. Substance P and the opioids enkephalin and endorphin are now known to belong to families of peptides whose neurotransmitter status has been not only conserved, but elaborated upon during the course of evolution. Tom Jessell and M. D. Womack, and John Hughes respectively introduce the reviews in these two areas, building on the genetic theme introduced by Rossier. David Marsden discusses our present understanding of the role played by dopamine in various disease states; and finally Sue Iversen discusses the relevance of current research on the role of individual transmitter systems in the control of behaviour, in health and disease.

The book is intended for students, teachers and researchers who want a compact guide to some of the major themes in neuroscience today, and, in a modest way, I hope that both it and the magazine will help to hasten future discoveries.

DAVID BOUSFIELD, *Editor*

Acknowledgement

I would like to acknowledge both the help given to me by Drs Leslie Iversen and David Brown in the early stages of planning the collection, and the efforts of the authors themselves, many of whom have updated their original articles.

Contents

	page
Preface	v

Introductions

Mechanisms of action, *R. A. Nicoll* — 1
The peptide 'explosion' and the new genetics, *J. Rossier* — 4
Neurotransmitter systems, *P. C. Emson* — 6
Substance P and the novel mammalian tachykinins, *T. M. Jessell and M. D. Womack* — 10
Opioid peptides – families of receptors and neurotransmitters, *John Hughes* — 13
Dopamine and disease, *C. D. Marsden* — 17
Neurotransmitters and behaviour, *S. D. Iversen* — 20

Reviews

Evolution of neuropeptides, *Roger Acher* — 25
✶ Recombinant DNA strategies and techniques, *Robert J. Milner* — 34
~ New approaches to the identification and isolation of hormonal polypeptides, *Victor Mutt* — 41
~ New approaches to the study of rapid events underlying neurotransmitter action, *Robert N. McBurney* — 47
Slow cholinergic excitation – a mechanism for increasing neuronal excitability, *D. A. Brown* — 55
Inhibitory cholinergic synapses in autonomic ganglia, *John P. Horn and Jane Dodd* — 65
Neural regulation of the heart: a model for modulation of voltage-sensitive channels and regulation of cellular metabolism by neurotransmitters, *Tony Creazzo, Louisa Titus and Criss Hartzell* — 74
Modulation of gated ion channels as a mode of transmitter action, *S. A. Siegelbaum and R. W. Tsien* — 81
A LHRH-like peptidergic neurotransmitter capable of 'action at a distance' in autonomic ganglia, *Yuh Nung Jan and Lily Yeh Jan* — 94
Coexistence of peptides and classical neurotransmitters, *Jan M. Lundberg and Tomas Hökfelt* — 104
Purinergic mechanisms: recent electrophysiological evidence, *G. Burnstock* — 119
✶ A single gene encodes multiple peptide-transmitter candidates involved in a stereotyped behavior, *Richard H. Scheller, Barry S. Rothman and Earl Mayeri* — 123
Neurohormones and lobsters: biochemistry to behavior, *Edward A. Kravitz, Barbara S. Beltz, Silvio Glusman, Michael F. Goy, Ronald M. Harris-Warrick, Michael F. Johnston, Margaret S. Livingstone, Thomas L. Schwarz and Kathleen K. Siwicki* — 135
The history of substance P, *U. S. von Euler* — 143
The tachykinin peptide family, *Vittorio Erspamer* — 151
Three tachykinins in mammalian brain, *Anthony J. Harmer* — 157
Substance P – the first peptide neurotransmitter?, *Masanori Otsuka and Shiro Konishi* — 163

Substance P antagonists, *Michael R. Hanley*   170

Sir Thomas Lewis's nocifensor system, histamine and substance-P-
    containing primary afferent nerves, *F. Lembeck*   173

Capsaicin's action on the nervous system, *J. I. Nagy*   180

Multiple endogenous opioid peptides, *Volker Höllt*   188

Multiple endogenous ligands for opioid receptors, *Eckard Weber,*
    Christopher J. Evans and Jack D. Barchas   194

The case for multiple opiate receptors, *R. Suzanne Zukin and*
    Stephen R. Zukin   201

Metabolism of enkephalins and the inactivating neuropeptidase concept,
    Jean-Charles Schwartz   209

How do opiates act?, *Richard Miller*   216

How do opiates inhibit neurotransmitter release?, *R. Alan North and*
    John T. Williams   220

Peptide hormone gene expression in heterogeneous tissues: the pro-
    opiomelanocortin system, *James L. Roberts, Ching-Ling C. Chen,*
    France T. Dionne and Connie E. Gee   226

The mesocortico-prefrontal dopaminergic neurons, *J. Glowinski,*
    J. P. Tassin and A. M. Thierry   233

Dopamine receptors explained, *Ian Creese*   242

✳ Recent advances in the study of Parkinson's disease, *T. Andreo Larsen*
    and Donald B. Calne   252

✳ 'On–off' effects: the new challenge in parkinsonism, *Peter A. Lewitt and*
    Thomas N. Chase   257

✳ Dopamine-rich transplants in experimental parkinsonism,
    Stephen B. Dunnett, Anders Björklund and Ulf Stenevi   261

✳ The pathophysiological basis of tardive dyskinesia, *Ross J. Baldessarini* 270

Neurobiological substrates of tardive dyskinesia: the GABA hypothesis,
    Hans C. Fibiger and Kenneth G. Lloyd   275

✳ Two syndromes in schizophrenia?, *T. J. Crow*   279

✳ High dopamine in the left amygdala, *A. V. P. Mackay*   286

Antipsychotic drug effects on the electrical activity of dopaminergic
    neurons, *Benjamin S. Bunney*   289

✳ Acetylcholine, aging and Alzheimer's disease: implications for treatment,
    Suzanne Corkin   297

✳ What is the importance of vasopressin in memory processes?, *Don M. Gash*
    and Garth J. Thomas   305

The anatomy of the CNS cholinergic neurons, *A. Claudio Cuello and*
    Michael V. Sofroniew   309

Monoamines and peptides in cerebral cortex: contrasting principles of
    cortical organization, *John H. Morrison and Pierre J. Magistretti*   319

Vasopressin and oxytocin in the mammalian brain and spinal cord,
    Michael V. Sofroniew   329

NPY – a new member of the pancreatic polypeptide family, *P. C. Emson*
    and M. E. De Quidt   338

Mechanisms of action

Our understanding of the processes involved in neuronal signalling is derived in large part from studies on the squid giant axon and the vertebrate neuromuscular junction. These studies have led to the concept that there are two categories of ion channels in nerve cell membranes. In the first category are the ligand-gated channels. The nicotinic acetylcholine (ACh) receptor at the vertebrate neuromuscular junction provides the best example of this type of channel. The channel opens only when ACh binds to the receptor. The synaptic potential, which lasts for only a few milliseconds, results from the flow of sodium and potassium ions through the channel. Changes in membrane potential are entirely ineffective in opening this channel, although when opened by ACh, the channel does exhibit a small voltage-sensitivity. The second category of channel is controlled by the voltage of the membrane. The best characterized channel in this category is the sodium channel which is responsible for action potential generation[1]. Nerve cell membranes can also possess voltage-dependent calcium channels as well as a variety of voltage-dependent potassium channels[2].

Traditionally it has been held that transmitters act solely by opening ion channels which are otherwise undetectable and do not contribute to the resting current-voltage relationship. This has been shown to be true for a large number of transmitters. By acting on different receptors, different transmitters or in some cases even the same transmitter, can open different types of ion channels. Depending on the type of channel opened, the transmitter will either depolarize and excite the cell or hyperpolarize and inhibit it. Virtually all of the synaptic potentials analysed in the vertebrate CNS conform to this scheme.

During the past decade studies on invertebrate and vertebrate ganglion neurons as well as vertebrate heart muscle have made it increasing clear that ion channels controlled by membrane voltage can also be affected by transmitters. Not only can well-established transmitters, such as norepinephrine and acetylcholine, act on voltage-dependent channels, but so also can the newly discovered peptide transmitters. Many of the reviews referred to here deal with the issue of transmitters acting on voltage-dependent channels.

If transmitters can act on voltage-dependent channels, how might this affect neuronal signalling? In attempting to answer this question, it is important to realize that for most neurons, two sites control the output; the initial segment and the nerve terminal. At the initial segment, transmitters acting on voltage/calcium-dependent channels can control the number of impulses that can be produced by a given excitatory input. At the presynaptic nerve terminal the amount of transmitter released per impulse can be altered by transmitters acting on the terminal.

Let us focus, for the moment, on the initial segment. In many neurons the frequency of action potential discharge falls off or adapts during a constant depolarizing stimulus. Two mechanisms are responsible for this adaptation: the M-current, which is a voltage-dependent potassium current, and the calcium-dependent potassium current. Both of these currents turn on slowly when the cell is depolarized and act as a brake to limit further discharge. As discussed later in this volume by **David Brown***, the M-current in sympathetic ganglia is blocked by synaptically released ACh acting on muscarinic receptors. As a result, the brake is released so that the cell fires many more action potentials for a given depolarization. An important observation is that this same current is blocked by a number of other transmitters including the peptide LHRH (see below). In hippocampal pyramidal cells the calcium dependent potassium current plays a role similar to that of the M-current in sympathetic ganglion cells. It too can be blocked by a number of transmitters[3].

Now let us consider the second site which controls the output of the neuron, i.e. the presynaptic nerve terminal. In general transmitters either facilitate or inhibit transmitter release by changing the amount of free intracellular calcium involved in exocytosis. Theoretically this can occur by (1) a direct action on voltage-sensitive calcium channels, (2) an indirect action resulting from changes in the morphology of the presynaptic action potential, or (3) an alteration in the buffering of calcium in the presynaptic terminal. Since one cannot record intracellularly from most nerve terminals, the analysis has usually involved (1) recording from the soma of the neuron, with the expectation that similar processes might occur at the nerve terminal, or (2) measuring transmitter release either chemically or by recording from the postsynaptic cell. A number of articles in this section address transmitter modulation of transmitter release. Serotonin can facilitate transmitter release at a number of synapses and two mechanisms appear to be involved. **Siegelbaum and Tsien** discuss the mechanism involved in facilitation of transmitter release for *Aplysia* sensory neurons by serotonin. Serotonin blocks a specific potassium channel which broadens the presynaptic action potential, thereby increasing the amount of transmitter released. At the lobster neuromuscular junction **Kravitz** and his colleagues have shown that serotonin also facilitates neurotransmitter release. However, at this synapse serotonin is thought to decrease the buffering of calcium in the nerve terminal. It is well known that opiates reduce transmitter release and it has been suggested that this might result from a direct effect on calcium channels (see **Miller**, also Ref. 4). Based on the finding that opiates can open potassium channels in the cell body of certain neurons, **North and Williams** propose that, at least in some systems, opiates may decrease calcium entry into nerve terminals indirectly by increasing potassium conductance. In this case, then, opiates would decrease transmitter release by acting in a conventional manner. The most convincing evidence that transmitters can directly modulate calcium channels comes from studies on the facilitatory action of β-adrenergic agonists on calcium currents in heart muscle (see **Creazzo et al.,** also **Siegelbaum and Tsien**). Based upon the analysis of single channels using the patch clamp technique (see **McBurney**) it appears that β-receptor activation may increase both the probability of calcium channel opening[5] and the number of functional calcium channels[6]. Another transmitter which may act on presynaptic terminals, although the mechanism is not understood, is dopamine. Indeed, specific receptor types may be associated with presynaptic, as opposed to postsynaptic membranes (see **Creese**).

Voltage-dependent channels are distributed over large areas of membrane, whereas the subsynaptic membrane is very restricted and may in fact not contain

---

* When referred to, the authors of review articles published in this volume will be highlighted in **bold**.

voltage-dependent channels. How then do transmitters exert their effects on voltage-dependent channels? This spatial problem has been solved in three ways. First, many of the effects on voltage-dependent channels are mediated by diffusible intracellular second messengers, such as cyclic AMP (**Creazzo et al.; Siegelbaum and Tsien; Kravitz et al.**). Second, the fiber systems that contain transmitters that act on voltage-dependent channels are usually extraordinarily diffuse, thus having the opportunity of influencing large areas of the cell (**Morrison and Magistretti**). Third, some transmitters may be able to diffuse an appreciable distance from their site of release, allowing them to act on areas of membrane that are not in the immediate vicinity of the synapse and, indeed, on neurons that are not directly contacted by the presynaptic fiber (**Jan and Jan**). These factors may in turn explain another fundamental property of transmitters that act on voltage-dependent channels: their slow time course. This is particularly characteristic of peptide transmitters (see below) and may be the only feature, aside from their different mode of synthesis, which separates them from non-peptide transmitters. The long duration of action appears to result primarily from the long lifetime of the peptide in the external environment of the cell (**Jan and Jan**). The duration of action is not the same for all peptides and it has been proposed that the structure of the peptide and therefore its susceptibility to proteolysis may explain this difference (**Scheller et al.**). Indeed, it has been shown (**Schwartz**) that the effects of enkephalin on target cells can be potentiated by selective peptidase inhibitors, thus supporting the idea that the duration of peptidergic signals is determined not only by diffusion but also by enzymatic degradation.

A major recent discovery which is emphasized, not only in this section but throughout this book, is that peptides clearly play an important role in interneuronal communication. The elegant work of **Otsuka and Konishi** on substance P, and **Jan and Jan** on LHRH, convincingly show that these two peptides fulfil all of the criteria required for establishing a substance as a transmitter. Even more intriguing is the realization that peptide transmitters can coexist in the same terminals with classical transmitters, or with other peptide transmitters derived from the same gene. The advantages conferred on a system by the use of multiple transmitters is only beginning to be understood. **Scheller et al.** suggest that the multiple peptides released from the bag cells of *Aplysia* could provide a way of co-ordinating events in the egg-laying program. In the frog sympathetic ganglion where ACh and LHRH are released from the same terminals (**Jan and Jan**), **Horn and Dodd** suggest that such a system can provide for a patterned firing of the postsynaptic cell. They have found that synaptically released ACh directly inhibits the C-cells of certain autonomic ganglia by increasing potassium conductance and that this effect lasts for a few seconds. On the other hand, as shown by others, LHRH decreases potassium conductance which results in intense discharge that lasts for minutes. If the presynaptic fiber is again stimulated during this discharge the inhibitory action of ACh will briefly interrupt this firing.

The issue of coexistence is discussed in detail by **Lundberg and Hökfelt** (see also **Burnstock**) who provide a particularly intriguing example of how co-transmitters may interact on the postsynaptic cell. They have found that the peptide VIP coexists with ACh in the parasympathetic fibers to the submandibular salivary gland of the cat. Although VIP alone does not cause secretion, it can potentiate the secretory action of ACh (see also introductory section by

Emson). VIP appears to cause this potentiation by increasing the affinity of muscarinic receptors for ACh.

In summary the papers referred to in this introduction deal with a number of new and exciting topics in the field of synaptic transmission, including (1) transmitter action on voltage dependent ion channels, (2) the role of peptides as transmitters and (3) the coexistence of transmitters. There can be no doubt that we are in the midst of a revolution in our understanding of the mechanisms by which neurons communicate with each other.

R. A. NICOLL

Departments of Pharmacology and Physiology, University of California School of Medicine, San Francisco, CA 94143, USA.

Reading list
1 Catterall, W. A. (1984) *Science* 223, 653–661
2 Adams, P. R. (1982) *Trends NeuroSci* 5, 116–119
3 Madison, D. V. and Nicoll, R. A. (1982) *Nature (London)* 299, 636–638
4 Mudge, A. W., Leeman, S. E. and Fischbach, G. D. (1979) *Proc. Natl Acad. Sci. USA* 76, 526–530
5 Cachelin, A. G., de Peyer, J. E., Kokubun, S. and Reuter, H. (1983) *Nature (London)* 304, 462–464
6 Beam, B. P., Nowycky, M. C. and Tsien, R. W. (1984) *Nature (London)* 307, 371–375

The peptide 'explosion' and the new genetics

In the early seventies it was widely believed that most of the important neurotransmitters utilized by the brain had been discovered. It was thought that the CNS could function effectively with the dozen or so known excitatory or inhibitory substances, an assumption reflected in much theoretical modelling of brain function even today. This complaicency has been completely shattered by the recent rapid (and continuing) increase in the number of putative neurotransmitters – currently totalling around 50. Many of these new substances are peptides and it has been the application of molecular genetic techniques that has been largely responsible for their discovery. Indeed it is not unrealistic to expect many more neuroactive peptides to be discovered in the years to come. The neurotransmitter 'explosion', together with the discovery of coexistence and slow transmitter actions, has made the study of information flow in the nervous system an increasingly complex topic.

During the late sixties and early seventies the usual procedure leading to the isolation and identification of a new neurotransmitter began with the discovery of some salient feature of the substances' physiology or pharmacology. For example, substance P was originally identified in tissue extracts by its effects on smooth muscle motility and non-cholinergic pharmacology (see article by **von Euler**). A similar strategy led to the discovery of the various hypothalamic releasing hormones following Geoffrey Harris' hypothesis that hypophyseal secretion was controlled by factors in portal blood released by the hypothalamus. Here too most of the factors were found to be peptides. The first to be characterized was TRH, then came LHRH and somatostatin, and more recently, CRF and GRH. The discovery of enkephalins provides another example of this 'logical' approach to the discovery of new transmitters. Ten years ago it was shown that opiate drugs produced their psychotropic actions via a specific type of receptor, and this led naturally to the search for an endogenous ligand, culminating in the discovery of the enkephalins and, later, the endorphins.

Although modern chromatographic techniques provide highly sensitive methods for isolating any peptide present in an extract, the amount of tissue that must be processed is often prohibitively large. One novel approach is to design techniques which 'recognize' molecular features common to other, already-characterized neuropeptides. For example, around 50% of the peptides that may play a neurotransmitter role in the brain are amidated at their C-terminus. This observation led Tatemoto to search for amidated peptides in brain and in the gut with an assay specific for amidated peptides leading to the discovery of several new peptides (NPY, PPY, PYY, PHI etc.). (See article by **Viktor Mutt**.) In contrast, recombinant DNA techniques provide far greater sensitivity and when used simply as a method of determining peptide sequences offers the bonus of providing information on the structure of the preprohormone and on the organization of the gene itself (see articles by **Milner, Hollt, Harmar,** and **Scheller** *et al.*). However, a less desirable consequence of the power of the new genetic techniques has been what one commentator has dubbed 'an embarrassment of peptides', an attitude that is neatly summarized in the opening paragraph of his article; viz. 'As molecular biology sweeps through pastures new, it tends to generate a mixture of despair, excitement and frustration in roughly equal parts. The despair is of those who see the limelight shifting to the molecular upstarts. The excitement stems from the amount of new information that is generated in short order by the new techniques. And the frustration comes in trying to translate the molecular information back into physiological terms'[1].

Time alone will tell whether this view is overly pessimistic. Certainly the discovery of gene families such as the group encoding the prepro-opiomelanocortin, and preprodynorphin precursor molecules has led to a great simplification in our understanding of opioid peptides (see articles by **Hollt** and by **Weber** *et al.*). A similar breakthrough seems close for the tachykinin peptide family, of which the best known member is substance P (see articles by **Erspamer** and by **Harmar**). As data on these gene families accumulates we may begin to reap some rewards in terms of our understanding of the evolution of neurotransmitter systems (**Acher**), their tissue specific regulation (**Roberts** *et al.*), and their role in the integration of complex behavioral patterns (**Scheller** *et al.*).

However there are caveats which must be borne in mind. It is possible that not all of these newly discovered peptides have a function. An example of that proposal is given in the paper on POMC by **Roberts** *et al*. Pro-opiomelanocortin (POMC) the precursor for ACTH and β-endorphin is also the precursor for α-MSH. This latter hormone is a skin-darkening hormone in frogs. This role has been lost in higher vertebrates and in humans the intermediate lobe, that normally secretes α-MSH, no longer exists. Thus, in humans the presence of α-MSH may have no physiological relevance and may simply be a vestige of evolution.

We are thus at a turning point in our understanding of brain function and we need to think more carefully of the role these new molecules might play in information transmission. Before the era of molecular genetics, physiologists thought they were in front of a jigsaw puzzle with a few missing pieces. Now some feel they have only a handful of pieces and, what is worse, no idea where to put them.

J. ROSSIER

CNRS, Laboratoire de Physiologie Nerveuse, 91190 Gif sur Yvette, France.

Reading list
1 Newmark, P. (1983) Nature (London) 303, 655

Neurotransmitter systems

In the 1960s a review of the organization of the mammalian CNS would probably have distinguished two classes of transmitter candidates, the biogenic amines (acetylcholine, noradrenaline, dopamine and 5-hydroxytryptamine) and the amino acids (γ-aminobutyric acid, glutamic acid, aspartic acid and glycine[1]). Of these various candidates only acetylcholine, acting at the neuromuscular junction fulfilled all the various criteria established by the physiologists for acceptance as a neurotransmitter[2,3]. Noticeably absent from our list of putative transmitters would have been the neuropeptides which, with perhaps a token glance towards substance P (see **von Euler**, also Ref. 4), would have been discussed only in relation to the neurohypophyseal hormones, vasopressin and oxytocin, and the 'dubious' occurrence of the hypothalamic releasing hormones proposed by Geoffrey Harris[5].

Since this date the neurosciences have experienced a positive deluge of information about the chemical organization of the mammalian brain based on developing histochemical and immunological techniques for visualizing monoamines, transmitter synthesizing enzymes and the ubiquitous neuropeptides. In particular, the burgeoning number of biologically active neuropeptides occurring in specific identifiable neurones means that the structural units of the brain are gradually breaking down into smaller and chemically distinct sub-systems, each of which may possibly act as a functional unit. The other conceptual advance that has arisen from the neuropeptide revolution has been the realization that some, or perhaps all neurones, contain two or more putative transmitters. These histochemical observations on coexistence, due in large part to the pioneering studies of Tomas Hökfelt and his colleagues[6], mean that the physiological regulation of neuronal activity is likely to be considerably more complex than originally envisaged, and the potential for synergistic or antagonistic interactions between transmitters is considerable.

Examples of coexistence are now numerous (see **Lundberg and Hökfelt, Burnstock** also Ref. 7), though in most cases the function of such coexistence is only poorly understood. One interesting example, where vasoactive intestinal polypeptide (VIP) coexists with acetylcholine in parasympathetic neurones innervating exocrine glands, has been studied in detail by Lundberg and colleagues[8]; it is worth examining here in a little detail as it may provide a model for the type of interacting control we are likely to find as we discover and study other examples of coexistence.

Histochemical studies have shown that the parasympathetic neurones innervating the cat salivary gland contain VIP-like immunoreactivity and are acetyl-cholinesterase-positive, consistent with these neurones containing both VIP and acetylcholine. Physiological studies show that nerve stimulation releases acetyl-choline which in turn enhances salivary secretion, and contributes to the vasodilation following stimulation. However, there is a component of the vasodilatory response, not blocked by the muscarinic cholinergic antagonist atropine, that is due to VIP released from the parasympathetic fibres innervating the gland. This synergism between VIP and acetylcholine (ACh) is most interesting. Application of VIP produces a small vasodilation and application of ACh produces some secretion, but application of the same amount of each transmitter together produces a response which is much greater than each individual response. This synergistic interaction has been investigated further and it has been shown that VIP will enhance the binding of muscarinic antagonists to salivary gland membranes, and further that muscarinic agonists will potentiate the formation of cAMP catalysed by VIP acting at its receptors. How these interactions between distinct receptors present in the cell membrane are mediated remains to be established.

Apart from its presence in peripheral parasympathetic ganglia, VIP is one of an increasing group of neuroactive peptides also found in interneurones in the cerebral cortex (**Morrison and Magistretti** and Ref. 9). These peptides include VIP, neuropeptide Y (NPY), somatostatin and cholecystokinin (CCK). It is also presumably no coincidence that two peptides which are vasoactive, the potent vasodilator VIP and vasoconstrictor NPY are found in similar cerebral cortical neurones[10]. Our original observations on the organization of cerebral cortical interneurones, such as those containing VIP, CCK or NPY, indicated that these cells may be suitably placed to receive thalamic inputs and to respond to such a stimulus by activating local neurones and enhancing local blood flow. This idea was developed further by Morrison and Magistretti who suggested that the cortical noradrenergic neurones providing a diffuse tangential innervation might activate large areas of cortex whilst the VIP, and presumably also the NPY and CCK cells might provide a more discrete local effect. This scheme has been extended recently by work of Magistretti and Schorderet[11], who showed that α-adrenergic agonists and VIP, although acting through separate receptors, interact synergistically to increase the cAMP formation catalysed by each agonist. This observation suggests that a general activation of cortical activity, produced by activation of the locus coeruleus noradrenergic neurones, would also result in an amplification of the much more localized response to activation of the VIP cortical neurones. Recently, to complicate this story further, it has been demonstrated that the cortical VIP neurones, like the peripheral parasympathetic neurones containing ACh and VIP, are also cholinergic neurones[12].

Although the presence of some intrinsic cholinergic cortical interneurones has now been confirmed by immunocytochemistry for the marker enzyme choline acetyltransferase (ChAT), the main cholinergic innervation to the cerebral cortex arises from ascending fibres, originating principally from the basal fore brain cholinergic neurones, which in primates form the nucleus basalis or substantia inominata (**Cuello and Sofroniew**). These neurones, like many other amine-containing neurones, can be thought of as autonomic sympathetic or parasympathetic neurones translocated into the CNS, and they share with neurones of this type containing serotonin, noradrenaline, and dopamine their high content of acetylcholinesterase and ability to accumulate biogenic amines (i.e. they belong to a class of neurones Pearse termed APUD cells – *a*mine *p*recursor *u*ptake and *d*ecarboxylation[13]). So far, the coexistence of a peptide or peptides with the majority of cholinergic basal fore-brain neurones has not been demonstrated, but it is likely that peptide transmitters will be found in these cells.

Apart from the interest that the phenomenon of coexistence produces, it has also enabled us to subdivide the class of previously apparently 'homogeneous' monoamine neurones. Thus immunocytochemical techniques distinguish CCK and neurotensin (NT)-positive mesencephalic dopamine neurones contributing to the mesolimbic dopamine system, providing a chemical distinction between these meso-limbic dopamine neurones and the meso-striatal dopamine neurones projecting to the basal ganglia[14]. The meso-cortical neurones of the meso-limbic dopamine system are also characterized by high rates of dopamine turnover and the absence of inhibitory presynaptic autoreceptors (see **Glowinski *et al.*** for discussion). Our own studies[15,16], suggest that many dopamine neurones may carry presynaptic neurotensin receptors capable of potentiating dopamine release. In a similar fashion CCK-octapeptide (CCK-8) has also been shown to inhibit dopamine release[17]. In this situation local release of CCK or NT from the terminals of dopamine neurones in which they coexist may allow for positive feed-forward and negative feed-back mechanisms to control dispamine release. Thus, in the cerebral cortex (where there are apparently no presynaptic inhibitory dopamine autoreceptors[18]), dopamine release may be regulated by co-released peptides, or alternatively influenced by local CCK-containing, or NT-containing neurones[19].

Functionally, CNS APUD neurones, whether noradrenergic, cholinergic, serotoninergic or dopaminergic, seem to serve a modulatory role by providing a diffuse signal to the area innervated without providing much patterned information content. This point is nicely illustrated by studies in rat in which neurotoxins or lesions remove dopaminergic or cholinergic innervation of the striatum or cerebral cortex[20,21]. Removal of the amines results in behavioural effects which can be at least partially reversed by transplantion of dopaminergic or cholinergic neurones to the denervated area (see **Dunnet and Björklund**). In this situation, in which the graft is not connected to its normal inputs and controls, it seems to act like a mini pump liberating acetylcholine or dopamine to the region reinnervated.

As noted earlier it is reasonable to regard the monoamine containing APUD neurones as autonomic ganglia translocated into the CNS. A further part of this autonomic system, and intimately connected to the CNS APUD neurones, are the magnocellular hypothalamic neurones containing neurohypophyseal hormones (see **Sofroniew**). These magnocellular neurones are the archetypal mammalian peptidergic neurones, and primarily innervate the neural lobe controlling lactation and diuresis. In addition they project to other parts of the autonomic system including the substantia nigra (dopamine), solitary tract (noradrenaline), vagal nuclei (acetycholine), locus coeruleus (noradrenaline) and raphé (5-hydroxytryptamine), providing the possibility of influencing aminergic neurones (such as those in the locus coeruleus) innervating and controlling the magnocellular neurones. Two other features of these neurones are of interest: the first one is the now expected coexistence of various peptides, with the neurohypophyseal hormones (which is even more complicated than in the APUD neurones, see **Lundberg and Hökfelt**); and the second is that there is an evolutionary series of vasopressin and oxytocin analogues[22] with different hormone sequences characterizing the different vertebrate classes (see **Acher**). In this respect the neurohypophyseal hormones may be unusual (although this has not been examined in detail) as most other neuroactive peptides, or at least the biologically active sequence, are strongly conserved during evolution. Thus NT-like immunoreactivity has been reported in bacteria[23], and in the simple nervous system of the coelenterate *Hydra*, substance P, CCK, NT and enkephalin-like immunoreactivity have all been reported[24]. Furthermore a peptide sequenced from *Hydra* (Hydra-head-activating-peptide) seems also to be found in the mammalian brain[25].

This type of information suggests that many of the peptide/transmitters that we are familiar with in mammals developed early in evolution, perhaps as local paracrine hormones, and have been preserved during evolution. So far a systematic study of, for example, substance P-like peptides has not been made through the phylla but it will be fascinating to see how amino acid substitutions and/or additional peptide hormones arise following gene mutation or gene duplication. It does seem clear that a physiologically active sequence, such as that in the carboxy-terminus of substance P, will be conserved, and the peptide may be used at any level of development or evolution when a particular physiological effect is required. Of course, it is likely that there will be a parallel development and evolution of the relevant receptor but nothing is yet known of the phyllogeny of receptor structure.

To conclude, transmitter histochemistry now enables the visualisation of neurotransmitter subsystems, and will continue to reveal more and more detail in what had originally been considered to be homogeneous systems. It is important to recognize that this complexity, and the variety and subtlety of cellular regulation that this implies, is an essential to understanding of the way the brain works. To echo Floyd Bloom, we will continue to find 'that the gains in the brain are mainly in the stain'.

P. C. EMSON

MRC Neurochemical Pharmacology Unit, Medical Research Council Centre, Medical School, Hills Road, Cambridge, CB2 2QH, UK.

Reading list

1 Cooper, J. R., Bloom, F. E. and Roth, R. H. (1970) in *The Biochemical Basis of Neuropharmacology*, Oxford University Press, Oxford
2 Orrego, F. (1979) *Neuroscience* 4, 1037–1057
3 Werman, R. (1966) *Comp. Biochem. Physiol.* 18, 745–766
4 von Euler, U. S. and Gaddum, J. B. (1931) *J. Physiol. (London)* 72, 74–87
5 Harris, G. W. (1948) *Physiol. Rev.* 28, 137–179
6 Hökfelt, T., Lundberg, J., Schultzberg, M., Johansson, O., Skirboll, L., Änggård, A., Fredholm, B., Hamberger, G., Pernow, B., Rehfeld, J. and Goldstein, M. (1980) *Proc. Soc. London Ser. B* 210, 63–77
7 Gilbert, R. F. T. and Emson, P. C. (1983) in *Handbook of Psychopharmacology* (Iversen, L. L., Iversen, S. D. and Snyder, S. H., eds), Vol. 16, pp. 519–556, Plenum Press, New York
8 Lundberg, J. M. (1981) *Acta Physiol. Scand.* 115, 525–528
9 Emson, P. C. and Hunt, S. P. (1981) in *The Organisation of the Cerebral Cortex* (Schmitt, F. O., Worden, F. G., Adelman, G. and Dennis, S. G., eds), pp. 325–346, M.I.T. Press, Cambridge
10 Emson, P. C. and De Quidt, M. E. (1984) *Trends NeuroSci.* 7, 31–35
11 Magistretti, P. J. and Schorderet, M. (1984) *Nature (London)* 308, 280–282

12 Eckenstein, F. and Baughman, R. (1984) *Nature (London)* (in press)

13 Pearse, A. G. E. (1968) *Proc. R. Soc. London Ser.* B 170, 71–80

14 Björklund, A. and Lindvall, O. (1978) in *Handbook of Psychopharmacology* (Iversen, L. L., Iversen, S. D. and Snyder, S. H., eds), Vol. 9, pp. 139–231, Plenum Press, New York

15 De Quidt, M. E. and Emson, P. C. (1983) *Brain Res.* 274, 376–380

16 De Quidt, M. E. and Emson, P. C. (1983b) *Neurosci. Lett.* Suppl. 14, S89

17 Markstein, R. and Hökfelt, T. (1984) *J. Neurosci* 4, 570–576

18 Bannon, M. J. and Roth, H. (1983) *Pharmacol. Rev.* 35, 53–68

19 Hara, Y., Shiosaka, S., Seraba, E., Sakanaka, M., Inagaki, S., Takagi, H., Kawa, Y., Takatsuki, K., Matsuzaki, T. and Tohyama, M. (1982) *J. Comp. Neurol.* 208, 177–183

20 Björklund, A., Dunnett, S. B., Stenevi, U., Lewis, M. E. and Iversen, S. D. (1980) *Brain Res.* 199, 307–333

21 Fine, A., Dunnett, S. R., Björklund, A. and Iversen, S. D. *Nature (London)* (in press)

22 Acher, R. (1980) *Proc. R. Soc. London Ser. B* 210, 21–43

23 Bhatnagar, Y. M. and Carraway, R. (1981) *Peptides* 2, 51–59

24 Grimmelikhuijzen, C. P. J., Balfe, A., Emson, P. C., Powell, D. and Sunmdler, F. (1981) *Histochemistry*, 71, 325–333

25 Bodenmuller, H. and Schaller, H. C. (1980) *Nature (London)* 293, 579–580

Substance P and the novel mammalian tachykinins

The isolation and characterization of substance P by Leeman and colleagues in the early 1970s has been responsible for much of the interest over the last decade in the potential role of peptides as synaptic transmitters in the nervous system. The presence of substance P in the cell bodies and terminals of small-diameter primary sensory neurons has focused particular attention on the actions of peptides on peripheral and central sensory targets. With the demonstration that substance P is released from the terminals of primary sensory neurons in sympathetic ganglia, and that it mediates slow excitatory synaptic potentials, **Konishi and Otsuka** have established that substance P can act as a synaptic transmitter. Substance P is also released from the central terminals of primary sensory neurons and recent studies have indicated that it is probably one of the transmitters that mediates the slow excitatory potentials that can be recorded in spinal cord neurons following dorsal root stimulation[1,2].

It is likely, however, that many of the physiological roles previously attributed to substance P may in fact be mediated by other peptides. One of the primary reasons for this reassessment has been the isolation and structural characterization of two new mammalian tachykinin peptides, substance K and neuromedin K (see **Harmar**). Substance K derives from the same polyprotein precursor that encodes substance P, and may be expressed and released obligatorily by all neurons that process this precursor. Evidence that these two peptides could have different physiological actions derives from the pharmacological characterization of multiple receptor subclasses for synthetic and naturally occurring tachykinin peptides (see **Erspamer** and Ref. 3). Iversen and colleagues[3] have provided evidence that the variation in biological activity of tachykinin peptides in different bioassay systems reflects the presence of two distinct receptor sub-types. Substance P and physalaemin interact preferentially with receptors of the substance

P-P subclass, whereas the tachykinins eledoisin and kassinin represent ligands with selectivity for substance P-E sites. Substance K is a potent agonist in bioassay systems that express substance P-E sites,[4,5] suggesting that it may be one of the mammalian ligands for this class of receptor.

The presence of multiple endogenous tachykinins and several different tachykinin receptors may begin to explain some of the discrepancies that have arisen from a comparison of the distribution of substance P and its receptors in the CNS. Substance P-containing neurons that originate in the caudate-putamen supply the substantia nigra with an extremely dense plexus of immunoreactive nerve terminals. Autoradiographic studies to map the distribution of substance P receptors, using radiolabelled substance P, have revealed a complete absence of binding sites in this region[6]. One explanation for this surprising observation is that nigral neurons may express, exclusively, the substance P-E receptor site. If autoradiographic studies confirm this possibility, substance K may represent the physiologically relevant tachykinin released from striato-nigral neurons.

While most of the excitatory effects of substance P seem to be mediated by the activation of specific tachykinin receptors, the inhibitory actions which have been described result from the modulation of receptors for other transmitters. The most intensely studied of these interactions has been the inhibition of nicotinic cholinergic responses, first described at motoneuron collateral synapses with Renshaw cells in the spinal cord, and subsequently examined in more detail on adrenal chromaffin cells and on the PC-12 cell line[7]. Studies on PC-12 cells indicate that substance P produces this effect by enhancing agonist-induced desensitization of nicotinic receptors. A kinetic analysis of the effects of substance P on carbachol-activated ion channels in chromaffin cells has led to similar conclusions[8]. Single channel studies are consistent with a model in which substance P stabilizes the desensitized state of the nicotinic receptor, but have not ruled out the possibility that the peptide produces a carbachol-dependent ion channel blockade.

Recent biochemical studies have demonstrated that the ability of substance P to inhibit nicotinic responses is critically dependent on conservation of both the N- and C-terminal amino acid sequence[9]. Moreover, the actions of substance P are not mimicked by physalaemin or eledoisin, suggesting that substance P-P and substance P-E receptors do not mediate these effects. While there may then be a third class or tachykinin receptor, it is possible that substance P binds in a selective manner to sites on, or near, the nicotinic receptor. Since micromolar concentrations of substance P are necessary to inhibit nicotinic responses, and the peptide concentration at synaptic sites is unknown, the physiological role of substance P induced nicotinic modulation is unclear. Resolution of the problem may be difficult. The low potency of substance P at this site effectively precludes the use of synthetic substance P antagonists (**Hanley**) that have been important in establishing the role of substance P as a synaptic transmitter acting via conventional tachykinin receptors.

A second example of modulatory interactions, this time between substance P and β-adrenergic ligands has recently been described. Substance P enhances the ability of β-adrenergic agonists to increase levels of cyclic AMP in cultured astrocytes, although there is no demonstrable effect of the peptide when administered alone[10]. At present it is unclear whether the enhancement of β-adrenergic responses is mediated by the activation of tachykinin receptors or by a modulation of β-adrenergic sites.

These studies, showing an effect of substance P on astrocytes, make it clear that any future assessment of the function of substance P within the CNS will have to include analysis of its actions on both neuronal and glial cells. The neural regulation of cerebral blood flow is an example of a system where such an interaction could have important physiological consequences. Cerebral blood vessels are richly innervated by substance P-containing nerve fibres and terminals which derive from sensory neurons located in the trigeminal ganglion[11]. The majority of sensory terminals actually make contact with endothelial cells that surround the vascular smooth muscle. The vasoactive effects of substance P appear to be dependent on the release, from endothelial cells, of an unidentified vasodilatory agent[12]. Endothelial cells also respond to β-adrenergic agents with an increase in cyclic AMP production that may trigger the secretion of the endo-thelial-derived vasodilatory agent. The enhancement of β-adrenergic responses by substance P released from sensory terminals could, therefore, represent a mechanism by which peptides regulate cerebral vascular permeability and blood flow.

The role of substance P released from the peripheral terminals of sensory neurons in cutaneous structures has been examined in detail, and there is now convincing evidence for its involvement in mediation of antidromic vasodilation (see **Lembeck**). The actions of substance P released from these terminals may not, however, be confined to neuronal and vascular targets in the vicinity of the sensory ending. Receptors for substance P have recently been described on subpopulations of T lymphocytes[13] and activation of these receptors leads to T cell proliferation. The stimulatory effects of substance P are abolished by synthetic substance P antagonists, indicating that the receptor present on lymphocytes resembles the tachykinin receptors found on neurons and secretory cells. These observations raise the possibility that peptides may play a physiological role in regulating the immune response and in triggering a variety of cellular events that modify the sensitivity of the primary sensory ending[14].

The mechanisms by which substance P receptor activation leads to the opening of ion channels, and to other cellular events, is not known. On non-neuronal secretory cells, and perhaps also on lymphocytes, substance P binding is associ-ated with a stimulation of polyphosphoinositol (PI) metabolism (see **Downes**). Some of the excitatory effects of substance P on neuronal cells may also be mediated by intermediates of the PI cycle. In fact, there is recent evidence that the density of substance P binding sites in the CNS correlates well with the ability of substance P to enhance PI turnover in discrete brain regions[15].

The identification of metabolic changes that can be elicited by substance P should provide a motivation for examining long term effects of peptides on central neurons. In a striking series of experiments, Jonsson and Hallman[16] have reported that substance P produces a dramatic increase in the regenerative capacity of central noradrenergic neurons after chemical lesions are produced by neonatal administration of 6-hydroxydopamine. In addition, some substance P receptor antagonists appear to exhibit neurotoxic properties after central administration[17]. Although these results do not yet indicate a trophic role for substance P within the CNS, they highlight the need for further studies on peptide effects of cellular metabolic events. The identification of substance P-linked PI responses in the CNS provides one possible mechanism that might underly changes in the regener-ative capacity of neuronal cells.

Since the first description of its physiological actions more than 50 years ago (see **von Euler**), many of the concepts derived from research on substance P have been useful in formulating ideas about the mechanisms of peptide action on neurons. Many of the articles cited in this introduction document the gradual erosion of the concept that substance P acts exclusively as a transmitter. Identification of substance P receptors on a variety of cell types in the nervous system and the realization that substance P can alter cellular metabolism, suggest that only a fraction of the effects of substance P may be detected with electrophysiological techniques. With the identification of novel mammalian tachykinins, multiple receptors and new target cells, it may soon be possible to provide a more comprehensive description of the physiological roles of one of the many peptide families present in the nervous system.

T. M. JESSELL

M. D. WOMACK

Department of Neurobiology, Harvard Medical School, Boston, MA 02115, USA.

Reading list

1 Urban, L. and Randić, M. (1984) *Brain Res.* 290, 336–341
2 Konishi, S. *et al.* (1983) *Neurosci. Lett.* Suppl. 13, S107
3 Iversen, L. I. *et al.* (1982) in *Substance P in the Nervous System* (Porter, R. and O'Connor, M., eds), CIBA Foundation Symposium 91, 186–205
4 Nawa, H. *et al.* (1984) *Life Sci.* (in press)
5 Hunter, J. C. and Maggio, J. E. (1984) *Eur. J. Pharmacol.* 97, 159–160
6 Quirion, R. *et al.* (1983) *Nature (London)* 303, 714–716
7 Stallcup, W. D. and Patrick, J. (1980) *PNAS* 77, 634–638
8 Clapham, D. E. and Neher, E. (1984) *J. Physiol.* 347, 255–277
9 Boyd, N. D. *et al.* (1983) *Soc. Neurosci. Abstr.* 9, 142
10 Rougon, G. *et al.* (1983) *Nature (London)* 305, 715–717
11 Liu-Chen, L. Y. *et al.* (1983) *Brain Res.* 268, 162–166
12 Zawadzki, J. V. *et al.* (1981) *Fed. Proc.* 40, 689
13 Payan, D. G. *et al.* (1983) *J. Immunol.* 131, 1613–1615
14 Payan, D. G. *et al.* (1984) *J. Immunol.* 132, 1601–1604
15 Mantyh, P. W. *et al.* (1983) *Soc. Neurosci. Abstr.* 9, 1206
16 Jonsson, G. and Hallman, H. (1982) *Science* 215, 75–77
17 Hökfelt, T. *et al.* (1981) *Acta Physiol. Scand.* 113, 571–573

Opioid peptides – families of receptors and neurotransmitters

Research on opioid peptides has formed part of the cutting edge of neurobiological research for close on ten years. The opiates are among the most potent of centrally acting drugs and the social and medical implications of their actions are profound. Scientists have long viewed the effects of morphine as a 'window into the brain' and the enthusiasm generated by the discovery of the endogenous opioid peptides partly reflects this view. However, it was also realized that the information and pharmacological tools generated from work on the opiates and narcotic analgesics provided a splendid opportunity to probe an endogenous peptide system in depth. The initial impetus of the early studies has been maintained, or even increased, by the development and application of the latest molecular and neurobiological techniques: immunocytochemical mapping techniques, receptor binding and receptor autoradiography, and recombinant DNA analysis of precursor mRNA species, are but a few examples.

From a personal viewpoint, my laboratory first detected opioid-like activity in brain extracts in early 1973. An unequivocal demonstration of naloxone reversible activity on the mouse vas deferens was made in September 1973. Despite a growing personal excitement during that year, I remained sceptical even when the 'occasional partial naloxone reversal' was superseded by a purified extract with effects that could be almost completely blocked by naloxone. One problem was the difficulty of repeating the results in the guinea pig ileum – the classical opiate bioassay. The very much larger amounts of brain extract that were needed to inhibit electrically evoked twitches in the ileum were an early indication of the variations in bioassay potency observed with different opioids; this is discussed later. Further doubts were aroused by the need to use much greater amounts of naloxone to block the effects of the extracts compared to that needed to block equi-active doses of the opiates. This observation lead Hans Kosterlitz and myself to consider the further subdivision of opioid receptors even before the full identification of the enkephalins.

I have been asked why we did not also 'discover' the endorphins or dynorphins. In fact, a number of chromatographic scans during the purification of the enkephalins showed minor unexplained peaks of opioid activity, and we reported on one of these[1]. However, following the announcement of the discovery of the opioid peptides by Lars Terenius and myself at the May 1974 Neuroscience Research Programme Conference at Boston, it was necessary to concentrate on identification of the major brain activity.

The bioassayable activity [Met]-enkephalin and [Leu]-enkephalin in most brain areas exceeds that of the other opioid peptides by at least tenfold. It should be mentioned that we indirectly discovered the endorphins by pointing out the structural homology between β-lipotropin and [Met]-enkephalin in our 1975 report of the enkephalin structures[2].

Definitions

There still appears to be confusion as to the nomenclature in the opioid field. *Opioid* is any substance with agonist activity at opioid receptors. The latter are operationally defined by the ability of naloxone to block biological responses mediated through activation of these receptors. The naloxone antagonism is stereoselective and although the limits of specificity can never be fully defined, it is generally accepted that specific antagonism is associated with a K_e of less than 40 nM. Even at this value, concentrations of 1 to 10 μmol^{-1} are required to totally block the maximal effects of the enkephalins. At high concentrations, naloxone does have GABA antagonist properties[3]. Naturally additional supporting evidence (e.g. relative agonist potencies) is required for a full 'definition' of the opioid receptor but the keystone remains naloxone. An *opiate* it should be recalled is strictly any product of poppy juice, whilst a narcotic analgesic is an opioid with antinociceptive activity that is specifically blocked by naloxone. Under these criteria the so-called σ-receptor is not an opioid receptor, and some of the effects mediated by the opioid peptides are clearly not opioid receptor mediated.

Physiological significance of opioid peptides

There is now a vast body of evidence implicating the involvement of endogenous opioid peptides in: (1) the control of sensory transmission at segmental and cranial levels; neuroendocrine mechanisms involving almost all the major hormones; (2) all central autonomic responses including cardiovascular, respiratory, temperature and exocrine responses; (3) extrapyramidal motor responses; and (4) most elusively, cognitive responses. It is relatively easy to demonstrate opioid agonist modulation of all the preceding functions, but an overt involvement of endogenous systems is difficult to demonstrate in the absence of an external perturbation. Thus the most clearly defined effects of opioid antagonists are seen in young animals (neuroendocrine responses), or animals subjected to stress or chronic drug treatment. Opioids may therefore be involved in subtle adjustments to changes in internal equilibrium which are normally difficult to detect but which doubtless operate even under normal conditions. Unfortunately, there is an almost complete dearth of studies on opioid peptide turnover under normal or mildly perturbed conditions.

It appears that the endogenous opioid systems may also be involved in an overcompensation to stressful situations. Naloxone or naltrexone can effectively reduce the autonomic manifestations of toxaemic or hypovolaemic shock[4,5]. The clinical significance of these and related observations may be profound.

Behaviour and the opioids

Some peptides are thought to exert specific behavioural effects consonant with their homeostatic physiological role, e.g. angiotensin and drinking behaviour. Naturally analgesia, or more correctly, antinociception, has been a major preoccupation in the opioid field. It is doubtful whether analgesia can be viewed as a physiological response. Rather, it may be the extreme, or even pathological, behavioural manifestation of a response to extreme stress. In my opinion many of the sterile controversies of the past ten years have revolved around the nature of the endogenous 'analgesic factor'. I have never understood why anyone would expect an endogenous agent to exactly reproduce the actions of morphine with its unique pharmacodynamics. β-Endorphin, by intracerebral injection, most nearly reproduces the actions of morphine but this does not necessarily denote a physiological significance.

A much more important problem is to link the behavioural actions of the opioids to cellular and molecular events. The inhibition of ascending noradrenergic systems by μ-receptor mediated mechanisms, and the activation of dopaminergic neurones by δ-receptor mediated mechanisms, may give us clues to the effects of opioids on reward and memory systems.

Three opioid families and receptors – a coincidence?

It is now generally accepted that naloxone blocks or displaces opioids with varying degrees of efficacy. In broad terms the antagonist is active at μ-sites between 1 and 4 nM, at κ-sites between 5 to 15 nM and at δ-sites between 15 to 40 nM. These three sites have been the subject of extensive investigation and are reviewed here by **Zukin and Zukin**.

There are also three clearly defined opioid peptide precursors giving rise to the enkephalins, endorphins and dynorphins (see articles by **Hollt** and **Weber** *et al.*).

TABLE I. Receptor activity of endogenous opioid peptides

Precursor	Activity at opioid sites[1]		
	μ	δ	κ
Proenkephalin			
tyr-gly-gly-phe-met[2]	++	+++	0
tyr-gly-gly-phe-met-arg-phe	++	+	+
tyr-gly-gly-phe-met-arg-gly-leu	++	++	+
tyr-gly-gly-phe-met-arg-arg-val-NH$_2$	+++	++	+++
tyr-gly-gly-phe-leu	+	+++	0
Peptide-E	+++	++	+++
Peptide-E (1–12) or BAM 12	++	++	++
Prodynorphin			
tyr-gly-gly-phe-leu[3]	+	+++	0
tyr-gly-gly-phe-leu-arg-arg-ile	++	+	++
tyr-gly-gly-phe-leu-arg-lys-tyr-pro-lys	+++	+	++
tyr-gly-gly-phe-leu-arg-lys-tyr-pro	+++	++	+
Dynorphin-A	+++	++	+++
Dynorphin-B	+++	++	+++
Pro-opiomelanocortin			
β-endorphin	+++	++	0
β-endorphin (1–27)	++	+	0
β-endorphin (1–26) or α-endorphin	++	+	0

[1] The table is only meant as a rough guide since the peptides have been tested under different assay conditions in many cases. Direct binding activity is not available for most of the peptides and true estimates of receptor affinity in bioassay preparations (as opposed to ED_{50} values) have rarely been made.

0	No activity
+	Weak activity >25 nM ED_{50} (bioassay) or IC_{50} (binding)
++	Active 5–25 nM
+++	Very active <5 nM

[2] Note that there is a misconception with respect to the activity of [Met]-enkephalin at μ-receptors. Indeed, when metabolism of the small peptides is blocked, they showed marked increases in potency.

[3] It is likely that [Leu]-enkephalin may be formed from both proenkephalin and prodynorphin.

At one time it appeared that the products of each precursor could be closely assigned to one of the three receptor types, but this is no longer so (Table 1).

Several factors prevent the construction of a simple model of the endogenous opioid-receptor relationships. First it is probably incorrect to view the opioid receptors as three distinct entities. There is more likely to be a continuum of receptor types, and more importantly these receptor types still require further investigation with respect to the activity of the endogenous ligands. Binding studies, which do not by themselves classify a receptor type, have rarely been carried out with the endogenous ligand as a primary ligand. When this has been done, a much higher selectivity has often been observed than would be inferred from indirect displacement studies[6,7]. Even more important is the fact that, apart from some behavioural studies, there have been few attempts to correlate current opioid receptor classifications with central opioid activity. Central bioassays utilizing biochemical or biophysical assessments of opioid action are sadly lacking. The greater use of brain slice preparations for release and electrical recording studies should yield important information in this respect.

A further complicating factor in relating the actions of the opioids to their receptors is the coexistence, and presumably co-release, of the precursor products. The possibility of 'receptor modulation' by co-released products of enkephalin, dynorphin or endorphin action has barely been explored (but see Ref. 8.) At the present time, I would consider the pharmacological evidence for multiple opioid receptors to be overwhelming. However, it remains to be seen if, at the molecular level, there is one receptor oligomer with multiple subsites or several quite separate molecular species.

Concluding comments

To those intimately involved in opioid research in the last few years it will be no surprise if I comment that a number of issues have centred around what may be termed trivia. The potency, selectivity or even validity of individual peptides has often been a matter of hot dispute. All too often it has been forgotten that physiological or pharmacological responses depend on a combination of temporal and spatial factors. It has also been forgotten that ligand binding is meaningless, except as a discipline by itself, in the absence of physiologically or pharmacologically meaningful correlations.

What are the most likely growth areas or outstanding problems in the opioid field? There will almost certainly be a steady growth in our understanding of the factors controlling the processing of the opioid peptide precursors. There is a pressing need to study biochemical and biophysical events at defined enkephalin, endorphin and dynorphin synapses. The biochemical linkages between opioid receptor activation and biological response at both the cellular and organismal levels will be the subject of even more detailed study. More selective pharmacological tools will become available, in particular the need for selective δ- and κ-receptor antagonists will become urgent. Finally, the number of opioid receptor types and endogenous ligands will threaten to outnumber all other neurotransmitter-endocrine systems until order is restored by some as yet unsung hero.

JOHN HUGHES

Parke-Davis Research Unit, Addenbrooke's Hospital Site, Cambridge CB2 2QB, UK.

Reading list
1 Hughes, J., Kosterlitz, H. W. and Smith, T. W. (1977) *Br. J. Pharmacol.* 61, 639–647
2 Hughes, J., Smith, T. W., Kosterlitz, H. W., Fothergill, L. A., Morgan, B. A. and Morris, H. R. (1975) *Nature (London)* 258, 577–579
3 Dingledine, R., Iversen, L. L. and Breuker, E. (1978) *Eur. J. Pharmacol.* 47, 19–27
4 Holaday, J. W. and Faden, A. I. (1978) *Nature (London)* 275, 450–451
5 Wright, D. J. M. (1981) *Neuropeptides* 1, 181–202
6 Young, E. A., Walker, J. M., Houghton, R. and Akil, H. (1983). *Eur. J. Pharmacol.* 91, 327–328
7 Quirion, R. and Pilapil, C. (1984) *Eur. J. Pharmacol.* 99, 361–363
8 Smith, A. P., Lee, N. M. and Loh, H. H. (1983) *Trends in Pharmacol. Sci.* 4, 163–164

Dopamine and disease

Dopamine was the first neurotransmitter to attain clinical significance. The critical discovery was the profound depletion of dopamine in the striatum of patients with Parkinson's disease. This led to the introduction and refinement of high dose oral L-Dopa replacement therapy, which remains the cornerstone of current treatment of the disease. Soon after its introduction, overdosage of L-Dopa was found to cause the whole range of abnormal involuntary movements (dyskinesias) reminiscent of spontaneous disorders. Thus, L-Dopa can provoke chorea, ballism, tics, myoclonus and dystonia in susceptible parkinsonian patients. From this observation came the hypothesis that many of these drug-induced dyskinesias are due to dopaminergic overactivity, a hypothesis that is most secure for chorea. At about the same time it became apparent that the drugs used to control the positive symptoms of psychotic illnesses such as schizophrenia (see article by **Crow**), all possessed a common mode of action, namely the antagonism of the effects of dopamine in the brain. This notion, along with the observation that amphetamine can provoke a schizophreniform psychosis in some individuals, led to one of the major biological concepts of schizophrenia, namely that it too is due to cerebral dopaminergic overactivity. Finally, it was appreciated that long-term treatment with antipsychotic drugs (neuroleptics) could lead to the appearance of tardive dyskinesias, similar to chorea, dystonia and other movement disorders, whose clinical pharmacology suggested cerebral dopaminergic overaction. All these interrelated principles were established by the early 1970s. Obviously they are simplistic, as attributing such a wide array of neurological and psychiatric illness to over- or under-activity of one neurotransmitter system in the brain leaves much to be explained. The following articles in this collection explore these simple concepts in more detail.

One of the many stimuli for subdividing dopamine receptors into different categories was the need to explain the variety of clinical phenomena apparently associated with dopamine. Of course, it is known that there are different dopamine systems in the brain. The motor disorders of parkinsonism and the dyskinesias are attributed to abnormalities mainly in the nigrostriatal dopamine system, while psychotic illness may be due to changes predominantly in the meso-limbic-cortical dopamine regions. The function of the cortical dopamine system is a subject of current debate. Undoubtably it regulates subcortical dopamine mechanisms, as is discussed by **Glowinski** *et al.*, but whether it is also concerned with cortical cognitive functions remains a tantalizing mystery.

In addition to the presence of different dopamine systems in different brain areas, evidence has accrued for the presence of both post- and pre-synaptic dopamine receptors, some of the latter being on dopaminergic terminals and cell bodies (autoreceptors). Preferential actions of some dopamine agonists, and antagonists on the latter, have been invoked to explain the paradoxical effects of dopaminergic drugs, such as the capacity of low doses of dopamine agonists to improve schizophrenia and dyskinesias. However, complexity of further orders of magnitude are introduced by the contemporary concept of multiple classes of the dopamine receptor itself.

Many conflicting classifications of dopamine receptors have been introduced, but **Creese** attempts a rationalization of the evidence. The original classification into D-1 receptors linked to adenylate cyclase and D-2 receptors identified by radioactive antagonist ligands stands, although there have been interesting reports recently of interaction between the two. Subdivision of the D-2 receptor into different categories is seen as less secure, although the D-2 receptor may exist in interchangeable high- and low-affinity states. Interestingly, most cerebral actions of dopamine agonists and antagonists, in man and animals, appear linked to their effects on D-2 receptors. The functions of the D-1 receptor in the brain is uncertain, although cAMP accumulation clearly is responsible for hormonal formation elsewhere.

How do these concepts of dopamine systems and receptors relate to human disease? Both **Lewitt and Chase**, and **Larsen and Calne** discuss the problems of modern treatment and pharmacology of Parkinson's disease. Central to their comments is the enigma of the 'on–off' effect which appears in about a half of patients treated with L-Dopa for several years. Some have held that the sudden loss of benefit of the drug at intervals throughout the day may be due to receptor changes, a belief given some support by the rather variable and transient improvement afforded by a drug holiday. However, recent experience with constant intravenous infusions of L-Dopa, which can abolish all forms of the 'on–off' problem, suggest that the latter arises from failure of delivery of L-Dopa to the brain, and/or failure of synthesis and storage of dopamine in the brain.

A completely novel method of overcoming such problems may have been introduced by the dramatic demonstration that transplants of embryonic substantia nigra into rodents with experimental parkinsonism can reverse the biochemical and behavioural effects of dopamine depletion, as is discussed by **Dunnett et al**. Much experimental work has to be done before such an approach can realistically be applied to man; not least it is necessary to show that the same can be achieved in primates. However, this discovery refutes, once and for all, the belief that the brain is incapable of functional regeneration, and opens fascinating prospects for the future.

In the field of schizophrenia, the search for a 'perfect' neuroleptic continues. The aim is to produce an effective anti-psychotic drug devoid of extrapyramidal side effects, and a number of novel atypical agents have been studied, as reviewed by **Bunney**. Some of these drugs, such as clozapine, appear to have preferential action on the mesolimbic, and perhaps also the mesocortical dopamine systems, thus decreasing their propensity to cause movement disorders. Certainly this should reduce their capacity to induce pseudo-parkinsonism, although the high inherent anticholinergic properties of drugs such as clozapine and thioridazine may also be responsible. Whether novel neuroleptics can avoid the risks of tardive dyskinesias remains an open question. The origins of tardive dyskinesia appear to lie in the capacity of conventional neuroleptics to induce dopamine receptor supersensitivity on long term administration, as discussed by **Baldessarini**. Such a course of events is well-established in the experimental animal, at least in the stratium, from which tardive dyskinesias may originate. However, presumably such a course of events does not take place in other dopaminergic areas of the brain, such as the mesocortical area, where continuing dopamine blockade preserves their anti-psychotic action. An alternative hypothesis is discussed by **Fibiger and Lloyd**.

The effects of chronic drug treatment on brain dopamine receptors have confounded the search for abnormalities of dopaminergic mechanisms in the schizophrenic brain. Initial discoveries of increased numbers of dopamine receptors have been attributed by many, though not all, to prior drug treatment, and no obvious changes in dopamine metabolism have been found. However, **Mackay** reviews the recent demonstration of high dopamine levels in the left amygdala, which re-opens the dopamine hypothesis of schizophrenia. Not all will be convinced by the specificity of this hypothesis, for dopamine antagonists are widely used to control the psychotic disturbance of many illnesses other than schizophrenia, for example acute confusional states and mania. Indeed, dopamine may

be concerned more with psychotic behaviour in general, rather than schizophrenia alone. In this context, **Crow's** clear distinction between the positive
psychotic symptoms of schizophrenia (which respond to neuroleptic drugs) and
the negative symptoms of the defect state (which do not), leads him to distinguish
two syndromes in the disease, only one of which may be related to dopamine.

Dopamine has been around for a long time, and has been threatened with
extinction by the overwhelming number of new neurotransmitters. However, the
essays in this section clearly show that dopamine still takes pride of place when it
comes to explanations for many human diseases, even if there remain many
unanswered questions.

C. D. MARSDEN

Department of Neurology, Institute of Psychiatry, Denmark Hill, London SE5 8AF, UK.

Neurotransmitters and behaviour

Do peptides integrate body and brain?
The brain contains a plethora of neuropeptides many of which, despite initial
scepticism, have established themselves as respectable neurotransmitter
candidates. They are localized to specific anatomical pathways, often in company
with classical monoamine transmitters. In behavioural studies, a number of
contentious issues have already emerged typified in the article by **Gash and
Thomas.**

de Wied and Bohus[1] were the first to demonstrate that an extract of the
posterior pituitary delayed the extinction of active shock avoidance behaviour in
the rat. Subsequent experiments indicated that the active substance was vasopressin; ACTH or synthetic Lys[8]-vasopressin given in a single dose (3.0 μg),
subcutaneously, caused a long-lasting delay in extinction. In their article, Gash
and Thomas question the reproducibility of this effect and its interpretation as a
facilitation of memory, and suggest that until the effects of arginine-vasopressin
(AVP) on autonomic responses are dissociated from the effects on CNS, it is safer
to assume that the behavioural changes are secondary to the pressor effect of
AVP. Vasoconstriction and the consequent increase in blood pressure provide
powerful visceral stimuli sufficient, it is claimed, to alter behaviour.

Sahgal *et al.*[2] have shown that the effect of AVP on the extinction of passive
avoidance behaviour varies depending on the ability of the rat to learn the initial
avoidance response. Memory for this response is enhanced in slow learners and
disrupted in faster learners, results, it is claimed, which can be interpreted within
the framework of arousal theory. Under conditions of low arousal, AVP-induced
visceral input increases arousal towards optimum levels, and enhances behaviour
efficiency. In rats, already operating close to maximum arousal, further visceral
input leads to over arousal and behavioural inefficiency. There is good reason to
believe that activation of brainstem visceral arousal centres by AVP is perceived
as aversive. Rats learn to avoid a distinctive environment in which they have
experienced injections of AVP; similar results have been obtained with
cholecystokinin (CCK) and substance P.

The arousal hypothesis is appealing, but it does not contribute materially to the view that AVP acts via visceral feedback to modify behaviour. Such effects could equally well be accounted for in terms of arousal induced by direct central actions of AVP since many sites in the brain, in addition to visceral integrative centres of the brainstem, influence arousal levels. How strong then is the evidence that AVP can act directly at CNS sites?

Intracerebroventricular (i.c.v.) injection of a thousandfold lower dose of AVP than that needed with subcutaneous injection, produces the same effect on extinction behaviour, suggesting that AVP acts directly on brain to modify behaviour. Central administration of [p Glu^4, Cyt^6] AVP(4-8), the potent desglycinamide derivative of AVP enhances passive avoidance behaviour, but has no pressor effect[3]. Furthermore, an AVP antagonist given centrally blocks the behavioural, but not the pressor effect, of systemically administered AVP.

Further support for a central site of action comes from a more recent study of Sodersten et al.[4], who reported that doses of AVP as low as 1 ng, injected centrally, inhibited sexual receptivity in oestradiol-17B-treated ovariectomized female rats but did not result in changes in blood pressure. However, higher doses (1 μg) administered systemically, increased blood pressure but had no effect on sexual behaviour.

This controversy extends to a number of other peptides with peripheral and central sites of action. CCK, for example, reduces food intake, and it has been demonstrated that vagal input from the stomach to the area postrema contributes to this satiety effect. A section of the vagus nerve, or a lesion to the projection site in the brain, attenuates the effect of CCK on food intake.

Viewing the organism holistically, it may well be that peripheral and central mechanisms sensitive to peptides function synergistically to maintain physiological and behavioural homeostasis[5]. It is interesting to note that AVP-containing neurons of the paraventricular nucleus project to brainstem sites controlling the input and output of the autonomic nervous system.

The reluctance to accept that AVP alters memory functions specifically then is justified; though it is unsatisfactory that this controversy rests largely on results obtained in the one-trial shock avoidance task. Varied tests of memory function, particularly some not involving electric shock or other negative reinforcers, need to be explored.

The neurochemistry of Alzheimer's disease

The discovery that the brain contains many neurotransmitters, in addition to the classical excitatory and inhibitory amino acids and the monoamines, has thrown new light on the interpretation of the chemical deficiencies of brain observed in patients dying from specified neuropsychiatric conditions. Most recently attention has focused on Alzheimer's dementia, characterized by severe disorders of memory leading to a more general cognitive deterioration. **Suzanne Corkin** reviews the evidence for a lesion to the cholinergic forebrain projections in this disease (see also article by **Cuello and Sofroniew**). It is important to stress that a number of issues relating to this question remain unresolved.

Is Alzheimer's dementia a specific dementia or merely premature ageing?

The rapid and global intellectual deterioration in this condition presents special problems to the clinical psychologist attempting to answer this question. Longitudinal studies using standardized neuropsychological test batteries are now needed to provide, first a psychological profile and rating of cognitive impairment to correlate with post-mortem neuropathological and neurochemical measurements in brain, and second to record a progressive history of the disease state to aid better diagnosis in the early stages of the illness. Advantage should be taken of microprocessors to automate appropriate neuropsychological screening and to develop a standardized evaluation for general use.

How do we model Alzheimer's disease in animals?

In many laboratories attempts are being made to study the behavioural effects of lesions to the nucleus basalis, thought to be one of the major sources of cortical cholinergic innervation. This may not be the correct approach for a number of reasons. First, it has been reported in post-mortem material that although degeneration occurs in the cortical ACh terminals, the cell bodies in the nucleus basalis remain, albeit severely shrunken. If this is verified, it has important implications for therapy since a pharmacological response may be elicited from a system in retrograde degeneration, but not from one that has totally degenerated. Second, does Alzheimer's dementia involve only a cholinergic degenerative process? The answer to this is almost certainly no. It has been demonstrated that in sub-groups of patients loss of noradrenaline-containing (NA) neurons in the locus coeruleus, deficiencies in 5-HT, and somatostatin in the cortex, may also occur. A progressive degeneration of several interacting neurochemical pathways is difficult to induce experimentally.

However, such findings present new possibilities for the pharmacological treatment of dementia. Neuropeptides play an important role in cortical integration and in some cases actually coexist with monoamine transmitters. Referring back to the de Wied studies, there is good reason to believe that the effect of AVP on central function involves an interaction of the peptide with brain stem noradrenaline neurones, innervating hippocampus and cortex. Peptide drugs to modulate cortical integration thus provide a challenge for the future.

Finally, is the loss of neurotransmitters primary to Alzheimer's dementia (AD) or secondary to a more fundamental degenerative process in cortex? It has been suggested that the plaques and neurofibrillary tangles represent the core pathology, and that perhaps the predisposing factors for their development should be a target for therapy.

The drugs currently available to treat AD, when effective, improve the patient's daily behaviour as viewed by the relatives and nursing staff, and as Corkin stresses, this will be an essential feature of any new drug. There is little evidence, however, that the present drugs improve cognitive functioning, the most important property required.

AD raises the general issue of methods available for restoring neurotransmitter efficacy in the damaged nervous system. The monoamine neurons implicated in the pathology of AD, Parkinson's disease, Huntington's Chorea and schizophrenia are components of the iso-dendritic core, embedded in the reticular activating system, and extending from the brain stem to the basal forebrain. The neurons which contain NA, dopamine (DA), 5-HT or ACh, sometimes together with neuropeptides, collateralize, have extensive axon and dendritic trees, and release transmitter diffusely over large areas of the CNS at synaptic and non-synaptic junctions. Thus they have the architecture to influence, simultaneously, vast arrays of precisely connected neurons, in cortex, hippocampus or striatum. The extensive projection tree maintained by the cell bodies of these neurons may make them particularly vulnerable to any condition which stresses the nervous system (e.g. nutrient, oxygen or cerebrovascular insufficiency, viruses and febrile conditions).

It may, therefore, be no coincidence that progressive degeneration in these systems results in clearly defined neuropsychiatric disease characterized by global losses of neural integration within specific forebrain areas; in Parkinson's disease of sensorimotor integration related to striatum, and in AD of processing in association cortex leading to impairment of perception, attention, memory and language.

Replacing brain neurotransmitters

Monoamines serve enabling functions in their target areas rather than information processing, and for these reasons replacement therapy which achieves diffuse activation of the post-synaptic monoamine receptors may well be clinically effective. The use of L-DOPA in the treatment of Parkinson's disease provides the best example of this approach, which is now being pursued in the cholinergic system for the treatment of AD.

Dunnett *et al.* present an alternative approach to the problem of restoration of neurotransmitter function in the damaged adult nervous system. Foetal neurons of the iso-dentritic core have another fascinating property; they survive grafting to the damaged adult nervous system, and re-establish the level of biochemical activity of a given transmitter in a damaged target area sufficient to reverse the behavioural deficits associated with the lesion. The paper describes experiments on the nigro-striatal DA pathway.

It has also been demonstrated that a severe spatial memory impairment, induced by sectioning the connections of the hippocampus, can be reversed by grafts of foetal cholinergic septal neurons to the damaged hippocampus[6].

Thus a graft of monoamine neurons, despite isolation from normal input/output connections, can apparently diffusely release sufficient transmitter to modulate integration in the target area. Basic research on the conditions for survival of foetal neurons, the elucidation of growth promoting factors and methods for sorting and culturing classes of neurotransmitter neurons will be necessary if these fascinating findings are to find application in the treatment of degenerative and traumatic diseases of the nervous system.

S. D. IVERSEN

Merck Sharp & Dohme Research Laboratories, Neuroscience Research Centre, Terlings Park, Eastwick Road, Harlow, Essex, CM20 2QR.

Reading list

1 de Wied, D. and Bohus, B. (1966) *Nature (London)*, 212, 1484–1486
2 Sahgal, A., Keith, A. B., Wright, T. and Edwardson, J. A. (1982) *Neurosci. Lett.* 28, 87–92
3 de Wied, D., Gaffori, O., van Ree, J. M. and de Jong, W. (1984) *Nature (London)* 308, 276–278
4 Sodersten, P., Henning, M., Melin, P. and Ludin, S. (1983) *Nature (London)* 301, 608–610
5 Iversen, S. D. (1981) *Nature (London)* 291, 454
6 Dunnett, S. B., Low, W. C., Iversen, S. D., Stenevi, V. and Bjorklund, A. (1982) *Brain Res.* 251, 335–348

Evolution of neuropeptides

Roger Acher

Virtually all of the small peptide hormones have been identified immunologically in the brain and can therefore be termed neuropeptides. The same chemical messengers, possibly after further processing, seem to have switched from a neuromediator function to a second integrative system specialized in endocrine communication. The dual evolution of the neural cell and the peptide biosynthesis on one hand, and of the recipient cell and the molecular receptor on the other, has probably been involved in the tailoring of present-day neuropeptides.

Recently about 20 of the known peptide hormones (virtually all the small hormones) have been identified immunochemically in the brain and can therefore be termed neuropeptides[5] (Fig. 1). Apparently each of these molecules may fulfill a variety of functions in the same organism, e.g. by acting as both hormones and neuromodulators. Because intercellular communication depends primarily upon the interaction of an active peptide and a receptor, the evolution of neuropeptides can be examined at both the cellular and molecular levels.

Dual function of the primitive neuron

As pointed out by Bertha Scharrer[11], because it is derived from a 'potential epithelial element'*, the primitive nerve cell was probably able to dispatch both long distance and localized signals. Phylogenetically speaking, neurons with elementary synaptic contacts first appear in the lowest eumetazoans, the coelenterates, and some of these cells display cytological evidence of secretory activity. Tests with isolated neurosecretory granules from the coelenterate *Hydra* have shown that they contain a substance which regulates growth and also participates in both gametogenesis and

sexual differentiation[11]. Neurosecretory granules are also abundant in the nervous system of planarians and annelids. Here, non-neural internal glands have not been identified suggesting that the nervous system in these primitive invertebrates is responsible for both neural and endocrine functions. From this point of view the so-called neurosecretory neuron of higher vertebrates may be regarded as retaining more of the ancient characteristics of this nerve cell precursor than either the conventional neuron, or endocrine cell. It is not surprising therefore that the products of these three cell types should be similar.

Processing and differentiation

Secretory peptides and proteins are produced by cleavage(s) from a larger precursor polypeptide chain. Thus, a pre-pro-protein, emerging from the ribosome attached to reticular endoplasmic epithelium by its recognition sequence, is truncated by a specific enzyme to form a pro-protein. This pro-protein may be truncated again, excised, or divided into fragments by specialized enzymes belonging either to the cathepsin B family (trypsin-like specificity) or to the cathepsin D family (pepsin-like specificity). Each fragment may have its own function so that the initial chain acts as a polyprecursor and may be processed differently at different locations in the body.

For example, three peptides have so far

---

* This term was used by Scharrer to denote the fact that the precursor cell could give rise to several types of differentiated cell, including an epithelial cell.

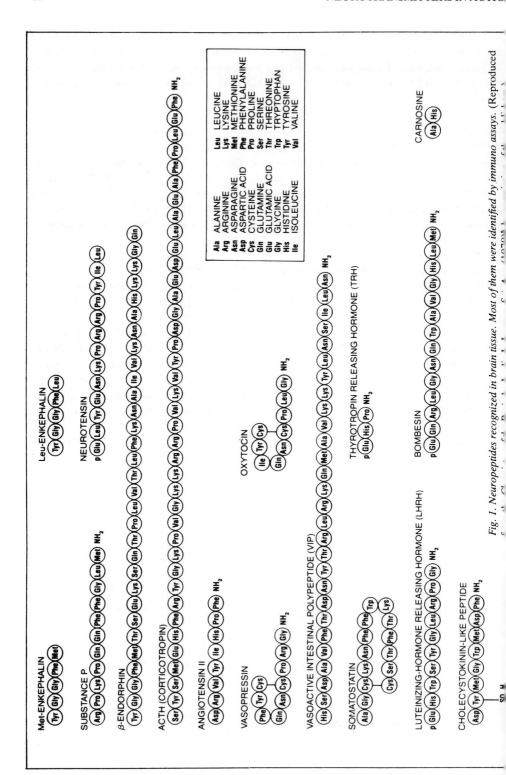

Fig. 1. Neuropeptides recognized in brain tissue. Most of them were identified by immuno assays. (Reproduced

been isolated from brain and gastrointestinal tissues in identical forms – substance P (11 residues), neurotensin (13 residues) and somatostatin (14 residues) (Fig. 1). However, an N-terminal-extended form of somatostatin (somatostatin-28) has also been identified in the hog intestine, suggesting that processing of the macromolecular precursor may differ in neural and gut tissues.

In the case of cholecystokinin, an intestinal hormone responsible for gall bladder contraction and pancreatic secretion, these differences in processing have been more clearly demonstrated by Dockray and Gregory[3]. Two active forms, one having 33 residues (CCK-33), the other with an N-terminal extension of six residues (CCK-39), have been chemically characterized in hog intestine[7] (Fig. 2). After trypsin hydrolysis a C-terminal octapeptide (CCK-8) with strong biological activity was obtained; this fragment has also been found in the intestine[3] (Fig. 1). A macromolecular precursor of cholecystokinin of about 150 residues has been detected in the brain[10]. Reports of brain CCK-33

immunoreactive product have been made but additional studies have shown that in fact CCK-33 is virtually absent whereas CCK-8 accounts for about 95% of the active material[3].

A similar situation occurs in the myenteric plexus; precursors peptides are converted almost completely to CCK-8 in central and peripheral neurons whereas this processing is only partial in endocrine cells[3]. It may be assumed that CCK-8 is a neuromodulator in neural tissue whereas CCK-33 fulfills a hormonal function in digestion.

Ontogeny and phylogeny

Another interesting observation is the change in peptide processing which occurs during development. Corticotropin (39 residues), the adrenocorticotropin hormone (ACTH), is primarily found in the anterior lobe of the pituitary gland whereas α-melanocyte stimulating hormone (α-MSH), which represents the first 13 residues of corticotropin, is found in the intermediate lobe (Fig. 1). These molecules have both been detected

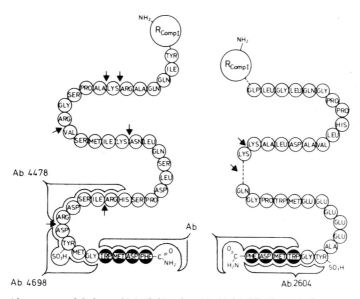

Fig. 2. Amino acid sequences of cholecystokinin (left) and gastrin (right). The C-terminal sequences are identical. R_comp.1 indicates the N-terminal extensions of unknown amino acid sequence in the largest precursor forms (From Ref. 10.)

immunologically in the brain. Using the complementary DNA of the mRNA, the sequence of a macromolecular precursor (265 residues) which includes a glycopeptide, corticotropin and endorphin has been deduced. Silman and co-workers[12] have found a switch in the processing of this precursor during the development of rhesus monkey. The fetal pituitary mainly produces α-MSH whereas the infant or adult gland mainly makes corticotropin. Likewise the fetal adrenal gland is stimulated by α-MSH but not by corticotropin whereas this response is reversed in the adult organ. Most importantly, this metamorphosis of the adrenal at birth is temporally associated with the change in polypeptide processing in the pituitary. Thus, the same precursor may give rise to different products at different stages of development.

Concerning the phylogenetic distribution of neuropeptides it is interesting that caerulein, a decapeptide that has been isolated from the skin of an Australian hylid frog, *Hyla caerulea*, has a C-terminal sequence identical to CCK-8 except for the substitution of a methionine residue by threonine. At the N-terminal a pyroglutamyl group is found. This is usually the result of the spontaneous conversion of glutamine after cleavage of an adjacent peptide bond and indicates that caerulein is probably a fragment of a larger precursor. The role of caerulein in frog skin is unknown but it is clear that a CCK-like precursor not only exists in the frog but is processed in the same way as the CCK precursor in the sheep brain.

Bombesin, a tetradecapeptide which has been purified from the skin of the frog *Bombina bombina*, is probably also derived from a larger precursor because of its N-terminal pyroglutamyl and its amidated C-terminal end (Fig. 1). In the rat, two populations of bombesin-containing neurons have been detected immunologically. One is found in the brain and intestine and mainly contains a form which is similar in size to the amphibian peptide, the other is found in the stomach and is larger[3].

Duplication of function

Identical amino acid sequences can be found within peptides having distinct biological properties, e.g. cholecystokinins and gastrins (Fig. 2). Gastrins, peptides which stimulate gastric acid secretion when cholecystokinins act on the gall bladder and pancreas, were first isolated from hog antral mucosa. Two main forms, G-17 (17 residues) and G-34 (G-17 with an N-terminal extension of 17 residues) have been characterized[3]. By purifying the appropriate mRNA and then making the corresponding 'complementary' DNA (cDNA) from this using the 'reverse transcriptase' enzyme, it has been possible to decode not only the portion of cDNA coding for the peptide, but also the neighboring sequences. In this way it has been deduced that these particular peptides are derived from a precursor containing 110–140 residues in antral mucosa. G-17 and G-34-like immuno-reactive factors have been detected in small amounts in neurohypophysis, hypothalamus and the vagus nerve[3,7]. The existence of G-4 (which is identical to CCK-4) remains in question. It is tempting to explain the similarity between cholecystokinins and gastrins as being the result of a gene duplication, followed by divergence through point mutations (see below). However, the similarity is limited to the last five residues and it is difficult to explain why only the N-terminal parts have undergone so many substitutions. Another interpretation could be that both peptides have the same mRNA but that two different 'splicings' of this RNA have brought together two distinct sequences with the same nucleotide sequence coding for the active pentapeptide. If such a mechanism exists, it could provide an economical mechanism for peptide diversification.

Duplication seems to be a fundamental mechanism for increasing the number of

Fig. 3. Putative common precursor of arginine vasopressin (AVP) and specific neurophysin (Np-AVP). (From Ref. 2 with permission. Copright 1980 by the American Association for the Advancement of Science.)

neuropeptides. An example can be given by neurohypophysial hormones and neurophysins. These are isolated from neurohypophysis and are believed to share common macromolecular precursors. According to Brownstein and Gainer[2], each precursor is a 200-residue polypeptide chain with an N-terminal peptide (mol. wt about 10,000), a central 'hormone' sequence (mol. wt about 1000) and a C-terminal neurophysin (mol. wt about 10,000) (Fig. 3). In mammals, two active peptides, oxytocin and vasopressin, and two neurophysins, MSEL and VLDV (distinguished by their sequence and designated by residues in positions 2, 3, 6 and 7), have been found[1].

Examination of over 40 species representing the entire vertebrate phylum has revealed that each animal usually makes two hormones and that oxytocin and vasopressin are the final links of two lineages of molecules – the former probably involved in reproduction, the latter in hydromineral regulation. Ten active peptides have been characterized to date. All are nonapeptides with the same general molecular pattern, and with substitutions occurring at positions 4 and 8, and very rarely in positions 2 and 3 (Fig. 4). Because of the similarity between the two hormone lineages and because only a single hormone is found in a very primitive vertebrate, the lamprey, it has been assumed that a gene duplication occurred between Cyclostomes (lampreys) and true fishes. After this the two lines of molecules evolved separately (Fig. 5). Thus, each vertebrate species usually has an 'oxytocin-like' peptide and a 'vasopressin-like' peptide. Oxytocin and vasopressin themselves are characteristic of mammals, whilst mesotocin and vasotocin are found in non-mammalian tetrapods, and isotocin and vasotocin in bony fishes. In cartilaginous fishes, glumitocin and vasotocin are found in rays whereas two oxytocin-like peptides, valitocin and aspargtocin, as well as vasotocin are present in the shark *Squalus acanthias* (Fig. 6). Because in this last case the isolation was performed from pooled glands it is not possible to decide whether there was a true

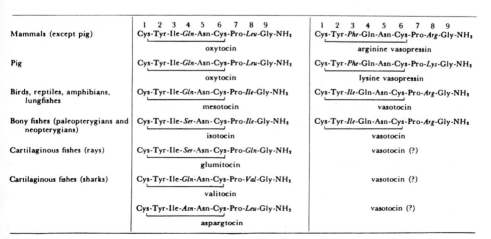

	1 2 3 4 5 6 7 8 9	1 2 3 4 5 6 7 8 9
Mammals (except pig)	Cys-Tyr-Ile-*Gln*-Asn-Cys-Pro-*Leu*-Gly-NH₂ oxytocin	Cys-Tyr-*Phe*-Gln-Asn-Cys-Pro-*Arg*-Gly-NH₂ arginine vasopressin
Pig	Cys-Tyr-Ile-*Gln*-Asn-Cys-Pro-*Leu*-Gly-NH₂ oxytocin	Cys-Tyr-*Phe*-Gln-Asn-Cys-Pro-*Lys*-Gly-NH₂ lysine vasopressin
Birds, reptiles, amphibians, lungfishes	Oys-Tyr-Ile-*Gln*-Asn-Cys-Pro-*Ile*-Gly-NH₂ mesotocin	Cys-Tyr-*Ile*-Gln-Asn-Cys-Pro-*Arg*-Gly-NH₂ vasotocin
Bony fishes (paleopterygians and neopterygians)	Cys-Tyr-Ile-*Ser*-Asn-Cys-Pro-*Ile*-Gly-NH₂ isotocin	Cys-Tyr-*Ile*-Gln-Asn-Cys-Pro-*Arg*-Gly-NH₂ vasotocin
Cartilaginous fishes (rays)	Cys-Tyr-Ile-*Ser*-Asn-Cys-Pro-*Gln*-Gly-NH₂ glumitocin	vasotocin (?)
Cartilaginous fishes (sharks)	Cys-Tyr-Ile-*Gln*-Asn-Cys-Pro-*Val*-Gly-NH₂ valitocin	vasotocin (?)
	Cys-Tyr-Ile-*Asn*-Asn-Cys-Pro-*Leu*-Gly-NH₂ aspargtocin	vasotocin (?)

Fig. 4. Structure of vertebrate neurohypophysial hormones (From Ref. 1.)

duplication of oxytocin-like peptides or simply a mixture from two strains of shark, one which synthesized valitocin, the other aspargtocin.

Duplication of the vasopressin-like peptide has been found, however, in Australian marsupials belonging to the family *Macropodidae*, namely the red kangaroo and the tammar. Systematic examination of individual glands always shows two vasopressins as well as an oxytocin-like peptide. One is lysine vasopressin (Lys^8-vasopressin), exceptional in eutherians but found in the pig, the other phenypressin (Phe^2-Arg^8-vasopressin) which is found only in macropodids. Interestingly, duplication was not observed in the possum, another Australian marsupial belonging to the family *Phalangeridae*. This species only has arginine vasopressin as does the prototherian echidna and most eutherians. A single duplication followed by divergent mutations probably occurred during macropodid evolution. Although the two vasopressins have a high antidiuretic activity

in the rat, no specific functions are apparent. Curiously, duplication of the vasopressin-like peptide is also observed in American marsupials but chemical identification has not yet been carried out. The comparison might provide a new perspective not only on the evolution of neuropeptides but also of metatherians and the influence of the continental drift on gene dispersion.

This duality in eutherian hormone structure is also observed for neurophysins. Two types have been characterized in each species: MSEL-neurophysins (fully sequenced for ox, sheep, pig, horse and whale) and VLDV-neurophysins (sequenced for ox, pig and horse)[1]. These two proteins are 93–95 residues long and in a given species show about 80% homology. The central sequences (residues 10–75) are nearly identical and variations between families occur in the N-terminal part (residues 1–9) and in the C-terminal part (76–95) within the families[1]. (Fig. 7).

It is generally assumed that vasopressin

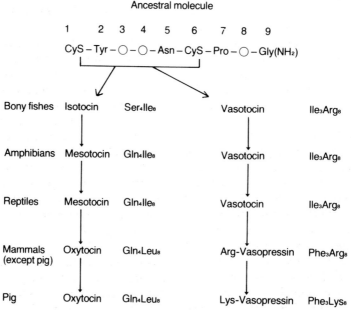

Ancestral molecule

1   2   3   4   5   6   7   8   9

CyS – Tyr – ◯ – ◯ – Asn – CyS – Pro – ◯ – Gly(NH$_2$)

Bony fishes	Isotocin	Ser$_4$Ile$_8$	Vasotocin	Ile$_3$Arg$_8$
Amphibians	Mesotocin	Gln$_4$Ile$_8$	Vasotocin	Ile$_3$Arg$_8$
Reptiles	Mesotocin	Gln$_4$Ile$_8$	Vasotocin	Ile$_3$Arg$_8$
Mammals (except pig)	Oxytocin	Gln$_4$Leu$_8$	Arg-Vasopressin	Phe$_3$Arg$_8$
Pig	Oxytocin	Gln$_4$Leu$_8$	Lys-Vasopressin	Phe$_3$Lys$_8$

Fig. 5. Hypothetical scheme of the evolution of neurohypophysial hormones. One-gene duplication and a series of subsequent single substitutions in positions 3, 4, or 8 produce two molecular lines. The substituted amino acids and their positions in a hormone are listed to the right of each hormone. (From Ref. 1.)

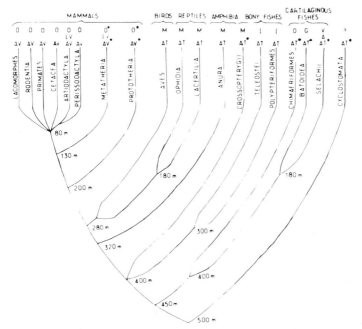

Fig. 6. Neurohypophysial hormones and species evolution according to palaeontological data. Letters indicate hormones identified in modern representatives of the groups: O, oxytocin; AV, arginine vasopressin; LV, lysine vasopressin; M, mesotocin; I, isotocin; A, aspargtocin; V, valitocin; G, glumitocin; AT, arginine vasotocin. The numbers give the time in millions of years (ma) since the divergence. (From Ref. 1.)

...nd MSEL-neurophysin on the one hand, ...nd oxytocin and VLDV-neurophysin on ...he other, share common precursors. The ...atter would have an additional N-terminal ...equence of about 100 residues, which is ...ucosylated in the case of vasopressin pre-...ursor[2] (Fig. 3). The function of this third ...part or of its cleavage product is unknown. ...The two precursors, which can be sepa-...ated by isoelectric focusing (pIs 5.4 and ...).1), are synthesized in supra-optic and ...paraventicular nuclei of the hypothalamus ...nd processed intra-axonally during trans-...port to the neurohypophysis. The loss of ...asopressin in the Brattleboro mutant rat is ...pparently accompanied by the disappear-...nce of the more basic precursor. It is not ...lear if there is a deficiency of the precursor ...ynthesis or a default in the subsequent ...processing in the strain. It would also be of ...nterest to ascertain whether the additional ...phenypressin of macropodids is accom-...panied by an additional neurophysin.

Repetitive neuropeptide genes

Genes are sequences of DNA which are transcribed into complementary sequences of mRNA which, in turn, are translated into polypeptides. Gene duplication, fol-lowed by fusion, can give rise to a DNA molecule containing multiple copies of the same sequence. Later point mutations will introduce diversification into these repeti-tive units and, if all of them are expressed individually, a family of isopeptides or isoproteins will be created. Repetitive sequences may be found either in the polypeptide precursors or directly in DNA.

Both α-MSH and its putative precursor, corticotropin, have been detected in the brain. On the other hand the active melanocyte-stimulating heptapeptide is also contained within the pituitary peptide β-MSH, and in the corresponding putative precursor, lipotropin, which also contains the endorphin sequence. A large common precursor which includes a glycopeptide,

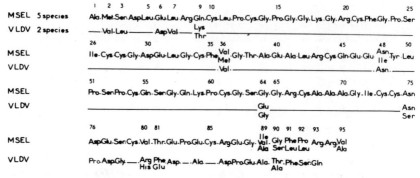

Fig. 7. Comparison between MSEL- and VLDV-neurophysins. (From Ref. 1.)

corticotropin and lipotropin, termed pro-opiocortin, has been synthesized using the appropriate mRNA. Finally, the complementary DNA (cDNA) of the mRNA has been made using reverse transcriptase and directly sequenced. In this manner the complete amino acid sequence of pre-pro-opiocortin (265 residues) has been deduced and a third repetition of the melanocyte-stimulating peptide, called γ-MSH, has been found within the decoded N-terminal sequence of the protein[9]. Peptide fragments containing γ-MSH have now been isolated from the pituitary (Fig. 8). Although pro-opiocortin-like immunoreactive material has been detected in the hypothalamus, it seems that the brain opioid penta-peptides, the

enkephalins (Fig. 1), are not derived from pro-opiocortin, despite the fact that the (Met)-enkephalin sequence is contained within the endorphin molecule.

A second example concerns the opioid pentapeptides (Leu)- and (Met)-enkephalins. These were first discovered in the brain[10] but have now been identified in many tissues, particularly the adrenal medulla. Two putative precursors, which upon digestion with trypsin yield peptides that bind to opiate receptors, have been purified from adrenal chromaffin granules. One is apparently a (Met)-enkephalin precursor containing two copies of the peptide, the other contains both (Leu)- and (Met)-enkephalin and is presumably a common precursor of the two forms[6] (Fig.

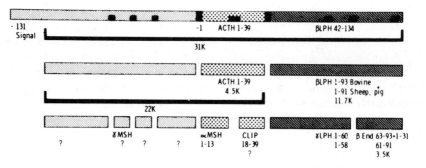

Fig. 8. The pre-pro-opiocortin and its multi-step processing. ACTH; corticotropin; LPH: lipotropin; End: endorphin; MSH: melanotropin; CLIP: corticotropin-like intermediate lobe peptide. Note the triplication of MSH sequence. (From Ref. 13.)

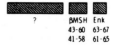

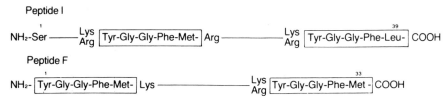

Fig. 9. Dual precursor of [Met]- and [Leu]-enkephalins (boxes) isolated from adrenal medulla. (From Ref. 6.)

). Repetitive DNA sequences are not rare: it may be recalled that 12 interferon-related sequences have been detected in the human gene bank and there are indications for at least eight interferon-related genes[8].

Evolution can act at three levels. At the level of DNA itself gene multiplication followed by diversification via point mutations can increase the number of neuropeptides, by producing a family of sequence-related peptides in which each member is associated with a particular physiological role (e.g. oxytocin and vasopressin). At the level of mRNA, transcriptional and post-transcriptional events, involving one or several splicings (i.e. removal of an excised sequence – intron – with ligature of the two ends – exons. This mechanism can build new proteins or peptides by joining up separate sequences. The number of combinations would be limited by the specificity of the splicing enzymes, but these themselves are subjected to evolution. At the level of proteins, translational and post-translational events may also modify the information content of a neuropeptide.

Although the active neuropeptide is the result of a precise program, the chain of intermediate molecules and of enzymes involved appears intricate. Thus, evolutionary variations can occur at many places. The program must build a peptide with a conformation that can fit a specific receptor; on the other hand, the conformation of the receptor is itself the result of a program subjected to evolution. How the dual evolution was co-ordinated and recorded in the relevant genes remains a mystery.

Reading list

1 Acher, R. (1980) *Proc. R. Soc. London, Ser. B* 210, 21–43
2 Brownstein, M., Russel, J. T. and Gainer, H. (1980) *Science* 207, 373–378
3 Dockray, G. J. and Gregory, R. A. (1980) *Proc. R. Soc. London, Ser. B* 210, 151–164
4 Hughes, J., Smith, T. W., Kosterlitz, H. W., Fothergill, L. A., Morgan, B. A. and Morris, H. R. (1975) *Nature (London)* 258, 577–579
5 Iversen, L. L. (1979) *Sci. Am.* 241, 118–129
6 Kimura, S., Lewis, R. V., Stern, A. S., Rossier, J., Stein, S. and Udenfriend, S. (1980) *Proc. Natl Acad. Sci. U.S.A.* 77, 1681–1685
7 Mutt, V. (1976) *Clin. Endocrinol. N.Y.* (Suppl.) 175s–183s
8 Nagata, S., Mantei, N. and Weissmann, C. (1980) *Nature (London)* 287, 401–408
9 Nakanishi, S., Inoue, A., Kita, T., Nakamura, M., Chang, A. C. Y., Cohen, S. N. and Numa, S. (1979) *Nature (London)* 278, 423–427
10 Rehfeld, J. F. (1980) *Trends NeuroSci.* 3, 65–67
11 Scharrer, B. (1977) *47th James Arthur Lecture on the evolution of the human brain*, pp. 1–17, The American Museum of Natural History, New York
12 Silman, R. E., Holland, D., Chard, T., Lowry, P. J., Hope, J., Robinson, J. S. and Thornburn, G. D. (1978) *Nature (London)* 276, 526–528
13 Smith, I. (1980) *Biochem. Ed.* 8, 1–4

Roger Acher is Professor of Biochemistry at the Université Pierre et Marie-Curie (Université de Paris VI), Laboratoire de Chimie Biologique, 96, Boulevard Raspail, 75006-Paris, France.

Recombinant DNA strategies and techniques

Robert J. Milner

Imagine setting out to purify and characterize all of the proteins in a rat brain: each protein would require a specifically designed purification scheme, perhaps kilogram quantities of starting material, and the determination of each primary amino-acid sequence would be complex and time consuming. To do this for each of the many thousands of proteins in a mammalian brain would be a daunting task indeed! Yet a few micrograms of rat brain mRNA contain molecules coding for every protein in the brain: by means of recombinant DNA techniques we can use the information encoded in each mRNA to investigate not only the structure of the corresponding protein but also its genetic regulation. The mRNA molecules are first converted into a form which can be inserted into a bacterial plasmid. The population of plasmids, each containing a different piece of inserted material, is then used to infect bacteria, in such a way that each bacterium receives a different plasmid. The complex mixture of plasmids, and hence the original mRNA population, can now be very easily separated into its different components by growing up each bacterium which received a plasmid as an individual colony or clone. This simple cloning procedure is the essence of recombinant DNA technology.

The power of recombinant DNA technology is actually threefold: first, we can completely and absolutely fractionate a complex mixture of biological molecules into its individual components; second, we can obtain unlimited quantities of a molecule of interest and, lastly, we can translate an experimental problem in protein chemistry into the language of nucleic acids, providing access to a range of experimental techniques, not the least being the rapid determination of primary structures by nucleotide sequence analysis. For these reasons recombinant DNA technology has had an enormous impact on modern biology and for the first time it has been possible to investigate the molecular genetics of complex eukaryotic systems. As the articles in this issue bear witness, the potential of these approaches is now starting to be felt in the neurosciences. The purpose of this article is to give an overview of the available molecular genetic methodologies and their capabilities and to provide some idea of how these are and will be applied to problems in neuroscience.

Strategies for molecular cloning

In most cases the desired product is a clone (known as a cDNA clone) of a particular mRNA coding for a defined protein and several possible strategies to obtain a clone of interest exist. Each strategy will contain two essential elements: the production of cDNA clones from mRNA and the selection of clones of interest.

For most investigations the starting material will be a mRNA population from a tissue source and the exact choice of strategy will depend very much on the abundance of the desired mRNA in that RNA population. For highly abundant mRNA molecules (greater than 1% of total mRNA), such as the mRNA coding for insulin, it is quite feasible to enrich these mRNAs further, usually by sucrose density gradient fractionation monitored by *in-vitro* translation of the mRNA into its protein products. The purified mRNA is then cloned in bacteria and virtually all the resulting cDNA clones will correspond to the desired mRNA. For mRNA molecules with low abundance (0.1% or lower of total mRNA), however, purification is considerably more difficult and different strategies have been developed for this. For example, using synthetic oligonucleotides, appropriate clones are selected from a 'cDNA library', a collection of clones derived from a total tissue mRNA population. Between these extremes there are many possible combinations of partial mRNA purification and some selection of clones. A good illustration of such a combined strategy is given by the recent isolation of cDNA clone for tyrosine hydroxylase[12].

Whatever the purity of the mRNA used as a starting material, the production of the clones is virtually the same in each case. The enzyme reverse transcriptase is first used to produce a single stranded DNA copy of the mRNA i.e. complementary DNA (cDNA), hence the name cDNA clone. This reaction requires a short oligonucleotide 'primer' to initiate the cDNA strand; usually an oligonucleotide of 12–18 thymidylate residues, oligo (dT), is bound to the polyadenylate tail which terminates most mRNA molecules. After removal of the mRNA template with alkali, a second DNA strand is produced, usually with the enzyme DNA polymerase, to produce a double-stranded cDNA. This double-stranded DNA is then trimmed with the enzyme S_1 nuclease to remove any single-stranded regions. A single-stranded stretch of deoxycytidylate residues (dC tail) is now attached to each end of the double-stranded cDNA insert with the enzyme terminal deoxynucleotide transferase. To clone the cDNA insert it must now be inserted in a vector, most usually the plasmid pBR322, which can be used to infect bacteria. The DNA of the plasmid is circular and can be made linear by cutting with a specific endonuclease. A deoxyguanylate tail (dG tail) is then added to each end of the linear plasmid. The dC tailed cDNA inserts and dG tailed plasmid are mixed and the complementary dG and dC tails annealed to form recombinant DNA circles containing both plasmid and cDNA insert material.

The recombinant DNA plasmids are then used to infect bacteria, usually *Escherichia coli*. For a selection of bacterial clones containing recombinant plasmids, most plasmid vectors carry genes conferring antibiotic resistance to their bacterial hosts. Insertion of the cDNA in the plasmid usually destroys one of these genes, enabling bacterial clones containing recombinant plasmids to be selected by their antibiotic resistance. Each separate bacterial colony or clone derived by this procedure will contain a recombinant plasmid corresponding to a single member of the starting mRNA population. There are many variations on this general method of clone production (for experimental details of these and the other techniques described here see Refs 6, 9, 24, 25); a particularly elegant method of cloning with a reputation of producing long cDNA clones with high efficiency has recently been described by Okayama and Berg[17].

There are two methods generally used to select desired clones from collections of cloned bacteria: colony hybridization and hybridization-translation. As with many of the techniques involving recombinant DNA, both depend on the ability of nuclei acids to hybridize or 'base-pair' specifically with a complementary nucleic acid sequence. In colony hybridization, the clones are grown on a nitrocellulose filter support, lysed to expose the plasmid DNA and incubated with a radioactively labelled nucleic acid probe. Under appropriate conditions of temperature and salt concentration the probe will bind only to complementary sequences in the plasmid DNA and the location of the hybridization can be detected by autoradiography. Many different kinds of nucleic acid can be used in this technique. For example, the probe may be derived from purified mRNA (usually a cDNA produced from the RNA): in this case only the cloned copies of the same mRNA will be detected.

A recent development of this technique is to use a labelled oligonucleotide (10–20 bases in length) as a hybridization probe. This probe is synthesized chemically and its sequence is designed to be complementary to the assumed sequence for a region of the mRNA coding for a known protein. The assumed sequence of the RNA is derived by use of the genetic code from the amino-acid sequence of the peptide. This is illustrated below for a oligonucleotide probe complementary to the mRNA coding for the dynophin precursor (taken from Ref. 11):

---

peptide
  sequence ....Lys Trp Asp Asn Gln ....
mRNA
  sequence 5′ ....AA$_G^A$ UGG GA$_C^U$ AA$_C^U$ CA$_G^A$ ...... 3′
probe
  mixture 3′ ......TT$_C^T$ ACC CT$_G^A$ TT$_G^A$ GT .... 5′

Because the genetic code is degenerate, we cannot be absolutely certain of the sequence of the mRNA. Conse-

quently all possible variants of the probe are synthesized and the bacterial colonies hybridized with the mixture of labelled probes. Kakidani et al.[11] recently used the probe shown above to select 75 positive clones from a library of 250,000 clones derived from pig hypothalamic mRNA. Similar oligonucleotide probes have also been used to select for cDNA clones of the enkephalin precursor[3,10,15]. This approach is ideal for cloning low abundance mRNAs (the dynorphin and enkephalin mRNAs are 0.03% and 0.1%, respectively, of total mRNA) but it does depend on at least partial knowledge of the amino-acid sequence of the corresponding protein. The specific oligonucleotides may also be used to prime reverse transcriptase in place of the oligo (dT) primer normally used. Ideally this will produce only the cDNA copy of the complementary mRNA which can then be cloned. This approach has been developed in some detail for the gastrointestinal peptide gastrin[1].

Colony hybridization can also be used with probes derived from total or partially purified mRNA populations. For example, a library of clones derived from liver mRNA has been hybridized in parallel with probes derived from the total mRNA populations of liver, hepatoma cells or fibroblasts[5]: clones hybridizing only to the liver mRNA probe were found to be of mRNA molecules uniquely expressed in liver. This strategy could be applied to any pair of RNA populations. It differs considerably from the strategies already described in that it selects not for a clone coding for a specific molecule but rather for a class of clones, in this case those encoding mRNAs expressed only in one tissue.

The second general method of clone selection is positive hybridization-translation[18]. Plasmid DNAs containing insert sequences are isolated from the bacteria, bound to nitrocellulose filters and the filters are hybridized with a sample of mRNA. Only the appropriate mRNA will hybridize to its complementary sequence in the plasmid and will remain bound to the filter while the remainder of the mRNA is washed away. The specific mRNA can then be eluted from the filter and translated in protein synthesizing system *in vitro* in the presence of [^{35}S]methionine to produce a radioactively labelled protein product. The product can be visualized by polyacrylamide gel electrophoresis and may be characterized immunologically if a suitable antibody against the protein product is available. This technique evolved from an earlier procedure, hybrid-arrested translation, in which purified cDNA plasmids added to a protein synthesizing system *in vitro* would selectively inhibit the translation of their corresponding mRNA. Hybridization-translation can be used for less abundant mRNAs than hybrid-arrested translation since it produces a positive, rather than a negative signal. The technique is often used, even where selection is not required, as a definitive proof that a clone is of the desired mRNA. In addition, this technique may be used to characterize the proteins encoded by cDNA clones which have been selected, for example, for the unique expression of their corresponding mRNA in a particular tissue.

Structure and genetics

Once a cDNA clone has been isolated and its identity confirmed, a wide variety of different experiments are possible. By using the clone as a specific hybridization probe we can study both the structure of the mRNA and its distribution and regulation, and also the DNA structure of the gene which codes for the cloned mRNA. In addition, considerable information

may be obtained about the structure of the protein coded by the cDNA clone, both from the structural information encoded in the nucleotide sequence of the cDNA insert and by use of antibodies against synthetic peptide fragments derived from that sequence.

In almost all cases the first characterization of a clone is to determine the nucleotide sequence of the cDNA insert. The DNA sequencing methods developed by Maxam and Gilbert[14] and by Sanger *et al.*[20] are an almost essential complement to recombinant DNA technology. While the two procedures are quite different experimentally, the end product in each case is the same: the nucleotide sequence can be read directly from the autoradiographic pattern of radioactively labelled bands on a high resolution acrylamide gel. The techniques are extraordinarily rapid and accurate: a 1000-base sequence can be obtained in only a few days. As with most molecular biology techniques DNA sequencing is very dependent on the availability of a wide range of restriction endonucleases. Each enzyme cleaves DNA precisely at sites defined by a specific short nucleotide sequence and there are over 100 different enzymes now known, many specific for different cleavage sites. In this case, restriction enzyme digestion of the cDNA insert will provide sets of DNA fragments of suitable size for sequence analysis. The complete sequence can then be assembled from the sequences of different and overlapping restriction fragments.

The nucleotide sequence of the cDNA insert will, of course, provide the sequence of the cloned mRNA. In addition, by use of the genetic code, we can obtain the amino acid sequence of the corresponding protein, providing information about its structure and organization. This sequence may indicate regions of importance: for example, bioactive peptides are often bracketed in the precursor sequence by pairs of basic amino acids. These peptide sequences can be synthesized chemically and tested for biological activities[13]. Furthermore, it has now been well established that antibodies produced against synthetic peptide fragments of a larger protein may also react with the whole active protein[8], providing a means to proceed back to the brain or other tissue of origin. Lastly, novel protein sequences can be compared to computerized collections of known sequences to search for possible homologies and evolutionary relationships[4].

The cDNA clone is a perfect hybridization probe for studies of the corresponding mRNA. The size, abundance and distribution of the mRNA can be visualized by the 'Northern' blotting procedure[23]. Samples of mRNA are fractionated by electrophoresis on agarose gels, transferred (or blotted) in nitrocellulose filters, and the filter hybridized with a cDNA probe labelled with ^{32}P to high specific activity. Only the mRNA molecules complementary to the cloned cDNA will hybridize and these can be detected by autoradiography: the intensity of the signal is related to the abundance of the mRNA and the size of the mRNA can be determined by its mobility relative to known standards. A comparison of mRNA samples from different tissues will provide an estimate of the tissue distribution of the mRNA. Northern blotting can also be used to detect precursors of the mature cytoplasmic mRNA in nuclear RNA preparations: these will be visible as less intense bands of larger size. For many purposes, however, gel fractionation is not essential as hybridization of the labelled probe to samples of mRNA bound directly to nitrocellulose ('dot blots') will give a measure of mRNA abundance. Alternatively, solution hybridization of either DNA

or RNA to a labelled probe will provide a more accurate measure of the frequency of a particular sequence. Any of these techniques could be used to measure changes in the steady state cytoplasmic concentration of a particular mRNA following perturbation, a lesion or drug treatment, for example. Measurements of changes in the actual rate of transcription require more detailed studies, usually involving isolated nuclei preparations, and may give clues as to the mechanism of genetic regulation of that mRNA. A recent development with great potential is to use the labelled cDNA clone to detect mRNA directly in tissue sections (*in-situ* hybridization, described by **Roberts** *et al.*

Lastly, a cDNA clone can be used to define the structure of the gene which codes for the cloned mRNA. The fragment of the genomic DNA containing the appropriate gene can be visualized by 'Southern' blotting[21], which is actually the forerunner of Northern blotting. In Southern blotting, genomic DNA is digested with a restriction enzyme and the fragments separated by agarose gel electrophoresis and transferred to nitrocellulose. Hybridization with a labelled cDNA clone will detect fragments with complementary sequences: for a single copy gene only one or two bands will be found; a larger number of bands may indicate a family of related genes. For isolation of the genes it is usual to screen a genomic clone library. The entire genome is fragmented into pieces 19–20,000 bases in length and cloned in bacteriophage. Collections of bacterial clones infected with the bacteriophage can be screened by colony hybridization using the cDNA clone as a hybridization role. In fact, the cDNA clone and the genomic library may be derived from different but closely related species. Thus, a rat cDNA clone may be used to isolate a human gene or vice versa.

Once an appropriate clone has been isolated, it is common to subclone fragments of the clone in a plasmid vector in order to characterize the gene of interest by DNA sequencing. The nucleotide sequence of the gene will provide information about possible regulatory sequences in the DNA and about the intron (intervening sequence) and exon (expressed sequence) structure of the gene. The latter may also be obtained by hybridizing mRNA to the genomic DNA clone: regions of the DNA which are not expressed in the mature mRNA (introns) will form single stranded loops (R loops) which can be detected by electron microscopy or by their sensitivity to nucleases. The cDNA clones corresponding to defined protein products are also very suitable for population genetic studies.

The present and the future

In the past 5 years recombinant DNA techniques have been directly responsible for several major advances in biology, most notably the discoveries of the intron–exon structure of genes and of DNA rearrangements in the genes coding for immunoglobulins. The impact of this technology on the neurosciences, however, has been much less extensive and has been limited largely to the characterization of neuropeptide precursors. One reason for this may be that the production of a cDNA clone for a particular protein has often been dependent on a previous characterization of the protein itself. The cases, particularly interferon[16] and the dynorphin precursor[11], where this is not true are the most interesting and suggest that recombinant DNA techniques are now overtaking the established approaches of the protein chemist.

In theory it is possible to obtain a cDNA clone corresponding to any protein, provided that there is a suitable source of mRNA and that it is possible to select the appropriate clone. In practice the major problems are involved in clone selection, particularly when there is no appropriate assay for the corresponding protein. For example, except for the cloning of mRNA encoding an AchR subunit, no clones coding for neurotransmitter receptors have been produced to date, largely because the only assays for these proteins are functional. One possible solution would be to screen for expression of the cloned protein in the bacteria and there have been several reports that this can occur (e.g. Ref. 2). This approach, however, has not been widely used with much success. One disadvantage is that proteins such as receptors may be composed of several dissimilar polypeptide chains, each coded by a separate mRNA. Each mRNA molecule will produce a separate cDNA clone and it is very unlikely that a functional receptor would be reconstituted in a single clone.

An exciting alternative is offered by eukaryotic transfection and cloning systems. It is now possible to transfer DNA to eukaryotic cells, either as naked DNA[19] or inserted in vectors such as SV40. We may be able to select for DNA segments coding for proteins which produce new activities or which complement mutated or missing functions in the recipient cells. DNA cloning techniques, known appropriately as 'search' or 'rescue', have been developed to recover the cloned DNA segments of interest[7].

A different approach to the identification of novel proteins in brain, which Greg Sutcliffe and I have taken in collaboration with Floyd Bloom, Tom Shinnick and Richard Lerner at Scripps Clinic and Research Foundation, is to select for cDNA clones of rat brain mRNA molecules which are expressed in brain but not in other tissues. Apart from the isolation of several clones for novel brain proteins which are currently under intensive study[26-28], this strategy has led to the identification of a common nucleotide sequence that may function in the regulation of brain-specific genes[22,28-30].

Clearly, recombinant DNA techniques, despite their great attraction, are not the universal solution to every problem in neuroscience. Nevertheless, I feel strongly that we have not yet tapped the full potential of this technology and molecular genetics will make a real contribution to neuroscience.

Reading list

1 Agarwal, K. L., Brunstedt, J. and Noyes, B. E. (1981) *J. Biol. Chem.* 256, 1023–1028

2 Broome, S. and Gilbert, W. (1978) *Proc. Natl Acad. Sci. U.S.A.* 75, 2746–2749

3 Comb, M., Seeburg, P. H., Adelman, J., Eiden, L. and Herbert, E. (1982) *Nature (London)* 295, 663–666

4 Dayhoff, M. O., Schwartz, R. M., Chen, H. R., Barker, W. C., Hunt, L. T. and Orcutt, B. C. (1981) *DNA* 1, 51–58

5 Derman, E., Krauter, K., Walling, L., Weinberger, C., Ray, M. and Darnell, J. E. (1981) *Cell* 23, 731–739

6 Fritsch, E. F., Maniatis, T. and Sambrook, J. (1982) *The Molecular Cloning of Eukaryotic Genes*, Cold Spring Harbor Laboratory, Cold Spring Harbor, N.Y.

7 Goldfarb, M., Shimizu, K., Perucho, M. and Wigler, M. (1982) *Nature (London)* 296, 404–409

8 Green, N., Alexander, H., Olsen, A., Alexander, S., Shinnick, T. H., Sutcliffe, J. G. and Lerner, R. A. (1982) *Cell* 28, 477–487

9 Grossman, L. and Moldave, K. (eds) (1980) *Methods in Enzymology*, Vol. 65, *Nucleic Acids* (part 1), Academic Press, New York

10 Gubler, U., Seeburg, P., Hoffman, B. J., Gage, L. P. and Udenfriend, S. (1982) *Nature (London)* 295, 206–208

11 Kakidani, H., Furutani, Y., Takahasi, H., Noda, M., Morimoto, Y., Hirose, T., Asai, M., Inayama, S., Nakanishi, S. and Numa, S. (1982) *Nature (London)* 298, 245–249

12 Lamouroux, A., Fancon Biguet, N., Samolyk, D., Privat, A., Salomon, J. C., Pujol, J. F. and Mallet, J. (1982) *Proc. Natl Acad. Sci. U.S.A.* 79, 3881–3885

13 Ling, N., Ying, S., Minick, S. and Guillemin, R. (1979) *Life Sci.* 25, 1773–1780

14 Maxam, A. M. and Gilbert, W. (1977) *Proc. Natl. Acad. Sci. U.S.A.* 74, 560–564

15 Noda, M., Furutani, H., Takahasi, H., Toyosato, M., Hirose, T., Inayama, S., Nakanishi, S. and Numa, S. (1982) *Nature (London)* 295, 202–206

16 Nogata, S., Taira, H., Hall, S., Johnsrud, L., Streuli, M., Escodi, J., Boll, W., Cantell, K. and Weissmann, C. (1980) *Nature (London)* 284, 316–320

17 Okayama, H. and Berg, P. (1982) *Mol. Cell. Biol.* 2, 161–170

18 Parnes, J. R., Velan, B., Felsenfeld, A., Ramanathan, L., Ferrini, U., Appella, E. and Seidman, J. G. (1981) *Proc. Natl Acad. Sci. U.S.A.* 78, 2253–2257

19 Ruddle, F. H. (1981) *Nature (London)* 284, 115–120

20 Sanger, F., Nicklen, S. and Coulson, A. R. (1977) *Proc. Natl Acad. Sci. U.S.A.* 74, 5463–5467

21 Southern, E. M. (1975) *J. Mol. Biol.* 98, 503–517

22 Sutcliffe, J. G., Milner, R. J., Bloom, F. E. and Lerner, R. A. (1982) *Proc. Natl Acad. Sci. U.S.A.* 79, 4226–4230

23 Thomas, P. (1980) *Proc. Natl Acad. Sci. U.S.A.* 77, 5201–5205

24 Williams, J. G. (1981) in *Genetic Engineering* (Williamson, R., ed.), Vol. 1, Academic Press, New York

25 Wu, R. (ed.) (1979) *Methods in Enzymology*, Vol. 68, *Recombinant DNA*, Academic Press, New York

26 Milner, R. J. and Sutcliffe, J. G. (1983) *Nuc. Acid Res.* 11, 5497–5520

27 Sutcliffe, J. G., Milner, R. J., Shinnick, T. M. and Bloom, F. E. (1983) *Cell* 33, 671–682

28 Sutcliffe, J. G. and Milner, R. J. (1984) *Trends in Biochemical Sciences* 9, 95–99

29 Milner, R. J., Bloom, F. E., Lai, C., Lerner, R. A. and Sutcliffe, J. G. (1984) *Proc. Natl Acad. Sci. U.S.A.* 81, 713–717

30 Sutcliffe, J. G., Milner, R. J., Gottesfeld, J. M. and Lerner, R. A. (1984) *Nature (London)* 308, 237–241

Robert J. Milner is an Assistant Member, Division of Preclinical Neuroscience and Endocrinology, Research Institute of Scripps Clinic, La Jolla, CA 92037, U.S.A.

New approaches to the identification and isolation* of hormonal polypeptides†

Viktor Mutt

The classical strategy for discovering peptide hormones via their actions is still in use but newer techniques are gaining in importance. These include looking at tissues containing cells with peptide secretory characteristics, searching for peptides with structural detail(s) characteristic of known hormone(s) and the analysis of amino acid sequences of proteins, whether determined directly or deduced from the nucleotide sequences of the corresponding mRNA.

The purification of a hormonal polypeptide from a complex mixture such as a tissue extract seldom, if ever, leads to a preparation that consists of a single polypeptide. Usually, small amounts of other polypeptides will be present in addition to the principal component. Even if purification is monitored by following the increase in specific hormonal activity as measured by bioassay, for example, there is no easy way of determining whether one of these minor 'contaminants' might be the hormone and the major one only an inert substance that co-purified with it. One way to dispel such doubts was shown by Vincent du Vigneaud and his colleagues in their work on oxytocin in 1953. They synthesized a peptide with the same sequence as a peptide isolated from the posterior pituitary, and found that both the synthetic and natural peptide showed identical oxytocic activity[13].

The situation is somewhat different when a previously known peptide is claimed to occur in organs other than those from which it was originally isolated. Here too, isolation and determination of the peptides' amino acid sequence is needed to prove identity and this has been done in some cases. However, the work sometimes stops after the determination of amino acid composition. If the composition of the isolated

material is identical with that of the previously known peptide, then it is likely that the peptides are identical, though theoretically of course, this need not be so. Peptides with identical compositions can have different sequences.

In practice, fortunately, situations such as this hardly ever occur. Sometimes, however, the results of isolation work are used to suggest that a known peptide occurs in a previously unknown location without any compositional data at all being provided. Two examples, chosen at random, may illustrate this problem. From extracts of dog

* Sometimes no clear distinction is made between identification and isolation. Here 'identification' is used in a sense synonymous with discovery, whereas 'isolation' means that the polypeptide in question has been obtained in a state of purity high enough to permit unambiguous determination of its amino acid sequence.

† The term 'hormonal polypeptide' is used here in a broad sense to describe any endogenous polypeptide capable of altering the state of activity of an organ – regardless of whether this takes place in an endocrine fashion by the peptide being released into the bloodstream and carried to its target organ, in a paracrine fashion by diffusion of the peptide to target cells in the vicinity of its cells of biosynthesis, or in a neurocrine fashion after the release of the peptide from nerves. This should be in accordance with the original derivation of the word 'hormone' from the Greek ὁρμάω, 'I rouse to activity'[4] – and nothing else.

gastric fundic mucosa, Doi and co-workers[12] purified peptide material reacting with antisera to glucagon. They found that one component of it, besides migrating like glucagon on polyacrylamide gel electrophoresis, also behaved like glucagon chromatographically, on a molecular sieving gel, and on a cation- and an anion-exchanger. In addition, the purified material behaved identically to glucagon in several bioassay systems, and, calculated on the basis of immunoreactivity, was found to be equiponent to glucagon. Does this then mean that it has been shown beyond reasonable doubt that glucagon occurs in dog fundic mucosa? Doi and co-workers consider this to be 'most likely', which it undoubtedly is.

The second example is taken from an article, by Lazarus and co-workers, with the title 'Physalaemin: an amphibian tachykinin in human lung small-cell carcinoma'[25]. The authors describe their finding that a peptide in extracts of human lung small-cell carcinoma reacted identically to the amphibian skin undecapeptide amide physalaemin with three different antisera to physalaemin. They found that the tumor material chromatographed identically to physalaemin on reverse-phase high-performance liquid chromatography (HPLC) under different chromatographic conditions. Further, the tumor material and physalaemin appeared to be affected in an identical fashion by treatment with two different proteolytic enzymes and had, on the basis of their immunoreactivities, identical pharmacological effects in a bioassay system. It is indeed tempting to conclude that the authors have shown physalaemin to be present in lung tumor tissue. This is a fascinating finding, especially in view of the extensive structural similarity of physalaemin to substance P, which is commonly held to be the mammalian counterpart of physalaemin[14]. Nevertheless, at variance with the title of their paper, the authors do not claim to have actually shown physalaemin to be present in the tumor extracts. They claim only that their results

'suggest the absence of any significant structural differences' between the tumor peptide and physalaemin. Evidently there is nothing as convincing as actual isolation and structural analysis. Structural analysis may, however, not always remain as stepwise determination of amino acid sequences but, at least in the case of small peptides, may come to imply mass-spectrographic analyses[2].

The changing methodology of peptide identification and isolation

It is a notable fact that the important polypeptide hormones insulin[1], somatotropin[27] and glucagon[43] were all isolated using the classical methods of preparative protein chemistry developed around the turn of the century; i.e. via the fractionation of aqueous polypeptide solutions with organic solvents or neutral salts, under controlled conditions of pH and temperature. However, such methods did not suffice for the isolation of certain other polypeptide hormones. For instance, despite a tremendous amount of work in many laboratories, starting with the discovery by Bayliss and Starling of secretin in 1902 (Ref. 5), neither this peptide nor any other of the subsequently discovered gastrointestinal hormones such as gastrin, cholecystokinin or pancreozymin could be isolated by this type of methodology alone. (Although information of importance for later work with more efficient methods was obtained.) The reason for this has become evident in retrospect. In terms of amount of hormone per gram of tissue, there is more than a hundred times as much insulin in the pancreas[40] and somatotropin in the pituitary[47], and ten times more glucagon in the pancreas[40], than there is, for example, secretin in the intestine[6]. However, when the old methodology was supplemented by the then new techniques of counter-current distribution, ion-exchange chromatography, molecular sieving chromatography, and various types of electrophoresis and partition and adsorption chromatography (references to these techniques may be found in

Morris and Morris)[33], the isolation of several peptide hormones became possible and additional hormones were both discovered and isolated. Thus, in the 1950s, oxytocin, vasopressin, angiotensin, α-melanotropin and corticotropin were isolated, followed in the 1960s by bradykinin, gastrin, secretin, cholecystokinin and pancreozymin (the final pair unexpectedly turned out to be a single substance), β-lipotropin, thyroliberin, the 'pancreatic polypeptide', and also the hormone-like amphibian skin peptides caerulein and physalaemin, and eledoisin from a cephalopod. The 1970s brought the isolation of substance P and luliberin, and the discovery and isolation of alytesin, bombesin, neurotensin, somatostatin, the gastric inhibitory polypeptide (GIP), the vasoactive intestinal polypeptide (VIP), motilin, the bombesin- and alytesin-related gastrin-releasing polypeptide (GRP), the enkephalins, and the endorphins (references given in Refs 11, 14 and 34).

By the mid-1960s techniques were available for the isolation of any peptide that had been identified in a tissue extract, provided that the amount of tissue available was reasonably large. In other words any porcine, bovine, ovine or chicken peptide could be isolated but many human peptides were out of reach, as were peptides from various exotic species. There would, moreover, have been little point in isolating a small amount of peptide from a small amount of tissue, even if this had been possible, since the amount of peptide would not have been enough for sequence determination with the equipment then available.

Today, however, it is often possible‡ to determine the amino acid sequence of a peptide of several tens of residues using only a few nanomoles of material[48]. Once a peptide has been isolated and its sequence determined, antibodies may be raised either

‡ Perhaps one should not generalize, since peptides differ greatly: this is especially applicable if they have been subject to unusual types of post-translational modifications, when considerably larger amounts of material may be required.

against the native or synthetic peptide and used for the isolation, by immunoadsorbent techniques, of more of the same peptide, some other form of it (for example chain elongated or shortened), or of homologous peptides from other species, provided, of course, that there is cross-reactivity with the antibodies. The adaptation of various types of liquid chromatography to high-performance forms (HPLC) has considerably facilitated peptide isolation. HPLC, which was first applied to the isolation of hormonal peptides in the case of the enkephalins[22], has quickly become a common technique in isolation work. Now it has been used for the final stages of purification of at least ten hormonal polypeptides: amunin (corticotropin-liberin)[42], dynorphin[15], glicentin[46], NPY[44], oxyntomodulin[3] (although recognized, after isolation, as a polypeptide earlier isolated from another source), PHI[44], PYY[44], the hydra head activator[7], the somatotropin-releasing factor[18,37], and urotensin[29]. No HPLC step was, however, found to be necessary in the isolation of dermophin[32] or sauvagine[31]. This list also shows that, far from abating, polypeptide isolation work seems to be gaining momentum[10].

Still further methods for peptide isolation will undoubtedly be developed. Metal chelate chromatography[36] may have wider applicability than previously recognized. The use of monoclonal antibodies[24] may prove useful not only for the isolation by affinity chromatography of known peptides or peptides cross-reacting with antibodies to such, but also for the isolation of peptides of unknown structure – provided that a sufficiently sensitive detection method can be found for identifying the clone producing antibodies to the peptide in question[28]. In general, the methods for peptide isolation, like those for determining the amino acid sequences of peptides once isolated, have reached a high degree of efficiency and continue to become ever more refined. This means that the problem of peptide isolation is becoming less difficult than that of finding a peptide worth isolating. The classical method of identifying a hormone, peptide or other substance, has been via its biological activity, either by observing the effects that the elimination of the source of the hormone has on a particular function, or by observing the effects of administration of tissue extracts known to contain the hormone in question. This method will undoubtedly continue to be used, though perhaps in more sophisticated forms, i.e. as was the case for the discovery and isolation of various liberins and statins, where changes in organ activity were not recorded directly but where the release or inhibition of release of hormones known to effect such changes[17,38] was recorded by radio-immunoassay[49]. Peptide hormones have occasionally been discovered by looking at the biological activities of side fractions obtained during the isolation of other hormones[23,26]. Now that the structures of many peptides are known, unknown hormones can be detected in tissue extracts by looking for structural features typical of known peptide hormones. For example, the search for peptides with C-terminal α-amide structures led to the isolation of the peptides NPY[44], PHI[44] and PYY[44] – which have subsequently been shown to have hormonal properties. Morphological and cytochemical investigations may reveal cells of endocrine type containing novel hormones[16].

Finally, work with receptors found by using exogenous substances may lead to the discovery of endogenous peptide ligands for these receptors, as was the case for the morphine receptor[22,45].§

Possible future developments

Theoretically, it should now be possible to isolate and sequence every peptide in a

§ Since this review was submitted for publication, Costa et al. have described the isolation and partial amino acid sequence determination of an endogenous polypeptide with agonistic action of the benzodiazepine receptors [Guidotti, A., Forchetti, C. M., Corda, M. G., Konkel, D., Bennett, C. D. and Costa, E. (1983) Proc. Natl Acad. Sci. USA 80, 3531–3535].

tissue extract and leave it to the physiologists and pharmacologists to infer which, if any, of the isolated native or synthetic peptides have hormonal properties. This approach could be taken, but the work would be rather dreary. The peptide patterns of many tissues are complex and it could be exasperating if, when sequenced, a peptide from some such extract was found to be an inactive fragment formed by proteolytic degradation of some well-known protein.

A recent and far more elegant approach is as follows. It is now known, though for reasons that are poorly understood, that protein precursors to several polypeptide hormones incorporate more than one hormone. This was first clearly shown for pro-opiomelanocortin which was found to contain both corticotropin and β-lipotropin – corticotropin in turn incorporating α-melanotropin, and β-lipotropin incorporating γ-lipotropin – and also the endorphins[9,20]. This led to an intensive and continuing search for unknown hormones in precursors to other hormonal polypeptides. Such work is now being conducted along two lines, either by the isolation and sequencing of the precursor proteins themselves[9] or, with increasing frequency, by prediction of the amino acid sequences of the precursor proteins from the sequences of the nucleotides encoding them[35]. The amino acid sequences are then scanned for segments that might, because of a sequence homology to known hormones or the presence of known peptide hormone cleavage sites, represent new hormones. So far, this approach has indeed led to the identification of new, putative hormones[21] as a result of the analyses of precursors to known hormonal peptides, but there is no reason why hormones may not be identified by scanning the amino acid sequences of other kinds of proteins‖. Determining nucleotide sequences is technically much easier than directly determining amino acid sequences, and it has been remarked that the protein-coding nucleotide sequences of the human genome will be known in their entirety within the forseeable future[30]. Could this mean that the isolation of hormonal polypeptides is becoming an unnecessary and obsolete undertaking? Should one not wait instead until the amino acid sequences of all human proteins are known from their underlying DNA sequences and then simply scan them for presumptive polypeptide hormones?

There are several reasons for assuming that this is not so. First, we have no decisive evidence as to between which amino acid residues cleavage of the protein chain to release a hormonal peptide will take place. It is true that in many instances proteolytic cleavage does occur at double-basic amino acid residues[39] and C-terminal amide groups are formed by cleavage of peptide bonds to glycine[8]. However, there are in many peptide hormones double-basic residues which may not be cleaved without the hormone losing its activity, and there is as yet no general principle stating which ones may be cleaved with release of the hormone and which result in its inactivation. Second, there are important peptide hormones whose formation does not imply the cleavage of any double-basic bonds. An example is angiotensin, which is released from its precursor by the cleavage of a leucyl–leucyl bond[41]. Third, there may be post-translational modifications, other than peptide bond cleavage, which may be necessary for hormonal activity and which will not be apparent from the analysis of amino acid sequences of precursor forms. The esterification of the phenolic group of a tyrosine residue in cholecystokinin is an example of one such modification[34]. Even if the nucleotide sequence of the human

genome is elucidated, it is improbable that the genomes of millions of other species ever will be, and among these species there may be found peptide hormones of great interest for the understanding of evolutionary and other mechanisms. Finally, not all peptides are biosynthesized by the cleavage of precursor proteins and it may be that non-ribosomally synthesized peptides with hormonal properties will be discovered, as indeed has been suggested by the finding of the non-ribosomally synthesized glutathione as a constituent of one of the hormone-like leukotriens[19]. There is, consequently, reason to believe that the identification and structural analysis of peptide hormones will remain a field of active research for a long time to come.

Reading list

1 Abel, J. J. (1926) *Proc. Natl Acad. Sci. USA* 12, 132–136
2 Barber, M., Bordoli, R. S., Sedgwick, R. D., Tyler, A. N., Garner, G. V., Gordon, D. B., Tetler, L. W. and Hider, R. C. (1982) *Biomed. Mass Spectrom.* 9, 265–268
3 Bataille, D., Tatemoto, K., Gespach, C., Jörnvall, H., Rosselin, G. and Mutt, V. (1982) *FEBS Lett.* 146, 79–86
4 Bayliss, W. M. (1920) *Principles of General Physiology*, 3rd edn, Longman Green, London
5 Bayliss, W. M. and Starling, E. H. (1902) *Proc. R. Soc. London* 69, 352–353
6 Bloom, S. R. and Polak, J. M. (1978) *Gut Hormones* (Bloom, S. R., ed.), pp. 3–18, Churchill Livingstone, Edinburgh
7 Bodenmüller, H. and Schaller, C. (1981) *Nature (London)* 293, 579–580
8 Bradbury, A. F., Finnie, M. D. A. and Smyth, D. G. (1982) *Nature (London)* 298, 686–688
9 Chrétien, M., Benjannet, S., Gossard, F., Gianoulakis, C., Crine, P., Lis, M. and Seidah, N. G. (1979) *Can. J. Biochem.* 57, 1111–1121
10 Clark, B. F. C. (1981) *Nature (London)* 292, 491–492
11 Dayhoff, M. O. (ed.) (1972) *Atlas of Protein Sequence and Structure*, Vol. 5, Suppl. 1–3, The National Biomedical Research Foundation, Silver Spring, MD
12 Doi, K., Prentki, M., Yip, C., Muller, W. A., Jeanrenaud, B. and Vranic, M. (1979) *J. Clin. Invest.* 63, 525–531
13 du Vigneaud, V., Ressler, C., Swan, J. M., Roberts, C. W. and Katsoyannis, P. G. (1953) *J. Am. Chem. Soc.* 75, 4879–4880

|| Since this review was submitted for publication, Hoffman *et al.* have suggested that certain structurally closely related proteins, the amino acid sequences of which were deduced from the nucleotide sequences of clones of DNA complementary to mRNA isolated from the skin of *Xenopus laevis,* might be the precursors of a 24 amino acid hormonal polypeptide named PYL[a] (peptide with N-terminal tyrosine and C-terminal leucine amide) [Hoffmann, W., Richter, K. and Kreil, G. (1983) *EMBO J.* 2, 711–714].

14 Erspamer, V. and Melchiorri, P. (1980) *Trends Pharmacol. Sci.* 1, 391–395

15 Fischli, W., Goldstein, A., Hunkapiller, M. W. and Hood, L. E. (1982) *Proc. Natl Acad. Sci. USA* 79, 5435–5437

16 Grube, D. and Forssmann, W. G. (1979) *Horm. Metab. Res.* 11, 589–606

17 Guillemin, R. (1978) in *Les Prix Nobel,* pp. 160–193, Almqvist and Wiksell International, Stockholm

18 Guillemin, R., Brazeau, P., Böhlen, P., Esch, F., Ling, N. and Wehrenberg, W. B. (1982) *Science* 218, 585–586

19 Hammarström, S., Murphy, R. C., Samuelsson, B., Clark, D. A., Mioskowski, C. and Corey, E. J. (1979) *Biochem. Biophys. Res. Commun.* 91, 1266–1272

20 Herbert, E. and Uhler, M. (1982) *Cell* 30, 1–2

21 Hillyard, C. J., Abeyasekera, G., Craig, R. K., Myers, C., Stevenson, J. C. and MacIntyre, I. (1983) *Lancet* i, 846–848

22 Hughes, J., Smith, T., Morgan, B. and Fothergill, L. (1975) *Life Sci.* 16, 1753–1758

23 Kimmel, J. R., Pollock, H. G. and Hazelwood, R. L. (1968) *Endocrinology* 83, 1323–1330

24 Köhler, G. and Milstein, C. (1975) *Nature (London)* 256, 495–497

25 Lazarus, L. H., DiAugustine, R. P., Johnke, G. D. and Hernandez, O. (1983) *Science* 219, 80–81

26 Li, C. H. (1968) *Arch. Biol. Med. Exp.* 5, 55–61

27 Li, C. H., Evans, H. M. and Simpson, M. E. (1945) *J. Biol. Chem.* 159, 353–366

28 Luben, R. A., Brazeau, P., Böhlen, P. and Guillemin, R. (1982) *Science* 218, 887–889

29 MacCannell, K. L. and Lederis, K. (1983) *Fed. Proc. Fed. Am. Soc. Exp. Biol.* 42, 91–95

30 McKusick, V. A. (1980) *J. Hered.* 71, 370–391

31 Montecucchi, P. C., Anastasi, A., de Castiglione, R. and Erspamer, V. (1980) *Int. J. Peptide Protein Res.* 16, 191–199

32 Montecucchi, P. C., de Castiglione, R., Piani, S., Gozzini, L. and Erspamer, V. (1981) *Int. J. Pept. Protein Res.* 17, 275–283

33 Morris, C. J. O. R. and Morris, P. (eds) (1976) *Separation Methods in Biochemistry,* Pitman Publishing, Bath

34 Mutt, V. (1982) in *Vitamins and Hormones* (Munson, P. L., Glover, J., Diczfalusy, E. and Olson, R. E., eds), Vol. 39, pp. 231–427, Academic Press, New York

35 Nakanishi, S., Inoue, A., Kita, T., Nakamura, M., Chang, A. C. Y., Cohen, S. N. and Numa, S. (1979) *Nature (London)* 278, 423–427

36 Porath, J., Carlsson, J., Olsson, I. and Belfrage, G. (1975) *Nature (London)* 258, 598–599

37 Rivier, J., Spiess, J., Thorner, M. and Vale, W. (1982) *Nature (London)* 300, 276–278

38 Schally, A. V. (1978) in *Les Prix Nobel,* pp. 201–234, Almqvist and Wiksell International, Stockholm

39 Seidah, N. G., Gossard, F., Crine, P., Gianoulakis, C., Routhier, R. and Chrétien, M. (1980) in *Precursor Processing in the Biosynthesis of Proteins* (Zimmerman, M., Mumford, R. A. and Steiner, D. F., eds), Vol. 343, pp. 443–447, The New York Academy of Sciences, New York

40 Siedel, V. W. and Schöne, H. H. (1969) in *Handbuch des Diabetes Mellitus, Band I* (Pfeiffer, E. F., ed.), pp. 281–286, The New York Academy of Sciences, New York

41 Skeggs, Jr, L. T., Kahn, J. R. and Shumway, N. P. (1956) *J. Exp. Med.* 103, 301–307

42 Spiess, J., Rivier, J., Rivier, C. and Vale, W. (1981) *Proc. Natl Acad. Sci. USA* 78, 6517–6521

43 Staub, A., Sinn, L. and Behrens, O. K. (1955) *J. Biol. Chem.* 214, 619–632

44 Tatemoto, K. (1982) *Proc. Natl Acad. Sci. USA* 79, 5485–5489

45 Terenius, L. and Wahlström, A. (1974) *Acta Pharmacol. Toxicol.* 35, Suppl. 1, 55

46 Thim, L. and Moody, A. J. (1981) *Regul. Pept.* 2, 139–150

47 Wilhelmi, A. E. (1974) in *Handbook of Physiology,* Sect. 7, Vol. 4:2, pp. 59–78, American Physiological Society, Washington, DC

48 Wittmann-Liebold, B. (1982) in *Methods in Protein Sequence Analysis* (Elzinga, M., ed.), pp. 27–63, Humana Press, Clifton, New Jersey

49 Yalow, R. S. (1978) in *Les Prix Nobel,* pp. 243–264, Almqvist and Wiksell International, Stockholm

Viktor Mutt is at the Department of Biochemistry II, Karolinska Institute, S-104 01 Stockholm, Sweden.

New approaches to the study of rapid events underlying neurotransmitter action

Robert N. McBurney

The introduction of two new biophysical techniques, fluctuation analysis and single-channel recording, to the study of neurotransmitter action has greatly advanced our understanding of events in the postsynaptic membrane at synapses. Future application of these techniques to the membrane actions of putative peptide transmitters will undoubtedly provide essential information about the roles they play in the nervous system.

Our conventional ideas about synaptic transmission include a concept that the direct consequence of transmitter molecules binding to receptor sites is the opening of ion channels to increase membrane conductance in discrete regions of the postsynaptic cell. Although a number of situations have recently been revealed where neither such a direct nor localized action of neurotransmitters seems to occur (see other articles in this book), a direct activation of ion channels following transmitter–receptor binding is still thought to underlie most 'fast' synaptic potentials.

One aim of this article will be to examine the advances in our understanding of this process of channel activation that have been made over the past decade or so by the application to studies of synaptic transmission of two biophysical techniques: analysis of fluctuations in membrane current responses to receptor agonists; and patch-clamp recording of single-channel events. Each technique is outlined in a separate box on the following pages. Further aims of the article will be to draw on the results obtained by these techniques to comment on: the postsynaptic sites and modes of drug action; the question 'Why so many neurotransmitters?'; and the problem of identifying a particular neurotransmitter in a range of candidate molecules.

Since there have been many excellent reviews of this subject over the past few years[5, 6, 8, 9, 12, 17, 24, 27, 29, 31, 35], this commentary is not intended to be a definitive treatment of the techniques nor is it planned as an essentially biophysical treatise. Hopefully its main function will be to bring some interesting results and ideas to the attention of readers whose primary interest is in the other articles of this collection.

Contributions to our understanding of channel activation

To outline the insights that have been gained in recent years it is probably worthwhile starting from a primitive kinetic scheme which might describe channel activation by neurotransmitters and to point out where, in relation to this 'model', the advances have been made.

The direct activation of membrane ion channels by transmitter–receptor binding can be represented most simply by the kinetic scheme shown below in equation I.

$$nT + nR \sim \text{Closed channel } (\gamma_c) \underset{\alpha}{\overset{\beta}{\rightleftharpoons}}$$

$$n(TR) \sim \text{Open channel } (\gamma_o) \qquad (I)$$

where nT represents the n transmitter molecules that must bind to the n receptor sites (nR) associated with a closed ion channel (conductance γ_c) to induce channel opening with rate constant β and an increase in membrane conductance per open channel of $\gamma_o - \gamma_c$. Channel closure (and in this model the unbinding of transmitter molecules) occurs with rate constant α.

The early results obtained by fluctuation analysis[1,22] were interpreted as if they arose from an homogeneous population of ion channels activated by a process similar to

a. multiple conductance states

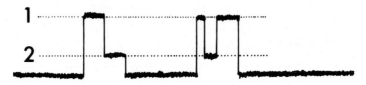

b. flicker

c. bursts

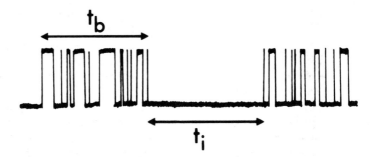

d. cluster

bursts

Fig. 1. *Sketches which illustrate some interesting features of single ACh-activated ion-channel events that have been revealed using recent developments of the extracellular patch-clamp technique. The features have been exaggerated in the sketches. The durations of the records shown in **a** and **b** are each about 50 ms. The durations of records **c** and **d** are about 2 s and 20 s, respectively.*

that described above. In early fluctuation studies, those spectra that could not easily be fitted by the curve representing equation II were not usually interpreted.

$$S(f)/S(0) = 1/[1 + (2\pi\tau f)^2] \qquad (II)$$

It was generally assumed that a single ion channel had only two conductance states and, once having been induced to open, it stayed open at the same conductance level until it closed.

One important finding of these investigations was that the average open-time of acetylcholine (ACh)-activated ion channels (and its sensitivity to temperature and membrane voltage) closely matched the time constant of the decay phase of end-plate currents[1]. This result strongly indicated that the decay of these synaptic currents was determined by the closure of the postsynaptic channels rather than by the falling transmitter concentration in the synaptic cleft, which must therefore have been much faster than the current decay. From the amplitude of miniature end-plate potentials or currents and the calculated amplitude of the corresponding single-channel events, it was possible to calculate the number of postsynaptic ion channels opened by a quantum of transmitter[1,22].

In the case of direct recording of the behaviour of single ion channels in the presence of receptor agonists, the early recordings[28] were made with such a low signal-to-noise (S/N) ratio and such limited recording bandwidth that it appeared that the simple closed-opened-closed sequence was confirmed. However, recently with the significant improvements in S/N ratio and bandwidth afforded by the creation of 'giga-seals'[21,33] some interesting characteristics of channel activation have been revealed in patch-clamp experiments.

(a) Multiple conductance states

O. Hamill and B. Sakmann have reported[21] that ACh-activated channels in cultured 'myoballs' occasionally exhibit transitions to a lower conductance state from the main conductance level of their open state (Fig. 1a). This behaviour is certainly not taken into account in the simple kinetic scheme outlined before. With further investigation it should be possible to discover whether such multiple conductance states are a general property of agonist-activated ion channels, and to modify the kinetic scheme to account for the observations. One interesting possibility is that the lower conductance state might be associated with the unbinding of an agonist molecule from the receptor–ionophore complex. This might also be revealed as a small component in equilibrium binding studies.

(b) Flicker

D. Colquhoun and B. Sakmann have reported[11] that single ACh-activated channel events recorded from the perisynaptic region of frog muscle consist of a transition from the closed state to the open state, followed by brief transitions towards the closed state and back to the open state before the channel finally closes (Fig. 1b). This 'flickering' seems not to result from blockage of the open channel, at least by the agonist, and the interpretation that Colquhoun and Sakmann favour is that the closures arise from multiple closed-open-closed transitions during single-receptor occupancy.

Once again a more complete analysis of this phenomenon should increase our understanding of the detailed kinetics of channel activation. Some of this analysis has already begun[2,18]. Since a similar phenomenon has been observed for glutamate-activated channels in locust muscle[16] and for muscimol-activated channels in cultured spinal neurons (Barker, Jackson, Lecar, McBurney and Mathers, unpublished observations), it may also prove to be a general feature of channel activation by neurotransmitters.

(c) Bursts during desensitization

Information about the behaviour of ion channels in their closed states has been gained by observing the patterns of occur-

Fluctuation analysis

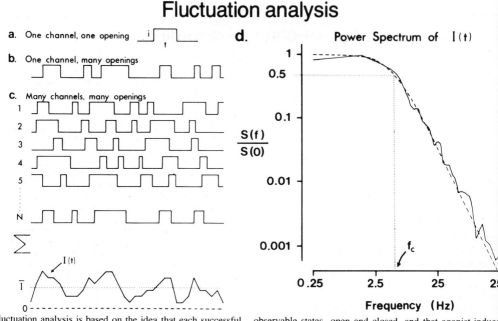

Fluctuation analysis is based on the idea that each successful activation of an ion channel produces a brief pulse of current of fixed amplitude, i, and of duration, t (see part **a** of the figure in this box). The amplitude of the current pulse is the product of the channel conductance, γ, and the driving force on ion movements, $V_m - V_n$, where V_m is the membrane potential of the cell and V_n is the null potential, at which no current flows when the ion channel opens (also called the reversal potential).

The time each channel stays open is the time taken for the open channel to gain sufficient energy to exceed the energy barrier for the channel closing step (see 'model' kinetic scheme in the main text). Since the process of acquiring energy depends on interactions between a channel molecule and its environment and since each individual molecule will not have the same initial energy content (Boltzman's distribution), open-times will be random variables drawn from a Poisson (exponential) distribution. The mean value of this distribution is the average open-time, τ, of the ion channel. τ is the reciprocal of the rate constant, α, for the closing step in the kinetic scheme outlined in the main text.

In the presence of a constant concentration of an agonist, each channel may be activated a number of times (see part **b** of the figure). Like the channel closing process the activation process will also be random – depending upon the random collisions of agonist molecules with receptors generating sufficient energy for the agonist–receptor–channel complex to exceed the energy barrier for the opening step. In a membrane containing many channels that can be activated by the same agonist, the independent activity of a large number of randomly activated ion channels will sum to produce an overall membrane current response, I(t), which fluctuates about a mean level, $\bar{I}$ (see part **c** of the figure).

This fluctuating current response can be analysed to yield estimates of γ and τ for channels activated by a particular agonist. The theoretical basis of this analysis has been presented in a number of reviews and will not be dealt with here. Suffice it to say that the analysis is based on two major relationships which can be derived by assuming that ion channels have only two

observable states, open and closed, and that agonist-induce transitions between closed and open states (and subseque open–closed transitions) are generated by Poisson processe The relationships are as follows:

$$\sigma^2/\bar{I} = i(1 - p)$$

where σ^2 is the variance of the current fluctuations about th mean level, $\bar{I}$, and p is the probability of a channel being open i the presence of a particular concentration of an agonist; and

$$S(f) = S(0)/[1 + (2\pi \tau f)^2]$$

where S(f) is the power spectrum of the current fluctuation essentially a measure of the contribution to the variance, σ^2, membrane current fluctuations from individual frequencies, of oscillation, S(0) is the zero frequency asymptote of S(f), an τ is the average open-time of the underlying ion-channel event

The technical details of recording membrane curre responses in particular preparations are outside the scope of th review. Voltage-clamp procedures, often using two intracell lar microelectrodes, are usually required to record curre responses without associated changes in membrane potentia Current records are usually filtered and then digitized at fixe time intervals by a laboratory computer. The mean level membrane current and additional variance in membrane curre caused by the agonist are calculated from the digitized record The power spectrum is also calculated from the digital values a Fourier Transform procedure. If a low probability, $p \ll 1$, channels being open is assumed, i can be calculated from equ tion 1, and γ can be calculated if the driving force is known. graph of the power spectrum (see part **d** of the figure) can be fi ted with the curve representing equation 2, and the frequenc f_c, at which S(f)/S(0) = 0.5 determined. At this value, τ $1/2\pi f_c$ (see equation 2). When these two procedures have bee completed the mean response, $\bar{I}$, to the agonist can be re resented in terms of three parameters, γ, τ, and n, the avera; frequency of channel openings for a particular agonist conce tration. Thus:

$$\bar{I} = n\tau\gamma(V_m - V_n)$$

Single-channel recording

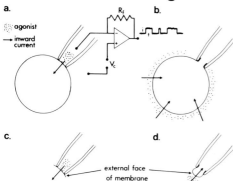

a. agonist; inward current; R_f; V_c

b.

c.

d. external face of membrane

tudes is usually consistent with a fixed open-state conductance (but see main text), while distributions of open-state lifetimes usually follow a falling exponential curve consistent with a Poisson process for the channel closing step.

The creation of adequate seals has been a key factor in the application of this technique to different preparations. The requirement for direct access to the cell's surface membrane has clearly prevented its application to many cell types. The most commonly used preparations have been nerve and muscle cells in culture, although the technique has also been applied to the perisynaptic region of frog muscle[11] and locust muscle[15, 16, 30].

An exciting development in this technique came in 1980 when F. Sigworth and E. Neher reported[33] that if suction was applied to the recording pipette as it was placed on a surface membrane, a very high resistance seal ($>10^9$ Ω) could be created. Since the seal resistance (R_{seal}) largely determines the baseline current noise (inversely proportional to $\sqrt{R_{seal}}$) of the recording system, the greatly increased resistance significantly improves the current resolution of the system and the recording bandwidth, which previously had been limited to improve resolution. Not only has the creation of 'giga-seals' improved current resolution and recording bandwidth, and revealed interesting details of channel activation (see main text), but the tight attachment of the electrode rim to the cell membrane has allowed a number of workers to develop variations of the patch-clamp technique to suit their particular application[20]. The 'excised patch' preparation (inside-out or outside-out) shown in parts c and d of the figure allows access to either the inside or outside surface of the cell membrane while recording, and 'whole-cell recording' (see part b of the figure) permits the application of voltage-clamp techniques to small cells or restricted regions of cells not amenable to conventional voltage clamping with intracellular microelectrodes.

The potential of this technique is enormous and the next few years will undoubtedly see the extracellular patch electrode achieve the same, but to some extent complementary, usefulness as the intracellular microelectrode.

Single agonist-activated ion-channel events can be observed directly with the extracellular patch-clamp technique. The first recordings, of acetylcholine-activated channel events in denervated frog muscle, were reported by E. Neher and B. Sakmann in 1976[28]. The past six years or so have seen a tremendous explosion in the use of the technique which is continually being developed to increase its resolving power and to extend its application to new experimental situations[20].

The basic features of the technique are illustrated in part a of the figure in this box. A specially constructed glass pipette seals off a small patch of membrane (about 1 μm in diameter) on the surface of a cell from the rest of the surface membrane. The successful interaction of agonist molecules (in the solution inside the pipette) with receptor–channel complexes on the patch of membrane generates pulses of ionic current (see part a of the figure) which are recorded with a low-noise current-to-voltage converter (R_f, feedback resistor; V_c, command voltage). If a sufficiently low concentration of agonist is used, individual current events can be seen and if a large number of events are measured the single-channel current, i, and average open-time, τ, can be determined. The distribution of channel current ampli-

---

rence of single-channel events in the presence of desensitizing concentrations of the agonist. B. Sakmann, J. Patlak and E. Neher have reported[32] that, in denervated muscle fibres of frogs, acetylcholine concentrations sufficient to cause desensitization generate single-channel current pulses which occur in groups (Fig. 1c). Their interpretation of these findings is that, unlike the ion channels of the simple scheme presented above, channels in this preparation can be found in at least three states: open; closed but activatable; and closed and not activatable (desensitized). The average duration of bursts of events, $\bar{t_b}$, and the average inter-burst interval, $\bar{t_i}$, reflect the rate constants of the conversion

between closed and desensitized states. At a slower time resolution it is apparent that groups of 'bursts' occur in 'clusters' with unusually long intervals between them (Fig. 1d). This very slow kinetic process has been tentatively related to the onset of and recovery from desensitization.

In the light of the multiple conductance states, flicker, bursts and clusters, which have been observed for ACh-activated ion channels, it is clear that the simple kinetic scheme is not adequate to account for the behaviour of these channels. Such an idea is certainly not very new since, in 1957, B. Katz and S. Thesleff came to similar conclusions about the characteristics of end-plate voltage responses to ACh in their article on desensitization[25]. What is new is the hope that this approach to defining the kinetic scheme of channel activation by receptor agonists through the use of single-channel recording will yield precise information about the states in which a receptor–channel complex can exist, and the rates of transition between the various states. Such information is an essential element in our understanding of postsynaptic events in general and of drug action at synapses in particular.

Modes of drug action

If the membrane current response to an agonist can be expressed as the product of the average frequency, n, of channel openings and the average effect, $\tau\gamma(V_m - V_n)$, produced by each opening (see 'Fluctuation analysis' box), then drugs which alter the responses of nerve and muscle cells to neurotransmitters can be studied in terms of their effects on n, γ and τ. For instance, drugs which potentiate the postsynaptic response to receptor agonists might be exerting their effects by increasing either n, γ or τ. An investigation of the effects of a particular drug on the properties of agonist-activated ion channels should reveal something about its mode of action.

To take just one example, this approach has been used very successfully by R. Study and J. Barker[34] to determine the modes of action of two quite different anticonvulsant drugs, $(-)$pentobarbital and diazepam, both of which potentiate membrane responses to γ-aminobutyric acid (GABA) in cultured central neurons. Although both drugs potentiate GABA-induced responses in these neurons, an effect consistent with their anticonvulsant properties, they achieve this end by different means. The barbiturate increased the response by prolonging the channel open-time, τ, while the benzodiazepine acts to increase the frequency of channel openings, n.

A similar conclusion might have been drawn if complete dose-response curves of membrane current versus GABA concen-

tration had been examined under control conditions and in the presence of each drug. However, since this is usually an almost impossible task in electrophysiological experiments, an examination of the effects of each drug on the properties of GABA-activated channels clearly provided the most direct evidence of the very different modes of action of these drugs.

The power of this approach in pharmacological investigations has been confirmed by many workers who have used either fluctuation analysis or single-channel recording to study the detailed modes of action of a wide range of drugs which modify the postsynaptic responses to receptor agonists in a variety of different tissues. A good deal of this work is reviewed in detail elsewhere[6, 17, 19, 27, 35].

Agonists' effects on channel properties

Wherever the properties of ion channels coupled to different receptor types (for example cholinergic, glutamatergic, GABA-ergic) have been determined for activation by a range of agonists, it has been found that each agonist of a particular receptor type generates ion-channel events with different average properties. The differences in channel properties are more commonly seen as different open-times (see Table I for some examples).

While there are many thermodynamic reasons to account for this observation, more important than an explanation of the phenomenon itself might be the hint it provides to help us answer the question 'Why so many neurotransmitters?', and the tool it provides for transmitter identification.

(a) 'Why so many neurotransmitters?'

The input–output function of neuronal networks is clearly important in the processing of information in the CNS, and the postsynaptic action of a particular neurotransmitter is an important aspect of this input–output function. If different transmitter molecules generate different postsynaptic effects, not just in terms of excitation and inhibition but in terms of the duration of the postsynaptic conductance change per released quantum, they will contribute different characteristics to the input–output function of neuronal networks. Perhaps the reason that the CNS uses so many different classes of molecules to produce either excitation or inhibition is to take advantage of the characteristics of their postsynaptic action to give different 'weights' to excitation and inhibition produced by different inputs in a particular network.

(b) Application to transmitter identification

One of the criteria used in transmitter identification is that the candidate substance must mimic the action of the natural transmitter[26]. In the light of the effect of different agonists on channel properties (see Table I) the word 'mimic' takes on a more precise meaning than simply 'depolarize (or hyperpolarize) the cell'. The candidate substance must generate ion-channel events whose characteristics (γ and τ) are identical to those produced by the natural transmitter.

If the decay of the synaptic current generated by a quantum of the natural transmitter is governed by the closure of ion channels rather than by the falling transmitter concentration in the synaptic cleft, then the time constant of this decay phase (τ_d) should equal the average open-time (τ) of transmitter-activated ion channels. Any transmitter candidate which activated channels whose average open-time was greater than τ_d could be eliminated from the list.

This general approach to transmitter identification has proved useful at neuromuscular junctions of vertebrates[1] and invertebrates[13,14], and for one class of spontaneous synaptic currents in cultured central neurons[3]. The use of this 'agonist fingerprint' in quantal synaptic currents has also been used in an elegant series of experiments by D. Colquhoun, W. Large and H. Rang[10] to study the incorporation of a false transmitter substrate, monoethylcholine (MECh), into the transmitter pool of nerve terminals at motor end-plates and its release as acetylmonoethylcholine (AMECh) in quanta which, due to the shorter open-time of AMECh-activated channels, generate synaptic currents with durations different from those of quanta containing only ACh.

TABLE I. Open-times of ion channels activated by different agonists

Experimental preparation	Agonist	Average channel open-time (ms)	Refs
Frog muscle, extracellular recording (20–25°C)	Acetylcholine	1.0	22, 23
	Carbachol	0.3	
	Suberyldicholine	1.6	
Frog muscle, voltage clamp (10–15°C)	Acetylcholine	3.2	7
	Suberyldicholine	5.6	
	3-Phenylpropyltrimethyl ammonium	0.8	
Crab muscle, extracellular recording (23°C)	Glutamate	1.4	13
	Aspartate	0.8	
	Cystate	0.9	
Locust muscle, patch clamp (23°C)	Glutamate	2.3	15
	Fluoroglutamate	1.4	
	Quisqualate	6.4	
Cultured spinal neurons, voltage clamp (23°C)	γ-Aminobutyric acid	30.4	4
	Taurine	2.3	
	Muscimol	76.3	
	Isoguvacine	16.5	

Relevance of the techniques to peptide neurotransmitters

Other articles of this book present the growing evidence that peptides might serve many functions in the transmission of information in the nervous system, including the generation of both 'fast' and 'slow' synaptic potentials. Clearly the techniques of fluctuation analysis and single-channel recording will play important roles in experimental work: to identify particular peptide transmitters; to reveal the detailed kinetics of channel activation by certain peptides; and to determine the sites and modes of action of drugs which effect peptidergic transmission. There is an enormous contribution still to be made by these techniques in studies of the postsynaptic action of neurotransmitters in general. In the particular case of postsynaptic events underlying peptide-mediated 'fast' synaptic potentials, the field is wide open.

Reading list

1 Anderson, C. R. and Stevens, C. F. (1973) *J. Physiol. (London)* 235, 655–692

2 Auerbach, A. and Sachs, F. (1983) *Biophys. J.* 42, 1–10

3 Barker, J. L. and McBurney, R. N. (1979) *Proc. R. Soc. London, Ser. B* 206, 319–327

4 Barker, J. L. and Mathers, D. A. (1981) *Science* 212, 358–361

5 Colquhoun, D. (1975) *Annu. Rev. Pharmacol.* 15, 307–325

6 Colquhoun, D. (1979) in *The Receptors* (O'Brien, R. D., ed.), Vol. 1, pp. 93–142, Plenum Publishing Company, New York

7 Colquhoun, D., Dionne, V. E., Steinbach, J. H. and Stevens, C. F. (1975) *Nature (London)* 253, 204–206

8 Colquhoun, D. and Hawkes, A. G. (1977) *Proc. R. Soc. London, Ser. B* 199, 231–262

9 Colquhoun, D. and Hawkes, A. G. (1981) *Proc. R. Soc. London, Ser. B* 211, 205–235

10 Colquhoun, D., Large, W. A. and Rang, H. P. (1977) *J. Physiol. (London)* 266, 361–395

11 Colquhoun, D. and Sakmann, B. (1981) *Nature (London)* 294, 464–466

12 Conti, F. and Wanke, E. (1975) *Q. Rev. Biophys.* 8, 451–506

13 Crawford, A. C. and McBurney, R. N. (1976) *Proc. R. Soc. London, Ser. B* 192, 481–489

14 Crawford, A. C. and McBurney, R. N. (1976) *J. Physiol. (London)* 258, 205–225

15 Cull-Candy, S. G., Miledi, R. and Parker, I. (1981) *J. Physiol. (London)* 321, 195–210

16 Cull-Candy, S. G. and Parker, I. (1982) *Nature (London)* 295, 410–412

17 De Felice, L. J. (1977) *Int. Rev. Neurobiol.* 20, 169–208

18 Dionne, V. E. and Leibowitz, M. D. (1982) *Biophys. J.* 39, 253–261

19 Gage, P. W. and Hamill, O. P. (1981) *Int. Rev. Physiol.* 25, 1–45

20 Hamill, O. P., Marty, A., Neher, E., Sakmann, B. and Sigworth, F. J. (1981) *Pfluegers Arch.* 391, 85–100

21 Hamill, O. P. and Sakmann, B. (1981) *Nature (London)* 294, 462–464

22 Katz, B. and Miledi, R. (1972) *J. Physiol. (London)* 224, 665–700

23 Katz, B. and Miledi, R. (1973) *J. Physiol. (London)* 230, 707–717

24 Katz, B. and Miledi, R. (1977) in *Motor Innervation of Muscle* (Thesleff, S., ed.), pp. 31–50, Academic Press, New York

25 Katz, B. and Thesleff, S. (1957) *J. Physiol. (London)* 138, 63–80

26 McLennan, H. (1963) *Synaptic Transmission*, W. B. Saunders, Philadelphia

27 Mathers, D. A. and Barker, J. L. (1982) *Int. Rev. Neurobiol.* 23, 1–34

28 Neher, E. and Sakmann, B. (1976) *Nature (London)* 260, 799–802

29 Neher, E. and Stevens, C. F. (1977) *Annu. Rev. Biophys. Bioeng.* 6, 345–381

30 Patlak, J. B., Gration, K. A. F. and Usherwood, P. N. R. (1979) *Nature (London)* 278, 643–645

31 Rang, H. P. (1975) *Q. Rev. Biophys.* 7, 283–299

32 Sakmann, B., Patlak, J. and Neher, E. (1980) *Nature (London)* 286, 71–73

33 Sigworth, F. and Neher, E. (1980) *Nature (London)* 187, 447–449

34 Study, R. E. and Barker, J. L. (1981) *Proc. Natl Acad. Sci. USA* 78, 7180–7184

35 Wray, D. (1980) *Prog. Drug Res.* 24, 9–56

Robert McBurney is at the Department of Physiological Sciences, The Medical School, University of Newcastle upon Tyne, Newcastle upon Tyne NE1 7RU, UK.

Slow cholinergic excitation – a mechanism for increasing neuronal excitability

D. A. Brown

There are two quite distinct types of cholinergic transmission in the vertebrate nervous system: a rapid form, mediated via nicotinic receptors; and a slow form, mediated via muscarinic receptors. Taking the sympathetic ganglion as an example of a system displaying both forms of transmission, it is argued that, as well as being mechanistically different, they subserve quite different functions: nicotinic transmission provides a 'fast-switching' mechanism for the faithful transfer of frequency-coded information through the synapse; whereas muscarinic transmission regulates neuronal discharge patterns over prolonged time-periods, by closing a specific subset of voltage-sensitive K^+ channels. Such 'modulation' of excitability may be fundamental to other forms of slow synaptic excitation.

Much current thinking about synaptic transmission derives from observations on nicotinic cholinergic transmission at loci such as the neuromuscular junction. Here, the cycle of transmitter release and post-junctional effect is complete within a very few milliseconds after the arrival of each incoming nerve impulse. Such rapidity of information transfer is assured by the close apposition of the pre- and post-junctional membranes, and by the tight and direct coupling between the acetylcholine (ACh) receptor and the ionic channel whose opening initiates the post-junctional response. In consequence, individual impulses can be transmitted across the junction with minimal disruption of their frequency coding. Such fast-switching transmission constitutes the basic process whereby the potential circuitry of the nervous system inherent in its anatomical connectivity can be rapidly and precisely activated. In the vertebrate nervous system the synaptic switches are probably operated by a relatively restricted group of transmitter substances – ACh (at nicotinic synapses), dicarboxylic excitat-

ory amino acids, and the inhibitory amino acids, glycine and γ-aminobutyric acid.

In contrast, it seems likely that the large (and rapidly increasing) number of other transmitters act in a very different way – not to transmit the individual signals through the circuit in a temporally faithful manner, but rather to control the rate and amount of information transfer in selected pathways within the nervous system over fairly extended time periods. Indeed, some synaptic events operated by ACh itself conform to this pattern: these are the 'slow' forms of cholinergic transmission which involve muscarinic (atropine-sensitive) postsynaptic receptors, and which constitute the prevalent form of cholinergic transmission in the CNS.

Fast and slow cholinergic excitatory transmission in sympathetic ganglia

The sympathetic ganglion provides an illuminating example of a neural pathway in which both fast and slow forms of cholinergic excitation are manifest in the same neurons. Fig. 1 shows these two types

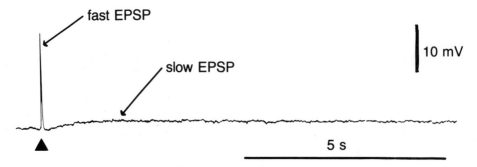

Fig. 1. *Two excitatory synaptic potentials (EPSPs) – fast (nicotinic) and slow (muscarinic) – recorded from a frog sympathetic neuron after a single shock to the preganglionic trunk* (from Ref. 2).

of excitatory postsynaptic potential (EPSP) in a large ('B-type') neuron in a frog sympathetic ganglion. Both potentials result from the release of ACh from the preganglionic fibres – possibly from the same preganglionic fibres, since each cell is innervated by only a very few, and sometimes one, fibre[45].

The initial 'fast' EPSP results from the action of the ACh on curare-sensitive nicotinic receptors. This potential lasts some 20–30 ms, and results from the transient opening of cation-selective ionic channels triggered by the ACh[31,32]. The same mechanism underlies the fast EPSP in mammalian sympathetic ganglia[38,41]. This fast EPSP is analogous to the transmission process at the neuromuscular junction, and serves to convey the individual afferent impulses through the synapse with minimal latency and distortion.

The 'slow' EPSP was first described some time ago by Libet and his colleagues[27,43] and by Nishi[35]. It differs from the fast EPSP in three important respects. Firstly, it is blocked by atropine, not by curare, and so results from the action of ACh on a quite different type of postsynaptic receptor – the muscarinic receptor. Secondly, it is slow to develop, with a latency of several hundred milliseconds, and lasts several seconds even after a single shock. Thirdly, it is not associated with an increased ionic conductance of the postsynaptic membrane[27,35]: on the contrary, Weight and Votava[44] obtained evidence to

suggest that it resulted from a reduced conductance to K^+ ions. Then, so long as the membrane potential is more positive than the equilibrium potential for K^+ ion distribution, such that there is a steady net outward movement of K^+ ions, the membrane will depolarize because the rate of outward positive charge transfer is reduced.

However, if viewed simply as a means of initiating postsynaptic spikes by depolarizing the cell to spike threshold, this channel-closure mechanism seems both cumbersome and inefficient – cumbersome, because a very large fraction of the resting K^+ channels need to be shut to produce an adequate depolarization; and inefficient, because a slowly rising depolarization would tend to raise the threshold for spike generation, by promoting inactivation of the Na^+ channels, and so reduce excitability. Moreover, the very slowness of the event would disrupt the normal frequency coding of information transfer through the pathway.

M-current inhibition

Recent experiments using voltage-clamp techniques[2–4,8] have provided a more precise definition of the ionic mechanism of the slow EPSP, and prompt some re-evaluation of its function. These experiments have revealed that the species of K^+ conductance blocked by the transmitter is not a passive linear component of resting membrane conductance, but instead is a particular type of voltage-sensitive K^+ con-

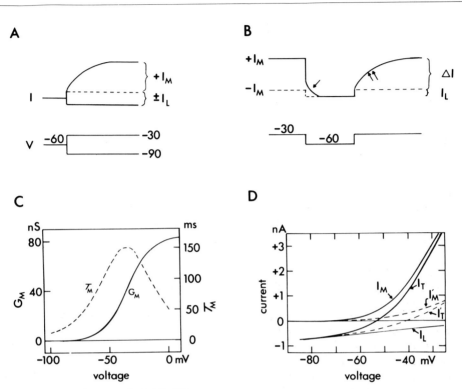

Fig. 2. *Some properties of the M current* (from Refs 11 and 12).

(A) *Schematic of the currents (I) generated by stepping the membrane potential (V) from −60 mV to −90 and −30 mV. At −60 mV most of the M channels are shut. A step to −90 mV reveals only the current flow through the residual leak channels (−IL): this is 'square' and proportional to the voltage step ('ohmic'). A step to −30 mV reveals, superimposed on the leak current (+IL, - - -), a slowly incrementing additional outward K⁺ current due to the slow opening of M channels induced by the membrane depolarization (+IM).*

(B) *Effect of a muscarinic agonist on the currents at a depolarized membrane potential. The schematic starts from a holding potential of −30 mV: the M channels opened in (A) remain open, and contribute a steady outward component to the net membrane current. On jumping the potential to −60 mV, these channels close, and the time-dependent decline in outward current gives rise to the slow inward relaxation marked ↓ . On returning to −30 mV, the channels reopen to give an outward relaxation as in (A) (↑ ↑). A large dose of of muscarinic agonist (- - -) shuts the M channels: the consequent loss of outward current generates a steady inward (depolarizing) current at −30 mV (Δl), and a step back to −60 mV now reveals only the leak current component IL. Figs 4A and B show examples of recordings using this type of protocol.*

(C) *Voltage-dependence of the steady-state M conductance (GM) and time-constant for the M-current relaxations (τM) in frog ganglion cells. GM behaves as though it represented the sum of the conductances of a finite number of single M channels, whose probability of being open or shut is determined by a single voltage-sensing particle of effective valency +2.5. Half of the channels are open at −35 mV. τM is given by 1/(αM + βM) where αM and βM are opening and closing first-order rate constants for the transition:*

$$closed \xrightarrow[\beta M]{\alpha M} open$$

(D) *The behaviour of the frog ganglion cell membrane between −100 and −30 mV can be modelled using two parallel current pathways: a leak pathway whose conductance GL does not change with voltage, and which carries inward (depolarizing) current IL (reversal potential about −10 mV); and an M pathway, whose conductance GM varies with voltage as shown in (C), and which carries outward K⁺ current IM (reversal potential −90 mV). The resting potential is set by the balance between these two currents and is given by the point at which net current IT crosses the zero-current line. Normally this is about −53 mV. When GM is reduced – in this example, by 80% (dashed line) – the reduced outward M current (I'M) leaves an unbalanced inward leak current and the cell depolarizes to −40 mV, at which point sufficient extra M channels have opened to counterbalance the leak current.*

ductance termed the M conductance (G_M: M for muscarinic inhibition). Some of the properties of G_M are summarized in Fig. 2. In frog ganglion cells, the G_M is switched on progressively between about −70 mV and 0 mV and, because it does not inactivate with time, forms a major component of the steady membrane conductance up to −30 mV. It differs from the 'delayed rectifier' conductance involved in spike repolarization by having slower kinetics and a 40 mV more negative activation threshold; and, unlike Ca^{2+}-dependent K^+ conductances, it is insensitive to changes in intra- or extracellular Ca^{2+} concentration.

Since G_M is partly activated at rest potential, inhibition of G_M will cause the cell to depolarize, in very much the manner originally proposed by Weight and Votava[44], as shown in Fig. 2D. However, the crucial

feature of G_M is that, because G_M increases steeply as the membrane is depolarized, the resultant time-dependent outward M current exerts a remarkably strong stabilizing influence on the neuron: it is the reduction of this stabilizing influence, and the consequent increase in excitability of the neuron, which constitutes the key feature of M-current inhibition. This is illustrated in Fig. 3, using the injection of positive current as a simplified example of an excitatory perturbation. The immediate effect of the current injection is to start the cell depolarizing; however, the initial depolarization causes more M channels to open, so there is a large increase in outward current which partially restores the membrane potential; and an increase in conductance which raises spike threshold. Because of this, sustained current injection does not generate the

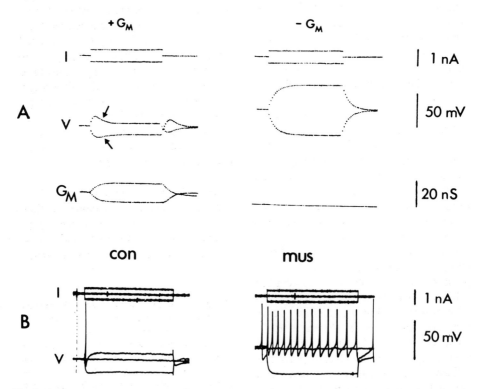

Fig. 3. (A) Reconstruction (see Ref. 4) of the membrane-potential changes (V) induced by a 100-ms current injection (I) under normal conditions (+G_M) and after inactivating the M channels (−G_M). Arrows show secondary voltage deflexions induced by the voltage-induced change in state of the M channels. **(B)** Responses of a rat sympathetic neuron to 500-ms current injections recorded before (con) and after (mus) adding muscarine (adapted from Ref. 9).

expected maintained train of spikes: instead, the spike train terminates after one or a few spikes (Fig. 3B). If, now, the G_M is inactivated, this adaptive influence is lost: the membrane responds passively to the current injection, without an increase in G_M, and sustained spike-trains can then be readily generated, as shown on the right-hand side of Fig. 3. In principle, a comparable M-current-induced adaptation may be expected during repetitive synaptically driven fast EPSPs, so that an increased efficiency of fast EPSP-mediated information transfer may be predicted during M-current inhibition: indeed, Shulman and Weight[39] have reported an appropriate potentiation of subthreshold fast EPSPs, with a greater probability of spike generation, when frog ganglia are exposed to an M-current inhibitor.

Thus, the slow EPSP is not primarily a means of direct synaptic activation: instead, it may serve as a facilitatory device which, by inhibiting the normal M-current brake, permits the cell to respond more faithfully to a train of input signals mediated via the other, nicotinic, fast EPSP.

Slow cholinergic excitation in the brain

The excitatory action of ACh on cortical cells closely resembles that seen in ganglia: it is mediated via muscarinic receptors; it increases neuronal input resistance; and excitation is delayed and sustained[7,14,18,28]. Recent experiments have revealed that two examples of ACh-sensitive cortical neuron – hippocampal[22] and olfactory cortical (A. Constanti and M. Galvan, unpublished observations) pyramidal cells – do indeed possess M currents like those in ganglion cells, and that these can be inhibited by ACh analogues (Fig. 4). Unlike sympathetic neurons, however, if these cells are rendered quiescent, by depriving them of their synaptic input or other depolarizing influences such as current injections, they are not directly depolarized by ACh because insufficient M channels are normally open to generate any steady outward current at the 'resting' potential of $-75\,\mathrm{mV}$

or thereabouts (J. V. Halliwell, unpublished observations; see also Ref. 24). This implies, even more strongly than in ganglion cells, that the function of the cholinergic innervation to cortical neurons is not the direct initiation of spikes but the facilitation of their response to other inputs. Observations according with this view have recently been made by Krnjevic and Ropert[30] in the rat hippocampus *in vivo*: even quite intense and high-frequency stimulation of the abundant cholinergic input from the septum to the CA$_1$ neurons did not, of itself, initiate spike activity as measured by focal extracellular field-potential measurements, but instead strikingly facilitated the synchronous spikes induced by single shocks applied to non-cholinergic commissural fibres. This facilitation was due to the activation of cholinergic fibres in the septal input because it was blocked by the muscarinic antagonist atropine and imitated by ACh. (A comparable facilitatory effect of septal stimulation of the dentate gyrus response to perforant path stimulation appears not to be blocked by atropine, and therefore might reflect a parallel effect of a non-cholinergic transmitter in the septal input[17].) As pointed out by Krnjevic *et al.*[29], this type of 'alerting' effect of septal stimulation may play a key role in cortical learning.*

Peptidergic slow excitation

In some neurons the cholinergic slow EPSP is replaced by an equivalent peptidergic response. Two particularly well-defined examples of this are discussed

---

* I do not wish to imply that M-current inhibition is the only effect of ACh on the hippocampus. Apart from indirect effects on pyramidal cells mediated via afferent or interneuronal inputs[29], there is some indication that pyramidal cell membrane currents other than the M current might be directly modified by muscarinic agonists[7,18] (Halliwell, J. V. and Nicoll, R. A., unpublished observations). Notwithstanding, M-current inhibition clearly plays a key role in the characteristic effects of muscarinic agonists on hippocampal pyramidal cell excitability[22].

elsewhere in this issue – the 'late slow' EPSP in amphibian sympathetic neurons mediated by an analogue of mammalian luteinizing-hormone-releasing hormone (LHRH) (**Jan and Jan**, see page 94) and a slow EPSP in guinea-pig inferior mesenteric ganglia mediated by substance P (SP) (**Otsuka**, see page 163). LHRH inhibits

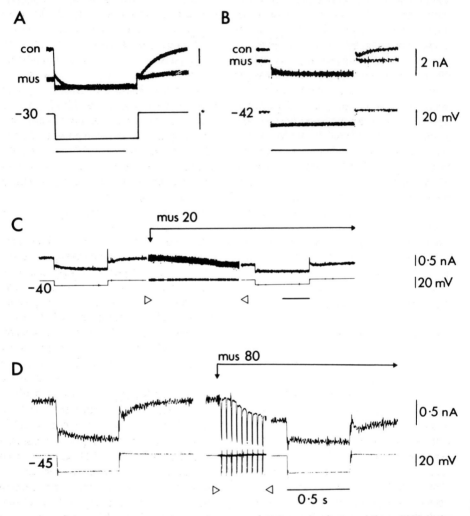

Fig. 4. *Examples of M-current inhibition by muscarine in* (**A**) *frog sympathetic ganglion cell,* (**B**) *rat sympathetic ganglion cell,* (**C**) *guinea-pig hippocampal pyramidal neuron, and* (**D**) *guinea-pig olfactory neuron. In each case the neuron was voltage clamped at a membrane potential where a proportion of the M channels are open and then subjected to a square hyperpolarizing command to shut the channels, as in Fig. 2B. The upper trace shows current, the lower trace shows voltage. The initial holding potential is shown against the voltage records. Muscarine produced an inward (depolarizing) current at the holding potential and reduced the amplitudes of the slow M-channel closure and reopening relaxations during and after the hyperpolarizing commands, showing that it had closed the M channels. Records* (**A**) *and* (**B**) *show superimposed currents before (con) and during (mus) 10 μM muscarine application, exactly as depicted schematically in Fig. 2B. Records* (**C**) *and* (**D**) *show continuous recordings before and after adding muscarine: the recorder speed was slowed by a factor of 100 during drug addition, between the marks* ▷ *and* ◁ *. Sources:* (**A**) *P. R. Adams and D. A. Brown, unpublished observations (cf. Ref. 4);* (**B**) *A. Constanti and D. A. Brown, unpublished observations (cf. Ref. 11);* (**C**) *W. H. Griffith and D. A. Brown, unpublished observations (cf. Ref. 10);* (**D**) *A. Constanti and M. Galvan, unpublished observations (cf. Ref. 12).*

the M current[1]: this effect probably under-lies the late EPSP in some, at least, of the amphibian ganglion cells[26] although activa-tion of a separate inward current may also contribute to the observed depolariza-tion[26,40]. SP can also inhibit the M current in amphibian neurons[5], but the response of mammalian prevertebral ganglion cells to SP appears rather complex[16] and it has yet to be clearly ascertained whether M-current inhibition contributes to the SP-mediated slow EPSP in these cells. The slow depolari-zation of spinal neurons produced by SP also shows some of the characteristic features associated with M-current inhibition[36], and the presence of muscarine-sensitive M currents in these neurons has recently been reported[37]. Thus it seems likely that some peptidergic slow excitations are mechanistically and func-tionally comparable to the cholinergic slow excitation described above, but further detailed study will be necessary to deter-mine the limits of this analogy.

Closure of voltage-insensitive K[+] channels

In contrast to the examples discussed above, there are also some instances where slow synaptic excitation is mediated, not through the closure of voltage-sensitive M channels, but through the closure of voltage-insensitive channels. One such example is provided by the myenteric neurons of the intestinal wall: here, the responsive K[+] channels appear to remain open down to potentials of -100 mV or so, so that the slow EPSP can be reversed to a hyperpolarization as the membrane poten-tial is driven beyond the normal equilibrium potential for K[+] ions[20,25]. In some of the myenteric neurons this particular K[+] cur-rent (unlike the M current) appears to be controlled by the level of intracellular Ca^{2+} ions, the primary effect of the transmitter being to modify the entry or availability of Ca^{2+} (Ref. 20). Even if not directly voltage gated, such a Ca^{2+}-activated K[+] current may have an effective voltage sensitivity conferred upon it by its sensitivity to Ca^{2+}

influx, and so may fulfil a comparable adaptational role on spike discharges to that provided by the M current. This is the case for those myenteric neurons with a pro-nounced K[+] current of this type[34]. In such a situation, synaptic inhibition of the current might convey the same form of facilitatory information as that conveyed by inhibiting the M current. An interesting manifestation of this type of facilitation has recently been reported by Madison and Nicoll[33] in the CA[1] cells of the rat hippocampus: here there appears to be a component of spike adaptation induced by a Ca^{2+}-activated K[+] current which, when blocked by norad-renaline, allows a more sustained repetitive spike discharge in much the same way as that induced in sympathetic neurons by muscarine.

On the other hand, cells which lack appropriate subthreshold voltage-sensitive currents can frequently sustain trains of spikes over very long periods during cur-rent injection, and may even be spontan-eously active. Examples include some myenteric neurons[34], certain mammalian parasympathetic neurons[21], and even sym-pathetic neurons after complete suppression of the M current[15]. The parasympathetic cells, illustrated in Fig. 5, are particularly interesting. These sustain steady spontan-eous discharges whose rate can be subtly controlled by small changes in membrane potential[21]. K[+]-channel closure may then provide a suitable method for depolarizing the cell by a small amount and increasing the rate of spike discharge without chang-ing spike threshold. Conversely, an increase in K[+] conductance would intro-duce an appropriate hyperpolarizing influ-ence to reduce firing rate (Figs 5C and D): this appears to be the basic mechanism of the inhibitory postsynaptic potential in ganglion cells[15,19]. Thus, the interplay of the slow EPSP and slow IPSP allows transmitters to 'fine-tune' the activity of such cells over relatively long time periods.

Receptor–channel coupling

Hartzell[23] has reviewed evidence – based

mainly on the time course of the response – that certain slow synaptic potentials may involve a more indirect coupling between the surface receptor and the affected channel than that obtained at the nicotinic receptor, and has discussed some plausible biochemical intermediary events. (These are further discussed later by **Siegelbaum and Tsien**, on page 81. The argument for an indirect coupling to the M channel is strengthened by the fact that several different transmitter receptors appear capable of closing the same population of

channels: in frog ganglion cells this includes receptors for ACh, LHRH, SP and (possibly) uridine and adenosine nucleotides[4,6,26]. There is excellent evidence that closure of the 'S-type' K$^+$ channels[42] and opening of other K$^+$ channels[13] in molluscan neurons by 5-hydroxytryptamine is mediated by the increased synthesis of cyclic AMP and consequent change in the state of phosphorylation of membrane protein, and it seems probable that the same biochemical events underly the β-mediated action

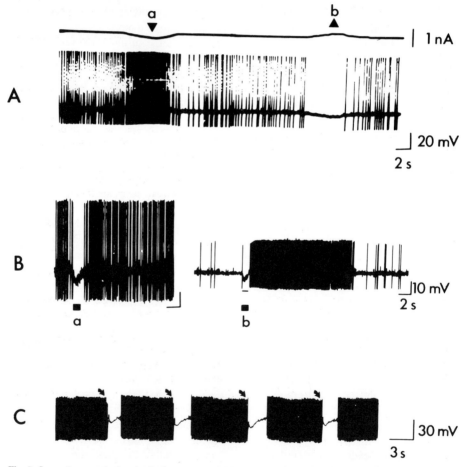

Fig. 5. *Synaptic control of tonic discharge rates in* (**A** *and* **B**) *cat parasympathetic neurons, and* (**C**) *a frog lumbar sympathetic neuron.* (**A**) *Modification of spontaneous firing rate by injecting depolarizing (a) and hyperpolarizing (b) current* (from Ref. 21). (**B**) *Inhibition (a) and acceleration (b) of spontaneous firing by neurally evoked slow IPSP and EPSP, respectively* (from Ref. 19; spikes attenuated by recorder). (**C**) *Slow IPSP-mediated inhibition of firing (at arrows) in a frog sympathetic neuron driven to spontaneous firing by a preceding intense period of preganglionic nerve stimulation: this generates a prolonged late slow EPSP, during which the M current is inhibited* (from Ref. 15; spikes attenuated).

of noradrenaline on the Ca^{2+}-activated K^+ current of hippocampal neurons[33]. However, there is no compelling evidence that the closure of M channels is mediated by cyclic nucleotides[4] and the precise biochemical mechanism underlying cholinergic and peptidergic slow potentials in vertebrates has still not been resolved at the cellular/electrophysiological level. This should be one of the more fruitful areas for future research into synaptic control mechanisms. Nevertheless, as indicated in the article, such mechanisms may be surprisingly varied, and extrapolated from one system to another might be unwise.

Acknowledgements

Most of the work described in this article was completed in collaboration with Dr Paul R. Adams, currently at the Department of Neurobiology and Behavior, SUNY, Stony Brook, and/or with Drs A. Constanti, J. V. Halliwell and W. H. Griffith, at the School of Pharmacy, University of London. The work was supported by grants from the UK Medical Research Council, the US National Institutes of Health, and the Wellcome Trust.

Reading list

1 Adams, P. R. and Brown, D. A. (1980) Br. J. Pharmacol. 68, 353–355

2 Adams, P. R. and Brown, D. A. (1982) J. Physiol. (London) 332, 263–272

3 Adams, P. R., Brown, D. A. and Constanti, A. (1982) J. Physiol. (London) 330, 537–572

4 Adams, P. R., Brown, D. A. and Constanti, A. (1982) J. Physiol. (London) 332, 223–262

5 Adams, P. R., Brown, D. A. and Jones, S. W. Br. J. Pharmacol. 79, 330–333

6 Akasu, T., Hirai, K. and Koketsu, K. (1983) Brain Res. 258, 313–317

7 Benardo, L. S. and Prince, D. A. (1981) Brain Res. 211, 227–234

8 Brown, D. A. and Adams, P. R. (1980) Nature (London) 283, 673–676

9 Brown, D. A. and Constanti, A. (1980) Br. J. Pharmacol. 70, 593–608

10 Brown, D. A. and Griffith, W. H. J. Physiol. (London) 337, 287–301

11 Constanti, A. and Brown, D. A. (1981) Neurosci. Lett. 24, 289–294

12 Constanti, A. and Galvan, M. (1983) J. Physiol. (London) 335, 153–178

13 De Peyer, J. E., Cachelin, A. B., Levitan, I. B. and Reuter, H. (1982) Proc. Natl Acad. Sci. USA 79, 4207–4211

14 Dodd, J., Dingledine, R. and Kelly, J. S. (1981) Brain Res. 207, 109–127

15 Dodd, J. and Horn, J. P. (1983) J. Physiol. (London) 334, 271–292

16 Dun, N. J. and Minota, S. (1981) J. Physiol. (London) 321, 259–271

17 Fantie, B. D. and Goddard, G. V. (1982) Brain Res. 252, 227–237

18 Gähwiler, B. and Dreifuss, J. J. (1982) Neuroscience 7, 1243–1256

19 Gallagher, J. P., Griffith, W. H. and Shinnick-Gallagher, P. (1982) J. Physiol. (London) 332, 473–486

20 Gräfe, P., Mayer, C. J. and Wood, J. D. (1980) J. Physiol. (London) 305, 235–248

21 Griffith, W. H., Gallagher, J. P. and Shinnick-Gallagher, P. (1980) J. Neurophysiol. 43, 343–354

22 Halliwell, J. V. and Adams, P. R. (1982) Brain Res. 250, 71–92

23 Hartzell, H. C. (1981) Nature (London) 291, 539–544

24 James, T. A. and MacLeod, N. K. (1981) J. Physiol. (London) 315, 32–33P

25 Johnson, S. M., Katayama, Y. and North, R. A. (1980) J. Physiol. (London) 301, 505–516

26 Katayama, K. and Nishi, S. (1982) J. Physiol. (London) 333, 305–313

27 Kobayashi, H. and Libet, B. (1968) Proc. Natl Acad. Sci. USA 60, 1304–1311

28 Krnjević, K., Pumain, R. and Renaud, L. (1971) J. Physiol. (London) 215, 247–268

29 Krnjević, K., Reiffenstein, R. J. and Ropert, N. (1981) Neuroscience 6, 2465–2474

30 Krnjević, K. and Ropert, N. (1982) Neuroscience 7, 2165–2183

31 Kuba, K. and Nishi, S. (1979) Pfluegers Arch. 378, 205–212

32 MacDermott, A. B., Connor, E. A., Dionne, V. E. and Parsons, R. L. (1980) J. Gen. Physiol. 75, 39–60

33 Madison, D. V. and Nicoll, R. A. (1982) Nature (London) 299, 636–638

34 Nishi, S. and North, R. A. (1973) J. Physiol. (London) 231, 471–491

35 Nishi, S., Soeda, H. and Koketsu, K. (1969) Life Sci. 8, 33–42

36 Nowak, L. M. and MacDonald, R. L. (1981) Brain Res. 214, 416–423

37 Nowak, L. M. and MacDonald, R. L. (1983) Neurosci. Lett. 35, 85–92

38 Rang, H. P. (1981) J. Physiol. (London) 311, 23–55

39 Schulman, J. A. and Weight, F. F. (1976) Science 194, 1437–1439

40 Sejnowski, T. (1982) Fed. Proc. Fed. Am. Soc. Exp. Biol. 41, 2923–2928

41 Selyanko, A. A., Derkach, V. A. and Skok, V. I.

(1979) *J. Auton, Nerv. Syst.* 1, 127–137

42 Siegelbaum, S. A., Camardo, J. S. and Kandel, E. R. (1982) *Nature (London)* 299, 413–417

43 Tosaka, T., Chichubu, S. and Libet, B. (1968) *J. Neurophysiol.* 31, 396–409

44 Weight, F. and Votava, J. (1970) *Science* 202, 772–775

45 Weitsen, H. A. and Weight, F. F. (1977) *Brain Res.* 128, 197–211

D. A. Brown is at the Department of Pharmacology, The School of Pharmacy, University of London, 29/39 Brunswick Square, London WC1N 1AX, UK.

Inhibitory cholinergic synapses in autonomic ganglia

John P. Horn and Jane Dodd

Slow synaptic potentials may provide mechanisms for long-term regulation of neuronal integration in the vertebrate nervous system. Autonomic ganglia, because of their structure and accessibility, have proved useful for studying several mechanisms of slow synaptic inhibition and excitation. Our purpose here is to review recent work on ganglionic slow inhibitory postsynaptic potentials (IPSPs). Although slow IPSPs are present in many ganglia, there is no consensus as to the transmitter(s) or ionic mechanism(s) that produce these responses. Furthermore, the ways in which slow IPSPs function physiologically to inhibit neuronal excitability have been largely a matter of speculation. Our recent experiments on sympathetic ganglia may serve to resolve controversies over mechanisms while also suggesting that interactions between slow cholinergic IPSPs and slow peptidergic excitatory postsynaptic potentials (EPSPs) function specifically to modulate the repetitive firing behavior of neurons.

The study of slow IPSPs in ganglia began over 30 years ago. Laporte and Lorente de No[19] first demonstrated that presynaptic stimulation of the turtle superior cervical sympathetic ganglion (SCG) could evoke a relatively slow 'positive' extracellular potential that was independent of more rapid nicotinic excitatory postsynaptic potentials (EPSPs) and postsynaptic action potentials. In the 1960s similar positive or 'P' extracellular waves were shown to be compound synaptic potentials resulting from the membrane hyperpolarization of many neurons[16, 26]. In these experiments the SCG of the rabbit and the 9th and 10th paravertebral sympathetic ganglia of the bullfrog were used. Since then, slow IPSPs have also been studied in preparations of parasympathetic ganglia[10,11]. Thus it seems likely that slow IPSPs influence the integrative properties of many autonomic neurons in lower vertebrates and in mammals. However, some aspects of popular theories accounting for the pharmacology

and the ionic dependence of slow IPSPs now appear to be incorrect and it remains unknown how many different types of IPSPs are expressed by autonomic neurons and how each of them functions.

Unlike fast nicotinic EPSPs, muscarinic IPSPs are present in some, but not all, sympathetic and parasympathetic neurons. For example, in the 9th and 10th paravertebral ganglia of the bullfrog, where neurons can be classified according to the segmental origin of their fast nicotinic innervation, IPSPs are seen only in the subset of cells that are cholinergically innervated by spinal nerves 7 and 8 (Refs 6, 25, 26). The solitary IPSP elicited by a single nerve stimulus has a latency of about 50 ms and a duration of about 1 s (Ref. 7). In response to repetitive stimulation at rates as low as 4 Hz, the IPSP summates in amplitude and may last for tens of seconds[7]. Although it has been asserted that the IPSP is intrinsically small, we have recently found that IPSPs as large as 40 mV can be recorded with conventional intracellular methods.

Pharmacology of the slow IPSP

Two models have been proposed to account for the pharmacology of slow IPSPs recorded from different ganglia (Fig. 1). In the first model, acetylcholine released by presynaptic nerve terminals activates inhibitory muscarinic receptors on the surface of ganglionic neurons. This scheme was first substantiated in the parasympathetic cardiac ganglion of the mudpuppy by Kuffler and his colleagues[11]. In 1977 they showed that the slow IPSP in the cardiac ganglion is blocked reversibly by low doses of atropine, a competitive antagonist of muscarinic receptors. They found that the synaptic response can be closely mimicked by iontophoresing acetylcholine directly onto the neuronal surface. Moreover, the hyperpolarizing action of exogenous acetylcholine is not altered by blocking transmitter release with low Ca^{2+}, high Mg^{2+} Ringer solution, showing that this IPSP is monosynaptic.

The second model, first articulated in 1961 by Eccles and Libet[9], postulates an obligatory role for a catecholamine-releasing interneuron. According to this scheme, acetylcholine released by preganglionic nerve terminals activates excitatory muscarinic receptors on ganglionic chromaffin cells that function as interneurons. This, in turn, stimulates the chromaffin cells to release a catecholamine that activates inhibitory adrenergic receptors on the principal neurons. The notion of a disynaptic IPSP comes from experiments on sympathetic ganglia in the rabbit and bullfrog, and the basic argument for the hypothesis is straightforward. Atropine-sensitive IPSPs in sympathetic ganglia are also depressed by adrenoceptor antagonists, suggesting that muscarinic and adrenergic receptors both mediate the response[2,9,20]. Bath-applied acetylcholine and catecholamines each cause hyperpolarization in sympathetic neurons, but the action of acetylcholine is depressed by low Ca^{2+}, high Mg^{2+} (Ref. 20). This is consis-

tent with the concept that a catecholamine, acting as a second transmitter, is released by the muscarinic action of acetylcholine. Finally, evidence that chromaffin cells can release catecholamines in response to presynaptic stimulation or application of acetylcholine supports their postulated role as interneurons[21].

The fact that two models have been proposed to account for the muscarinic IPSP is problematic. Since the strongest evidence in favor of each hypothesis has been obtained from different ganglia, it is possible that both models are correct. Accordingly, one might suppose that the two mechanisms are differentially expressed, possibly on the basis of species (e.g. lower vertebrates vs. mammals) or function (e.g. parasympathetic vs. sympathetic ganglia). The difficulty arises because both mechanisms have been ascribed to the IPSP in bullfrog sympathetic ganglia. However, a re-examination of the old data in the context of new findings suggests that one scheme may describe all atropine-sensitive IPSPs.

Disynaptic mediation of the atropine-sensitive IPSP in bullfrog paravertebral sympathetic ganglia was first proposed in 1968 by Tosaka, Chichibu and Libet[26]. Using intracellular recording methods, the stimulus threshold of the presynaptic nerve that elicited the IPSP was found to be indistinguishable from that required to elicit the nicotinic EPSP. This was interpreted as evidence that the same preganglionic fibres initiate both synaptic potentials. The authors assumed, by analogy with previous observations in the rabbit SCG, that the IPSP in bullfrog ganglia would be sensitive to adrenergic blockers. Furthermore, they thought it implausible that acetylcholine, the transmitter released from the presynaptic fibers, could directly activate both excitatory nicotinic and inhibitory muscarinic potentials in individual postganglionic neurons. Consequently, Tosaka *et al.*[26] proposed that an adrenergic interneuron in bullfrog ganglia was required to convert the excitatory action of acetylcholine to one of inhibition. This view was challenged in 1973 by Weight and Padjen[28] who found that, in nicotinized ganglia, the extracellulary recorded hyperpolarizing response to bath-applied acetylcholine was not antagonized by low Ca^{2+}, high Mg^{2+}. In 1974, Libet and Kobayashi[20] did similar experiments and found that, after extensive washing in low Ca^{2+}, high Mg^{2+}, the acetylcholine response was reduced in curarized but not in nicotinized ganglia. Since the actions of nicotine appeared more complex than those of curare, these authors asserted that the latter were more relevant to the 'normal' IPSP. Libet and Kobayashi[20] also found that 200 μM phentolamine, an α-adrenergic antagonist, strongly depressed the IPSP and concluded that their experiments supported the interneuron hypothesis. However, the large doses of phentolamine used in these experiments also produced non-specific depression of nicotinic transmission.

More recently, Weight and Smith[29] re-

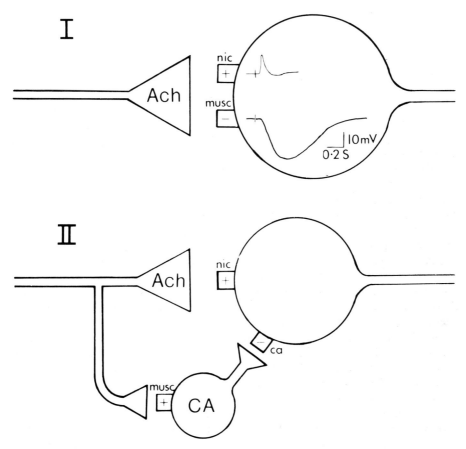

Fig. 1. *Two models proposed for the pharmacology of the IPSP.* (**I**) *The monosynaptic IPSP: acetylcholine (Ach), released from the presynaptic nerve terminal, acts upon nicotinic (nic) and muscarinic (musc) receptors located on the same postganglionic principal neuron. Activation of the two receptors results in a fast EPSP (upper trace) and the slow IPSP (lower trace), respectively.* (**II**) *The disynaptic IPSP: ACh is released from all terminals of the presynaptic nerve. It acts upon nicotinic receptors located on the principal neuron and muscarinic receptors located on a catecholamine-containing interneuron (CA). Activation of the nicotinic receptors produces the fast EPSP as in model (**I**). Activation of the muscarinic receptors produces a muscarinic EPSP in the interneuron. The depolarization of the interneuron, whose time course is unknown, causes the release of a catecholamine which itself acts upon catecholamine (ca) receptors, on the principal neuron, to evoke the IPSP.*

peated these experiments and reported that in curarized ganglia low Ca^{2+}, high Mg^{2+} did not block the inhibitory response to acetylcholine at a time when the IPSP was blocked. They also found that α-adrenoceptor antagonists, at doses that block responses to exogenous catechol-amines, did not antagonize the IPSP. Unfortunately, interpretation of all these results is hampered by the fact that they consist of extracellular recordings from whole ganglia. In this preparation, the IPSP occurs in only one of three identifiable neuronal cell types[6]. Therefore, the cellular origin of responses to exogenous agents is always uncertain. Comparing the effects of bath-applied agents to synaptic potentials is further complicated by the fact that the former are much slower. Finally, the effects of diffusion barriers that might limit drug access to the ganglion's interior are difficult to assess.

Recent results of experiments in which the IPSP has been recorded intracellularly from identified neurons on the surface of bullfrog sympathetic ganglia[7,12] provide direct evidence that this synaptic potential, like that in the cardiac parasympathetic ganglia[11], is a monosynaptic muscarinic response. We have extended Tosaka et al.'s[26] analysis of stimulus thresholds for the IPSP by examining C cells with two cholinergic inputs. In such cells, it can be seen that a single presynaptic stimulus elicits a nicotinic EPSP and a muscarinic IPSP, each of which has two components with distinct thresholds. However, the low and high thresholds of the EPSP are identical to those of the IPSP. This confirms that a close correlation exists between the release of acetylcholine onto the neuronal surface and the genesis of the IPSP. In a second series of experiments, the time course of the IPSP was compared to that of the response to iontophoretically applied acetylcholine. We found that the mus-carinic action of a brief pulse of acetyl-choline can mimic the latency and time course of the synaptic response, but only when it is applied very close to the neuronal surface. In conjunction with the fact that chromaffin cells are sparsely distributed and lack processes in bullfrog ganglia[30], it therefore seems unlikely that these putative interneurons release a second transmitter to produce the IPSP. This possibility was tested directly by measuring the effect of blocking evoked release on inhibitory acetylcholine responses. First, a pipette containing acetylcholine was positioned so that the iontophoretic response mimicked the time course and amplitude of the IPSP. Then the normal Ringer was exchanged with one containing low Ca^{2+}, high Mg^{2+}, and when release was blocked, as deter-mined by the total disappearance of the synaptic response, the muscarinic response to iontophoretically applied acetylcholine was found to persist undiminished. In addi-tion, we could show that the ionic conduc-tance changes during responses to acetyl-choline and during the IPSP are identical. These findings demonstrate that inhibitory muscarinic receptors on ganglionic neurons mediate a hyperpolarizing response that is indistinguishable from the IPSP but they do not exclude the possibility that some small fraction of the IPSP is disynaptically medi-ated by a catecholamine. However, this possibility appears remote since antagonists of three adrenoceptors, in doses known to be effective on well-characterized neuronal receptors, were found to have no effect on the IPSP. These results and those from the cardiac ganglion demonstrate conclusively that the muscarinic IPSPs in parasympathe-tic and sympathetic ganglia of lower verte-brates are monosynaptic.

In mammalian ganglia, the pharmacol-ogy of atropine-sensitive IPSPs remains debatable, although recent experiments suggest that they too may be purely cholinergic. Catecholamine antagonists suppress muscarinic IPSPs, but it has been known for some time that these agents (e.g. phenoxybenzamine, dibenamine, phen-tolamine, haloperidol) act non-specifically at high concentrations. In a careful extracel-lular study, Cole and Shinnick-Gallagher[4,5] have characterized the α-adrenoceptor that

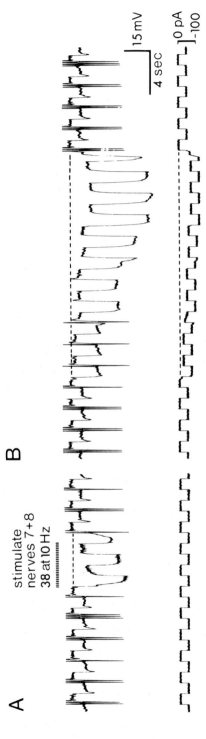

Fig. 2. *The IPSP is accompanied by a decrease in membrane resistance. The membrane resistance of a bullfrog sympathetic C cell was estimated by measuring the amplitude of membrane potential (upper trace) excursions resulting from 50 pA pulses of injected current (lower trace). (**A**) During an IPSP, evoked by stimulation of spinal nerves 7 and 8, the potential change produced by the current pulses increased. This represents an increase in membrane resistance. (**B**) A constant current, in addition to the pulses, was injected in order to hyperpolarize the membrane to the same potential as that reached during the IPSP. At this potential the voltage excursion resulting from the current pulses was much larger than that recorded at rest. This means that hyperpolarization alone causes a substantial increase in membrane resistance. Comparison of the resistance increase due to this intrinsic membrane rectification (**B**) with that during the IPSP (**A**) indicates that the net change during the IPSP is a decrease in membrane resistance. It is also interesting to note that, in the absence of a continuous hyperpolarizing current, the membrane potential reaches threshold for one or more action potentials (tops cropped) in response to each depolarizing current step. During the IPSP, and during hyperpolarization caused by current injection, the action potentials cease to appear.*

mediates hyperpolarization induced by bath-applied catecholamines in the rabbit SCG. They found that while 10 μM phentolamine can block 80% of the response to 50 μM noradrenaline, it has no discernible effect on the slow IPSP. Higher doses of phentolamine depress all synaptic potentials in a non-selective manner. Another recent study from the same lab[10] has shown that the IPSP in the parasympathetic vesical pelvic ganglion of the cat is probably also a monosynaptic muscarinic response mediated by acetylcholine alone. However, until additional intracellular experiments are done, further comparisons between IPSPs in mammals and in lower vertebrates are premature. It should also be kept in mind that this recent work does not rule out the possibility that atropine-insensitive slow IPSPs are extant in the autonomic nervous system.

Ionic basis of the muscarinic IPSP

Slow IPSPs are notorious for being difficult to record intracellularly and this has impeded the rigorous analysis of their underlying mechanisms. The earliest data came from bullfrog sympathetic ganglia in which, it was reported[27,28], an increase in membrane resistance accompanied the IPSP, and the IPSP amplitude diminished when the membrane potential was depolarized from rest. Based largely on these findings, Weight and Padjen proposed that a decrease in membrane sodium conductance produced the IPSP. The first systematic investigation of an inhibitory muscarinic conductance was done in the mudpuppy cardiac ganglion. Kuffler and his colleagues[11] showed that the IPSP reversed polarity near -100 mV and that this reversal potential varied as a Nernstian function of extracellular potassium concentration. When published in 1977, this definitive demonstration of an increase in membrane potassium conductance during an IPSP appeared to contradict the previous results. More recently, we have found that the IPSP in bullfrog sympathetic neurons, like that in mudpuppy parasympathetic neurons,

reverses polarity near -100 mV and that this reversal potential varies as a simple function of extracellular potassium concentration[7,12]. The analysis of these two IPSPs, which now seem to resemble each other closely, has several interesting implications.

IPSP amplitude is not a simple linear function of membrane potential, and near rest (about -50 mV) it can be depressed by either depolarization or hyperpolarization. This phenomenon occurs in the cardiac ganglion[11], in the rabbit SCG (Refs 8, 13), and in bullfrog paravertebral ganglia[7,12]. On the basis of conductance calculations, Kuffler and his colleagues concluded that at potentials depolarized from rest, the muscarinically activated conductance is voltage sensitive and decreases. Thus during depolarization from rest the IPSP becomes smaller as the voltage-sensitive muscarinic conductance decreases, and during hyperpolarization from rest the IPSP becomes smaller as the reversal potential is approached and the driving force on potassium decreases. In the bullfrog we observed another mechanism that contributes to the voltage sensitivity of the IPSP (Ref. 12). The steady-state input impedence of bullfrog neurons is voltage dependent. Hyperpolarized to -70 mV, the input resistance is constant and the IPSP amplitude varies as a simple linear function of membrane potential. However, as a neuron is depolarized beyond -70 mV, its input resistance decreases sharply and this shunts the muscarinically activated current, thereby producing a smaller synaptic potential. The curvature of the steady-state current–voltage relation also accounts for the apparent increase in membrane resistance during the IPSP (Fig. 2). If the membrane resistance at the peak of the IPSP is compared with that of the membrane when brought to the same potential by injecting current, a decrease is always observed. Although the rectifying properties of the membrane can account qualitatively for the non-linear relation between IPSP amplitude and membrane potential, more careful measurements will be required to distinguish further between this effect and the voltage dependence of the muscarinic conductance.

The IPSP is difficult to record intracellularly because it is produced by a small (2–4 nS) increase in membrane conductance[11,12], a change that is about 50 times smaller than that underlying the nicotinic EPSP in autonomic neurons[18,22,24]. Microelectrode impalement can easily reduce the steady-state input resistance of bullfrog neurons to values of 20 MΩ (Ref. 23). Under such conditions, the 100 pA outward current generated by a 2 nS conductance increase and a driving force of 50 mV will displace the membrane potential by only 2 mV. However, using fine microelectrodes it is possible routinely to record input resistances of 200–500 MΩ and IPSP amplitudes of 20–40 mV.

Slow inhibition in action

Perhaps the most interesting aspect of the muscarinic IPSP is the inhibition that it produces. A synaptic potential caused by an increase in membrane potassium conductance will tend to drive the membrane away

from the action potential threshold and thereby inhibit firing. The first sign of slow muscarinic inhibition in action came from Koketsu and Nishi's[17] extracellular recordings of afterdischarges in nicotinized sympathetic ganglia. In the 9th and 10th ganglia of the bullfrog, they found that tetanic presynaptic stimulation was followed by intense, asynchronous firing of postganglionic action potentials and that this afterdischarge was inhibited during the muscarinic P wave. Recently, we have pursued muscarinic inhibition at the intracellular level.

In the 9th and 10th paravertebral sympathetic ganglia of the bullfrog the IPSP occurs in only one of three cell types, the C cells[6]. In C cells, three different synaptic potentials can be evoked. In addition to the nicotinic EPSP and muscarinic IPSP that have already been discussed there is a slow peptidergic EPSP mediated by an LHRF-like peptide[7,14]. This EPSP develops very slowly in response to long trains of presynaptic stimuli and outlasts the IPSP by many tens of seconds. It appears that a single set of nerve terminals produces the

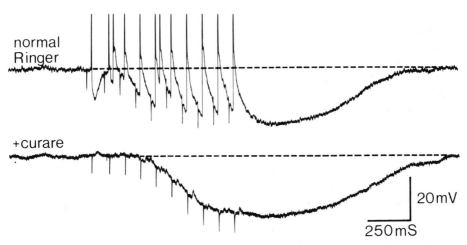

Fig. 3. *The IPSP does not inhibit nicotinic excitation of bullfrog sympathetic neurons. In normal Ringer (upper trace) a train of ten presynaptic stimuli produces 12 suprathreshold nicotinic EPSPs followed by the IPSP. The tops of the action potentials produced by the EPSPs have been cropped. When the cell was bathed in 100 μM tubocurarine (lower trace) and the same train applied, the nicotinic EPSPs were almost completely blocked, leaving stimulus artefacts superimposed upon the intact muscarinic IPSP. It now becomes clear that the IPSP starts as early as the 4th stimulus artefact and is almost fully developed by the 10th. Comparison of the two records demonstrates that the IPSP, even as it approaches its maximum amplitude, does not inhibit nicotinic EPSPs from initiating action potentials.*

three different synaptic potentials by releasing two transmitters, acetylcholine and the peptide[14,15]. We have studied muscarinic inhibition by recording the interactions between the IPSP and action potentials, and between the IPSP and the two EPSPs[7]. The IPSP cannot inhibit action potentials when they are stimulated by either antidromic shocks or suprathreshold nicotinic EPSPs (Fig. 3). However, C cells can fire repetitively at resting membrane potentials near −50 mV and these action potentials are inhibited by the IPSP (Fig. 4). Physiologically, repetitive firing can be initiated or enhanced by the slow peptidergic EPSP and it has been proposed that suppression by LHRF of a voltage-sensitive potassium conductance is responsible for this effect[1,3].

The ability of muscarinically induced potassium currents to inhibit repetitive firing selectively is a direct result of their size. The conductance changes during nicotinic and peptidergic EPSPs have not been measured in C cells, but can be estimated from work on other bullfrog sympathetic neurons. Such a comparison[7] indicates that the nicotinic excitatory postsynaptic current (EPSC) may be an order of magnitude larger than the muscarinic inhibitory postsynaptic current (IPSC). However, the magnitude of the peptidergic EPSC is probably quite similar to that of the muscarinic IPSC. Consistent with this prediction, small injected currents in the range of 25 pA, compared to the 100 pA that may be generated during the IPSP, can block the repetitive firing induced by the slow EPSP.

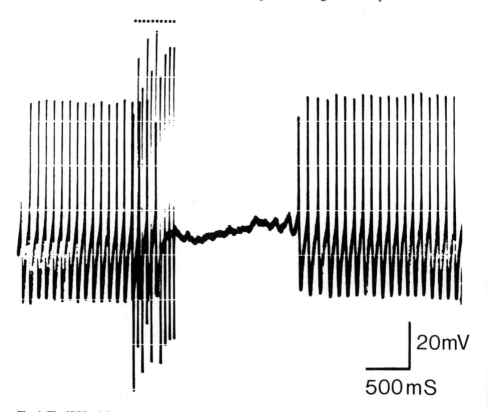

20mV

500 mS

Fig. 4. *The IPSP inhibits repetitive firing of bullfrog sympathetic neurons. This intracellular recording was taken from a C cell during a period of repetitive firing induced by the slow peptidergic EPSP. 100 μM tubocurarine was present to block nicotinic synapses. At the times indicated by dots, a train of presynaptic stimuli was applied and an IPSP was produced. As the IPSP developed the repetitive firing was inhibited. As the IPSP subsided the membrane potential began to oscillate and repetitive firing recommenced.*

The consequences of the IPSP's ability to inhibit peptidergic excitation, while leaving nicotinic excitation intact, are illustrated by the experimental finding[7] that phasic bursts of repetitive action potentials, lasting for tens of seconds, can be produced by interaction between the peptidergic EPSP and the muscarinic IPSP. Thus, a single suprathreshold or convergent subthreshold nicotinic EPSPs will always give rise to a single postsynaptic action potential. On the other hand, a long train of presynaptic impulses will give rise to repetitive firing that can be punctuated and reinforced by subsequent short trains of presynaptic impulses. In other words the dual expression of slow inhibitory and excitatory mechanisms permits a complex transformation between pre- and post-synaptic activity in which comparatively few presynaptic impulses will generate intense, patterned postsynaptic firing. Understanding the uses to which this type of synaptic transmission has been adapted by the vertebrate nervous system awaits future study.

Reading list

1 Adams, P. R. and Brown, D. A. (1980) *Br. J. Pharmacol.* 68, 353–355
2 Ashe, J. H. and Libet, B. (1982) *Brain Res.* 242, 345–349
3 Brown, D. A. and Adams, P. R. (1980) *Nature (London)* 283, 673–676
4 Cole, A. E. and Shinnick-Gallagher, P. (1980) *Brain Res.* 187, 226–230
5 Cole, A. E. and Shinnick-Gallagher, P. (1981) *J. Pharmacol. Exp. Ther.* 217, 440–444
6 Dodd, J. and Horn, J. P. (1983) *J. Physiol. (London)* 334, 255–269
7 Dodd, J. and Horn, J. P. (1983) *J. Physiol. (London)* 334, 271–291
8 Dun, N. J. and Karczmar, A. G. (1978) *Proc. Natl Acad. Sci. U.S.A.* 75, 4029–4032
9 Eccles, R. M. and Libet, B. (1961) *J. Physiol. (London)* 157, 484–503
10 Griffith, W. H., Gallagher, J. P. and Shinnick-Gallagher, P. (1981) *Brain Res.* 209, 446–451
11 Hartzell, H. C., Kuffler, S. W., Stickgold, R. and Yoshikami, D. (1977) *J. Physiol. (London)* 271, 817–846
12 Horn, J. P. and Dodd, J. (1981) *Nature (London)* 292, 625–627
13 Ivanov, A. Y. A. and Skok, V. I. (1980) *J. Auton. Nerv. Syst.* 1, 255–263
14 Jan, L. Y. and Jan, Y. N. (1982) *J. Physiol. (London)* 327, 219–246
15 Jan, L. Y., Jan, Y. N. and Brownfield, M. S. (1980) *Nature (London)* 288, 380–382
16 Kobayashi, H. and Libet, B. (1968) *Proc. Natl Acad. Sci. U.S.A.* 60, 1304–1311
17 Koketsu, K. and Nishi, S. (1967) *Life Sci.* 6, 1827–1836
18 Kuba, K. and Nishi, S. (1979) *Pfluegers Arch.* 378, 205–212
19 Laporte, Y. and Lorente de No, R. (1950) *J. Cell. Comp. Physiol.* 35, Suppl. 2, 61–106
20 Libet, B. and Kobayashi, H. (1974) *J. Neurophysiol.* 37, 805–814
21 Libet, B. and Owman, C. (1974) *J. Physiol. (London)* 237, 635–662
22 MacDermott, A. B., Connor, E. A., Dionne, V. E. and Parsons, R. L. (1980) *J. Gen. Physiol.* 75, 39–60
23 Nishi, S., Soeda, H. and Koketsu, K. (1965) *J. Cell. Comp. Physiol.* 66, 19–32
24 Rang, H. P. (1981) *J. Physiol. (London)* 311, 23–55
25 Skok, V. I. (1965) *Fed. Proc. Fed. Am. Soc. Exp. Biol., Translation Suppl.* 24, T363–T367
26 Tosaka, T., Chichibu, S. and Libet, B. (1968) *J. Neurophysiol.* 31, 396–409
27 Weight, F. F. and Padjen, A. (1973) *Brain Res.* 55, 219–224
28 Weight, F. F. and Padjen, A. (1973) *Brain Res.* 55, 225–228
29 Weight, F. F. and Smith, P. A. (1980) *Histochemistry and Cell Biology of Autonomic Neurons, SIF Cells, and Paraneurons* (Eranko, O., Sonila, S. and Paivarinta, H., eds), Raven Press, New York
30 Weight, F. F. and Weitsen, H. A. (1977) *Brain Res.* 128, 213–226

Note added in proof: Since this paper was first written, two intracellular studies have demonstrated that the muscarinic IPSP in both parasympathetic and sympathetic mammalian ganglia is indistinguishable from that in lower vertebrates.

Gallagher, J. P., Griffith, W. H. and Shinnick-Gallagher, P. (1982) *J. Physiol.* (London) 332, 473–486
Cole, A. E. and Shinnick-Gallagher, P. (1984) *Nature (London)* 307, 270–271

In addition, a non-cholinergic slow IPSP has been demonstrated in parasympathetic neurons.

Akasu, T., Shinnick-Gallagher, P. and Gallagher, J. P. (1984) *Nature (London)* 311, 62–65

John P. Horn is in the Department of Physiology, University of Pittsburgh School of Medicine, Pittsburgh, PA 15261 U.S.A. and Jane Dodd is at the Department of Neurobiology Harvard Medical School, 25 Shattuck Street, Boston, MA 02115, U.S.A.

Neural regulation of the heart

A model for modulation of voltage-sensitive channels and regulation of cellular metabolism by neurotransmitters

Tony Creazzo, Louisa Titus and Criss Hartzell

The effects of neurotransmitters on the heart are multifarious. The autonomic transmitters influence the function of a variety of ionic channels as well as several intracellular proteins. Effects on beat rate are mediated by effects on ionic channels in the membrane. The effects on peak systolic tension are probably largely due to changes in the Ca^{2+} influx during the action potential and release of Ca^{2+} from the sarcoplasmic reticulum. Changes in relaxation rate may be due to changes in the state of the contractile apparatus itself. In addition to the diversity of effector systems is a variety of mechanisms coupling the neurotransmitter receptors to these effectors. Some responses are coupled by cyclic-nucleotide-dependent phosphorylation, whereas other effectors are coupled by as yet unidentified mechanisms. Thus, there are multiple points of divergence in the action of autonomic transmitters on the heart. We do not yet understand, however, how these various points of divergence are independently controlled or how the various effector systems quantitatively contribute to the final physiological response of the heart to nervous input. It will be challenging and exciting to try to answer these questions.

Ten years ago, the nervous system was much more simple than it is today; or so it seemed. It appeared that signalling in the brain might be understood in terms of synapses which worked in ways similar to the excitatory neuromuscular junction and inhibitory synapses on spinal motor neurons: that is, neurotransmitters were thought to produce their effects by opening ionic channels which were always closed in the absence of transmitters. The only interesting differences between synapses seemed limited to the ionic selectivity of the channels which were opened.

Understanding neuronal signalling has become much more challenging as we have learned that neurotransmitters can close – as well as open – membrane channels and that some channels are controlled both by neurotransmitters and by $ \jmath $ ianges in transmembrane potential. Furthermore, some neurotransmitters have effects on intracellular enzymes which are likely to be important in long-term signalling.

The heart is a very favorable system for studying these newly recognized kinds of postsynaptic responses. Autonomic neurotransmitters modulate voltage-sensitive channels involved in pacemaker activity and the action potential and also affect a variety of processes in the cell interior, notably processes which affect cytoplasmic Ca^{2+} concentration and the sensitivity of the contractile apparatus to Ca^{2+}.

Regulation of the heartbeat

The vertebrate heart contracts spontaneously, but the force and frequency of contraction are increased by noradrenaline (NA) released from sympathetic nerves and decreased by acetylcholine (ACh) released from parasympathetic nerves[6,21]. At the molecular level, these transmitters act upon several different effector systems. The effects on beat frequency are produced by modulation of several different kinds of ionic channels in the plasma membrane and consequent alteration of pacemaker currents[21]. The effects on contractile force, on the other hand, are mediated by changes in myosin cross-bridge activity[3,9,11,28], which is regulated by (1) the influx of Ca^{2+} during the action potential, (2) Ca^{2+} sequestration and release by the sarcoplasmic reticulum (SR), and (3) the functioning of proteins in the contractile apparatus itself.

Normal cardiac cycle

We will begin by summarizing the events which occur during the normal cardiac cycle. Although the details of these events may differ somewhat in different regions of the heart, the main features seem similar. The following description is of pacemaking activity in the primary pacemaker, the sino-atrial (SA) node. When the membrane potential reaches its most negative value (the maximum diastolic potential, MDP), two important ionic currents are flowing: an inward (depolarizing) 'background' current; and a current due to the slow decay of the outward repolarizing K^+ current that turns off during the falling phase of the action potential (pacemaker K^+ current). From the MDP, the membrane potential slowly depolarizes due to the slow turn-off of the pacemaker current and the gradual activation of an inward current carried by Ca^{2+}/Na^+. As the membrane further depolarizes, the inward Ca^{2+}/Na^+ current is maximally activated, producing an action potential lasting ~300 ms. The cells of the SA node, unlike other heart cells of the atria and ventricles, do not have a fast Na^+ current. Their action potential is dependent on the kinetically slower Ca^{2+}/Na^+ current. The influx of Ca^{2+} ions then probably stimulates Ca^{2+} release from the SR. The resulting increase in intracellular Ca^{2+} activates the contractile apparatus by binding to troponin on the actin thin filaments. The binding of Ca^{2+} to troponin alters the interaction between troponin, tropomyosin and actin. In relaxed muscle, tropomyosin non-competitively inhibits the ability of actin to activate myosin ATPase, but when Ca^{2+} binds to troponin this inhibition is relieved[1]. Relaxation of the muscle after the contraction is due to: (1) repolarization of the membrane by activation of an outward K^+ current (the repolarization current), which results in closure of the voltage-sensitive Ca^{2+}/Na^+ channels and thus terminates Ca^{2+} influx; (2) reduction of free intracellular Ca^{2+} by active uptake into the SR and by extrusion of Ca^{2+} into the extracellular fluid by sodium–calcium exchange; and (3) dissociation of Ca^{2+} from troponin and subsequent inhibition of the ATPase by tropomyosin.

The description of the pacemaker current in secondary pacemakers (e.g. Purkinje fibers) has recently been reinterpreted by DiFrancesco[2]. In the old view, pacemaking in secondary pacemakers was due to the slow turn-off of a specific K^+ current different from the repolarizing K^+ current. The new view is that the pacemaker current is carried largely by Na^+ ions and that the pacemaker depolarization is due to the turn-on of this Na^+ current which is activated at hyperpolarizing (negative to -60 mV) potentials. The difficulty in identifying the ionic components of the pacemaker current is caused by depletion of K^+ from the extracellular clefts during prolonged voltage clamp pulses. What was at first thought to be a K^+ specific pacemaking current is really the result of an artefact (i.e. a time-dependent K^+ depletion current). The K^+ depletion current causes the Na^+ pacemaker current reversal potential to vary in parallel with the K^+ equilibrium potential. As a result, the reversal potential of the current is not a reliable indicator of the current carrying ionic species. Pacemaking in the SA node is still considered to be due to the decaying K^+ repolarizing current. The Na^+ pacemaker current, while present in the cells of the SA node, normally contributes little to the pacemaker depolarization since the MDP of these cells is about -60 mV and, therefore, it is not significantly activated. An excellent discussion of pacemaking currents and the DiFrancesco reinterpretation may be found in a review by Noble (1984)[29].

Mechanism of action of NA

NA has three effects on the heartbeat: NA increases (1) beat frequency, (2) peak systolic tension, and (3) rate of relaxation after peak tension has been reached. Each of these effects can be partly explained by effects on ionic channels in the plasma membrane. The increase in beat frequency is probably due to an increase in the magnitude of the repolarizing K^+ current. This increases the rate of repolarization and thereby shortens the action potential. The pacemaker

Na^+ current is also increased by NA[30]. This produces a more rapid pacemaker depolarization. The increased peak tension is largely due to an increase in the influx of Ca^{2+} during the action potential (Ca^{2+}/Na^+ current)[25] and, consequently, an increase in the peak levels of free intracellular Ca^{2+} during systole. The increase in the Ca^{2+}/Na^+ current may possibly result from an increase in mean open-time of this channel caused by NA[26]. The increased rate of relaxation which occurs in response to NA is due partly to an increase in the repolarization current which is responsible for terminating Ca^{2+} influx[21].

Although these three effects of NA can be largely explained by effects on ionic channels, NA also has effects on proteins of the contractile apparatus and sarcoplasmic reticulum. These effects are very likely involved in regulation of contractile activity although the exact roles are not yet proven. NA speeds up Ca^{2+} sequestration by the SR[11,13]. Exposure of cells to NA results in phosphorylation of phospholamban, an 8 000 mol. wt protein located in the membrane of the SR. When phospholamban is phosphorylated, the affinity of the Ca^{2+} transport protein for Ca^{2+} and the velocity of Ca^{2+} transport increase. It has been proposed that this increased Ca^{2+} sequestration is responsible for the increased relaxation rate, but recent studies have failed to correlate relaxation rate with phospholamban phosphorylation[14]. Alternatively, the increased ability of the SR to accumulate Ca^{2+} may increase the Ca^{2+} store of the SR and result in a greater release of intracellular Ca^{2+} during each beat. This would be an additional mechanism for increasing peak systolic tension.

In addition, NA stimulates phosphorylation of two contractile proteins. NA stimulates the phosphorylation of troponin-I[13,24]. Troponin-I is the subunit of troponin which regulates the affinity of troponin-C (the Ca^{2+}-binding subunit) for Ca^{2+}. Phosphorylation of troponin-I results in an increase in the dissociation rate of Ca^{2+} from troponin-C and a decrease in the sensitivity of myofibrillar ATPase for Ca^{2+}. This increased rate of dissociation of Ca^{2+} from troponin-C could be important in producing the increased rate of relaxation which is observed in response to NA[3,13,27].

C-protein phosphorylation

Another very interesting protein in the contractile apparatus which is phosphorylated in response to NA is C-protein[8]. C-protein is an integral component of the thick filament[17]. We have proposed that C-protein phosphorylation, like troponin phosphorylation, may be involved in regulating the rate of relaxation of the cardiac twitch. The evidence supporting this idea is that the phosphorylation state of C-protein correlates with twitch relaxation[31]. Furthermore, C-protein has a variety of interesting properties which suggest that it may play a regulatory role in the myofibril: it binds to both actin and myosin and has complex effects on the actin-activated myosin ATPase activity[17]. Recently we have purified cardiac muscle C-protein and have found that it is phosphorylated at 3–5 sites by cAMP-dependent protein kinase and by an endogenous Ca^{2+}-calmodulin dependent protein kinase[32]. We are currently examining the effect of phosphorylated and dephosphorylated C-protein on reconstituted actomyosin systems in order to test the hypothesis that C-protein is involved in regulation of the actomyosin ATPase.

Mechanisms of action of ACh

ACh and NA have opposite effects on force and frequency of heartbeat.

Some of these effects are produced by opposing actions on the same molecular effector systems. For example, ACh and NA have opposite effects on the Ca^{2+}/Na^{+} current (ACh decreases this current while NA increases it)[5] and on phosphorylation of troponin-I[24] and C-protein[8]. However, ACh decreases the rate of pacemaker depolarization by the activation of a background K^{+} current not affected by NA[4]. The activation of this K^{+} current is responsible for the hyperpolarization of the cardiac cell which is seen in response to ACh.

This hyperpolarizing response is particularly interesting because it is very slow[7]. Application of a brief (5 ms) pulse of ACh from an iontophoretic micropipette produces a hyperpolarization which begins after a lag period of ~100 ms and lasts ~5 s. This response is several orders of magnitude slower than the fast excitatory postsynaptic potential produced by ACh on nicotinic receptors. Why this response is so slow is not clear. The duration of the response is 3–4 orders of magnitude longer than expected from free diffusion and is at least 1–2 orders of magnitude greater than the single-channel lifetime measured by noise analysis[23] or patch-clamp (Hartzell, unpublished observations). Thus, it appears that the rate-limiting step is not diffusion, binding, or channel lifetime[19]. The lag period and the high sensitivity of this lag period to temperature suggest that enzymatic mechanisms may be partly responsible for this response.

In summary, autonomic neurotransmitters have effects on at least four different kinds of ionic channels in the cardiac muscle membrane: (i) NA increases and ACh decreases Ca^{2+}/Na^{+} current; (ii) NA increases the repolarization K^{+} current; (iii) NA shifts the current–potential relationship of the pacemaker current in a depolarizing direction; and (iv) ACh increases a background K^+ current. It is important to emphasize that the effect of these transmitters on the Ca^{2+}/Na^+ channel and the pacemaker channel is to modulate how these channels respond to changes in trans-membrane potential. In addition, these transmitters alter the levels of intracellular Ca^{2+} by changing the pumping of Ca^{2+} by the SR and the sensitivity of the contractile apparatus for Ca^{2+}. In these respects, the heart exhibits several features which would be useful to a presynaptic terminal: transmitter release from presynaptic terminals could effectively be modulated by neurotransmitters which act on the terminals to alter Ca^{2+} influx, Ca^{2+} sequestration, and the Ca^{2+}-sensitivity of cytoskeletal elements involved in synaptic vesicle mobilization and fusion.

Molecular mechanisms mediating sympathetic effects

The heart's response to catechol-amines is mediated by both α- and β-adrenergic receptors. Most of the increased rate and force appears to be due to β-receptor activation of adenyl-ate cyclase and subsequent elevation of the cAMP 'second messenger'[28]. The stimulatory effect of α-adrenergic-receptor activation is independent of cAMP and may be the result of increased Ca^{2+} influx due to suppression of the repolarization K^+ current.

Binding of NA to β-adrenergic receptors activates adenylate cyclase, which synthesizes cAMP. This activation involves coupling of the receptor and cyclase via a regulatory, guanyl-nucleotide-binding protein and GTP. The receptor exists in two states. The high-affinity state is not coupled to the cyclase, but can be converted to the low-affinity, cyclase-coupled state by GTP. The newly synthesized cAMP then preferentially activates a mem-brane-bound cAMP-dependent pro-tein kinase[10] by binding to the regula-tory subunit of the protein kinase. The catalytic subunit of the protein kinase dissociates from the regulatory subunit and phosphorylates proteins asso-ciated with various effector systems. The phosphorylation of phospholam-ban, troponin-I, and C-protein are all mediated by cAMP-dependent protein kinase. In addition, it is likely that the increase in the Ca^{2+}/Na^+ current produced by NA is mediated by cAMP-dependent phosphorylation.

The involvement of cAMP in these effects was controversial for some time. Although some investigators reported good correlation between the level of cAMP and contractile force, small doses of β-receptor agonists, which stimulated contractile force, sometimes had no measurable effects on cAMP levels. This problem has been resolved by more recent studies which show that there is a large population of 'spare' β-receptors: that is, only a small percentage of the total β-receptors need to be occupied by agonist to achieve a maximal effect. Elevation of cAMP which occurs with submaximal doses of NA is often not detectable in measurements of whole-cell cAMP, particularly because the relevant changes in cAMP levels occur only in a certain subcellular pool[10]. The best evidence favoring the cAMP hypothesis is that application of cAMP analogs or treatment with drugs which elevate endogenous cAMP levels mimic many of the effects of NA. For example, external application or intra-cellular injection of cAMP analogs or injection of catalytic subunit of cAMP-dependent protein kinase into heart cells[22] causes an increase in the Ca^{2+}/Na^+ current.

Although many of the effects of β-adrenergic agonists are mediated by the cAMP system, not all effects of NA can be mimicked by cAMP application. For example, NA shortens action potential duration and increases activity-dependent K^+ efflux (the repolarization current?), but cAMP analogs have the opposite effects[20]. These results suggest that the repolarization K^+ current is not mediated by cAMP.

Molecular mechanisms mediating parasympathetic effects

The effects of ACh in heart are produced exclusively via muscarinic ACh receptors. The molecular mechanisms which mediate these effects are very poorly understood. It has been proposed that some of the effects of ACh are mediated by the cGMP–protein kinase system; however, whole-cell cGMP levels often do not correlate with the force of contraction[15]. Although extracellular application of 8-bromo-cGMP mimics the effect of ACh on action potential duration and Ca^{2+} influx, it does not affect the K^+ permeability. Furthermore, there are several studies which argue that the response to ACh can clearly be dissociated from increases in cGMP levels. Elevation of cGMP by ACh seems to require the presence of high levels of extracellular Ca^{2+}, whereas the decrease in contractile force and increased $^{42}K^+$ efflux produced by ACh is insensitive to Ca^{2+} (Ref. 16). Compartmentalization of cGMP may complicate interpretation of many experiments. There seem to be multiple pools of cGMP, one of which is elevated by nitroprusside and is not coupled to protein kinase and another which is altered by ACh and is coupled to a cGMP-dependent protein kinase. Final resolution of the role of cGMP will require understanding the nature of these subcellular pools and identification of proteins which are specifically phosphorylated by cGMP-dependent protein kinase. However, evidence for specific cGMP-dependent phosphorylation in heart has been largely lacking to date.

Other evidence suggests that some effects of ACh are mediated by decreases in cAMP levels[12]. ACh and NA have antagonistic effects on glycogen phosphorylase activity, phosphorylation of troponin-I and C-protein, and on the Ca^{2+}/Na^+ current. Since these effects of NA are very likely mediated by cAMP-dependent phosphorylation, it is attractive to suppose that ACh acts oppositely by inactivating adenylate cyclase. In addition, since the affinity of the muscarinic receptor for agonists is modulated by GTP in much the same way that β-adrenergic receptors are modulated, this suggests that muscarinic receptors are coupled to adenylate cyclase via a GTP-binding protein. ACh does have inhibitory effects on adenylate cyclase in broken cells and produces modest decreases in cAMP levels in whole cells which have been stimulated by NA. However, the decreases in whole-cell cAMP levels which are observed are not large enough to account for the decreases in phosphorylation which occur.

Although the role of cyclic nucleotides as second messengers in mediating many of the responses to ACh remains controversial, there are reasons to believe that a second messenger is involved. One of the reasons is that the hyperpolarization produced by ACh in the heart is very slow and exhibits a long latency of onset after ACh application. Although these findings are most attractively explained by a second-messenger mechanism, there is no direct evidence to support this hypothesis.

Reading list

1 Chalovich, J. M. and Eisenberg, E. (1982) *J. Biol. Chem.* 257, 2432–2447
2 DiFrancesco, D. (1981) *J. Physiol. (London)* 314, 359–376
3 England, P. (1980) in *Recently Discovered Systems of Enzyme Regulation by Reversible Phosphorylation* (Cohen, P., ed.), Elsevier/North-Holland, Amsterdam

4 Garnier, D., Nargeot, J., Ojeda, C. and Rougier, O. (1978) *J. Physiol. (London)* 274, 381–396

5 Giles, W. and Noble, S. J. (1976) *J. Physiol. (London)* 261, 103–123

6 Giles, W. and Shibata, E. (1981) *Fed. Proc. Fed. Am. Soc. Exp. Biol.* 40, 2618–2624

7 Hartzell, H. C. (1981) *Nature (London)* 291, 539–544

8 Hartzell, H. C. and Titus, L. (1982) *J. Biol. Chem.* 257, 2111–2120

9 Hauswirth, O., Noble, D. and Tsien, R. W. (1968) *Science* 162, 916–917

10 Hayes, J. S., Brunton, L. L. and Mayer, S. E. (1980) *J. Biol. Chem.* 255, 5113–5119

11 Katz, A. (1979) *Adv. Cyclic Nucleotide Res.* 11, 303–343

12 Keeley, S. L., Lincoln, T. M. and Corbin, J. D. (1978) *Am. J. Physiol.* 234, H432–438

13 Kranias, E. G. and Solaro, R. J. (1982) *Nature (London)* 298, 182–184

14 Lindemann, J. P., Jones, L. R., Hathaway, D. R., Henry, B. G. and Watanabe, A. M. (1983) *J. Biol. Chem.* 258, 464–471

15 Linden, J. and Brooker, G. (1979) *Biochem. Pharmacol.* 28, 3351–3360

16 Mirro, M. J., Bailey, J. C. and Watanabe, A. M. (1979) *Circ. Res.* 45, 225–233

17 Moos, C., Mason, C. M., Besterman, J. M., Feng, I.-N. M. and Dubin, J. H. (1978) *J. Mol. Biol.* 124, 571–586

18 Mope, L., McClellan, G. B. and Winegrad, S. (1980) *J. Gen. Physiol.* 75, 271–282

19 Nargeot, J., Lester, H. A., Birdsall, N. J. M., Stockton, J., Wassermann, N. H. and Erlanger, B. F. (1982) *J. Gen. Physiol.* 79, 657–678

20 Nawrath, H., Blei, I. and Gegner, R. (1980) *Experientia* 36, 72–74

21 Noble, D. (1975) *The Initiation of the Heart Beat*, Oxford University Press, London

22 Osterrieder, W., Brum, G., Hesheler, J., Trautwein, W., Flockerzi, V. and Hofmann, F. (1982) *Nature (London)* 298, 576–578

23 Osterrieder, W., Noma, A. and Trautwein, W. (1980) *Pfluegers Arch.* 386, 101–109

24 Ray, K. P. and England, P. J. (1976) *FEBS Lett.* 70, 11–16

25 Reuter, H. and Scholz, H. (1977) *J. Physiol. (London)* 264, 49–62

26 Reuter, H., Stevens, C. F., Tsien, R. W. and Yellen, G. (1982) *Nature (London)* 297, 501–504

27 Stull, J. T. (1980) in *Advances in Cyclic Nucleotide Research* (Greengard, P. and Robison, G. A., eds), pp. 39–93, Raven Press, New York

28 Tsien, R. W. (1977) *Adv. Cyclic Nucleotide Res.* 8, 363–420

29 Noble, D. (1984) *J. Physiol. (London)* 353, 1–50

30 Brown, H. F., DiFrancesco, D. and Noble, S. J. (1979) *Nature (London)* 280, 235–236

31 Hartzell, H. C. (1984) *J. Gen. Physiol.* 83, 563–588

32 Hartzell, H. C. and Glass, D. B. *J. Biol. Chem.* (in press)

Tony Creazzo, Louisa Titus and Criss Hartzell are at the Department of Anatomy, Emory University School of Medicine, Atlanta, GA 30322, USA.

Modulation of gated ion channels as a mode of transmitter action

S. A. Siegelbaum and R. W. Tsien

Ionic channels in nerve and muscle cells have until recently been divided into two broad classes: channels that participate in the generation of the action potential and channels that generate postsynaptic potentials in response to neurotransmitters. This distinction was based to a large extent on the classic analysis of the action of acetylcholine (ACh) at the frog neuromuscular junction[31] – where the cholinergic end-plate channels are different from the Hodgkin-Huxley Na^+ and K^+ channels that generate the action potential[62]. However, recent results suggest that in many other systems neurotransmitters can modulate the activity of channels that contribute to the action potential. This type of postsynaptic effect is responsible for several important physiological actions of transmitters[43]. Patch-clamp experiments provide insights into the mechanisms of modulation at the level of single-channel molecules.

What types of action potential ion channels are subject to control by transmitters and how do transmitters alter channel functioning? Table I summarizes some recent results, indicating the nature of the ion channel that is affected by the neurotransmitter as well as the mode of transmitter action on the ionic conductance. In nearly all of the examples reported so far, the major effect of transmitters is to increase or decrease the peak magnitude of specific ionic conductances involved in generating the action potential. This shows up in voltage-clamp experiments as a change in the size of the maximal ionic current. Table I also points out that different neurotransmitters can modulate a single type of ion channel in a given preparation. For example, in cardiac cells the magnitude of the slow inward calcium current (I_{si}) is enhanced by catecholamines[53] and the peptide angiotensin II[30], while in bullfrog sympathetic ganglion cells, ACh and luteinizing-hormone-releasing factor (LRF) act to decrease the voltage-dependent M current[2]. Conversely, a single

transmitter can often modulate several different types of channels in a single preparation. In cardiac Purkinje fibers, adrenaline increases the magnitude of both I_{si} and the delayed rectifier K^+ current I_x, and shifts the voltage-dependent kinetics of the pacemaker current (see Ref. 68).

The actions of modulatory transmitters on action potential channels differ from the more conventional type of transmitter action (for example ACh on end-plate channels) in two other important respects. First, the time course of such transmitter actions is in general quite slow, lasting in the order of seconds to minutes, compared to the brief depolarization (lasting only a few milliseconds) produced by ACh at the end-plate[25,32]. Second, transmitters do not in general directly interact with action potential channels. Rather, their action is often mediated by intracellular messengers, including Ca^{2+} (Ref. 41) and cyclic AMP[23,38]. The work of Krebs[37] and Greengard[23] and colleagues suggests that cAMP-dependent neurotransmitter effects resemble the actions of certain peptide

TABLE I. Selected examples of neurochemical modulation of channels that participate in normal electrical activity of neurons and heart cells[a]

Tissue	Cell type	Channel type (ion)	Modifier	Messenger mechanism	Response	Physiological effect	Refs
Neuron	Frog sympathetic and others (see Ref. 6)	$I_M(K^+)$	ACh(muscarinic)	Unknown	$\downarrow I_M$	Release inhibition of repetitive firing; slow EPSP	2, 7
	Frog sympathetic and others (see Ref. 6)	$I_M(K^+)$	LRF	Unknown	$\downarrow I_M$	Release inhibition of repetitive firing; late slow EPSP	2
	Chick sensory	Ca^{2+}	Noradrenaline; GABA; 5-HT; enkephalin; somatostatin	Unknown	$\downarrow I_{Ca}$	$\downarrow$ Action potential duration; $\downarrow$ transmitter output?	18
	Rat sympathetic	Ca^{2+}	Noradrenaline (α-adrenergic)	Unknown	$\downarrow I_{Ca}$	$\downarrow$ Action potential duration	19, 26
	Xenopus, Rohon–Beard	Ca^{2+}	Met-enkephalin	Unknown	$\downarrow I_{Ca}$	$\downarrow$ Action potential duration	16
	Rat hippocampal pyramidal	Ca^{2+}-activated K^+	Noradrenaline (β-adrenergic)	$\uparrow$cAMP	$\downarrow I_{K(Ca)}$	$\downarrow$ Spike adaptation	40
	Guinea-pig myenteric	Ca^{2+}-activated K^+	5-HT	?	$\downarrow I_{K(Ca)}$	Slow EPSP; $\downarrow$ spike adaptation	22
	Guinea-pig myenteric	K^+ (rest)	ACh(muscarinic)	?	$\downarrow I_K$	Slow EPSP	42
	Otala cell 11	$I_B(Na^+?)$	Lysine vasopressin	?	$\uparrow I_B$	Bursting pacemaker	3
	Helix identified	K^+ (rest)	5-HT	$\uparrow$cAMP	$\downarrow I_K$	$\uparrow$ Action potential duration	46
	Helix identified	Ca^{2+}-activated K^+	5-HT	?$\uparrow$ cAMP; $\downarrow C_{ai}$	$\downarrow I_{K(Ca)}$	$\uparrow$ Action potential duration	5

	Preparation	Channel	Transmitter	Second messenger	Current	Effect	Ref.
	Aplysia LB, LC	Ca²⁺	5-HT	↑cAMP	↑I_{Ca}	↑ AP duration	47
	Aplysia R15	I_B(Na⁺?)	Dopamine	Unknown	↓I_B	Inhibit pacemaker activity	71
	Aplysia R15	Inward rectifier (K⁺)	5-HT	↑cAMP	↑I_K	Deepens interburst hyperpolarizations	17
	Aplysia sensory	I_S(K⁺)	5-HT	↑cAMP	↓I_S	Broadens spikes; ↑transmitter output; slow EPSP	33, 60
	Aplysia L10	Ca²⁺	Histamine(?)	Unknown	↓I_{Ca}	↓Transmitter output	59
	Aplysia bag cell	K⁺	Atrial peptide(?)	↑cAMP	↓I_K	↑Afterdischarge; ↑hormone output	29
Cardiac	All	Ca²⁺	Adrenaline; noradrenaline (β-adrenergic)	↑cAMP	↑I_{Ca}	↑Rate; ↑contraction	50, 67, 69
	Purkinje	Ca²⁺	Angiotensin	Unknown	↑I_{Ca}	↑Contraction	30
	Atrial; ventricular; nodal	Ca²⁺	ACh(muscarinic)	↓cAMP;? ↑cGMP	↓I_{Ca}	↓Rate; ↓contraction	20, 21, 28
	Atrial; nodal	K⁺ (rest)	ACh(muscarinic)	?	↑I_K	↓Rate; ↓contraction	48, 58
	Purkinje	K⁺ (rest)	Adrenaline; noradrenaline (β-adrenergic)	? ↑cAMP	↑I_K	Hyperpolarization	14
	All	I_x(K⁺)	Adrenaline; noradrenaline (β-adrenergic)	↑cAMP	↑I_x	Restrict action potential duration	8, 67
	Purkinje	I_f(Na⁺, K⁺)	Adrenaline; noradrenaline	?↑ cAMP	Shifted p(V)	↑Spontaneous firing	15, 65, 72

[a] This table does not include channels controlled by light or channels known to show activity only in the presence of transmitters.

hormones on target cells and involve the following sequence of events. First, binding of transmitter to its membrane receptor activates a membrane-bound adenylate cyclase, which increases the intracellular concentration of cAMP. This activates a cAMP-dependent protein kinase, which then phosphorylates one or more substrate proteins. One attractive possibility, widely proposed but never directly demonstrated, is that the channel itself is the substrate for protein kinase and that channel phosphorylation leads to the observed change in ionic conductance.

It is not surprising that channel modulation by transmitters should involve a freely diffusible intracellular messenger. The action potential channels are widely distributed throughout the cell membrane, whereas transmitter release is often localized to the small area under the presynaptic nerve terminal. Through production of an intracellular messenger, local application of transmitter can alter channel activity throughout the cell. As a consequence of this topologically widespread modulation of ion channels, these transmitter effects are often associated with a variety of changes in basic cellular electrical properties, including alterations in the threshold for the action potential, changes in the amplitude and/or duration of the action potential, and alterations in the rate of spontaneous pacemaker activity. Such changes in the electrical activity of nerve and muscle cells are often associated with changes in Ca^{2+} influx into the cell, either due to the direct modulation of the overall current carried by a population of Ca^{2+} channels (I_{Ca}), by transmitter, or indirectly through changes in the duration and firing rate of the action potential[36]. Changes in Ca^{2+} influx will, in turn, affect certain cellular processes such as contractility and transmitter release.

How might action potential channels be modulated?

One way of answering this question is to describe the overall current carried by a population of channels (I) as the product of three factors:

$$I = N_f \cdot p \cdot i$$

where N_f is the number of functional channels, p is the probability that an individual channel is open, and i is the current through a single channel when it is open. The unitary current i is often expressed as $\gamma (E - E_{rev})$ where γ is the single-channel conductance and $E - E_{rev}$ is the electrochemical driving force.

Changes in the total current I could arise from alterations in N_f, p or i (or any combination of these factors). Fig. 1 illustrates how such changes might be detected with single-channel recordings. For convenience, we discuss mechanisms which would increase ionic current; the opposite processes represent possible explanations for decreased ionic current. Panel A depicts an increase in the number of functional channels and its electrical consequences. The rise in N_f could come about through fusion of membrane vesicles and incorporation of new channels, a mechanism that seems to mediate vasopressin-induced water permeability in the toad bladder[70]. In this case, the density of channel proteins would actually increase (as illustrated). Alternatively, non-functional channels that are already in the membrane could become available.

Panel B describes what would happen if the probability of a channel being open increased, due to a change in the properties of the channel gate. Kinetically, the effect could involve a decrease in the rate of channel closure (expressed at the single-channel level as an increase in the average time that each channel spends open), or an accelerated rate of channel opening (showing up as a decrease in the time that the channel spends closed), or both (as illustrated).

The third possibility, represented in panel C, is an increase in the current flow through the open channel. This could come about through changes in fixed charge near the channel and an altered local concentration of permeant ions. It might also result from a decreased channel affinity for protons or some other rapidly equilibrating ion that blocks the channel (see Ref. 68). If the on- and off-rates for the blocking substance are very fast, moment-to-moment variations in current intensity will be smoothed out by the recording system and only the average will be expressed by the observable current amplitude i. (This illustrates the fact that distinctions between N_f, p and i are not absolute, but depend to some extent on how rapidly current varies relative to the time resolution of the measurements.)

Changes in any one of the factors N_f, p or i could plausibly arise from phosphorylation or some other covalent modification of the channel protein or a modifier protein. At one extreme, phosphorylation might remove a distinct, voltage-independent gate that would otherwise prevent current flow, and thus increase N_f (for example, see Ref. 52). Alternatively, one might also imagine

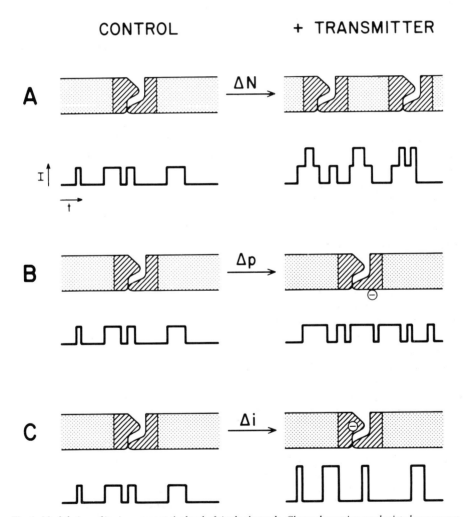

Fig. 1. *Modulation of ionic current at the level of single channels. Channel proteins are depicted as aqueous pores. An outer narrowing called a 'selectivity filter' plays a major role in deciding which ion species can pass through the pore, and the local concentration of permeant ions controlling the unitary-current amplitude i. An inner 'gate' acts as an on-off switch to control current flow in an all-or-none way. In many cases, the probability that the gate is open (p) varies with membrane potential. Idealized current recordings from a small patch of membrane show channel opening as upward deflections.*

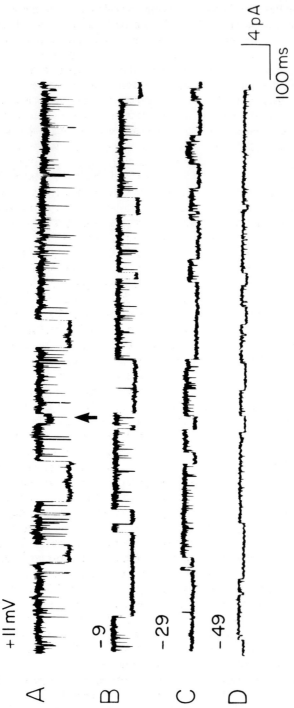

Fig. 2. 5-HT-sensitive K^+ channel. Single-channel current records from mechanoreceptor sensory neurons (LE cluster) in the abdominal ganglion of Aplysia californica. Both the bath and recording pipette contain artificial sea water. Current records at four different patch membrane potentials (indicated to left of each trace). The patch membrane potential was altered by changing the potential inside the recording pipette while the intracellular resting potential (-39 mV) was kept constant. Channel openings appear as step increases in outward current (outward current plotted in upward direction). The current fluctuates between two levels corresponding to the closed and open channel. At all potentials the channel shows both brief closures (downward flickers) and longer closures, but is in the open configuration for most of the time. The arrow indicates a rare event representing a closure of the channel to an intermediate conductance level. Addition of 10 μM 5-HT to the bath caused this channel to close (record not shown) (from Ref. 60).

effects on gating, through changes in the electrical or chemical energies of the open or closed conformations of the channel protein (see Refs 63, 65). The mere addition of the extra negative charge of a phosphate group might have a powerful electrostatic effect on rearrangement of charged groups during channel gating (Fig. 2B). Finally, phosphorylation or other covalent modifications might alter the structure of the selectivity filter or change the local concentration of a permeant ion or a rapidly equilibrating blocker (Fig. 2C).

The development of the patch-clamp technique for single-channel recording[24] has greatly aided investigations of how transmitters modulate channel function at the molecular level. Two recent examples of modulatory transmitter actions on single-channel currents are presented below.

Modulation of a K^+-current channel by serotonin

In *Aplysia* sensory neurons, serotonin (5-HT) produces a slow depolarizing excitatory postsynaptic potential (EPSP) that is associated with an increase in the cell resting-membrane resistance, a broadening of the action potential, and an increase in transmitter release from the sensory cell terminals[10]. Voltage-clamp studies[33,35] have shown that the slow EPSP is due to a decrease in a specific outward K^+ current (S current) that is distinct from the previously identified K^+ currents in molluscan cells[1]. Several lines of evidence support a role for cAMP-dependent protein phosphorylation in mediating the effects of 5-HT. Biochemical studies have shown that 5-HT (but not other transmitters) increases cAMP in single identified sensory neurons[4] and increases protein phosphorylation[45]. Intracellular injections of cAMP[34] or catalytic subunit of protein kinase[11] mimic many of the electrophysiological actions of 5-HT, while injections of a specific inhibitor of protein kinase blocks the effects of 5-HT[12].

The 5-HT-sensitive K^+ channel (S channel) in the sensory neuron membrane has been identified recently with single-channel recording techniques[60]. These experiments have also provided some insight into how 5-HT modulates the K^+ channel. Fig. 2 shows channel-current records from a membrane patch that contains only a single S channel. The channel carries outward current over a wide range of membrane potentials and is in the open state for a large fraction of time, even at potentials negative to the cell resting potential ($V_r = -40$ mV). As the membrane potential is made more positive, the magnitude of the single-channel current increases (due to the increase in outward driving force on K^+), although the probability that a channel is open, p, changes little (p = 0.7–0.8).

The effect of 5-HT on this type of K^+ channel is illustrated in Fig. 3. This membrane patch initially contained four active S channels. The top trace (Fig. 3A) shows the onset of 5-HT action on channel currents on a slow time base. Fig. 3B shows a brief stretch of the control-current record at an expanded time-scale before addition of drug to the bath. The current record jumps among several discrete levels due to the random opening and closing of the four S channels in the patch. At the arrow (Fig. 3A), 5-HT (100 μM) was added to the bath and within a few seconds the cell slowly began to depolarize and there was an increase in the cell resting-membrane resistance (measured with an intracellular microelectrode). Simultaneous with these changes in the whole-cell membrane properties, the single-channel current record shows a slow stepwise decrease in the total current carried by the S channels as three of the four active S channels close in response to 5-HT (Fig. 3A). Fig. 3C is another fast time-scale display which shows that, in the presence of 5-HT, the remaining active channel continues to open and close normally with an unaltered single-channel current amplitude.

This type of experiment argues that 5-HT does not convert channels to a state with a reduced channel conductance (see Fig. 1A) or with modified gating (see Fig. 1B).

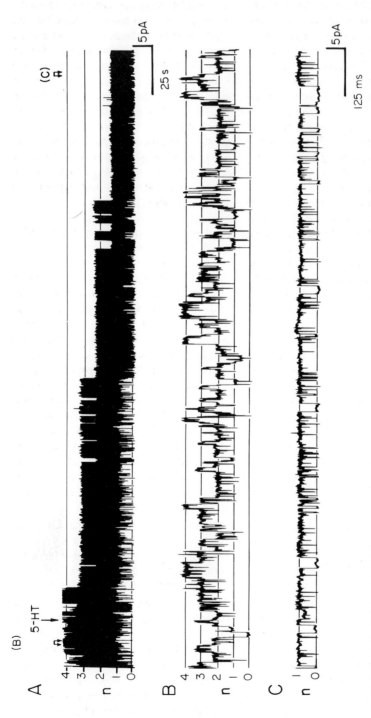

Fig. 3. *Effect of 5-HT on single-channel current. Single-channel current recordings from a sensory-cell membrane patch containing four channels.* **A.** *Channel currents shown on a slow time base. At the arrow a concentrated drop of 5-HT was added to the bath to achieve a 5-HT concentration of 100 μM. The numbers on the left-hand ordinate indicate the number of open channels in the patch. The small arrows labelled (**B**) and (**C**) indicate regions of trace **A** from which expanded records shown in traces **B** and **C** were obtained. Cell resting potential = −41 mV before 5-HT. In presence of 5-HT the cell depolarized to −37 mV and there was a 33% increase in membrane resistance. Patch membrane potential was 0 mV before 5-HT and +4 mV after 5-HT. (Unpublished experiment by J. S. Camardo and S. A. Siegelbaum.)*

Rather, 5-HT appears to act on S channels in an all-or-none manner, completely closing some channels while leaving others unaffected. In the context of the models for channel modulation discussed above (see Fig. 1), 5-HT decreases the effective number of open channels in the patch. We cannot, of course, distinguish experimentally whether 5-HT actually renders channels non-functional (equivalent to a true decrease in Nf) or drastically reduces their probability of opening (for example a reduction in p from 0.7 to $\ll 0.01$).

The experiment shown in Fig. 3 also provides independent support that 5-HT acts on the S channel via an intracellular messenger. To obtain the single-channel recordings, a mechanically tight giga-ohm seal is formed between the recording pipette and the cell membrane, and this effectively prevents the diffusion of molecules from the bath into the pipette. Since in these experiments no 5-HT is present inside the pipette, the transmitter can influence channels in the patch of membrane under the pipette only via some intracellular messenger. To test this more directly, single S-channel currents were recorded while cAMP was injected into the sensory cell by iontophoretic current pulses from a cAMP-filled microelectrode. The intracellular cAMP injections closed the S channels in a manner that was identical to the action of 5-HT.

How well do these single-channel studies agree with previous results from conventional electrophysiological measurements? Since the S channel is normally open at the resting potential, its closure can account for the slow depolarization and increase in resting-membrane resistance observed with 5-HT. Another characteristic feature of the action of 5-HT is that it lengthens the sensory-cell action potential. This too can be explained by closure of the S channel:

since this channel normally contributes outward repolarizing current throughout the action potential, its closure will prolong the repolarization phase. One fundamental question that remains concerns the substrate protein for the cAMP-dependent protein kinase. Is it the S channel itself or some intracellular protein (for example an ion pump) that indirectly alters S-channel activity? Experiments involving the addition of purified catalytic subunit of protein kinase to cell-free inside-out patches (where the cytoplasmic surface of the membrane patch is exposed to the bath) provide a promising approach to these questions.

Modulation of cardiac Ca^{2+} channels by β-adrenergic agonists

The modulatory effect of noradrenaline and adrenaline on cardiac Ca^{2+} channels plays a large part in controlling the rhythm and strength of the heartbeat. The increase in Ca^{2+} conductance by β-adrenergic agents was one of the first known examples of neurochemical regulation of an action potential channel[50]. Like serotonergic regulation of S channels, β-adrenergic modulation of Ca^{2+} channels leads to increased Ca^{2+} influx during the action potential – in this case, by a direct effect on Ca^{2+} conductance. Like the S-channel modulation the Ca^{2+}-channel modulation is mediated by cAMP and protein phosphorylation. The sequence of events can be summarized as in equation 1.

$$\begin{array}{c} \text{Transmitter-} \\ \beta\text{-receptor} \\ \text{complex} \end{array} \rightarrow \uparrow \begin{array}{c} \text{Adenylate} \\ \text{cyclase} \end{array} \rightarrow \uparrow \text{cAMP} \rightarrow \begin{array}{c} \uparrow \text{Protein} \\ \text{phosphorylation} \end{array} \rightarrow \begin{array}{c} \text{Altered} \\ \text{channel} \\ \text{properties} \end{array} \rightarrow \uparrow I_{Ca} \quad (1)$$

The role of cyclic AMP has been substantiated by experiments where Ca^{2+} currents or Ca^{2+}-dependent action potentials are enhanced by direct injection of cAMP or by other interventions known to increase intracellular cAMP (for examples, see Refs 39, 51, 64). Strong evidence for involvement of protein phosphorylation comes from experiments showing that the β-adrenergic response can be mimicked by injection of the catalytic subunit of cAMP-dependent protein kinase and opposed by injection of regulatory subunit[49].

Voltage-clamp recordings from multicellular preparations showed no change in either the time course of Ca^{2+}-channel current or its reversal potential[54]. This encouraged the hypothesis that β-adrenergic agents enhance the Ca^{2+} current by increasing the number of functional Ca^{2+} channels, and not by changing the properties of individual channels such as i or p[44,51,54,61,66]. This hypothesis has now been tested with patch-clamp recordings from rat heart cells exposed to isoproterenol or 8-bromo-cyclic AMP[9,53,55] (see Fig. 4). The recordings of unitary current show that the unitary current amplitude (i) remains unchanged during the increase in the averaged Ca^{2+}-channel activity. So far, there is no evidence for the increase in the number of functional channels as previously hypothesized. What the unitary recordings do show clearly is an increase in the probability that a single channel is open at any given time. Thus, the experiment illustrated in Fig. 4 fits with the pattern described in Fig. 1B. Further analysis shows that the increase in probability is brought about by a prolongation of the average duration of channel openings and, more importantly, by an abbreviation of the closed intervals between successive openings[9,53,55]. The enhancement of p was also associated with fewer 'nulls' (depolarizations which produced no detectable channel openings)[9,53].

The demonstrated increase in p was unexpected because the earlier voltage-clamp analysis did not reveal any change in the time course of Ca^{2+}-channel activation or deactivation due to β-adrenergic stimulation[54]. On the other hand, patch-clamp recordings indicate that the rate constants leading up to the open-channel state are accelerated[9], and predict faster turn-on kinetics; this prediction needs to be tested further. Another unsettled question is whether the number of functional Ca^{2+}

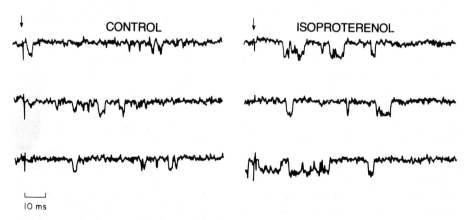

Fig. 4. *Effect of isoproterenol on current through a single Ca^{2+} channel. Current recordings from a cell-attached membrane patch on a cultured ventricular cell from neonatal rat heart. Patch pipette contained Ba^{2+} (96 mM) as the current-carrying species, and tetrodotoxin (TTX) (20 μM) to block Na^{+} channels. Ca^{2+}-channel openings were evoked by depolarizations from $V_m \cong -90$ mV to $V_m \cong +10$ m V; the step change occurred at the time marked by the arrow and was associated with a downward spike of imperfectly subtracted capacitative current. Records taken during a control run (left) and a run after exposure of the cell to 10 μM isoproterenol (right). Analysis of these runs gave the following values:*

  control: $N_f = 1, i = -1.00 pA, p = 0.059$
  isoproterenol: $N_f = 1, i = -1.05 pA, p = 0.094$

In this particular experiment, the enhancement of the average Ca^{2+}-channel current was largely accounted for by the increased probability of channel opening. (Unpublished experiment by H. Reuter, C. F. Stevens, R. W. Tsien and G. Yellen.)

channels really remains the same during the β-adrenergic response. Despite the lack of direct evidence, there is still reason for suspecting that the number of channels can increase. At strong depolarizations, where p can exceed 0.5 in the absence of β-adrenergic stimulation[55], a maximal elevation of p could only account for a doubling of Ca^{2+}-channel current – much less than the full β-adrenergic response in many cardiac cells.

Multiple modulatory mechanisms?

The 5-HT-sensitive K^+ channel in *Aplysia* and the noradrenaline-sensitive Ca^{2+} channel in heart are only the first of many conductances whose modulation will be investigated at the level of single-channel molecules. These two cases have already illustrated how variations in the magnitude of an ionic current can come about in different ways, through changes in N_f and p. It seems likely that we will continue to see a diversity of regulatory mechanisms with analysis of other systems.

One major challenge for the future is to relate electrical measurements of channel function to information about channel structure and biochemistry. Ion channels can be considered as a special class of enzymes, comparable perhaps with other enzymes that are regulated by covalent modifications such as phosphorylation. Some soluble enzymes are controlled by phosphorylation at a single site (for example glycogen phosphorylase), others at multiple sites (for example glycogen synthetase). There is also precedent for modulation of membrane enzymes through the phosphorylation of a relatively small regulatory peptide (for example Ca^{2+}-ATPase of cardiac sarcoplasmic reticulum, phospholamban). In comparison to these relatively well studied examples, analysis of channel modulation is still at an early stage where the relationship of biochemical events to channel behavior is not understood. There is evidence demonstrating cAMP-dependent phosphorylation of Na^+ channels[13] and nicotinic ACh-sensitive channels[27], but the

functional significance of these modifications is not clear. The presumed role of phosphorylation is more obvious in the case of Ca^{2+} channels. Enhancement of 'potential-sensitive' Ca^{2+} uptake into cardiac sarcolemmal vesicles by protein kinase treatment seems to be correlated with phosphorylation of a 23 000 mol. wt protein called 'calciductin'[56,57]. It is intriguing that this protein is similar in molecular weight and amino acid composition to the regulatory protein phospholamban, but its relationship to the Ca^{2+}-channel protein itself is uncertain[73]. Much work needs to be done to unify biophysical and biochemical approaches to ion-channel modulation.

Acknowledgement
We wish to thank E. R. Kandel, J. S. Camardo, S. DeRiemer and M. C. Nowycky for advice.

Reading list and references in Table I
1 Adams, D. J., Smith, S. J. and Thompson, S. H. (1980) *Annu. Rev. Neurosci.* 3, 141–167

2 Adams, P. R., Brown, D. A. and Constanti, A. (1982) *J. Physiol. (London)* 332, 223–262

3 Barker, J. L. and Smith, T. G., Jr (1976) *Brain Res.* 103, 167–170

4 Bernier, L., Castellucci, V. F., Kandel, E. R. and Schwartz, J. H. (1982) *J. Neurosci.* 2, 1682–1691

5 Boyle, M. B. and Smith, S. J. (1982) *Soc. Neurosci. Abstr.* 8, 523

6 Brown, D. A. (1983) *Trends NeuroSci.* 6, 302–307

7 Brown, D. A. and Adams, P. R. (1980) *Nature (London)* 283, 673–676

8 Brown, H. F., McNaughton, P. A., Noble, D. and Noble, S. J. (1974) *Phil. Trans. R. Soc. London, Ser. B* 270, 527–537

9 Cachelin, A. B., dePeyer, J. E., Kokubun, S. and Reuter, H. *Nature (London)* (in press)

10 Castellucci, V. and Kandel, E. R. (1976) *Science* 194, 1176–1178

11 Castellucci, V. F., Kandel, E. R., Schwartz, J. H., Wilson, F. D., Nairn, A. L. and Greengard, P. (1980) *Proc. Natl Acad. Sci. USA* 77, 7492–7496

12 Castellucci, V. F., Nairn, C., Greengard, P., Schwartz. J. H. and Kandel, E. R. (1982) *J. Neurosci.* 2, 1673–1681

13 Costa, M. R. C., Casnellie, J. E. and Catterall, W. A. (1982) *J. Biol. Chem.* 257, 7918–7921

14 Cranefield, P. F. and Gadsby, D. C. (1981) *J. Physiol. (London)* 318, 34–35

15 DiFrancesco, D. (1981) *J. Physiol. (London)* 314, 359–376

16 Bixby, J. L. and Spitzer, N. C. (1983) *J. Neurosci.* 3, 1014–1018

17 Drummond, A. H., Benson, J. A. and Levitan, I. E. (1980) *Proc. Natl Acad. Sci. USA* 77, 5013–5017

18 Dunlap, K. and Fischbach, G. D. (1981) *J. Physiol. (London)* 317, 519–535

19 Galvan, M. and Adams, P. R. (1982) *Brain Res.* 244, 135–144

20 Giles, W. and Noble S. J. (1976) *J. Physiol. (London)* 261, 103–123

21 Giles, W. and Tsien, R. W. (1975) *J. Physiol. (London)* 246, 64–66P

22 Grafe, P., Mayer, C. J. and Wood, J. D. (1980) *J. Physiol. (London)* 305, 235–248

23 Greengard, P. (1976) *Nature (London)* 260, 101–108

24 Hamill, O., Marty, A., Neher, E., Sakmann, B. and Sigworth, F. J. (1981) *Pfluegers Arch.* 391, 85–100

25 Hartzell, H. C. (1981) *Nature (London)* 291, 539–544

26 Horn, J. P. and McAfee, D. A. (1980) *J. Physiol. (London)* 301, 191–204

27 Huganir, R. L. and Greengard, P. (1983) *Proc. Natl Acad. Sci. USA* 80, 1130–1134

28 Ikemoto, Y. and Goto, M. (1975) *Proc. Jpn Acad.* 51, 501–505

29 Kaczmarek, L. K. and Strumwasser, F. (1981) *J. Neurosci.* 1, 626–634

30 Kass, R. S. and Blair, M. L. (1981) *J. Mol. Cell. Cardiol.* 13, 797–809

31 Katz, B. (1966) *Nerve, Muscle and Synapse*, McGraw-Hill, New York

32 Kehoe, J. and Marty, A. (1980) *Annu. Rev. Biophys. Bioeng.* 9, 437–465

33 Klein, M., Camardo, J. S. and Kandel, E. R. (1982) *Proc. Natl Acad. Sci. USA* 79, 5713–5717

34 Klein, M. and Kandel, E. R. (1978) *Proc. Natl Acad. Sci. USA* 75, 3512–3516

35 Klein, M. and Kandel, E. R. (1980) *Proc. Natl Acad. Sci. USA* 77, 6912–6916

36 Klein, M., Shapiro, E. and Kandel, E. R. (1980) *J. Exp. Biol.* 89, 117–157

37 Krebs, E. G. (1972) *Curr. Top. Cell Regul.* 5, 99–133

38 Kupfermann, I. (1980) *Annu. Rev. Physiol.* 42, 629–641

39 Li, T. and Sperelakis, N. (1982) *Circ. Res.* 52, 111–117

40 Madison, D. V. and Nicoll, R. A. (1982) *Nature (London)* 299, 636–638

41 Maruyama, Y. and Petersen, O. H. (1982) *Nature (London)* 300, 61–63

42 Morita, K., North, R. A. and Tokimasa, T. (1982) *J. Physiol. (London)* 333, 125–139

43 Nicoll, R. (1982) *Trends NeuroSci.* 5, 369–374

44 Niedergerke, R. and Page, S. (1977) *Proc. R. Soc. London, Ser. B* 197, 333–367

45 Paris, C. G., Castellucci, V. F., Kandel, E. R. and Schwartz, J. H. (1981) *Cold Spring Harbor Conf. Cell Proliferation* 8, 1361–1375

46 Paupardin-Tritsch, D., Deterre, P. and Gerschenfeld, H. M. (1981) *Brain Res.* 217, 201–206

47 Pellmar, T. C. and Carpenter, D. O. (1980) *J. Neurophysiol.* 44, 423–439

48 Ojeda, C., Rougier, O. and Tourneur, Y. (1981) *Pfluegers Arch. Gesamte Physiol. Menschen Tiere* 391, 57–59

49 Osterrieder, W., Brum, G., Hescheler, J., Trautwein, W., Flockerzi, V. and Hofmann, F. (1982) *Nature (London)* 298, 576–578

50 Reuter, H. (1967) *J. Physiol. (London)* 192, 479–492

51 Reuter, H. (1974) *J. Physiol. (London)* 242, 429–451

52 Reuter, H. (1979) *Annu. Rev. Physiol.* 41, 413–424

53 Reuter, H. (1983) *Nature (London)* 301, 569–574

54 Reuter, H. and Scholz, H. (1977) *J. Physiol. (London)* 264, 49–62

55 Reuter, H., Stevens, C. F., Tsien, R. W. and Yellen, G. (1982) *Nature (London)* 297, 501–504

56 Rinaldi, M. L., Capony, J.-P. and Demaille, J. G. (1982) *J. Mol. Cell. Cardiol.* 14, 279–289

57 Rinaldi, M. L., LePeuch, C. J. and Demaille, J. G. (1981) *FEBS Lett.* 129, 277–281

58 Sakmann, B., Noma, A. and Trautwein, W. (1983) *Nature (London)* 303, 250–253

59 Shapiro, E., Castellucci, V. F. and Kandel, E. R. (1981) *Proc. Natl Acad. Sci. USA* 77, 1185–1189

60 Siegelbaum, S. A., Camardo, J. S. and Kandel, E. R. (1982) *Nature (London)* 299, 413–417

61 Sperelakis, N. and Schneider, J. (1976) *Am. J. Cardiol.* 37, 1079–1085

62 Stevens, C. F. (1983) in *Molecular Biology of the Cell* (Alberts, B., Bray, D., Lewis, J., Raff, M., Roberts, K. and Watson, J. D., eds), pp. 1013–1098, Garland, New York

63 Tsien, R. W. (1973) *Neurosci. Res. Prog. Bull.* 11, 204–210

64 Tsien, R. W. (1973) *Nature (London) New Biol.* 245, 120–122

65 Tsien, R. W. (1974) *J. Gen. Physiol.* 64, 320–342

66 Tsien, R. W. (1977) *Adv. Cyclic Nucl. Res.* 8, 363–420

67 Tsien, R. W., Giles, W. and Greengard, P. (1972)

Nature (London) New Biol. 240, 181–183

68 Tsien, R. W. and Siegelbaum, S. A. (1978) in *Physiology of Membrane Disorders* (Andreoli, T. E., Hoffman, J. F. and Fanestil, D. D., eds), pp. 517–538, Plenum Press, New York

69 Vassort, G., Rougier, O., Garnier, D., Sauviat, M. P., Coraboeuf, E. and Gargouil, Y. M. (1969) *Pfluegers Arch.* 309, 70–81

70 Wade, J. E., Stetson, D. L. and Lewis, S. A. (1981) *Annu. NY Acad. Sci.* 372, 106–117

71 Wilson, W. A. and Wachtel, H. (1978) *Science* 202, 772–775

72 Hauswirth, O., Noble, D. and Tsien, R.W. (1968) *Science* 162, 916–917

73 Manalan, A. S. and Jones, L. R. (1982) *J. Biol. Chem.* 257, 10052–10062

S. A. Siegelbaum is at the Department of Pharmacology, Columbia University College of Physicians and Surgeons, New York, NY 10032, USA.

R. W. Tsien is at the Department of Physiology, Yale University School of Medicine, New Haven, CT 06510, USA.

A LHRH-like peptidergic neurotransmitter capable of 'action at a distance' in autonomic ganglia

Yuh Nung Jan and Lily Yeh Jan

Many peptides are localized in nerve terminals, suggesting that peptides may function as neurotransmitters. But do peptides really serve as neurotransmitters and, if so, are the actions of peptidergic transmitters qualitatively different from the actions of 'classical transmitters'? We chose to approach these questions by studying sympathetic ganglia in the bullfrog. The structural simplicity of the ganglia has enabled us to demonstrate that (i) a peptide resembling luteinizing-hormone-releasing hormone (LHRH) is a neurotransmitter, (ii) this LHRH-like peptide probably coexists with acetylcholine (ACh) in the same nerve terminals, and (iii) although the peptide transmitter is most probably released together with ACh from the same terminals that form conventional morphological synaptic contacts with sympathetic neurons, it can diffuse a far greater distance than ACh and can act on cells non-synaptically.

At present, more than twenty peptides are considered as putative neurotransmitters. Since most of these neuropeptides were discovered by chance rather than through systematic search, it is quite likely that many more will be found in the future. If many peptides indeed turn out to be neurotransmitters, one wonders why the nervous system utilizes so many different molecules as transmitters. To try to answer this question, one needs first to establish that peptides do serve as transmitters. A detailed analysis of the actions of a number of such transmitters may then reveal different modes of actions and thus shed light on the functional significance of having multiple transmitters.

Frog sympathetic ganglia are an excellent preparation for this purpose. Structurally, they are very simple. Neurons in these ganglia are unipolar and have no dendrites. Preganglionic fibers make synaptic contacts almost exclusively on the ganglionic cell bodies. This arrangement facilitates analysis of the physiological effects of neurotransmitters and allows accurate anatomical description of synaptic connections. It has been known for many years that ACh is a transmitter contained in the preganglionic fibers. Three types of synaptic responses are mediated by ACh, namely (i) the nicotinic fast excitatory postsynaptic potentials (EPSPs) which last for about 30–50 ms, (ii) the muscarinic slow EPSPs lasting 30–60 s, and (iii) the muscarinic slow inhibitory postsynaptic potential (IPSP) of 1–2 s duration. In 1968 a fourth synaptic potential was discovered by Nishi and Koketsu[17] and named the late slow EPSP. This response lasts for several minutes and is not mediated by ACh (Fig. 1). From studies done in the last few years we believe that the late slow EPSP is mediated by a peptide transmitter that resembles mammalian LHRH. Briefly, we will outline the evidence as follows.

I. A LHRH-like peptide is the transmitter mediating the late slow EPSP in bullfrog sympathetic ganglia

(1) Presence

A LHRH-like peptide is contained in the appropriate preganglionic fibers: radio-immunoassays using an antiserum highly specific for LHRH revealed that the bull-frog sympathetic ganglia contained a high level of LHRH-like peptide[9]. The LHRH-like peptide is localized to preganglionic nerve terminals by immunohistochem-istry[6]. Cutting the appropriate preganglionic fibers greatly reduces the staining in nerve terminals[6] and removes from ganglia almost all the LHRH-like peptide detect-able by radioimmunoassays[9], demonstra-ting that the LHRH-like peptide is contained in those preganglionic fibers that generate the late slow EPSP.

(2) Release

The LHRH-like peptide is released into the extracellular medium when the appro-priate preganglionic fibers are stimulated: by either stimulating the appropriate spinal nerves electrically or raising the extracellu-lar potassium concentration, one can detect the release of the LHRH-like peptide by radioimmunoassays[5,9]. This release requires the presence of extracellular calcium.

(3) Mimicry

The physiological effects of the late slow EPSP can be mimicked by applying LHRH to the surface of sympathetic neurons: a depolarizing response in sympathetic neurons is induced by synthetic LHRH, which may be applied either in the bath or locally through a micropipette via a brief

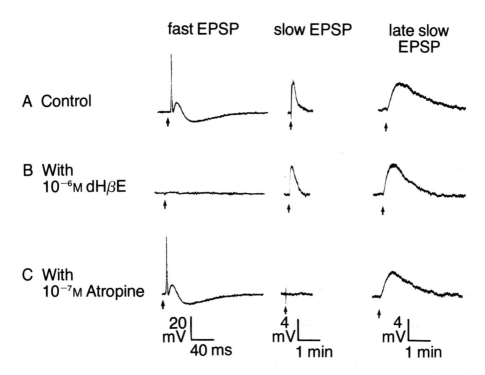

Fig. 1. *Effects of a nicotinic cholinergic blocker, dihydro-β-erythroidine (dHβE), and a muscarinic cholinergic blocker, atropine, on the fast EPSP and late slow EPSP recorded from the same B cell. Arrows indicate time of nerve stimulation. The fast EPSP was initiated by a single stimulus of the sympathetic chain above the 7th ganglion. The slow EPSP was induced by stimulating the chain at 30 Hz for 0.7 s. Two separate nerves, the 7th and 8th spinal nerves, were stimulated at 5 Hz for 20 s to induce the late slow EPSP. (From Ref. 5.)*

pulse of pressure. This depolarizing response persists in media devoid of calcium, indicating that LHRH acts directly on sympathetic neurons. The LHRH-induced depolarization resembles the late slow EPSP in considerable detail[5, 10, 11]. (a) Both are associated with similar conductance changes. (b) Their amplitudes vary in parallel as the membrane potential is shifted over a wide range, suggesting that similar ionic mechanisms are involved. (c) Both responses increase the excitability of the neurons. (d) The responses interact with the cholinergic responses in a parallel manner. The similarity between physiological changes during the LHRH-induced depolarization and those during the late slow EPSP suggest that LHRH acts on the same receptors as the natural transmitter for the late slow EPSP.

(4) Pharmacology

The late slow EPSP is blocked by antagonists of LHRH: several analogs of LHRH that function as antagonists in mammalian anterior pituitaries[19] also block the LHRH-induced depolarization in frog

sympathetic neurons[5, 10]. Furthermore, they also block the nerve-evoked late slow EPSP without affecting the resting membrane potential, membrane resistance, or the cholinergic synaptic potentials[5, 10] (Fig. 2). Therefore, pharmacologically the receptor for the late slow EPSP behaves like a LHRH receptor.

Based on the above four criteria, there seems to be very little doubt that a LHRH-like peptide is the transmitter mediating the late slow EPSP. However, several issues have yet to be resolved completely.

(i) The identity of the LHRH-like peptide.

This peptide is structurally very similar to mammalian LHRH but can be separated from it chromatographically[4]. A recent report suggested that this peptide from frog ganglia may be identical to fish hypothalamic LHRH, which differs from the mammalian LHRH by two (the 7th and 8th) amino acids[20]. This proposition is supported by electrophysiological experiments: Branton found that fish LHRH, and its various analogs that function as agonists or antagonists, are all more potent than their

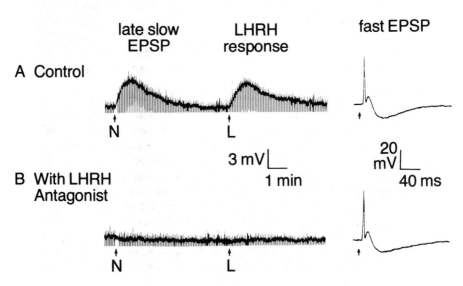

Fig. 2. *Effect of bath application of an antagonist of LHRH on the late slow EPSP (N), the LHRH-induced response (L), and the cholinergic fast EPSP. Applying an antagonist, [D-pGlu¹, D-Phe², D-Trp³,⁶]-LHRH, to the bathing medium to a final concentration of 10^{-5} M had no effect on the membrane potential, the membrane resistance, or the cholinergic fast EPSP but completely blocked both the late slow EPSP and the LHRH-induced response. (From Ref. 5.)*

∝HRP ∝LHRH

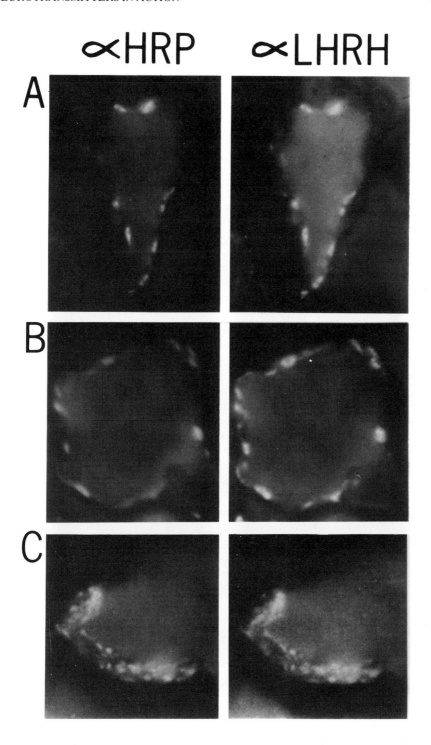

Fig. 3. *Double labelling of the same terminals of preganglionic C fibers with antibodies to LHRH and HRP. Preganglionic C fibers were first filled with HRP, then treated with fluorescein-coupled goat antibodies to HRP, rabbit antibodies to LHRH, and rhodamine-labelled goat antibodies to rabbit antibodies. Note that all terminals filled with HRP contain the LHRH-like peptide.* (From Ref. 7.)

mammalian counterparts in their physiological effects in bullfrog sympathetic ganglia[8]. Nevertheless, sequencing of the LHRH-like peptide from bullfrog sympathetic ganglia has yet to be done for a definitive determination of its structure.

(ii) The ionic basis of the late slow EPSP. Adams and Brown and their colleagues discovered that the late slow EPSP causes inactivation of a novel potassium channel, the M channel[1-3]. Although the M channel probably is an important component in generating the late slow EPSP, it cannot fully account for the ionic basis of the late slow EPSP. In addition to the M channel, at least one more ionic current must be involved, because the late slow EPSP and the LHRH-induced depolarization usually persist at potassium equilibrium potential[10,11,14,15]. This additional component has not yet been fully characterized.

(iii) Removal of the LHRH-like peptide after release. In the classical picture of synaptic transmission, the transmitter molecules are quickly removed after release either by enzyme degradation or by an efficient reuptake system. This does not seem to be the case for the LHRH-like peptide. As will be discussed later, the LHRH-like peptide appears to have a fairly long lifetime (many seconds) after it is released; apparently there are no efficient removal systems. Whether removal mechanisms other than simple diffusion are operative is not yet clear.

II. Features of peptidergic transmission

Given that a peptide can function as a transmitter for a slow synaptic potential, our next question is: do peptide transmitters serve functions qualitatively different from those of 'classical' transmitters? One striking difference is that the peptidergic responses in autonomic neurons and cultured spinal cord neurons are $10-10^4$ times slower than cholinergic responses[5,12-14,18,21]. It turns out that in frog ganglia the slow time course of the late slow

EPSP is partially due to the long lifetime of the nerve-released peptide transmitter. Further, the LHRH-like peptide appears to be contained and released from the same preganglionic fibers as ACh. While ACh acts only synaptically, the LHRH-like peptide can diffuse and activate sympathetic neurons that are not in synaptic contact with LHRH-positive nerve terminals. Experimental results in support of the above statements are reviewed in the following sections.

(1) The LHRH-like peptide and ACh are probably contained and released from the same preganglionic fibers

Sympathetic neurons and their preganglionic fibers can be subdivided into two distinct classes. In the last two ganglia of the lumbar chain, the 9th and 10th ganglia, there are two classes of sympathetic neurons: the larger B cells are in synaptic contact with preganglionic B fibers arising from the 3rd, 4th and 5th spinal nerves; while the smaller C cells are in synaptic contact with preganglionic C fibers arising from the 7th and 8th spinal nerves. As shown in Table I, stimulating the 3rd, 4th and 5th spinal nerves generates cholinergic synaptic potentials in B cells only. On the other hand, stimulating the 7th and 8th spinal nerves generates the late slow EPSP in both B cells and C cells, as well as cholinergic responses in C cells. This raises the following question: does the same preganglionic C fiber generate both cholinergic responses and the peptidergic late slow EPSP? In other words, does the same preganglionic C fiber contain and release both ACh and the LHRH-like peptide?

(i) Coexistence? In the absence of any known specific markers for ACh or choline-acetyltransferase in frog sympathetic ganglia, we have approached this question with indirect means. In double labelling experiments, we marked all terminals of preganglionic C fibers with horseradish peroxidase (HRP) or with a monoclonal antibody specific for a 65 000 mol. wt

membrane protein[16], and with the appropriate rhodamine-labelled second antibodies. The same terminals were then treated with rabbit antibodies against LHRH and with fluorescein-labelled second antibodies that bind rabbit antibodies, so that we could estimate the proportion of preganglionic C-fiber terminals that contain the LHRH-like peptide. It turned out that almost all terminals of preganglionic C fibers contained the LHRH-like peptide[7], as shown in Fig. 3. Since some of these terminals must also contain ACh, which in C cells generates the fast EPSP of only 1–2 ms latency, at least some of the terminals of preganglionic C fibers must contain both ACh and

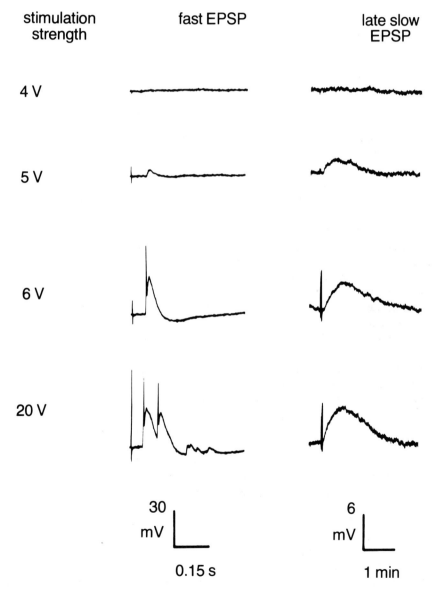

Fig. 4. *Fast EPSPs and late slow EPSPs recorded from the same C cell as the stimulation strength was varied from 4 V to 20 V. A single stimulus elicited the fast EPSP while a short-circuited train of stimuli were used to generate the late slow EPSP. The thresholds of the three cholinergic inputs correlated well with the thresholds of the peptidergic inputs. (From Ref. 7.)*

the LHRH-like peptide. Morphologically, terminals of preganglionic C fibers form conventional synaptic contacts with C cells and are uniform in appearance under an electron microscope. Therefore, conceivably all terminals of preganglionic C fibers may contain both ACh and the LHRH-like peptide.

(ii) Co-release? Physiological experiments indicate that each preganglionic C fiber probably releases both ACh and the LHRH-like peptide: a sympathetic C neuron typically receives several cholinergic inputs with different thresholds for stimulation, so that one may raise the stimulation strength gradually to recruit cholinergic preganglionic fibers one by one. In doing so, we found that each time a cholinergic fiber is recruited, repetitive stimulation at that stimulation strength also resulted in a larger late slow EPSP[7], indicating that the peptidergic inputs to a C cell have thresholds similar to the thresholds of its cholinergic inputs (Fig. 4). Most likely, the same preganglionic fibers are responsible for both the cholinergic fast EPSP and the peptidergic late slow EPSP.

(2) The LHRH-like peptide can diffuse for tens of micrometres before activating sympathetic neurons

Although stimulating preganglionic C fibers arising from the 7th and 8th spinal nerves generates the late slow EPSP in both B cells and C cells, preganglionic C fibers were found to make synaptic contacts on C cells exclusively. Therefore the late slow EPSP recorded in B cells must be due to peptide transmitters released from preganglionic C fibers which are at a distance from B cells. Evidence in support of these statements is reviewed as follows.

(i) Preganglionic C fibers make synaptic contacts with C cells but not B cells. If we cut all preganglionic B fibers by cutting the sympathetic chain between the 6th and 7th ganglia and allowed 5–10 days for their terminals to degenerate, electron microscopy revealed no synaptic boutons on the larger B cells, even though many synaptic boutons were found on smaller C cells. Similarly, filling the remaining preganglionic C fibers with HRP marked 30–50 nerve terminals around each C cell, but no terminals at all on the larger B cells[6]. These observations correlate well with immunohistochemistry which showed that LHRH-positive terminals are found on smaller C cells, but not on the larger B cells[5,6]. Taken together, they showed that no synaptic contacts exist between preganglionic C fibers and B cells.

(ii) The late slow EPSP recorded in B cells is due to non-synaptic action of the peptide transmitter. If we cut all preganglionic B fibers arising from the 3rd, 4th and 5th spinal nerves as described in the preceding paragraph and recorded from neurons in the denervated ganglia 5–10 days after the operation, we found no cholinergic synaptic potentials in B cells with nerve stimulation, while the late slow EPSP was still generated in those B cells when we stimulated the preganglionic C fibers arising from the 7th and 8th spinal nerves. Three of those B cells that showed the late slow EPSP but no longer the cholinergic synaptic potentials were serially sectioned. Electron microscopy revealed no synaptic boutons on the surface of these B cells[6]. Therefore, the late slow EPSP recorded in these B cells must be generated by preganglionic C fibers that are not in synaptic contact with their cell surface.

TABLE I. Segregation of preganglionic inputs to B and C cells in the 9th and 10th sympathetic ganglia

Stimulation/cell type	B cells	C cells
3rd, 4th and 5th spinal nerves	Cholinergic responses	None
7th and 8th spinal nerves	Peptidergic responses (late slow EPSP)	Cholinergic and peptidergic responses

(iii) The LHRH-like peptide remains active for at least thirty seconds after release and can therefore diffuse for many micrometres. A late slow EPSP normally lasts for several minutes, as shown in Fig. 5. Thirty seconds after the initiation of the late slow EPSP, applying an antagonist of LHRH through a micropipette caused the response to be truncated[5] (Fig. 5), suggesting that the LHRH analog can compete with the peptide transmitter for receptor binding thirty seconds after it is released. This is probably due to the long lifetime of the peptide transmitter after release, rather than prolonged release of peptide transmitters after nerve stimula-

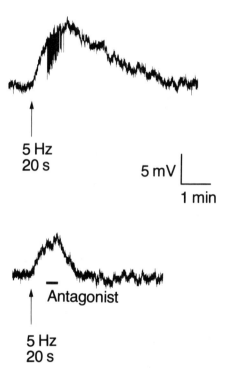

5 Hz
20 s

5 mV

1 min

Antagonist

5 Hz
20 s

Fig. 5. *Effect of an antagonist of LHRH on the late slow EPSP. After a late slow EPSP was initiated by stimulating the 7th and 8th spinal nerves at 5 Hz for 20 s, pressure application of [Ac-Δ³-Pro¹,pF-D-Phe²,D-Trp³,⁶]-LHRH, an antagonist of LHRH, (1 lb./sq. in., 25 s) reduced both the amplitude and the duration of the late slow EPSP. The antagonist by itself has no effect on the membrane potential of this cell. Notice that the spontaneously occurring action potentials during the late slow EPSP were also eliminated. (From Ref. 5.)*

tion, because applying antagonists thirty seconds after a brief pulse of LHRH also caused the LHRH-induced response to be truncated[5]. Thus, the slow time course of the late slow EPSP is partly caused by the long lifetime of the peptide transmitter. As expected, the rise-time and duration of the late slow EPSP in B cells are on average greater than those of the late slow EPSP in C cells[5].

In summary, the frog sympathetic ganglion is composed of two cell types, B cells (30–70 μm in diameter) and C cells (20–45 μm in diameter). LHRH-positive preganglionic C fibers make synaptic contacts exclusively with C cells, but are capable of generating late slow EPSPs in B cells. This non-synaptic activation of B cells is possible because the LHRH-like peptide transmitter remains active for at least thirty seconds after release and can diffuse some distance before activating receptors and generating the late slow EPSP. Since B cells and C cells are juxtaposed within the ganglion and most of the LHRH-positive synaptic boutons are clustered around the axon hillock region of C cells, the LHRH-like peptide probably has to diffuse for tens of micrometres before reaching the surface of B cells. On the other hand, although almost every B cell tested responded to LHRH with a depolarization, B cells from different regions of a sympathetic ganglion often showed late slow EPSPs of vastly different rise-time and amplitude. Most likely the peptide transmitter does not diffuse for distances comparable to the diameter of the ganglion ($\sim$ 1 mm). The action of this peptide transmitter is thus analogous to that of paracrine hormones.

III. Why do nervous systems need so many different chemical messengers?
. . . A hypothesis

In frog sympathetic ganglia, we have seen that a LHRH-like peptide mediates a slow synaptic potential and that it can diffuse for tens of micrometres before activating receptors on sympathetic neurons. Moreover, the LHRH receptors and muscarinic receptors on B cells apparently share the same ionic mechanism, which involves partly an inactivation of the voltage-sensitive M current[1-3,5,14,15]. Thus the mechanisms of action of this peptide transmitter seem to encompass features both of classical transmitters and of hormones. This raises the possibility that the types of action of chemical messengers in the nervous system may vary over a wide range, from that of a 'classical' transmitter like ACh at the neuromuscular junction to those more typical of paracrine hormones.

Is the 'action at a distance' a general fea-

ture of peptide transmitters? The answer is unclear, partly due to technical limitations. For instance, there is good evidence for peptides such as substance P to function as neurotransmitters for slow synaptic potentials in mammalian autonomic neurons[21]. However, these mammalian neurons have dendrites, which are the sites of synaptic contacts. This considerably complicates anatomical analysis of synaptic inputs to a neuron, and makes it difficult to demonstrate non-synaptic actions of peptides. Nonetheless, most of the peptide-induced membrane-potential changes appear indeed

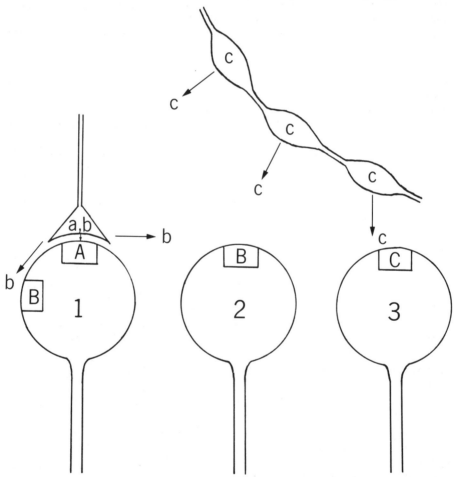

Fig. 6. *Hypothetical scheme for selective, long-range communication between neurons. The transmitter may be released either from varicosities or from nerve terminals that form synaptic contacts with other neurons. If the transmitter has a long lifetime, it may diffuse and activate those neurons in the vicinity that express the appropriate receptors. a, b and c represent different transmitter molecules. A, B and C represent different receptors for the respective transmitters.*

to be slow and long-lasting. The time course ranges from seconds to minutes in various autonomic neurons[5,12–14,21] and in cultured spinal cord neurons[18]. Such a slow time course is at least compatible with the possibility of peptides having long-range actions.

Suppose that, in general, peptide transmitters act in a range intermediate between the focal action of classical transmitters such as ACh and the global action of hormone: how would selective communication between neurons be achieved? One usually thinks of precise circuitry of synaptic contacts as the only means by which selective communications are achieved between neurons. However, in situations where the speed of action is not crucial or perhaps a slower and prolonged influence is more desirable, conceivably the presynaptic neurons may terminate in the vicinity of the postsynaptic neurons without making synaptic contacts with them. Such an arrangement could work if the transmitter released from the presynaptic neurons can diffuse for some distance before acting on receptors. Selective communication may be achieved if different neurons in a given region express different subsets of receptors, so that a transmitter released from a presynaptic neuron influences only those neurons nearby which have the right receptors on their surface (Fig. 6). Intuitively this arrangement seems more economical, and conceivably plasticity might evoke merely an alteration in the type of receptors expressed by the postsynaptic neuron. For this type of interneuronal communication to be used extensively in the nervous system without cross-talk between parallel pathways, a necessary requirement is that many different molecules are used as transmitters. Perhaps this is one reason for the multiplicity of peptides that are implicated as transmitters.

One important lesson learned from the frog sympathetic ganglia is that although a peptide transmitter is localized to nerve terminals that make classical synaptic contacts with other neurons, it may diffuse and act upon neurons that are not in synaptic contact with those peptidergic terminals. Thus, the conventional morphological criteria for synapses may actually be misleading in identifying target neurons for a peptide transmitter, while localization of peptide receptors could be more informative.

Reading list

1 Adams, P. R. and Brown, D. A. (1980) Br. J. Pharmacol. 68, 353–355
2 Adams, P. R., Brown, D. A. and Constanti, A. (1982) J. Physiol. (London) 330, 537–572
3 Adams, P. R., Brown, D. A. and Constanti, A. (1982) J. Physiol. (London) 332, 223–262
4 Eiden, L. E. and Eskay, R. L. (1980) Neuropeptides 1, 29–37
5 Jan, L. Y. and Jan, Y. N. (1982) J. Physiol. (London) 327, 219–246
6 Jan, L. Y., Jan, Y. N. and Brownfield, M. S. (1980) Nature (London) 288, 380–382
7 Jan, Y. N. and Jan, L. Y. Fed. Proc. Fed. Am. Soc. Exp. Biol. (in press)
8 Jan, Y. N., Bowers, C., Branton, W. D., Evans, L. and Jan, L. Y. Cold Spring Harbor Symp. Quant. Biol., Vol. XLVIII (in press)
9 Jan, Y. N., Jan, L. Y. and Kuffler, S. W. (1979) Proc. Natl Acad. Sci. USA 76, 1501–1505
10 Jan, Y. N., Jan, L. Y. and Kuffler, S. W. (1980) Proc. Natl Acad. Sci. USA 77, 5008–5012
11 Katayama, Y. and Nishi, S. (1982) J. Physiol. (London) 333, 305–313
12 Katayama, Y. and North, R. A. (1978) Nature (London) 274, 387–388
13 Konishi, S., Tsunoo, A. and Otsuka, M. (1979) Nature (London) 282, 515–516
14 Kuffler, S. W. (1980) J. Exp. Biol. 89, 257–286
15 Kuffler, S. W. and Sejowski, T. J. J. Physiol. (London) (in press)
16 Mattlew, W. D., Tsavaler, L. and Reichardt, L. F. (1981) J. Cell Biol. 91, 257–269
17 Nishi, S. and Koketsu, K. (1968) J. Neurophysiol. 31, 109–121
18 Nowak, L. M. and MacDonald, R. L. (1981) Brain Res. 214, 416–423
19 Rivier, J. and Vale, W. W. (1978) Life Sci. 23, 869–876
20 Sherwood, N. M., Eiden, L., Brownstein, M. J., Spiess, J., Rivier, J. and Vale, W. (1983) Neurosci. Abstr. 8, 12
21 Tsunoo, A., Konishi, S. and Otsuka, M. (1982) Neuroscience 7, 2025–2037

Yuh Nung Jan and Lily Yeh Jan are at the Department of Physiology, School of Medicine, University of California at San Francisco, San Francisco, CA 94143, USA.

Coexistence of peptides and classical neurotransmitters

Jan M. Lundberg and Tomas Hökfelt

Recent evidence suggests that biologically active polypeptides are present in certain populations of neurons which also contain classical transmitters such as noradrenaline (NA) or acetylcholine (ACh). Thus, it may be possible to subdivide a classical transmitter system on the basis of coexistence with specific peptides. Peptides and monoamines have differential mechanisms for synthesis and replacement after synaptic release, and possibly different subcellular storage sites as well. The release of the peptide and classical transmitter upon nervous activation may depend on the intensity of stimulation. Following release, peptides and monoamines may interact at the level of the receptor and/or second messenger before evoking a functional response. Data hitherto obtained in the peripheral nervous system indicate that the classical transmitter causes a rapid response of short duration, whereas the peptide is responsible for a more long-lasting effect. The concept of multiple synaptic messengers may explain why drug-induced blockade of classical receptors sometimes abolishes only partially the effects of nervous activation, for example atropine-resistant vasodilation in exocrine glands. It seems appropriate to consider the possibility that coexistence of multiple transmitters and/or modulators may have implications for our understanding of pathophysiological processes in nervous disorders. Furthermore, the coexistence concept may be of importance in strategies for developing new therapeutic drugs which interfere with neurotransmission.

Increasing evidence derived mainly from immunohistochemical studies indicates that neurons contain one or more biologically active polypeptides in addition to their monoamine transmitter[21,23,24,40]. Such coexistence of peptides and amines has previously been described in endocrine cells of the gastrointestinal tract[53,55]. The concept of coexistence of multiple synaptic messengers was extensively and timely discussed several years ago by Burnstock[4] and has been dealt with in a previous *TINS* article[51]. These papers also covered aspects of transmitter coexistence in invertebrates, a topic which will not be dealt with here. Neither will we cover the interesting issues of coexistence during development[54,57], of coexistence of ATP and NA or ACh[4], of peptide–peptide coexistence[24], or the presence of 5-hydroxytryptamine (5-HT) in sympathetic nerves[29]. It may be worth emphasizing, as has been done elsewhere[9,10,23,57], that the possible occurrence of multiple transmitters in a neuron does not, in fact, compromise Dale's principle as originally formulated by Eccles *et al.*[10] Although we focus here on an auxiliary role of peptides as co-messengers, it should be emphasized that peptides have been shown to meet several of the criteria established for a neurotransmitter[52] and thus also may act without classical transmitter.

Techniques for establishing coexistence

Evidence for coexistence of classical transmitters and peptides can be obtained with immunohistochemical techniques[60]. Adjacent thin sections are stained for two appropriate antigens, for example a monoamine-synthesizing enzyme and a peptide. Alternatively, elution-restaining experiments may be performed, where the same section is stained in sequence for two antigens[61].

The main problem in using immunohistochemistry is the question of specificity. Thus, the antibodies may cross-react with antigens which are structurally related but not identical to the immunogen. Since a full biochemical characterization of the immunoreactivity has not yet been performed we use, for the time being, expressions such as 'substance P-like immuno-reactivity (substance P-LI)' or 'substance P-immunoreactive (substance P-IR)' to describe the immunoreactive material. It may be that in some cases the peptides described here and in other immunohistochemical and radioimmunological studies will turn out to have a more or less different chemical structure. In fact, we have already experienced at least one such example, the avian and bovine pancreatic polypeptides (APP and BPP). Thus,

TABLE I. Coexistence of classical transmitters and peptides

Classical transmitter	Peptide[a]	Tissue/region (species)	Refs[b]
Dopamine	Enkephalin	Carotid body (cat)	
	CCK	Ventral tegmental area (rat, man)	
Noradrenaline	Somatostatin	Sympathetic ganglia (guinea-pig)	
		SIF cells (cat)	
	Enkephalin	Sympathetic ganglia (rat, bovine)	
		Adrenal medulla (several species)	
		SIF cells (guinea-pig, cat)	
		Locus coeruleus (cat)	8
	Neurotensin	Adrenal medulla (cat)	
	APP/BPP/NPY	Sympathetic ganglia (rat, cat, man)	
		Medulla oblongata (rat, man)	
		Locus coeruleus (rat)	
Adrenaline	Enkephalin	Adrenal medulla (several species)	
	APP/BPP/NPY	Medulla oblongata (rat)	
5-HT	Substance P	Medulla oblongata (rat)	
	TRH	Medulla oblongata (rat)	
	Substance P + TRH	Medulla oblongata (rat)	
	Enkephalin	Medulla oblongata (rat, cat)	
ACh[c]	VIP	Autonomic ganglia (cat)	
	Enkephalin	Preganglionic nerves (cat)	
		Cochlear nerves (guinea-pig)	2
	Neurotensin	Preganglionic nerves (cat)	
	LHRH	Sympathetic ganglia (bullfrog)	30
	Somatostatin	Heart (toad)	
	Substance P + enkephalin	Ciliary ganglion (avian)	13
GABA	Somatostatin	Thalamus (cat)	
	Motilin	Cerebellum (rat)	7

Abbreviations: 5-HT = 5-hydroxytryptamine; ACh = acetylcholine; GABA = γ-aminobutyric acid; CCK = cholecystokinin; TRH = thyrotropin-releasing hormone; VIP = vasoactive intestinal polypeptide; LHRH = luteinizing-hormone-releasing hormone; NPY = neuropeptide Y; APP = avian pancreatic polypeptide; BPP = bovine pancreatic polypeptide.

[a] In this column the peptide against which the antiserum used was raised is indicated. In view of the possibility of cross-reactivity, the exact nature of the peptide visualized with the immunohistochemical technique is uncertain.

[b] With regard to references, the following principles have been adopted in order to save space. The coexistence in Table I has been described in papers either cited in the text or in Refs 21, 23, 24, 40, or is indicated by the figure in Table I.

[c] The identification of ACh-containing neurons is based on indirect evidence, for example AChE staining, measurement of CAT, etc. (see Ref. 36), since no reliable marker, such as antibodies to CAT, has yet been used. Several groups have, however, now produced such antibodies, which may clarify this issue in the near future.

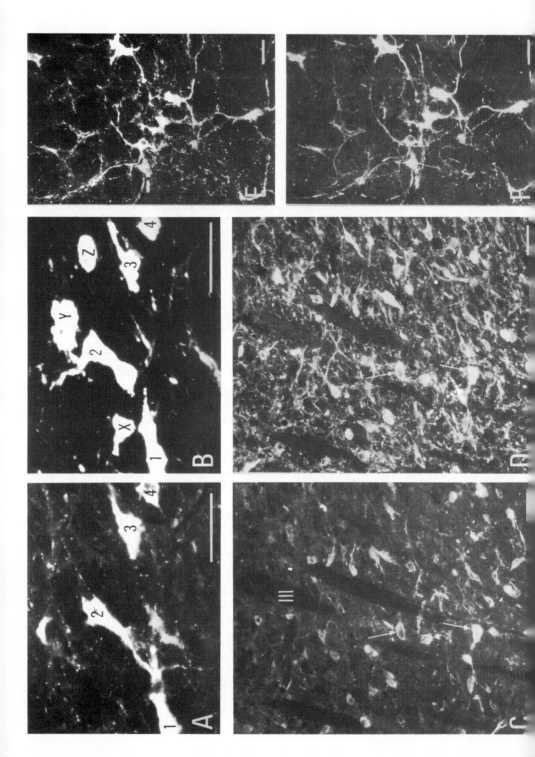

Fig. 1 – see p. 108 for caption

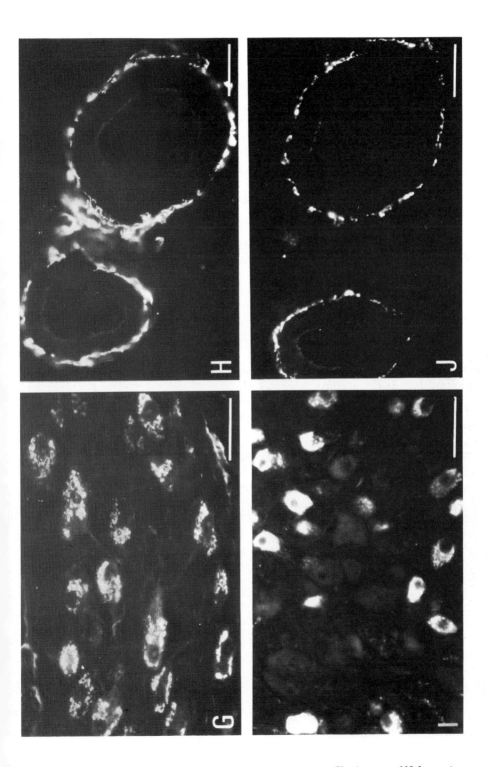

Fig. 1 – *see p. 108 for caption.*

APP-LI and BPP-LI have been observed both in some catecholaminergic[28,42,50] and other neurons[35,50], but recent evidence indicates that a novel peptide, neuropeptide Y (NPY), is in fact likely to be the endogenous APP- or BPP-like peptide[45]. We will therefore refer to this particular peptide as NPY.

A further problem with the immunohistochemical technique is its sensitivity, which in many cases is insufficient to demonstrate intraneuronal compounds. They are often not present in as high concentrations as, for example, hormones in endocrine cells. Negative results must therefore be interpreted with caution, since only those peptides which occur in particularly high concentrations may be visualized.

Overview of coexistence

Some years ago it was found that a population of noradrenergic ganglion cells of guinea-pig sympathetic ganglia were somatostatin-IR[20]. Since then, as Table I shows, several other cases of monoamine/peptide coexistence have been reported. In this list chromaffin cells of the adrenal medulla and some other paraneurons have also been included, since these cells are related to autonomic neurons. Thus, using immunohistochemistry, the presence of methionine- and leucine-enkephalin-LI but lack of β-endorphin-LI has been demonstrated both in noradrenergic and adrenergic cells of the adrenal medulla of several species[58]. Furthermore, preganglionic denervation of the adrenal medulla increased enkephalin-IR[58], reflecting accumulation of precursor molecules[33]. Subsequently, the subcellular storage and different molecular forms, as well as biosynthesis and mechanisms of release, of these opioid peptides have been thoroughly characterized in a series of elegant experiments[27,33,34,62].

It is evident from Table I that coexistence occurs in both central and peripheral neurons, and that ACh and γ-aminobutyric acid (GABA) can be involved as well as all three catecholamines (CA) and 5-HT. Interestingly, the same amines and peptides can be observed in several systems but in different combinations. For example, somatostatin may coexist with NA in postganglionic sympathetic neurons in the guinea-pig[20], with GABA in cat thalamus[49], and with ACh in the leech heart[5]. Conversely, 5-HT is present together with substance P[6,22], enkephalin[18] and/or thyrotropin-releasing hormone (THR)[31] in the brain. In most cases, the same patterns of coexistence can be found in many species including man, but species differences do exist. For example, somatostatin-LI occurs in sympathetic neurons of the guinea-pig[20] but apparently not in the cat[43]. Again, any interpretation must be made with caution, since these differences could represent differences in intraneuronal concentrations and/or structural dissimilarities of the peptides.

Several interesting examples of coexistence have been described in the CNS. As mentioned above, substance P-IR material is present in a population of serotonin

---

Fig. 1. *(pp. 106–107) Immunofluorescence micrographs of rat ventral medulla oblongata (**A,B,E,F**) and rat ventral mesencephalon (**C,D**), cat submandibular parasympathetic ganglion (**G**), cat superior cervical ganglion (**I**) and cat submandibular gland arteries (**H,J**), after incubation with antiserum to substance P (**A**), 5-HT (**B**), CCK (**C**), tyrosine hydroxylase (**D,F**), NPY (**E,I,J**) and VIP (**G,H**). A and B, and H and J represent pairs of adjacent sections. D and F show the same sections as C and E, respectively, after elution and restaining. (**A,B**) The same cell bodies (1–4) contain both substance P-LI and 5-HT-LI, whereas some cell profiles (X,Y,Z) are only 5-HT-positive. (**C,D**) Many dopaminergic (tyrosine-hydroxylase-positive) cells contain CCK-LI (arrows point to some). (**E,F**) In the C1 area all adrenergic cells [contain tyrosine hydroxylase (**F**) and, not shown, phenylethanolamine N-methyltransferase] are NPY-positive (**E**). (**G-J**) Almost all submandibular ganglion cells are VIP-IR (**G**) and many superior cervical ganglion cells are NPY-IR (**I**). VIP-positive (**H**) and NPY-positive (**J**) fibers have a similar distribution around small arteries in the submandibular hilus. Bars indicate 50 μm.*

neurons of the raphe nuclei of the brain stem[6,22] (Fig. 1A,B). At least some of these neurons also contain a TRH-IR substance[31], and some project to the ventral horn of the spinal cord, where nerve endings are seen close to α-motoneurons[22]. There is recent evidence that the same large, dense-core vesicles in nerve endings in the ventral horn store both 5-HT and substance P[56]. It is well known that the 5-HT precursor 5-hydroxytryptophan activates the stretch reflex, and recently TRH has been shown to exert a similar action in certain experimental models, possibly via an effect on the 5-HT receptor[3]. Other studies indicate that substance P too may amplify the action of 5-HT, but in a different way, namely by counteracting the autoreceptor-mediated inhibitory effect of 5-HT on 5-HT release[48]. These findings suggest that the peptides principally enhance the action of the classical transmitter on the postsynaptic cell, but that the effects are subtle and of a modulatory nature.

Some dopaminergic neurons also seem to contain a peptide. Thus, a population of ventral mesencephalic dopaminergic neurons contains a cholecystokinin (CCK)-IR substance[26] (Fig. 1C,D). These neurons project mainly to limbic areas of the forebrain such as the nucleus accumbens[26]. In electrophysiological experiments CCK has been shown to increase activity in dopaminergic neurons[59] and this peptide also seems to influence dopamine (DA) release[46]. Interactions between DA and CCK at the level of the DA receptor have also been reported[16]. A functional interaction between CCK and DA in this system may be of interest in view of the apparent over-activity of dopaminergic systems in schizophrenia[47].

Several catecholaminergic cell groups in the medulla oblongata contain an NPY-like peptide[25] (Fig. 1E,F), which may be signif-

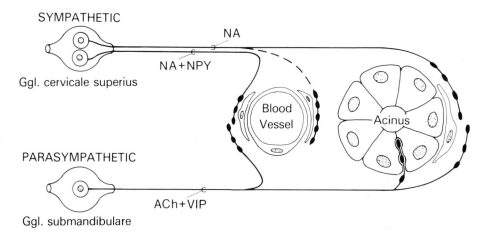

Fig. 2. *Schematic illustration of the autonomic motor innervation of the cat submandibular salivary gland. The secretory elements and blood vessels receive both sympathetic and parasympathetic innervation from the superior cervical ganglion and local submandibular ganglia, respectively. The latter ganglion cells are classically cholinergic but contain in addition the polypeptide VIP. A small population of the cholinergic neurons may, however, contain other peptides, for example enkephalin. The acetylcholinergic/vasoactive intestinal peptidergic nerves in the gland innervate blood vessels and secretory elements, whereby nerves are often found between the acini (secretory cells). Whether or not the same neuron can, in fact, innervate both blood vessel and acinus (as shown in the figure) has not been established with certainty. In the superior cervical ganglion about half of the noradrenergic ganglion cells contain an NPY-like peptide and these neurons seem to project selectively to blood vessels (mainly on the arterial side). In the remaining noradrenergic neurons of this ganglion in the cat no peptide has so far been identified. These noradrenergic nerves innervate secretory elements. Also, veins may receive noradrenergic nerves seemingly lacking NPY (dotted fiber).*

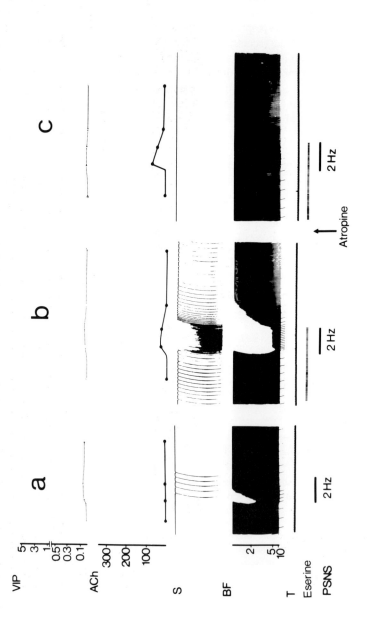

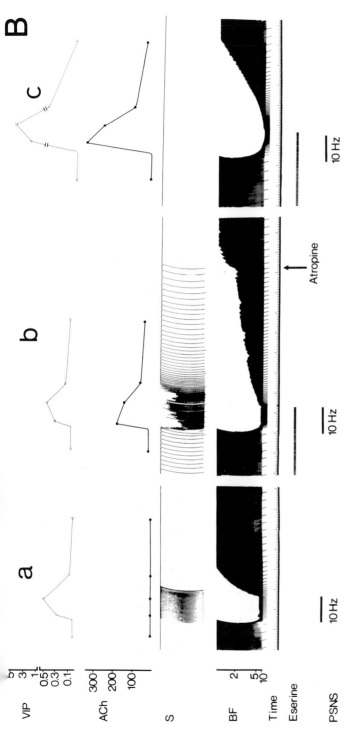

Fig. 3. *Effects of low (2 Hz) and high (10 Hz) frequency electrical stimulation of the submandibular branches of the chorda lingual nerve (parasympathetic nerve stimulation, PSNS) on salivary secretion (S; drops) and blood flow (BF; ml min^{-1}) from the cat submandibular gland. The output of VIP (fmol min^{-1} g^{-1}) and ACh (fmol min^{-1} g^{-1}) in the venous effluent from the gland is also shown. Local intra-arterial infusion of physostigmine (eserine) is indicated by the bar. Atropine administration (0.5 mg kg^{-1}, i.v.) is indicated by arrows. Time scale indicates 1 min between large bars.*

*(A) Low-frequency stimulation causes salivary secretion and a transient increase in blood flow (**a**). These responses are both markedly enhanced during local eserine infusion (**b**) and blocked by atropine (**c**), suggesting a major contribution by ACh for both secretion and vasodilation. ACh release can only be detected after inhibition of AChE by eserine (cf. **a** with **b** and **c**). Only a very slight VIP output can be seen at this low-frequency stimulation.*

*(B) High-frequency stimulation induces a much larger functional response, which is paralleled by an increase in ACh release and particularly by a dramatic increase in VIP output. Also at this frequency eserine infusion was a prerequisite for ACh detection. Eserine potentiates salivary secretion and prolongs the vasodilatory response (**b**) and this effect is abolished by atropine (**b,c**). After atropine pretreatment, the salivation response is abolished, while the vasodilatory response is atropine resistant and has a prolonged duration (cf. **a** and **c**). This may be due to the marked increase (about tenfold) in VIP output. Modified from Lundberg et al.[38]*

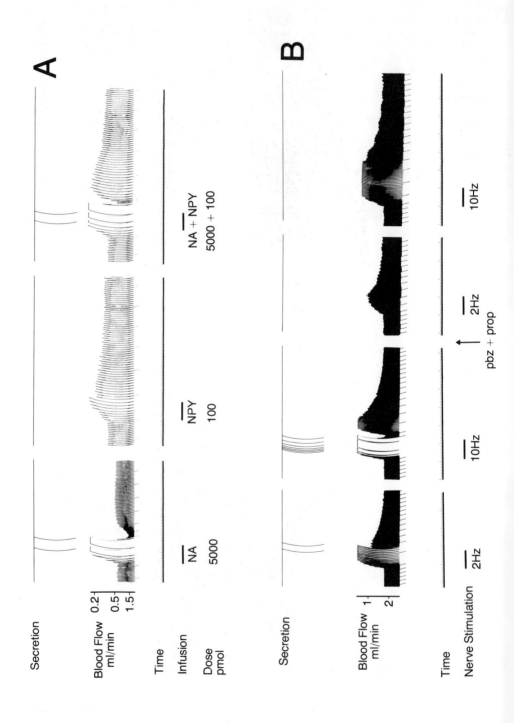

Fig. 4. *(see facing page) Effects of local arterial infusion of NA and NPY (A), and of low (2 Hz) and high (10 Hz) frequency stimulation of the cervical sympathetic trunk (B), on secretion and blood flow in the cat submandibular gland. For details on recordings, see Fig. 3.*

(A) Local infusion of NA induces both salivary secretion and a vasoconstriction which is followed by a rapid hyperemia. NPY infusion causes a slowly developing long-lasting reduction in blood flow but no salivation. Combined infusion of NA and NPY cause a functional response which has a very similar appearance to that caused by electrical nerve stimulation (cf. B).

(B) Sympathetic-nerve stimulation causes a frequency-dependent increase in secretion and decrease in blood flow. Combined blockade of α- and β-adrenoceptors by phenoxybenzamine (pbz) and propranolol (prop), respectively, abolishes the salivary response, while a slowly developing, long-lasting vasoconstrictory response is resistant to adrenoceptor blockade. The brief poststimulatory hyperemia seen during the control condition is abolished by adrenoceptor blockade.

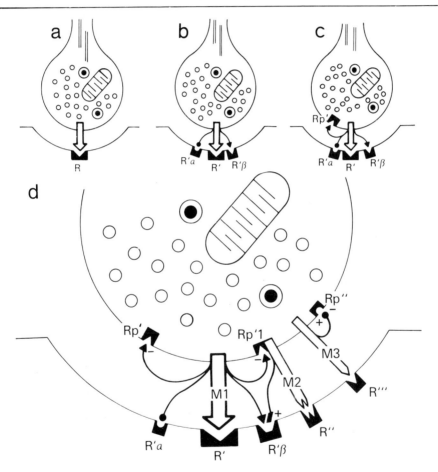

Fig. 5. *Schematic illustration of the development of the concept of chemical transmission. (a) One transmitter acts on one postsynaptic receptor (R'). (b) One transmitter acts on multiple types of postsynaptic receptors (R'α. R'β). (c) The transmitter acts in addition on a presynaptic receptor (Rp'). (d) Multiple compounds (M 1–3), possibly differentially stored in small vesicles (classical transmitter) and in large dense-core vesicles (classical transmitter plus peptide), are released from the same nerve ending. The main possible interactions indicated are: (1) inhibition of release of the second messenger (peptide M2) by the classical transmitter (M1)[40] via presynaptic action[40] (Rp'1); (2) interaction at the postsynaptic receptor (R'β) level between M1 and M2[16,41]; (3) facilitation or inhibition of release of the classical transmitter by the peptide (M3) via action on a presynaptic receptor (Rb')[45,46]; and (4) activation by the peptide (M3) of electrical activity in the presynaptic neuron via action on a presynaptic receptor (Rp'')[59].*

icant in view of a possible involvement of these cell groups in the central regulation of blood pressure.

Coexistence in the parasympathetic and sympathetic innervation of the cat submandibular gland

The submandibular gland of the cat is a classical organ for studies on autonomic neuroeffector mechanisms *in vivo*[12]. The parasympathetic nerves originate from local ganglia and innervate blood vessels and exocrine elements[17]. Activation of these nerves causes salivary secretion and a concomitant increase in local blood flow. Sympathetic nerves from the superior cervical ganglion show a similar innervation pattern and mediate vasoconstriction and salivary secretion[12,17]. Immunohistochemical analyses[36,37,40] have provided strong evidence for the view that the parasympathetic cholinergic neurons innervating blood vessels and exocrine elements contain a vasoactive intestinal polypeptide (VIP)-like peptide (Fig. 1G,H), and that the sympathetic noradrenergic neurons to blood vessels contain an NPY-like peptide[45] (Fig. 1 I,J; see also Fig. 2).

ACh–VIP coexistence

The evidence for the presence of VIP in a population of autonomic postganglionic neurons innervating cat exocrine glands and blood vessels has recently been reviewed[36,40] and can be summarized as follows: (1) VIP–IR cells contain high levels of acetylcholinesterase (AChE); (2) VIP-IR neurons seem to contain choline acetyltransferase (CAT), the ACh-synthesizing enzyme; (3) the ultrastructural features of VIP-IR nerve endings are similar to those assumed to be cholinergic, i.e. a dominance of small clear vesicles (diameter about 500 Å), which probably store most of the ACh, and some large dense-core vesicles (diameter about 1 000 Å), which most likely contain VIP.

Here we would like to discuss briefly the mechanisms of submandibular secretion and vasodilation based on the new concept of coexistence and co-release of VIP and

ACh from parasympathetic nerves, as outlined in a recent review[40]. As shown in Fig. 3, electrical stimulation in fact causes overflow of both ACh and VIP into the venous effluent from the gland, suggesting co-release[38]. Since both secretion and vasodilation were potentiated by AChE inhibition and abolished by atropine at low stimulation frequencies (Fig. 3A), it seems most likely that ACh is a prerequisite for salivation but also of importance for the increase in blood flow. This is also supported by results demonstrating that local infusion of ACh induces both salivation and vasodilation. At high stimulation frequencies, however, vasodilation is atropine resistant (Fig. 3B). It is likely that this effect is caused by the release of VIP, a potent vasodilatory agent[11,40]. Interestingly, upon high-frequency stimulation, atropine prolongs the duration of the vasodilatory response which is paralleled by a marked increase in VIP output (Fig. 3B). One possible explanation for this effect of atropine is that not only the release of ACh, but also that of VIP, is under presynaptic inhibitory control by muscarinic receptors.

Although VIP alone does not cause secretion, the peptide potentiates ACh-induced salivary secretion. This may be due to an effect either on blood flow or on acinar cells, or both. An exclusive effect on the vascular system seems less likely, since locally administered VIP antiserum also inhibits the salivary secretion response to nerve stimulation. Furthermore, the vasodilating agent isoprenaline does not cause potentiation of the ACh response to the same extent. In fact, *in-vitro* studies support an interaction between VIP and ACh directly on the secretory cells. Thus, VIP in low concentrations (10^{-9} M) enhances the association rate of muscarinic ligand binding to membranes of the submandibular salivary gland[41]. In addition, VIP considerably increases the affinity of carbachol and ACh for the muscarinic receptor[41]. Furthermore, carbachol enhances the cyclic AMP formation induced by VIP, which may suggest interactions between ACh and VIP at the second messenger level as well[15]. Finally, a morphological basis for vasoactive intestinal peptidergic effects on secretion exists, since VIP is present in nerves making close contact to acinar cells[36].

The present studies have also provided some information on the dynamics of storage, release and supply of ACh and VIP. It is important to note that the local stores in nerve endings of ACh are several hundred-fold higher than those of VIP on a molar basis[36]. Furthermore, the output of VIP upon stimulation is considerably lower than that of ACh (Fig. 3). Another interesting question is to what extent VIP stores can be depleted upon excessive stimulation, since the peptide cannot be synthesized in the nerve ending but has to be replaced by axonal transport[39]. Thus, long-term nerve stimulation (1 hour) leads to a marked reduction of the VIP content in the submandibular gland (to less than 50% of control levels), while the ACh levels remain unchanged (J. M. Lundberg, G. Lundgren, J. Fahrenkrug, A. Änggård and B. Holmstedt, unpublished observations). These findings point to marked differences between cholinergic and peptidergic transmission. It should, however, be pointed out that even after 30 minutes of supramaximal stimulation the presumptive, peptidergic functional response (non-cholinergic vasodilation) is largely maintained. It may be that the differences in levels of storage and release are, at least in part, 'compensated' for by less efficient inactivation mechanisms and/or a higher sensitivity of the receptors for the peptide as compared to, for example, ACh.

Pancreatic polypeptide (PP)-IR peptides – catecholamines

Antisera to several members of the PP family react with some populations of both central and peripheral catecholaminergic (adrenergic and noradrenergic) neurons of several species[25,28,42,45,50]. Recent studies suggest, as discussed above, that the endogenous peptide may be NPY or a similar peptide[25,45]. In the periphery, only a portion of the noradrenergic nerves seem to contain the NPY-like peptide, and these neurons may innervate specific target tissues, such as arteries and arterioles or the smooth-muscle cells of the vas deferens. Other populations of peripheral noradrenergic neurons may contain other peptides. Such heterogeneity of the sympathetic nervous system may provide a basis for its functional differentiation. Subpopulations of sympathetic neurons may represent the morphological basis, for example, of observations demonstrating that the sympathetic secretory response can be exerted without concomitant reduction in blood flow[12]. These subpopulations of neurons may therefore be under separate preganglionic control. Functionally[44,45], in the submandibular gland model, infusion of NPY causes a slowly developing, long-lasting vasoconstriction, which is in contrast to the strong, short-lasting effect caused by NA. NA, but not NPY, causes salivary secretion (Fig. 4A). When NPY and NA are administered together, a blood-flow response is obtained which mimics the one seen upon electrical stimulation, i.e. vasoconstriction followed by a rapid post-stimulatory hyperemia and subsequent prolonged vasoconstriction with a gradual decline (Fig. 4A,B). Interestingly, adrenoceptor blockade reduces the vasoconstriction and totally abolishes the rapid vascular escape response, but does not seem to affect markedly the prolonged reduction in blood flow seen upon sympathetic-nerve stimulation (Fig. 4B). Thus, these physiological experiments suggest the presence of a vasoconstrictor agent in sympathetic nerves, in addition to NA. This agent could be NPY or a very similar peptide. Recently, γ-adrenoceptors have been described at the neuromuscular junction of blood vessels[19]. Activation of these receptors has been suggested to mediate α-adrenoceptor-resistant sympathetic vasoconstriction. NPY-induced vascular smooth-muscle contractions may, however, also be of importance. In other systems, NPY exerts different actions. Thus, in the smooth muscle of rat vas deferens, NPY inhibits the electrically induced con-

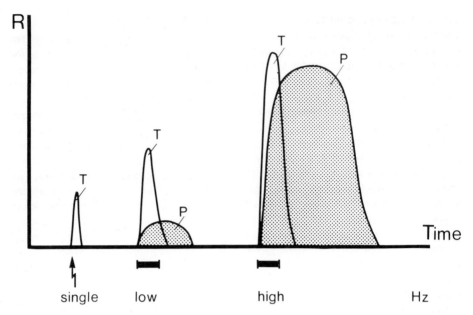

Fig. 6. *Schematic illustration showing the contribution of the classical transmitter (T) and coexisting peptide (P) to the functional response (R) upon various degrees of neuronal activation induced by electrical stimulation (single impulse, low and high frequency, Hz). A single nerve impulse preferentially induces a response which is due to release of the classical transmitter. Upon stimulation with higher frequencies there is an increasing functional effect caused by the peptide. The peptide-induced response is slower in onset, develops gradually and has a longer duration. Studies on the role of ACh and VIP for vasodilation induced by parasympathetic-nerve stimulation of the cat submandibular gland have provided the basis for this drawing but similar principles may prevail in other patterns of coexistence.*

traction possibly due to presynaptic inhibition of NA release[45].

The concept of chemical transmission

The 75th anniversary of the concept of chemical transmission was recently celebrated[14], a concept which has gone through many exciting phases. Originally the synthesis, storage and release of one transmitter acting on one type of receptor (R′) of the postsynaptic cell was demonstrated (Fig. 5a). Subsequently, subclasses of postsynaptic receptors were demonstrated (R′α, R′β), originally α- and β-adrenoceptors[1] (Fig. 5b). The occurrence of presynaptic receptors (autoreceptors) (Rp′), and thus the possibility that a transmitter may control its own release, has received much attention during recent years[32] (Fig. 5c). In the model of a chemical synapse shown in Fig. 5d, we have attempted to include the recent ideas of the storage and release of multiple synaptic

messengers and their interaction with post- and pre-synaptic receptors. It must be emphasized that this drawing is in many ways hypothetical, and that more or less indirect lines of evidence from several types of coexistence have been summarized. Particularly in the CNS, it is extremely difficult to prove that a result indicating interaction between a peptide and a classical transmitter does, in fact, reflect effects related to the coexistence of the two compounds.

Concluding remarks

Several examples of occurrence of a classical transmitter and a peptide in one and the same neuron have now been obtained with immunohistochemical techniques. A consistent finding is that the peptide only seems to be present in a subpopulation of neurons of a particular neurochemical type, and vice versa. The co-localization of peptide and classical transmitter in nerve endings makes it possible that both interact in chemical transmission. The functional significance of coexistence is still unclear, but in some models it seems that the peptides amplify the effects caused by the classical transmitters. Interestingly, one and the same peptide may have roles both as transmitter and modulator in the same tissue. Often the peptide seems to be responsible for a component of the response characterized by slow onset and long duration, whereas ACh and NA cause rapid and short-lasting effects (Fig. 6). There is also some evidence that release of the peptide requires a higher stimulation frequency than does the classical transmitter. It will be an important task to define more exactly the interactions between peptide and classical transmitter. Furthermore, it may be interesting to analyse to what extent the balance between multiple synaptic messengers is disturbed during various nervous disorders and how drugs of various types may affect the complex interplay between compounds released at synapses.

Acknowledgements

The present studies were supported by grants from the Swedish Medical Research Council (O4X-2887, 14X-6554, 17X-5438), Knut och Alice Wallenbergs Stiftelse, Astra Foundation, Svenska Läkarsällskapet, Karolinska Institutets Forskningsfonder, Wibergs Stiftelse, Hans och Leo Osterman Stiftelse and Magnus Bergvalls Stiftelse. We express our sincere appreciation to our collaborators and our gratitude for the supply of precious antisera and peptides. Two of the schematic drawings (Figs 2 and 5) were produced by the NIH medical illustration department while Tomas Hökfelt was a Fogarty Scholar. The support of Drs M. Brownstein and P. Condliffe at NIMH and NIH, Bethesda, MD, USA, is gratefully acknowledged. We thank Dr Barry Everitt for reading the manuscript and for valuable suggestions.

Reading list

1 Ahlqvist, R. P. (1948) *Am. J. Physiol.* 153, 586–600
2 Altschuler, R., Fex, J. and Parakkal, M. *Neuroscience* (in press)
3 Barbeau, H. and Bedard, P. (1981) *Neuropharmacology* 20, 477–481
4 Burnstock, G. (1976) *Neuroscience* 1, 239–248
5 Campbell, G., Gibbins, J. L., Morris, J. L., Furness, J. B., Costa, M., Oliver, J. R.,

Beardsley, A. M. and Murphy, R. (1982) *Neuroscience* 7, 2013–2023
6 Chan-Palay, V., Jonsson, G. and Palay, S. L. (1978) *Proc. Natl Acad. Sci. USA* 75, 1582–1586
7 Chan-Palay, V., Nilaver, G., Palay, S. L., Beinfeld, M. C., Zimmerman, E. A., Wu, J. Y. and O'Donohue, T. L. (1981) *Proc. Natl Acad. Sci. USA* 78, 7781–7791
8 Charnay, Y., Léger, L., Dray, F., Bérod, A., Jouvet, M., Pujol, J. F. and Dubois, P. M. (1982) *Neurosci. Lett.* 30, 147–151
9 Eccles, J. C. (1976) *R. Soc. London, Notes Rec.* 30, 219–230
10 Eccles, J. C., Fatt, P. and Koketsu, K. (1954) *J. Physiol. (London)* 126, 524–562
11 Edwards, A. V., Järhult, J., Andersson, P.-O. and Bloom, S. R. (1982) in *Systemic Role of Regulatory Peptides* (Bloom, S. R., Polak, J. M. and Lindenlaub, E., eds), pp. 145–168, Schattauer, Stuttgart
12 Emmelin, N. (1967) *Handbook of Physiology, Sect. 6: Alimentary Canal II*, pp. 595–632, American Physiological Society, Washington, DC
13 Erichsen, J. T., Karten, H. J., Eldred, W. D. and Brecha, N. C. (1982) *J. Neurosci.* 7, 994–1003
14 Euler, U. S., von (1981) in *Chemical Neurotransmission – 75 Years* (Stjärne, L., Hedquist, P., Lagercrantz, H. and Wennmalm, A., eds), pp. 3–12, Academic Press, London
15 Fredholm, B. and Lundberg, J. M. (1982) *Acta Physiol. Scand.* 114, 157–159
16 Fuxe, K., Agnati, L. F., Köhler, C., Kuonen, D., Ögren, S.-O., Andersson, K. and Hökfelt, T. (1981) *J. Neural Transm.* 51, 3–37
17 Garrett, J. R. (1974) in *Secretory Mechanisms of Exocrine Glands* (Thorn, N. A. and Petersen, O. H., eds), pp. 17–27, Munkgaard, Copenhagen
18 Glazer, E. J., Steinbusch, H., Verhofstad, A. and Basbaum, A. J. (1981) *J. Physiol. (Paris)* 77, 241–245
19 Hirst, G. D. S. and Neild, T. O. (1980) *Nature (London)* 283, 767–768
20 Hökfelt, T., Elfvin, L. G., Elde, R., Schultzberg, M., Goldstein, M. and Luft, R. (1977) *Proc. Natl Acad. Sci. USA* 74, 3587–3591
21 Hökfelt, T., Johansson, O., Ljungdahl, Å., Lundberg, J. M. and Schultzberg, M. (1980) *Nature (London)* 284, 515–521
22 Hökfelt, T., Ljungdahl, A., Steinbusch, H., Verhofstad, A., Nilsson, G., Brodin, E., Pernow, B. and Goldstein, M. (1978) *Neuroscience* 3, 517–538
23 Hökfelt, T., Lundberg, J. M., Schultzberg, M., Johansson, O., Ljungdahl, Å. and Rehfeld, J. (1980) in *Neural Peptides and Neuronal Communication* (Costa, E. and Trabucchi, M., eds), pp. 1–23, Raven Press, New York
24 Hökfelt, T., Lundberg, J. M., Skirboll, L.,

Johansson, O., Schultzberg, M. and Vincent, S. R. (1982) in *Cotransmission* (Cuello, A. C., ed.), pp. 77–125, MacMillan, London

25 Hökfelt, T., Lundberg, J. M., Tatemoto, K., Mutt, V., Terenius, L., Polak, J., Bloom, S. R., Elde, R. and Goldstein, M. (1983) *Acta Physiol. Scand.* 117, 315–318

26 Hökfelt, T., Skirboll, L., Rehfeld, J. F., Goldstein, M., Markey, K. and Dann, O. (1980) *Neuroscience* 5, 2093–2124

27 Höllt, V. (1983) *Trends NeuroSci.* 6, 24–26

28 Hunt, S. P., Emson, P. C., Gilbert, R., Goldstein, M. and Kimmel, J. R. (1981) *Neurosci. Lett.* 21, 125–130

29 Jaim-Etcheverry, G. and Zieher, L. H. (1971) *J. Pharmacol. Exp. Ther.* 178, 42–48

30 Jan, Y. N. and Jan, L. Y. (1982) in *Frontiers in Neuroendocrinology* (Ganong, W. F. and Martini, L., eds), Vol. 7, pp. 211–230, Raven Press, New York

31 Johansson, O., Hökfelt, T., Pernow, B., Jeffcoate, S. L., White, N., Steinbusch, H. W. M., Verhofstad, A. A. J., Emson, P. C. and Spindel, E. (1981) *Neuroscience* 6, 1857–1881

32 Langer, S. Z., Starke, K. and Dubocovic, M. L. (eds) (1979) *Presynaptic Receptors*, Pergamon Press, Oxford

33 Lewis, R., Stein, A. S., Kilpatrick, D., Gerber, L., Rossier, J. J., Stein, S. and Udenfried, S. (1981) *Neuroscience* 1, 80–82

34 Lewis, R. V., Stein, A. S., Rossier, J. J., Stein, S. and Udenfriend, S. (1979) *Biochem. Biophys. Res. Commun.* 89, 822–829

35 Lorén, I., Alumets, J., Håkanson, R. and Sundler, F. (1979) *Cell Tissue Res.* 200, 179–186

36 Lundberg, J. M. (1981) *Acta Physiol. Scand.* 112 (Suppl. 496), 1–57

37 Lundberg, J. M., Änggård, A., Fahrenkrug, J., Hökfelt, T. and Mutt, V. (1980) *Proc. Natl Acad. Sci. USA* 77, 1651–1655

38 Lundberg, J. M., Änggård, A., Fahrenkrug, J., Lundgren, G. and Holmstedt, B. (1982) *Acta Physiol. Scand.* 115, 525–528

39 Lundberg, J. M., Fahrenkrug, J. and Brimijoin, S. (1981) *Acta Physiol. Scand.* 112, 427–436

40 Lundberg, J. M., Hedlund, B., Änggård, A., Fahrenkrug, J., Hökfelt, T., Tatemoto, K. and Bartfai, T. (1982) in *Systemic Role of Regulatory Peptides* (Bloom, S. R., Polak, J. M. and Lindenlaub, E., eds), pp. 145–168, Schattauer, Stuttgart

41 Lundberg, J. M., Hedlund, B. and Bartfai, T. (1982) *Nature (London)* 295, 147–149

42 Lundberg, J. M., Hökfelt, T., Änggård, A., Kimmel, J., Goldstein, M. and Markey, K. (1980) *Acta Physiol. Scand.* 110, 107–109

43 Lundberg, J. M., Hökfelt, T., Änggård, A., Terenius, L., Elde, R., Kimmel, J., Goldstein, M. and Markey, K. (1982) *Proc. Natl Acad. Sci. USA* 79, 1303–1307

44 Lundberg, J. M. and Tatemoto, K. (1982) *Acta Physiol. Scand.* 116, 393–402

45 Lundberg, J. M., Terenius, L., Hökfelt, T., Martling, C.-R., Tatemoto, R., Mutt, V., Polak, J., Bloom, S. and Goldstein, M. (1982) *Acta Physiol. Scand.* 116, 477–480

46 Markstein, R., Skirboll, L. and Hökfelt, T. *Eur. J. Pharmacol.* (submitted)

47 Matthysse, S. W. and Kety, S. S. (eds) (1975) *Catecholamines and Schizophrenia*, Pergamon, Oxford

48 Mitchell, R. and Fleetwood-Walker, S. (1981) *Eur. J. Pharmacol.* 76, 119–120

49 Oertel, W. H., Graybiel, A. M., Mugnaini, E. L., Schmeckel, D. E. and Kopin, I. J. *J. Neurosci.* (in press)

50 Olschowka, J. A., O'Donohue, T. L. and Jacobowitz, D. M. (1981) *Peptides* 2, 309–331

51 Osborne, N. N. (1979) *Trends NeuroSci.* 2, 73–75

52 Otsuka, M. and Takahashi, T. (1977) *Am. Rev. Pharmacol. Toxicol.* 17, 425–439

53 Owman, Ch., Håkanson, R. and Sundler, F. (1973) *Fed. Proc. Fed. Am. Soc. Exp. Biol.* 32, 1785–1791

54 Patterson, P. H. (1978) *Am. Rev. Neurosci.* 1, 1–18

55 Pearse, A. G. E. (1969) *J. Histochem. Cytochem.* 17, 303–313

56 Pelletier, G., Steinbusch, H. W. and Verhofstad, A. (1981) *Nature (London)* 293, 71–72

57 Potter, D. D., Furshpan, E. J. and Landis, S. C. (1981) *Neurosci. Comment.* 1, 1–9

58 Schultzberg, M., Lundberg, J. M., Hökfelt, T., Terenius, L., Brandt, J., Elde, R. and Goldstein, M. (1978) *Neuroscience* 3, 1169–1186

59 Skirboll, L., Grace, A. A., Hommer, D. W., Rehfeld, J., Goldstein, M., Hökfelt, T. and Bunney, B. S. (1981) *Neuroscience* 6, 2111–2124

60 Sternberger, L. A. (1979) *Immunocytochemistry*, John Wiley, New York

61 Tramu, G., Pillez, A. and Leonardelli, J. (1978) *J. Histochem. Cytochem.* 26, 322–324

62 Viveros, O. H., Diliberto, E. J., Jr, Hazum, E. and Chang, K. J. (1979) *Mol. Pharmacol.* 16, 1101–1108

Jan M. Lundberg and Tomas Hökfelt are at the Departments of Pharmacology and Histology, Karolinska Institutet, S-104 01 Stockholm, Sweden.

Purinergic mechanisms: recent electrophysiological evidence

G. Burnstock

New insights into purinergic mechanisms have been provided by recent electro-physiological studies. In the original proposal of the purinergic nerve hypothesis in 1972, it was suggested that ATP might be the principal neurotransmitter released from the intrinsic, non-adrenergic, non-cholinergic neurones that supply the smooth muscle of the intestine and bladder, and possibly some other visceral and vascular organs as well[1]. There is now evidence, from both in situ *and culture studies, to show that ATP acts as a co-transmitter with the classical transmitters in autonomic fibres, and that a population of primary afferent sensory fibres release ATP to act on neurones in lamina II of the spinal cord. There is also evidence for purinergic transmission in ganglia, and for purinergic modulation of transmitter release and postjunctional action. Recent studies of the mechanisms of action of adenosine and ATP via P_1- and P_2-purinoceptors, respectively[2], in muscle and other cell types are also described. These findings suggest that purines are more widely involved in neuroregulatory mechanisms than originally envisaged.*

ATP as a co-transmitter

Recent reports have given electro-physiological support to the proposal that ATP acts as a co-transmitter with classical neurotransmitters in some autonomic nerves[16]. The mechanical response of the guinea-pig vas deferens to sympathetic nerve stimulation is biphasic; the initial twitch contraction is mimicked by ATP, and the second slow contraction is mimicked by nor-adrenaline (NA)[3]. Both responses are abolished by the adrenergic neurone blocking drug guanethidine, or by chemical sympathectomy, clearly indicating that the first phase is not due to release of a transmitter from separate non-adrenergic ('purinergic') fibres. The twitch contraction is associated with excitatory junction potentials (EJP's) that sum and facilitate until action potentials are initiatied. The EJP's and the twitch contractions are unaffected by α-adrenoceptor antag-

onists, but are blocked by the P_2-purinoceptor photoaffinity antag-onist arylazido aminopropionyl-ATP (ANAPP$_3$)[4] or by selective desensi-tization of the postjunctional P_2-purino-ceptor by exposure to the stable ana-logue of ATP, α,β-methylene ATP[25]. The EJP is mimicked by local applica-tion of ATP by pressure ejection from a micropipette; NA does not produce such a response[4,5]. In the vas deferens of animals pretreated with reserpine, which depletes most of the NA in sympathetic nerves, the second phase of the contractile response to nerve stimulation is virtually abolished, but the first phase of the contraction and the EJP are little affected[4]. Strong support has just appeared in *Neuro-science*, where Stjärne and Astrand[28] claim that the first time differentials of the rising phases of the EJP's recorded in the vas deferens ('discrete events') reflect the release of single quanta of

ATP from the sympathetic nerve terminals.

The response of a number of blood vessels to sympathetic nerve stimulation is similar. For example, intracellular recordings from smooth muscle cells of the rat tail artery during stimulation of the periarterial nerves revealed two components: EJP's produced by each stimulus and a slow maintained depolarization which develops as the train of stimuli progresses[6]. Recent experiments have shown that in the presence of the α-antagonist phentolamine the slow depolarization is virtually abolished, while the EJP's are unaffected; conversely, in the presence of α,β-methylene ATP, the EJP's are virtually abolished, while the slow depolarization persists[7]. Locally applied ATP, but not NA, mimics the EJP in the rat tail artery and also in several other blood vessels (H. Kuriyama, unpublished observations).

Further support for ATP as a co-transmitter in sympathetic neurones has come from the elegant studies of cultured rat sympathetic neurones by the Neurobiology group at Harvard. Recently, Potter, Furshpan and Landis[8] demonstrated, using microelectrode recordings from cardiac myocytes grown together with single neurones dissociated from the superior cervical ganglion, that some cultured neurones secrete a third transmitter in addition to NA and acetylcholine (ACh) this transmitter is probably adenosine or a phosphorylated derivative. They reported that 'this purinergic function is expressed with adrenergic or cholinergic function or with both (triple function) and that in some cases the main effect exerted by a neurone on co-cultured cardiac myocytes is purinergic'.

ATP as a central neurotransmitter

Recent experiments from several independent laboratories, using different approaches, have shown that certain primary afferent fibres may utilize ATP to excite a subpopulation of neurones in the sensory regions of the brain, as well as neurones in the outer layer of the dorsal horn of the spinal cord. This follows the earlier report by Holton[9] who found that ATP was released during antidromic stimulation of the primary afferent sensory nerves supplying the rabbit ear arteries.

Jahr and Jessell[10] demonstrated that ATP could selectively and potently excite a subpopulation of rat dorsal horn neurones maintained in dissociated culture. The following evidence suggests that a P_2-purinoceptor is involved: adenosine had no effect on these neurones; superfusion of dorsal horn nerves with 8-phenyltheophylline at a concentration sufficient to block P_1-purinoceptors did not decrease the depolarization produced by ATP, whereas the slowly degradable analogue β,γ-methylene ATP was effective.

Evidence from in-vivo studies of rat[11] and cat[12] suggests that a purinergic transmitter might mediate central synaptic excitation of neurones both in the trigeminal nucleus and in the outer layer of the spinal cord from a population of fine-diameter primary afferent fibres. Those central neurones consistently excited by ATP iontophoresis with very small currents (2–15 nA) responded to gentle mechanical stimulation of the skin and were associated with excitatory input from unmyelinated (C) primary afferent fibres[12]. Generally, the mechanoreceptor nerves excited by ATP were located in the deeper substantia gelatinosa or in the immediately adjacent nucleus proprius of the dorsal horn.

Krishtal et al.[13] showed that exogenously applied ATP produced a rapid and transient inwardly-rectifying Na^+ current in single sensory neurones that were enzymatically isolated from nodose, vestibular, trigeminal and spinal ganglia of rats.

Purinergic transmission in ganglia

Recent studies by Akasu and his colleagues suggest that purinergic transmission may occur in some autonomic ganglia. Slow hyperpolarizing synaptic potentials (slow HSP) in cat vesical parasympathetic ganglia produced by stimulating the preganglionic nerves appear to be mediated by adenosine[14] for the following reasons: exogenous application of adenosine closely mimicked the time course of the slow HSP; both responses were depressed by the P_1-purinoceptor antagonist caffeine, and by adenosine deaminase, while the adenosine-uptake inhibitor dipyridamole potentiated them; the reversal potential for both the slow HSP and the response to adenosine was comparable (about -93 mV), indicating activation of potassium conductance. Adenosine has also been shown to inhibit the voltage-dependent Ca^{2+} current via activation of P_1-purinoceptors on postganglionic neurones of the rat superior cervical ganglion[15].

Purinergic neuromodulation

There is increasing evidence that purines act as both pre- and post-junctional modulators of neuronal activity. Adenosine inhibits release of NA and ACh from sympathetic and parasympathetic nerve terminals[16], it inhibits spontaneous firing and reduces evoked excitatory post-synaptic potentials (EPSP's) in central neurones[17], and ATP and/or adenosine act as pre- and post-junctional modulators of membrane potentials recorded in autonomic ganglia[15,18,19].

The mechanism behind the modulatory actions of ATP on membrane potentials of bullfrog sympathetic ganglion cells has been examined[18]. ATP depolarized the membrane of the ganglion cell by decreasing resting K^+ conductance. Voltage-clamp studies

suggested that ATP also depressed the after-hyperpolarization of action potentials by suppressing both the M-current and the delayed rectifier K^+ current. In another study, ATP was shown to produce a long-lasting depolarization of spinal ganglion cells of the bullfrog that augmented the depolarizations produced by γ-aminobutyric acid (GABA), by modifying the GABA receptor channel complexes without changing the receptor affinity for GABA[20]. Postjunctional modulation by ATP of the actions of ACh released from motor nerves to the skeletal muscle has also been described [16].

An electrophysiological study of the mechanism by which adenosine receptor activation inhibits the release of acetylcholine from motor nerve endings[21] suggests that adenosine stimulates adenylate cyclase in presynaptic terminals leading to inhibition of ACh release by reducing the affinity of an intracellular component of the secretory apparatus for calcium.

ATP-regulated K^+ channels in muscles and some other cell types

While it has been recognized for some time that ATP evokes hyperpolarization of smooth muscle in the intestine by producing specific changes in K^+ conductance[22], the actions of purines on striated muscle have only recently been examined. Microelectrode or patch-clamp techniques have been applied to cardiac muscle[23] and to the skeletal muscle of the developing myotube[24]. The P_1-purinoceptor agonist adenosine, like ACh, hyperpolarizes and shortens the action potential in atrial muscle; analysis of reversal potentials suggest that micromolar concentrations of adenosine and ACh increase potassium conductance via a common mechanism.

In patch-clamp studies of cultured chick myoblasts and myotubes, external ATP in micromolar concentrations was shown to activate cation-selective channels[24]. In myoblasts, only one population of channels ($\gamma_1 = 43$ pS) was found, while in myotubes two populations ($\gamma_1 = 48$ pS and $\gamma_2 = 20$ pS) were observed. Treatment of myotube membranes with ACh or carbachol resulted in activation of two populations of channels which had conductance values and voltage-dependent mean channel open times similar to those produced in response to ATP. The authors concluded that 'the results show that embryonic skeletal muscle cells contain cation channels sensitive to ATP and provide evidence for a neurotransmitter-like action of ATP on these cells'.

Finally, there are recent reports that exogenous ATP acting on P_2-purinoceptors produces a transient hyperpolarization due to increased membrane permeability to K^+ of mouse fibroblasts[25], hepatocytes[26] and parotid acinar cells[27]. Speculations are made that P_2-purinoceptors activated by ATP (or ADP), released from injured cells or aggregating platelets, may mediate regulation of fibroblast function in wound healing[25].

The recent electrophysiological experiments reported here, taken together with earlier studies of storage, release and inactivation of purines from certain nerves[1,16], and the rapidly growing literature on the pharmacology of purinergic receptors in a range of tissues[2], suggest a wider involvement of purines in neuroregulatory mechanisms than was originally envisaged.

Selected references

1 Burnstock, G. (1972) *Pharmacol. Rev.* 24, 509–581
2 Burnstock, G., ed., (1981) *Purinergic Receptors* Chapman and Hall, London
3 Meldrum, L. A. and Burnstock, G. (1983) *Eur. J. Pharmacol.* 92, 161–163
4 Sneddon, P. and Westfall, D. P. (1984) *J. Physiol. (London)* 347, 561–580
5 Sneddon, P. and Burnstock, G. (1984) *Eur. J. Pharmacol.* 100, 85–90
6 Cheung, D. W. (1984) *Pflugers Arch.* 400, 335–337
7 Sneddon, P. and Burnstock, G. (1984) *Eur. J. Pharmacol.* 106, 149–152
8 Potter, D. D., Furshpan, E. J. and Landis, S. C. (1983) *Fed. Proc.* 42, 1626–1632
9 Holton, P. (1959) *J. Physiol. (London)* 145, 494–504
10 Jahr, C. E. and Jessell, T. M. (1983) *Nature (London)* 304, 730–733
11 Salt, T. E. and Hill, R. G. (1983) *Neurosci. Lett.* 35, 53–57
12 Fyffe, R. E. W. and Perl, E. R. (1984) *Proc. Natl Acad. Sci. USA* (in press)
13 Krishtal, O. A., Marchenko, S. M. and Pidoplichko, V. I. (1983) *Neurosci. Lett.* 41–45
14 Akasu, T., Shinnick-Gallagher, P. and Gallagher, J. P. (1984) *Nature (London)* 311, 62–65
15 Henon, B. K. and McAfee, D. A. (1983) *J. Physiol. (London)* 336, 607–620
16 Burnstock, G. (1983) in *Dale's Principle and Communication Between Neurones* pp. 7–35 (Osborne, N., ed.), Pergamon Press, Oxford
17 Schubert, P., Lee, K., Reddington, M. and Kreutzberg, G. (1983) in *Regulatory Function of Adenosine* (Berne, R. M., Rall, T. W. and Rubio, R., eds), pp. 439–454, Nijhoff, The Hague/Boston/London
18 Akasu, T., Hirai, K. and Koketsu, K. (1983) *Brain Res.* 258, 313–317
19 Silinsky, E. M. and Ginsborg, B. L. (1983) *Nature (London)* 305, 327–328
20 Morita, K, Katayama, Y., Koketsu, K. and Akasu, T. (1984) *Brain Res.* 293, 360–363
21 Silinsky, E. M. (1984) *J. Physiol. (London)* 346, 243–256
22 Tomita, T. and Watanabe, H. (1973) *J. Physiol. (London)* 231, 167–177
23 Hartzell, H. C. (1979) *J. Physiol. (London)* 293, 23–49
24 Kolb, H.-A. and Wakelam, J. O. (1983) *Nature (London)* 303, 621–633
25 Okada, Y., Yada, T., Ohno-Shosaku, T., Oiki, S., Ueda, S. and Machida, K. (1984) *Exp. Cell Res.* 152, 552–557
26 Burgess, G. M., Claret, M. and Jenkinson, D. H. (1979) *Nature (London)* 279, 544–546
27 Gallagher, D. V. (1982) *Nature (London)* 296, 83–86
28 Stjärne, L. and Astrand, P. (1984) *Neuroscience* 13, 21–28

Department of Anatomy and Embryology and Centre for Neuroscience, University College London, Gower Street, WC1E 6BT, UK.

A single gene encodes multiple peptide-transmitter candidates involved in a stereotyped behavior

Richard H. Scheller, Barry S. Rothman and Earl Mayeri

A multidisciplinary approach is being used to study the roles of peptides in neuronal function and the regulation of behavior in Aplysia. *Recent data indicate that a group of neuroendocrine cells, the bag cells, utilize two or more peptide neurotransmitters (and/or neurohormones) that are enzymatically cleaved from a common precursor protein. The gene for this precursor is a member of a small gene family that encodes several different precursor proteins for neuroactive peptides. The combined effects of the bag-cell peptides may serve to regulate the various neural and physiological events underlying a stereotyped pattern of behavior during egg laying.*

In the last several years more than 30 biologically active peptides have been discovered in the CNS of vertebrates and invertebrates. Combined immunocytochemical, pharmacological and electrophysiological studies suggest that these peptides act as neurotransmitters. However, little is known about the normal functioning of peptides in the CNS at the cellular and subcellular levels. This is because there are relatively few experimental systems where both the peptide-secreting cells and their target neurons in the abdominal defined and accessible at the cellular level.

One useful system for such studies consists of the peptidergic bag-cell neurons and their target neurons in the abdominal ganglion of the marine snail *Aplysia californica*[12]. These cells are large (50 μm–500 μm) and easily identifiable from preparation to preparation, making them accessible to detailed electrophysiological analysis. Furthermore, the bag cells are a large and relatively homogeneous population of neurons that can be surgically isolated from the rest of the ganglion.

Molecular genetic techniques, which have just begun to be used in neurobiology, are providing another powerful tool for investigating how gene products such as peptides, receptors for transmitters, and ion-channel proteins determine the individual properties of neurons. In *Aplysia* a variety of recombinant DNA techniques have been employed to isolate a family of 5–9 genes that encode the precursors for the neuroactive peptides used by the bag cells and a non-neuronal tissue, the atrial gland. By determining the nucleotide sequences of these genes the complete amino acid sequences of three of the precursor proteins have been determined. The genes encode related sets of peptides which are expressed specifically in the bag cells or the atrial gland. The protein precursors were found to contain new potentially active peptide sequences. Three previously described neuroactive peptides are found to be cleaved from a common precursor in the bag cells. Electrophysiological, biochemical, immunocytochemical and behavioral studies are delineating the actions of these peptides on targets in the CNS and periphery. These actions are thought to mediate the stereotyped behavior accompanying egg laying in *Aplysia*.

Egg-laying behavior and the role of the bag cells

Aplysia are non-self-fertilizing hermaphrodites which culminate their annual life cycle with the laying of many large egg masses, each containing up to 10^6 fertilized oocytes. As is the case with other reproductive processes in both vertebrates and invertebrates, egg laying is associated with a stereotyped pattern of behavior[2,17]. As an egg string emerges from the external genital groove, located near the mouth, it is deposited onto an appropriate substrate as an irregularly shaped mass; the shape due to a back-and-forth motion of the head. While these events occur there is an increase in respiratory pumping, and inhibition of locomotion and feeding.

The bag cells play a critical role in the generation of egg laying and the associated behavior pattern. Spontaneous egg laying in *Aplysia* is always preceded by firing of the bag cells[18]. Furthermore, the entire behavior pattern can be elicited by injection of bag-cell extract into the hemocoel of the animal[13]. Like other neuroendocrine cells, the bag cells, when electrically stimulated, release peptides which enter the general circulation; one of these peptides, egg-laying hormone (ELH), acts to release eggs from the ovotestis[21]. In addition, electrical activity in the bag cells produces several types of effects on the CNS, many of which last for hours[15,16] – in keeping with the duration of the behavioral array. These and other findings (see below) suggest that egg-laying behavior is generated by the release of bag-cell peptides which activate targets in the CNS and periphery.

The bag cells are thought to originate in a proliferative zone of the ectodermal lining in the body wall and then migrate to their final position in the rostral margin of the abdominal ganglion (L. B. McAllister, unpublished observations), resulting in a homogeneous population of about 800 neurons[9]. The bag cells are electrically coupled[14] and it is this feature that allows them to fire synchronously. This synchronous activity, termed the burst discharge, lasts from 20 to 30 minutes, and is probably necessary to generate the appropriate amount of circulating hormone required for laying large masses of eggs. The bag cells send granule-filled processes into the vascularized sheath surrounding the abdominal ganglion[9]. The sheath serves as a site for release of bag-cell peptides.

The atrial gland may also play a role in reproduction, since extracts of this gland initiate egg laying when injected into mature animals[3]. The atrial gland is situated at the distal end of the genital tract where it forms a continuous lumen with the large hermaphroditic duct. It consists of two major cell types: the large exocrine cells, which contain electron-dense granules; and ciliated capping cells. The dense-core granules fuse prior to release into the lumen of the duct, identifying the secretory modality as exocrine. Although the function of this tissue is unknown, the fact that it is located in the reproductive tract and contains large amounts of biologically active peptides suggests that it is likely to play an important role in reproduction.

Three peptides were the first to be isolated and characterized from the bag cells and atrial gland. ELH is a 36-residue peptide that is synthesized[1,7] and released[24] by the bag cells, and when injected into mature animals causes them to lay eggs[7]. Peptides A and B, each 34 residues long, have been isolated from the atrial gland[10]. The A and B peptides differ from each other by four amino acids in the NH_2-terminal portion of the molecule, and are not structurally related to ELH. When applied to the bag cells *in vitro*, the A or B peptides depolarize these neurons, resulting in a burst discharge.

Genes coding for reproductive behavior

During the reproductive season the bag cells and the atrial gland synthesize large amounts of ELH and peptides A/B, respec-

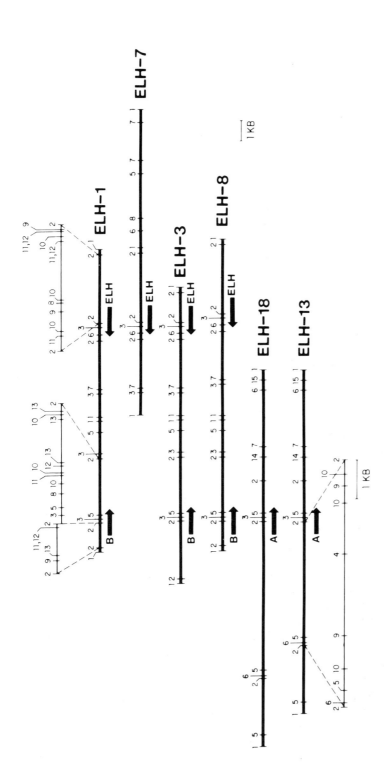

Fig. 1. *Restriction-enzyme maps of ELH recombinant clones. Restriction-enzyme maps were determined by a combination of single, partial and double digests on intact clones and isolated fragments. The arrows indicate the position of mRNA homologous sequences and point in the direction of transcription as determined from DNA sequencing. Restriction enzymes: (1) Eco RI; (2) Pst I; (3) Xho I; (4) Stu I; (5) Pvu II; (6) Hind III; (7) Bgl I; (8) Xba I; (9) Ava II; (10) Hinc II; (11) Hae II; (12) Hha I; (13) Hpa II; (14) Bam HI; (15) Sal I.*

tively. It was therefore possible to isolate the genes encoding the precursors of these peptides by screening a genomic library derived from the sperm DNA of a single animal. Radiolabelled cDNA was prepared by reverse transcription of poly A$^+$ RNA from the bag cells, atrial gland, abdominal ganglion and hepatopancreas. About 10^6 clones were screened with each cDNA preparation, and clones that hybridized only to prevalent sequences in the bag cells and the atrial gland were selected. A partial nucleotide sequence for one clone was determined and shown to contain an ELH-coding region. This sequence was then used to isolate additional recombinants until further screening failed to result in the isolation of unique clones[22,23].

Analysis of six different clones (Fig. 1) along with genomic blotting studies revealed that the A, B and ELH peptides are encoded on a family of 5–9 genes. The results of hybridization experiments suggest that each gene is transcribed in only one tissue; that is, no member of the gene family is expressed in both the bag cells (ELH genes) and the atrial gland (A- and B-peptide genes)[22]. Using immunocytochemical and *in-situ* hybridization techniques it has recently been shown that in addition to the bag cells, a small network of neurons throughout the *Aplysia* CNS[7] (L. B. McAllister, unpublished observations) express members of the gene family. At present, the function of these other cells is not known. It is possible, however, that certain members of the gene family are expressed only in these cells. It is often the case that individual members of a multigene family are expressed either at different times in development or in different adult tissues, presumably satisfying the functional requirements of the tissue in which they are expressed. In contrast to the proopiomelanocortin system[11], in which a single precursor undergoes different processing pathways in different tissues, the ELH gene family appears to use tissue-specific expression of related genes to generate different sets of peptides.

Restriction-enzyme and DNA-sequence analyses suggest that clones ELH-1, -3 and -8 contain two members of the gene family, the ELH gene and the B-peptide gene (Fig. 1). The nucleotide sequences of the two genes on clone ELH-1 revealed extensive homology, suggesting that they arose from a common ancestral gene. Detailed studies of the organization of sequences in clone ELH-1 showed that a particular element 1.7 kilobases (kb) in length is present at the 5′ end of the ELH gene but not the B-peptide gene. In clone ELH-3 the opposite organization is observed. The 1.7-kb element is present at the 5′ end of the B gene but not the ELH gene. Recent genomic blotting experiments have demonstrated that the Eco R1 restriction-enzyme fragments in clone ELH-3 are not present in the genome and suggest that the 1.7-kb element has been rearranged during the cloning procedure. It is possible therefore that this element has a mobile nature within the *Aplysia* genome as well. The fact that the 1.7-kb element is present at or near the 5′ end of some genes (for example ELH-1), but not others, suggests that this element may play an important role in governing the tissue-specific expression of the gene family. The resolution of this issue awaits further experimentation.

DNA-sequence analysis has been used to define the structure of the precursor proteins encoding the ELH, A and B peptides (Fig. 2). These data predict that one gene codes for a 33 000-mol. wt precursor expressed in the bag cells, and two others code for precursors expressed in the atrial gland, one of mol. wt 21 000 encoding peptide A and one of mol. wt 14 000 encoding peptide B. The results of *in-vitro* translation of total poly A$^+$ RNA from these tissues followed by immunoprecipitation with antibodies directed against ELH or peptide A reveal major protein species with molecular weights in agreement with those predicted from the genetic data[23].

The DNA-sequence analysis further reveals that the three genes have a 90%

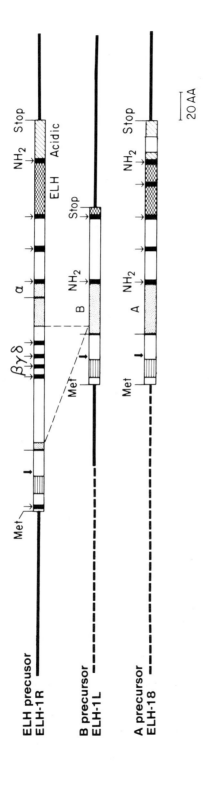

Fig. 2. *Comparison of the precursors encoding the ELH, A and B peptides. Each of the three proteins is initiated by a methionine followed by a hydrophobic region (■). Thick arrows represent the putative cleavage site of the signal sequence (↓). Line above the sequence represents potential cleavages at single arginine residues (↑), while arrows represent potential or known cleavages at dibasic, tribasic or tetrabasic residues. If COOH-terminal amidation is believed to occur, an NH₂ appears above the arrow. The A/B peptide homology is represented by stippled boxes (▨), the ELH homology by cross-hatched boxes (▨), and the AP homology by parallel lines enclosed in boxes (▨). Solid lines symbolize sequenced non-coding regions, and dashed lines depict regions not sequenced.*

sequence homology, yet they give rise to different sets of peptides (Fig. 2). Many of the differences between genes occur in regions which alter the proteolytic processing of the precursor proteins. This implies that these changes have become fixed in the population because of the selective advantage they provide. It also argues that the different peptide components are functionally important to the organism.

All three genes begin with a hydrophobic signal sequence necessary for membrane association, vesiculation and ultimately secretion[4]. Moving in a COOH-terminal direction the first six amino acids of the B peptide are observed in the ELH gene, followed by eighty amino acids which are not present in either the A- or B-peptide genes (see below). This sequence contains a direct repeat, TCATCA, at each of its ends, suggesting it is an insertion. Within this insertion there are four potential proteolytic cleavage sites, as indicated by the presence of four pairs of basic amino acids. If recognized, these cleavage sites would generate three small peptides, β-, γ- and δ-bag-cell peptide (BCP). After this region the homology with the A and B atrial peptides resumes. A single base change converts a methionine residue found in the atrial precursors to an arginine residue. This single amino acid appears to be the NH_2-terminal cleavage site for a candidate transmitter, α-BCP. The COOH-terminus of α-BCP is flanked by a tribasic cleavage sequence, Arg-Lys-Arg. In the atrial precursors this sequence is Gly-Lys-Arg, which presumably codes for cleavage followed by the destructive amidation of the A and B peptides at their COOH-termini. Further in the COOH-terminal direction on the bag-cell precursor is the DNA sequence encoding ELH, followed by the sequence Gly-Lys-Arg and a sequence of twenty-seven amino acids coding for the acidic peptide (AP)[1].

The sequence coding for peptides A and B on their respective atrial precursor proteins begins thirty-four amino acids after the initiator methionine. The NH_2-termini of peptides A and B are flanked by a single arginine residue and the COOH-termini by a Gly-Lys-Arg sequence. Forty-seven amino acids from the A-peptide-coding region there is a sequence that encodes an ELH-like peptide followed by a Gly-Lys-Arg sequence and an AP-like peptide. These peptides have recently been purified from atrial-gland extracts[19]. Their amino acid sequences are in agreement with those predicted by the genetic data and the ELH-like peptide causes the same neuronal effects as ELH. In the B-peptide gene a deletion of a single base pair puts a stop codon after the sixth amino acid of ELH. This peptide has not yet been identified in atrial extracts.

Purification and characterization of bag-cell peptides

Four peptides encoded on the ELH precursor have been purified from acidic bag-cell extracts using gel filtration chromatography followed by cation exchange or high-performance liquid chromatography[8,17,20]. Three peptides, ELH, α-BCP and AP, are recovered in roughly equimolar amounts from bag-cell extracts and their primary sequences agree perfectly with the molecular genetic data for the bag-cell precursor. A fourth bag-cell peptide was not sequenced, but the amino acid composition of this molecule suggests that it is a pentapeptide. A sequence of five amino acids (β-BCP) with the same amino acid composition as this peptide is encoded on the bag-cell precursor (Fig. 2). These data suggest that the ELH precursor is expressed by the bag cells and that most, if not all, bag cells process the precursor identically to yield one copy of each peptide. The other peptides predicted by the molecular genetic data have not yet been isolated, but they are expected to be present in the bag-cell extract.

Bag-cell peptides as candidate neurotransmitters

When given a brief electrical stimulus, the bag cells become depolarized and fire a burst discharge that lasts for 20–30 min.

The bag-cell discharge produces several types of profound effect on neurons located near them in the abdominal ganglion[15,16] (Fig. 3). These responses to bag-cell activity are specific to individually identified target neurons and are unusually prolonged. The responses have been divided into four types (Fig. 4): burst augmentation, an effect on the bursting pacemaker activity of cell R15; prolonged excitation in which normally silent cells of the left lower quadrant (LLQ) fire tonically; prolonged inhibition, in which left upper quadrant (LUQ) cells L2, L3, L4, L6 are hyperpolarized; and transient excitation in which cells L1 and R1 are depolarized, sometimes firing a short train of spikes. The first three responses last as long as several hours, while the fourth lasts about 5–10 min.

It is very likely that ELH mediates burst augmentation in cell R15 and prolonged excitation of LLQ cells. α-BCP inhibits LUQ cells and depolarizes the bag cells. A peptide with the amino acid composition of β-BCP mimics transient excitation of L1 and R1, although much less is known about its electrophysiological activities. AP, even at millimolar concentrations, has no effect on ganglion neurons and no function has been reported for this peptide. However, since it is released from the bag cells[24] it may have an important function.

Several lines of evidence strongly suggest that ELH is a neurotransmitter[5,17]. Arterial perfusion of purified ELH for a 2-min period at a concentration of about 5×10^{-7} M mimics both the time course and amplitude of two responses normally seen following discharge of the bag cells: burst augmentation and prolonged excitation. ELH produces these responses in low-calcium, high-magnesium solutions and in isolated clusters of LLQ somata, indicating

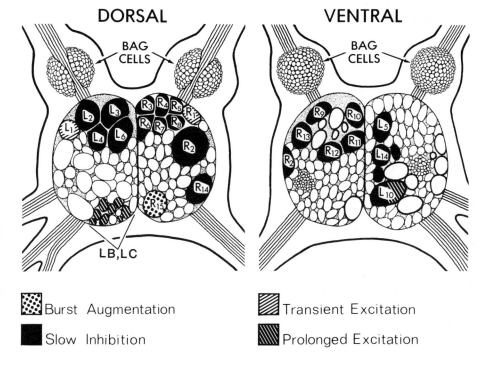

DORSAL **VENTRAL**

BAG CELLS BAG CELLS

LB,LC

▓ Burst Augmentation ▨ Transient Excitation

■ Slow Inhibition ◫ Prolonged Excitation

Fig. 3. *Schematic diagram of the dorsal and ventral views of the abdominal ganglion of* Aplysia californica *showing the locations of the two bag-cell clusters (400 cells each), and identified target cells and cell clusters that respond to bag-cell activity. The target cells are textured according to the type of response induced by bag-cell activity.*

that the actions are direct. No other purified fraction of bag-cell material mimics these distinctive neurally evoked responses. Other data indicate that ELH is synthesized[1,8], released[24] and localized[7] to the bag cells. It remains to be shown, however, whether the ionic mechanisms of ELH action are identical to the neurally evoked bag-cell actions.

It has been proposed that ELH is a 'nonsynaptic' transmitter (or alternatively, a locally acting hormone) that is dispersed into the vascular and interstitial spaces of the ganglion to act on those ganglion neurons that have receptors for the peptide[5,6,17]. Correspondingly, ultrastructural data indicate that the profusely branched axonal processes of the bag cells end blindly in the ganglionic sheath without making synaptic contacts with other ganglion neurons. The release of ELH and other bag-cell peptides is thought to occur at varicosities spaced along the bag-cell axons in a manner similar to release of transmitter from autonomic terminals on cardiac and smooth muscle.

Analysis of perfusate collected from ganglia in which there has been an electrically triggered discharge of the bag cells shows that transmitter is released in sufficient quantities to mediate the neuronal responses non-synaptically and that it is slowly inactivated compared to conventional synaptic transmitters, such as acetylcholine, at the vertebrate neuromuscular junction. As a transmitter within the CNS, ELH retains many of the physiological characteristics of peptide hormones acting on peripheral tissue. Compared to conventional synaptic transmitters, ELH has a slower onset (1–2 min), a more prolonged duration of action (>1 h), and is effective at lower concentrations (10^{-8} M).

As might be expected of a transmitter that is dispersed long distances to its targets, ELH acts only on certain targets. When arterially perfused at physiological concentrations, it affects only a subset of neurons that are affected by the bag-cell discharge and has no effect on cells that are unaffected by the bag-cell discharge. Even at high concentrations ELH has no effect on cells that undergo transient excitation (L1, R1) and has little or no effect on cells that undergo prolonged inhibition (LUQ cells)[17], suggesting that ELH neither directly nor indirectly mediates bag-cell actions on these particular neurons. Hence, other bag-cell transmitters are likely to mediate these responses.

α-BCP is a second candidate transmitter from the bag cells and appears to have a dual function: to inhibit certain ganglion neurons and to depolarize the bag cells[20]. Three neuroactive forms of α-BCP have been purified from bag-cell extracts: α-BCP[1–9], the 9-residue peptide encoded on the ELH precursor, and two NH$_2$-terminal fragments, α-BCP[1–8] and α-BCP[1–7]. α-BCP[1–7] acts directly on LUQ cells and mimics the duration of the bag-cell-induced response in two of the LUQs (L2 and L4). However, the neurally evoked response lasts longer in the other two LUQs (L3 and L6), suggesting that an additional bag-cell transmitter participates in the latter response. Application of α-BCP[1–7] at high concentration produces desensitization of the inhibitory response. Electrical stimulation of a bag-cell discharge under these conditions produces little or no inhibitory response in the LUQ neurons, suggesting that α-BCP is binding to the same receptors as the endogenous transmitter. The 7-residue peptide depolarizes the bag cells, suggesting that α-BCP serves as an excitatory transmitter among the bag cells themselves. This observation may explain why the bag-cell discharge far outlasts the electrical stimulus necessary to initiate it.

In assays on LUQ cells the 9-residue peptide is 1/30th as potent as the 8-residue peptide, and 1/10th as potent as the 7-residue form. Perhaps the 9-residue peptide is originally cleaved from the precursor and, either before or after release, the peptide is activated by proteolysis to the 8- and 7-residue forms.

Residues 2–7 in all three α-BCP forms

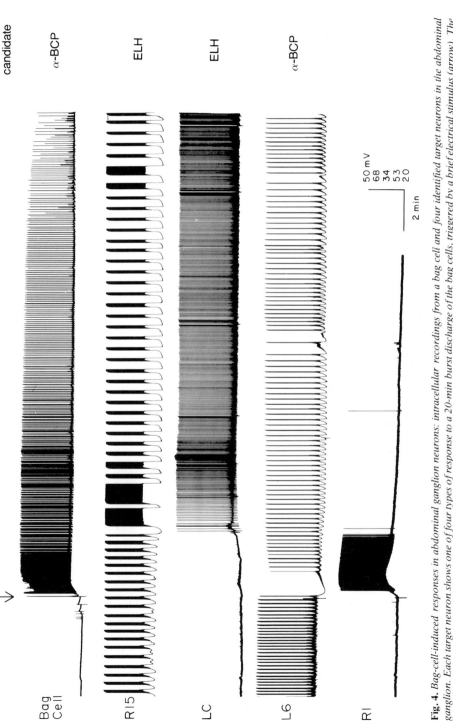

Fig. 4. Bag-cell-induced responses in abdominal ganglion neurons: intracellular recordings from a bag cell and four identified target neurons in the abdominal ganglion. Each target neuron shows one of four types of response to a 20-min burst discharge of the bag cells, triggered by a brief electrical stimulus (arrow). The names of the responses are: burst augmentation (R15); prolonged excitation (LC, and LLQ cell); slow inhibition (L6, an LUQ cell); and transient excitation (R1). The intracellular records are taken from several preparations. The records are aligned so that the times at which the respective bag-cell bursts began are positioned directly below the arrow. Column at right indicates peptide transmitter candidates for the corresponding response.

are identical to a 6-residue sequence in the COOH-terminal region of peptides A and B from the atrial gland. This reflects the fact that the bag-cell and atrial peptides are encoded on homologous precursors. The region of sequence homology is probably the active site for bag-cell excitation because peptides A and B also excite the bag cells.

The combined electrophysiological data strongly suggest that the bag cells are a multi-transmitter system, that communicates with target neurons by the release of peptides. Because one copy of each peptide is encoded on a precursor protein, and three of the peptides are recovered from bag-cell clusters in equimolar amounts, the simplest possibility is that the peptides are released in equimolar amounts. It is possible, by perfusing a combination of bag-cell peptides, to mimic several of the bag-cell-induced responses. As shown in Fig. 5, arterial perfusion of the ganglion with a sea-water solution containing equimolar amounts of ELH, α-BCP[1–7] and AP mimics prolonged excitation of an LLQ cell (LC) and the short-lasting component of slow inhibition in an LUQ cell (L6). This combination of peptides also mimics burst augmentation (R15) and depolarization of the bag cells (not shown). However, transient excitation, which occurs in cell L1 or R1 following a bag-cell burst discharge, does not occur. Ultimately, it may be possible to mimic the entire set of bag-cell actions by applying a combination of bag-cell peptides to the abdominal ganglion.

Role of bag-cell peptides in egg-laying behavior

Current data suggest that the bag cells mediate egg-laying behavior through the release of peptides. ELH is released by the bag cells[24] and is known to modify the activity of neurons located in the abdominal ganglion[5,17] and the head ganglia[25]. Target neurons in the abdominal ganglion regulate respiration, cardiac output and other autonomic functions while the head ganglia are thought to control locomotion, feeding and head movements[12]. ELH is also known to release eggs directly from fragments of the ovotestis[21]. These activities suggest that ELH functions both as a neurotransmitter within the abdominal ganglion and as a neurohormone outside this ganglion. By contrast, the other peptides, α-BCP and β-BCP, appear to act as neurotransmitters that are entirely degraded within the abdominal ganglion because, unlike ELH, their activities cannot be detected in ganglionic perfusates unless protease inhibitors are present in the medium. The role of AP in egg laying, if any, is unknown.

Overview

The bag-cell system as described above seems a reasonable way to regulate egg-laying behavior. However, it is important to consider what advantages are conferred on the system by the use of multiple transmitters that are encoded on a common precursor protein. Although the following points do not completely answer this question, they do provide the beginning to a discussion on this issue.

First, ELH and α-BCP have different durations of action and this is likely to be important in co-ordinating long- and short-lasting events in the egg-laying program. The actions of ELH last for hours, while those of α-BCP last for about 5–10 min. One possible source of these differences may be the structure of the peptides. ELH contains 36 amino acids and may be amidated at its COOH-terminus, and is therefore likely to fold into a stable tertiary configuration and be protected from COOH-terminal proteolysis. In contrast, α-BCP is only 7–9 amino acids in length and is not amidated at the COOH-terminus. It is therefore likely to have a shorter half-life, which is likely to lessen its duration of action.

Second, it may be especially adaptive that the multiple transmitters occur on a common precursor. The use of a common precursor ensures that all transmitters are synthesized and released together, yet might still allow a certain degree of plastic-

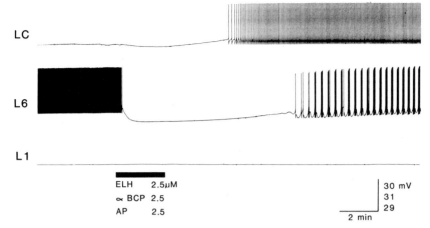

LC

L6

L1

ELH	2.5 μM		30 mV
α BCP	2.5		31
AP	2.5		29
		2 min	

Fig. 5. *Effect of three bag-cell peptides perfused into abdominal ganglion. A sea-water solution containing six protease inhibitors and 2.5 μM each of ELH, AP and α-BCP[1–7] was arterially perfused into the abdominal ganglion for 3 min (bar). All three peptides are encoded on the ELH precursor. Simultaneous recordings from three neurons show that the peptides mimic bag-cell-induced prolonged excitation of an LC cell (due to ELH), and part of the slow inhibition of cell L6 (due to α-BCP), but not transient excitation of cell L1.* (K. Sigvardt, B. S. Rothman and E. Mayeri, unpublished observations.)

ity in the system. During development, or as the result of a physiological event, an alteration of the processing of the precursor or in the post-translational modification of the resultant peptides might produce changes in the activities released, and corresponding changes in electrical signalling.

Third, the use of multiple transmitters encoded on a single precursor may have provided through the process of evolution a means for increasing the complexity of the behavior pattern. Perhaps the present behavioral program evolved from a more simple one that was regulated by a single peptide transmitter. The present complexity of behavior might therefore be caused by new peptide sequences being added to the precursor, as a result of duplication, mutation and translocation, and by new neuronal activities being brought into play by the effects of the new transmitters.

Acknowledgements

Part of the research described in this paper was supported by NIH grant No. NS 16490 (Earl Mayeri and Barry S. Rothman). We thank Karen Sigvardt for helpful discussions of the manuscript.

Reading list

1 Arch, S., Earley, P. and Smock, T. (1976) *J. Gen. Physiol.* 68, 197–210

2 Arch, S. and Smock, T. (1977) *Behav. Biol.* 19, 45–54

3 Arch, S., Smock, T., Gurvis, R. and McCarthy, C. (1978) *J. Comp. Physiol.* 128, 67–70

4 Blobel, G. and Dobberstein, B. (1975) *J. Cell Biol.* 67, 835–851

5 Branton, W. D., Arch, S., Smock, T. and Mayeri, E. (1978) *Proc. Natl Acad. Sci. USA* 75, 5732–5736

6 Branton, W. D., Mayeri, E., Brownell, P. and Simon, S. B. (1978) *Nature (London)* 274, 70–72

7 Chiu, A. Y. (1981) *Ph. D. Thesis*, California Institute of Technology, Pasadena

8 Chiu, A. Y., Hunkapiller, M. W., Heller, E., Stuart, D. K., Hood, L. E. and Strumwasser, F. (1979) *Proc. Natl Acad. Sci. USA* 76, 6656–6660

9 Frazier, W. T., Kandel, E. R., Kupfermann, I., Waziri, R. and Coggeshall, R. E. (1967) *J. Neurophysiol.* 30, 1288–1351

10 Heller, E., Kaczmarek, L. K., Hunkapiller, M. W., Hood, L. E. and Strumwasser, F. (1980) *Proc. Natl Acad. Sci. USA* 77, 2328–2332

11 Herbert, E., Birnberg, N., Lissitsky, J.-C., Civelli, O. and Uhler, M. (1981) *Neurosci. Comment.* 1, 16–27

12 Kandel, E. R. (1976) *The Cellular Basis of Behavior*, Freeman, San Francisco

13 Kupfermann, I. (1970) *J. Neurophysiol.* 33,

877–881

14 Kupfermann, I. and Kandel, E. R. (1970) *J. Neurophysiol.* 33, 865–876

15 Mayeri, E., Brownell, P. H. and Branton, W. D. (1979) *J. Neurophysiol.* 42, 1185–1197

16 Mayeri, E., Brownell, P. H., Branton, W. D. and Simon, S. B. (1979) *J. Neurophysiol.* 42, 1165–1184

17 Mayeri, E. and Rothman, B. S. (1982) in *Neurosecretion – Molecules, Cells and Systems* (Farner, D. S. and Lederis, K., eds), pp. 307–318, Plenum Press, New York

18 Pinsker, H. M. and Dudek, F. E. (1977) *Science* 197, 490–491

19 Rothman, B. S., Brown, R. O., Mayeri, E. and Shively, J. (1982) *Soc. Neurosci. Abstr.* 8, 14

20 Rothman, B. S., Mayeri, E., Brown, R. O., Yuan, P. M. and Shively, J. E. *Proc. Natl Acad. Sci. USA* (in press)

21 Rothman, B. S., Weir, G. and Dudek, F. E. *Gen. Comp. Endocrinol.* (in press)

22 Scheller, R. H., Jackson, J. F., McAllister, L. B., Rothman, B. S., Mayeri, E. and Axel, R. (1983) *Cell* 32, 7–22

23 Scheller, R. H., Jackson, J. F., McAllister, L. B., Schwartz, J. H., Kandel, E. R. and Axel, R. (1982) *Cell* 28, 707–719

24 Stuart, D. K., Chiu, A. Y. and Strumwasser, F. (1980) *J. Neurophysiol.* 43, 488–498

25 Stuart, D. K. and Strumwasser, F. (1980) *J. Neurophysiol.* 43, 499–519

Richard H. Scheller is at the Department of Biological Sciences, Stanford University, Stanford, CA 94305, USA.

Barry S. Rothman is at the Department of Physiology, University of California, San Francisco, CA 94143, USA.

Earl Mayeri is at the Department of Physiology, University of California, San Francisco, CA 94143; and at the Department of Basic Sciences, California College of Pediatric Medicine, San Francisco, CA 94115, USA.

Neurohormones and lobsters: biochemistry to behavior

Edward A. Kravitz, Barbara S. Beltz, Silvio Glusman, Michael F. Goy, Ronald M. Harris-Warrick, Michael F. Johnston, Margaret S. Livingstone, Thomas L. Schwarz and Kathleen K. Siwicki

Two amines, serotonin and octopamine, and a pentapeptide, proctolin, function as neurohormones in lobsters. The amines, when injected into lobsters, cause the production of stereotyped and opposing postures. This article explores the generation of these postures. It includes an examination of the distribution and localization of these substances in the lobster nervous system, a description of mechanisms of neurohormonal modulation at neuromuscular junctions, a presentation of the evidence that amines trigger the readout of central motor programs governing posture, and a discussion of the possibility that single identified neurons may regulate complex behaviors in lobsters and other invertebrate organisms.

The injection of serotonin into freely moving lobsters causes animals to assume a sustained and characteristic posture: animals stand high on the tips of their walking legs with their claws open in front of them and their abdomens loosely tucked underneath them. Octopamine injection causes animals to assume an opposing posture: they lie close to the substrate with their walking legs and claws pointed forward and lifted off the substrate, with their abdomens gently arching upwards[19]. One sees lobsters in similar poses during aspects of their normal behavior. For example, the animals are seen in serotonin-like postures when they are startled, at the beginning of agonistic encounters, and during parts of the mating behavior of males; the animals assume octopamine-like postures when they 'lose' an agonistic encounter, during parts of the female mating behavior, and in young animals in a 'playing dead' response[3]. In animals injected with serotonin, most or all of the postural flexor muscles in the body are contracted, while with octopamine, the postural extensors are contracted. The problem of understanding the production of the postures by amine injection can therefore be reduced to one of trying to learn how amines cause lobsters to contract their systems of postural flexor or extensor muscles. The control could be at the level of the peripheral flexor and extensor muscles, or at the level of the excitatory and inhibitory motoneurons that innervate the muscles, or possibly could involve some combined action at the two sites. The last explanation turns out to be the correct one. Moreover, the actions at the two sites are complex, and would not have been easily predicted.

This article will present a short review of our studies on serotonin and octopamine and the roles they serve in the lobster nervous system with particular emphasis on the generation of posture. We will also mention the peptide proctolin (Arg-Tyr-Leu-Pro-Thr) which shares a distribution with both amines in peripheral neurosecretory structures and appears to co-localize with serotonin in certain neurons of lobster central ganglia.

Distribution and cellular localization of amines

The lobster central nervous system consists of a chain of ventrally located ganglia (a 'brain' or supraesophageal ganglion, 2 circumesophageal, a subesophageal, 5 thoracic and 6 abdominal ganglia), each of which is concerned with control of a specific segment of the organism. Communication between the ventral nerve cord and peripheral tissues is through nerve roots, most of which contain mixtures of axons from peripherally located sensory receptors and axons of the excitatory and inhibitory motoneurons that innervate the exoskeletal muscles. Serotonin, octopamine and proctolin are found widely distributed in low concentration throughout the nervous system. Regions of particularly high concentration of all three substances, however, are found at two locations along the lengths of pairs of thoracic nerve roots (the second roots)[10,20,24]: (1) close to the ventral nerve cord near a bifurcation in the root where peripheral neurosecretory neurons are found; and (2) near the distal ends of the roots in a well-known crustacean neurohemal structure called the pericardial organs[1]. In both of these regions, the two amines are stored, synthesized and, with depolarization, released (Fig. 1). Proctolin too is found in both locations, and release from the pericardial

organs has been demonstrated (Schwarz et al., unpublished observations)[23]. Both regions of high concentration of these substances lie in haemolymph sinuses: material released from these sites therefore has ready access to the circulation (Fig. 1). Amines have been found in lobster haemolymph at concentrations of $10^{-10}–10^{-8}$ M (Ref. 19) but circulating proctolin has not yet been detected. With electron-microscope autoradiographic methods it has been possible to show that octopamine and serotonin are synthesized in distinct categories of nerve endings, each of which shows some of the classical features of neurosecretory terminals: the endings lie a few micrometres from the external surface of the nerve roots, surrounded by connective tissue, with no obvious postsynaptic target sites in their vicinity, and they contain a mixture of small vesicles and large dense-core granules[20]. Taken together the above results suggest that the two peripheral release sites along the thoracic second roots serve as a source of amines, and possibly proctolin, for roles as circulating neurohormones.

In recent studies we have used immunocytochemical methods to try to

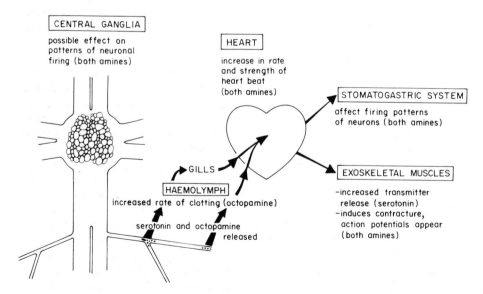

Fig. 1. *Peripheral and central targets of amines.* Reprinted with permission[18].

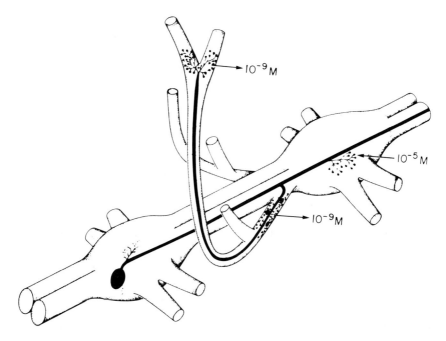

Fig. 2. *Composite drawing of a hypothetical lobster central ganglionic cell showing serotonin-like immunoreactivity. No single cell has yet been found showing all these features (see text). The concentrations shown on the figure (10^{-9} M, 10^{-5} M) are the effective concentrations of serotonin on peripheral and central targets.*

visualize the neurons that contain and release the two amines and proctolin. The data are most complete for serotonin. Using an antibody raised in rabbits against serotonin conjugated to bovine serum albumin[22] and a fluorescent second antibody as a marker, we have located cell bodies, axons and terminal arborizations of presumptive serotonin neurons[5]. Over 100 cells have been found with their cell bodies located almost exclusively in central ganglia. Each ganglion contains at least one cell body showing serotonin-like immunoreactivity. The richness of detail revealed by the immunocytochemical methods has allowed us to follow processes of cells into neuropil regions, through well-defined axonal tracts, and in some cases, to their terminal arborizations. Features of the organization of the serotonin neuron systems that are likely to be important in the postures we are examining include the following. (1) Certain central cells send nerve processes out to the thoracic second roots where they form a dense plexus of endings in the root regions rich in serotonin. In one case we have followed an axon from an identified central cell body directly to the peripheral plexus. In other cases identified cells send processes into nerve tracts that contribute to the peripheral sets of endings. (2) In all the thoracic ganglia, single nerve processes have been seen that give rise to two sets of endings: (a) in neuropil regions within the central ganglia; and (b) in the peripheral nerve root plexuses. (3) Probable dendritic arbors also show serotonin-like immunoreactivity. These are seen close to cell bodies in certain ganglia. (4) The major projections of many of the presumptive serotonin cells are in an anterior direction. They join fiber bundles that run through the entire thoracic region of the nerve cord. This suggests that these neurons are important in interganglionic communication. A composite drawing illustrating these design features and ascribing them to a single cell is shown in Fig. 2. We suspect that large pairs of cells in the 5th thoracic and 1st abdominal ganglia may contain all these features, but our immunocytochemical methods have not yet revealed any single cell showing them all. At present we are attempting to dye-inject these cells to obtain a precise picture of their neuronal geometry. We shall return later to how a cell, such as the one shown in Fig. 2, could participate in the generation of a flexed posture.

More recently antibodies have been generated in our laboratory to conjugates of octopamine and proctolin. While studies with these antibodies are at an early stage, we have been able to demonstrate, by immunocytochemical means, that proctolin-like material co-localizes with serotonin-like material in the pairs of large cells in the 5th thoracic and 1st abdominal ganglia. The co-localization raises the possibility that proctolin may be released along with serotonin when these neurons are activated.

Actions of serotonin, octopamine and proctolin on exoskeletal muscles

Many peripheral tissues of the lobster are responsive to serotonin, octopamine and proctolin (Fig. 1)[2,4,6,8,13,18]. Our focus has been on the exoskeletal muscles, both because they determine the postures we are interested in, and because they represent a large source of tissue for combined physiological and biochemical studies aimed at learning how neurohormones modulate synaptic efficacy. Lobster exoskeletal muscles are innervated by excitatory axons that are thought to use glutamate as a transmitter compound, and inhibitory axons using γ-aminobutyric acid (GABA) as a transmitter. The muscle preparation we use for most of our studies is the opener muscle of the dactyl (moveable finger) of the walking leg. All three of the neurohormonal substances we have been studying act on this preparation (Fig. 3). Serotonin has actions on both excitatory and inhibitory nerve terminals and directly on muscle fibers. On both kinds of nerve

terminals, serotonin increases transmitter release[9,12,14,16,18]. The enhancement of release, which has been studied best on excitatory terminals, involves both the nerve-evoked and spontaneous release of transmitter. The effect is long lasting: when serotonin is washed out of the bath, the response decays to the control size in two steps ($T_{1/2} = 1-2$ min; $T_{1/2} \cong 30$ min). The slower of the two components seems, at least in part, to result either from some metabolic change in the terminal having to do with the buffering or storage of Ca^{2+}, or with changes in the sensitivity of the release mechanism to Ca^{2+} (Ref. 14). In muscle fibers, serotonin induces a voltage- and Ca^{2+}-dependent contracture with little or no measured change in input resistance or membrane potential. In addition, serotonin causes the appearance of large Ca^{2+}-dependent action potentials in response to depolarization of the fibers. No action potentials were seen before serotonin treatment. Preliminary voltage-clamp studies demonstrate an increased inward Ca^{2+} current in the fibers after serotonin treatment, but we cannot tell yet whether this results from a direct action on Ca^{2+} channels or indirect actions on other channels[18]. All of the changes seen in muscle fibers after serotonin treatment are of long duration, lasting from 30 min to 1 h or longer. Octopamine behaves in a parallel fashion to serotonin on these preparations. It causes a small increase in transmitter release from excitatory nerve terminals[12] that requires a phosphodiesterase inhibitor to be seen in our experiments (not shown on Fig. 3), has little detectable action on inhibitory terminals, and has similar actions to serotonin on muscle fibers[4,12,18]. Proctolin has no detectable actions on either excitatory or inhibitory terminals, but causes contractures and action potentials to appear in muscle fibers[21].

In searching for possible molecular correlates of the physiological changes caused by serotonin, octopamine and proctolin, we have searched for neurohormonally linked alterations in cyclic nucleotide levels and protein phosphorylation patterns in intact opener-muscle preparations. While none of the three substances affects cyclic GMP levels, serotonin causes large changes in cyclic AMP levels and induces a cyclic AMP-dependent phosphorylation of a 29 000 mol. wt protein[4,15]. Octopamine is much less effective in raising cyclic AMP levels and in causing the phosphorylation: to see either, a phosphodiesterase inhibitor must be added to tissue incubations. Proctolin causes no change in cyclic nucleotide levels or in phosphorylation of the 29 000 mol. wt protein. At present we are using the drug forskolin (a direct activator of the enzyme adenylate cyclase) and other substances to increase cyclic nucleotide levels in these tissues and observe whether such manipulations duplicate any of the physiological changes caused by the neurohormones. Whatever the outcome of these experiments, however, it is unlikely that the long-lasting changes in muscle properties caused by proctolin can be due to cyclic nucleotides, since this peptide does not detectably alter cyclic nucleotide levels

in this tissue.

To return to the question of the opposing actions of serotonin and octopamine on postural flexor and extensor muscles: we see no opposite effects of the amines on opener-muscle preparations (or on several other flexor and extensor muscles from the walking legs). Instead the amines seem to prime these peripheral tissues to respond more vigorously to the normal stimuli that activate them.

Actions of amines on motoneurons of the ventral nerve cord

We next examined the responsiveness to serotonin and octopamine of the motoneurons that innervate the exoskeletal muscles. The motoneurons have their cell bodies in ganglia of the ventral nerve cord. We used preparations of the ganglionic chain (or individual ganglia) attached through nerve trunks to postural exoskeletal muscles, and recorded from muscle fibers and nerve trunks to examine the firing patterns of the excitatory and inhibitory motoneurons while superfusing test sub-

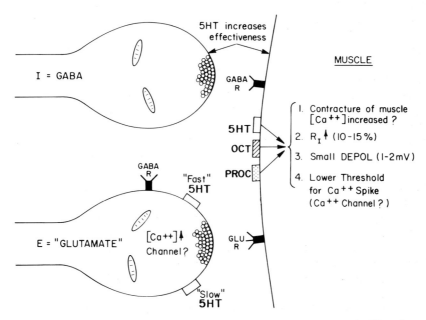

Fig. 3. *Summary diagram of sites of action and effects of serotonin (5-HT), octopamine (OCT) and proctolin (PROC) on the lobster opener-muscle neuromuscular preparation.* Reprinted in a slightly modified form with permission[18].

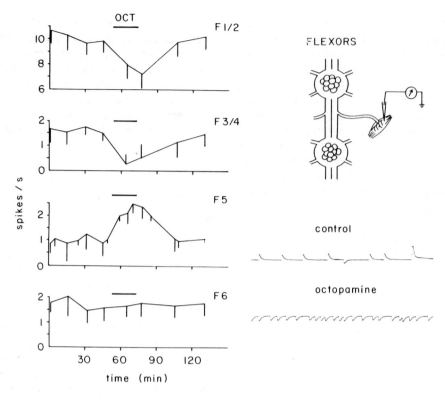

Fig. 4. *Effects of octopamine (3 × 10⁻⁵ M) on motoneurons innervating the superficial flexor muscles. The inset diagram illustrates the experimental arrangement. On the lower right a sample intracellular recording is shown. The left side of the figure shows the average action-potential frequency (one SD shown) in the five excitatory (F1, 2, 3, 4, 6) and one inhibitory (F5) motoneurons innervating the muscle. Action-potential frequency is measured with a pair of hook electrodes on the nerve root (not shown on inset drawing).*

stances on the isolated ganglia. The observed results were quite dramatic (Fig. 4). We saw amine-induced alterations in firing patterns that would be appropriate to cause flexor muscles to contract in response to serotonin or to relax in response to octopamine, and we saw opposite patterns with extensor-muscle preparations. For example, in Fig. 4 we show the results of recording from a postural flexor muscle and examining its response to octopamine. On the lower right of the figure, sample intracellular records from a muscle fiber are shown. In the control period several excitatory units are firing (the muscle is innervated by five excitatory neurons, F1, 2, 3, 4 and 6, and by one inhibitory neuron, F5) and the inhibitory unit is firing slowly: after octopamine treatment, the inhibitory

unit greatly increases its rate of firing and no excitatory units are seen. Data from another experiment are shown graphically on the left side of the figure. In this experiment octopamine decreased the firing of the excitatory neurons F1, 2, 3 and 4, increased the firing of the inhibitory neuron, F5, and caused no change in firing of the excitatory neuron F6. When the results of many experiments of this type on both flexor and extensor muscles were grouped together, the general result was that octopamine increased the firing of excitatory neurons innervating postural extensor muscles and of the inhibitory neurons innervating the postural flexors, while simultaneously decreasing the firing of the excitatory neurons innervating the flexors and the inhibitor to the extensors[19] (Fig. 5) (R. M.

Harris-Warrick and E. A. Kravitz, unpublished observations). We saw more variability with serotonin, particularly with regard to the firing of excitatory neurons, but the general pattern was opposite to that caused by octopamine. In other words, octopamine directs the readout of a central motor pattern causing extension (contract extensors, relax flexors) while serotonin leads to the readout of a pattern for flexion.

The idea that individual neurons may direct the readout of central motor patterns for flexion and extensions is an old one in the crustacean literature. Evoy and Kennedy and their colleagues[11] demonstrated in the 1960s that individual axons teased out of the connectives linking ganglia together could trigger flexion and extension motor programs when stimulated at high frequencies. They called such neurons 'command neurons'. We suspect that serotonin and octopamine play key roles in the command neuron circuitry (possibly as transmitters, possibly activating important elements), and we are now in the process of trying to clarify these roles.

Résumé

If we now return to our hypothetical serotonin cell (Fig. 2), we can see how such a cell might serve in the generation of a flexed posture in lobsters. The peripheral endings of this cell, along the second thoracic roots, could release serotonin into the general circulation where it would serve as a neurohormonal substance that primes peripheral muscles to respond more vigorously. Excitation, inhibition and muscle fibers all are sensitized. The central set of endings of the cell presumably would dictate the pattern of responsiveness by directing the readout of the central motor program for flexion or perhaps by sensitizing the central pattern generator to respond more vigorously. Single cells, or small groups of cells showing the features of the cell shown in Fig. 2, would then be the elements likely to regulate this behavior. It remains to be demonstrated that our presumptive serotonin cells actually serve the

role we ascribe to them in this model.

That amines and peptides serve essential roles in behavior, and that these roles can often be assigned to particular cells, is becoming well established in the invertebrate literature (learning models[17], swimming behavior[26], motor systems[7], metamorphosis[25]). The ability to analyse these com-

	Slow flexors		Slow extensors	
	E	I	E	I
Serotonin	↑	↓	↓	↑
Octopamine	↓	↑	↑	↓

Fig. 5. *Actions of serotonin and octopamine on the firing of excitatory (E) and inhibitory (I) motoneurons innervating postural flexor and extensor muscles.*

plex phenomena in simple systems, where the single neurons that participate in these events can be identified, should provide valuable models for the analysis of such events in the much more complicated vertebrate nervous systems.

Note added

Recently we have established by intracellular injections of horseradish peroxidase and cobalt hexamine chloride that the pairs of large serotonin-staining neurons in the 5th thoracic (T5) and 1st abdominal (A1) ganglia contain all the design features of the hypothetical cells shown in Fig. 2. Single cells have peripheral and central endings and cells project in an anterior direction with endings in many ganglionic segments (cells in A1 project at least as far as T2, cells in T5 at least as far as T1). In each ganglion A1 and T5 cells show a repeated and reasonably characteristic arbor of processes and endings.

Reading list

1 Alexandrowicz, J. S. (1953) *J. Mar. Biol. Assoc. UK* 32, 175–192
2 Anderson, W. W. and Barker, D. L. (1977) *Neurosci. Abstr.* 3, 522

3 Atema, J. and Cobb, J. S. (1980) in *The Biology and Management of Lobsters* (Cobb, J. S. and Phillips, B. F., eds), Vol. 1, pp. 409–450, Academic Press, New York

4 Battelle, B. A. and Kravitz, E. A. (1978) *J. Pharmacol. Exp. Ther.* 205, 438–448

5 Beltz, B. S. and Kravitz, E. A. (1983) *J. Neurosci.* 3, 585–602

6 Berlind, A. (1977) *J. Comp. Physiol.* 116, 77–90

7 Bishop, C. A. and O'Shea, M. (1982) *J. Comp. Neurol.* 207, 223–238

8 Cooke, I. M. (1966) *Am. Zool.* 6, 107–121

9 Dudel, J. (1965) *Naunyn-Schmiedebergs Arch. Exp. Pathol. Pharmakol.* 249, 515–528

10 Evans, P. D., Kravitz, E. A., Talamo, B. R. and Wallace, B. G. (1976) *J. Physiol. (London)* 262, 51–70

11 Evoy, W. H. and Kennedy, D. (1967) *J. Exp. Zool.* 165, 223–238

12 Fischer, L. and Florey, E. (1983) *J. Exp. Biol.* 102, 187–198

13 Florey, E. and Rathmayer, M. (1978) *Comp. Biochem. Physiol.* 61C, 229–237

14 Glusman, S. and Kravitz, E. A. (1982) *J. Physiol. (London)* 325, 223–241

15 Goy, M. F., Schwarz, T. L. and Kravitz, E. A. *J. Neurosci.* (in press)

16 Grundfest, H. and Reuben, J. P. (1961) in *Nervous Inhibition* (Florey, E., ed.), pp. 92–104, Pergamon Press, New York

17 Klein, M. E., Shapiro, E. and Kandel, E. R.

(1980) *J. Exp. Biol.* 89, 117–157

18 Kravitz, E. A., Glusman, S., Harris-Warrick, R. M., Livingstone, M., Schwarz, T. and Goy, M. F. (1980) *J. Exp. Biol.* 89, 159–175

19 Livingstone, M. S., Harris-Warrick, R. M. and Kravitz, E. A. (1980) *Science* 208, 76–79

20 Livingstone, M. S., Schaeffer, S. F. and Kravitz, E. A. (1981) *J. Neurobiol.* 12, 27–54

21 Schwarz, T. L., Harris-Warrick, R. M., Glusman, S. and Kravitz, E. A. (1980) *J. Neurobiol.* 11, 623–628

22 Steinbusch, H. W. M., Verhofstad, A. A. J. and Joosten, H. W. T. (1978) *Neuroscience* 3, 811–819

23 Sullivan, R. E. (1979) *J. Exp. Zool.* 210, 543–552

24 Sullivan, R. E., Friend, B. J. and Barker, D. L. (1977) *J. Neurobiol.* 8, 581–605

25 Truman, J. W. and Schwartz, L. M. (1980) in *Peptides – Integrators of Cell and Tissue Function* (Bloom, F. E., ed.), p. 55, Raven Press, New York

26 Willard, A. L. (1981) *J. Neurosci.* 1, 936–944

Edward A. Kravitz, Barbara S. Beltz, Silvio Glusman, Michael F. Goy, Ronald M. Harris-Warrick, Michael F. Johnston, Margaret S. Livingstone, Thomas L. Schwarz and Kathleen K. Siwicki are at the Department of Neurobiology, Harvard Medical School, 25 Shattuck Street, Boston, MA 02115, USA.

The history of Substance P
U. S. von Euler

This article provides an account for the early events which led to the discovery of Substance P in 1930 and some of the following studies aimed at the characterization of the substance. It is shown how improved preparation techniques helped to establish its peptide nature and to determine its distribution in the organism. While the early experiments were mostly concerned with its stimulating effect on smooth muscle and the vasodilator properties, later interest focussed more on the neurotropic effects and its presence in neural tissue, gradually suggesting its role as a neurotransmitter or neuromodulator.

Around 1930 a growing interest in biologically active, naturally occurring substances was noticeable. One important factor behind the rapid progress in this field was the development of a number of useful pharmacological methods. In the 'organ bath' inaugurated by Magnus in Utrecht it was possible to test and characterize not only various new and old drugs, but also biologically active extracts of natural origin. Examples of the usefulness of the blood pressure recording technique and of the Straub frog heart preparation are found in the classical experiments of Oliver and Schaefer in England (1895) and of Loewi in Graz (1921), both representing major breakthroughs in autopharmacology, to use a term introduced by H. H. Dale, who himself made basic contributions to the development of the new technology. The 'biogenic amines' became an important group of such active substances, the name implying that many of these were amines.

After its role as a chemical transmitter had been established interest in acetylcholine steadily increased, so it was not surprising that Dale, then Director of the National Institute of Medical Research in Hampstead, should suggest a theme within this field for a young post-graduate arriving during the summer of 1930. Shortly before, Dale and Dudley had demonstrated the presence of acetylcholine in the horse spleen. As a starting study it was proposed that I should prepare extracts of liver and spleen from the cat and test them for the presence of acetylcholine. The results were equivocal, however, and my interest gradually was transferred to the intestine. It was generally assumed that the 'motility hormone' of the intestine was choline or a choline ester, in spite of the fact that atropine was only moderately active in preventing the intestinal movements and the effect of vagus stimulation. At that time Dale and Gaddum[3] proposed that atropine might be ineffective as a blocker of released acetylcholine on account of spatial separation from the receptor at the nerve endings. Thus, they wrote: 'Where, in other cases, it (atropine) still suppresses the effects of choline esters artificially applied, but fails to paralyse the similar nervous effects, it is still possible that the latter might be due to the liberation of a choline ester, but in a relation of so much greater intimacy with the receptive mechanism that atropine cannot prevent its access thereto'. An alternative to this explanation that was evident was that vagus stimulation released from the intestine, in addition to acetylcholine, some other substance exerting a stimulating action on the intestine, which was not abolished by atropine.

Continued experiments with extracts of the gut from various laboratory animals actually revealed that some of these stimulated the movements of the isolated rabbit jejunum, which was used as test organ, even in the presence of atropine in a concentration which annulled the effect of added acetylcholine. This observation was considered of sufficient interest to warrant further studies along the same line, in which I had the good fortune to work together with J. H. Gaddum, whose experimental skill and extensive knowledge of pharmacology was very important to the continuation of the work. We examined extracts of a variety of organs for similar biological effects to those noticed for gut extracts (Fig. 1), but with the exception of some activity in stomach extracts, only those from brain had this kind of effect, suggesting that the same substance was involved. The purification work proceeded slowly, however, and in our first publication[5] we were not able to say much about the chemical nature of the active compound, except that it was thermostable at neutral or weakly acid reaction, dialysable and insoluble in lipid solvents.

In our studies we used, for comparison, a standard preparation in the form of a dry powder which could be dissolved in water and was sufficiently stable to serve in the quantitative assays. It was conveniently abbreviated in our tracings and in our notes to 'P'. In an introduction to a later paper Gaddum[9] wrote: 'We concentrated the active substance in the form of a stable dry powder known as preparation P. It is impossible to justify the widespread custom, started by Gaddum and Schild (1934), of calling the active principle itself Substance P, but it is probably too late to change that now'.

Recognition of peptide nature of Substance P

The organ extracts used in the first studies were contaminated by several other biologically active substances, and it was mainly its high concentration in the intestine and brain, and its insensitivity to atropine, which made it possible to distinguish Substance P (SP) from other active agents. In the early experiments minced tissue was extracted with 2–3 volumes of ethanol, followed by filtration and removal of ethanol and of fatty material, whereafter the aqueous solution was used for testing.

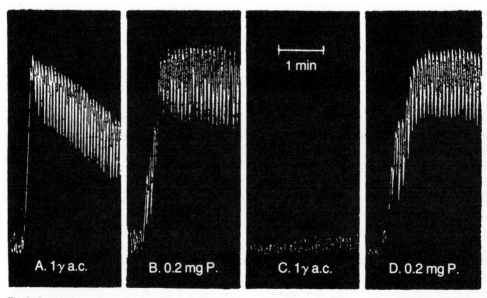

Fig. 1. Contractions of an isolated piece of small intestine from a rabbit suspended in a bath solution. In C and D: 1 p.p.m. atropine added; in A and C: 1 µg acetylcholine added; in B and D: 2 mg of preparation P added. (From Euler and Gaddum, 1936.)

Purification by adsorption of the active principle on benzoic acid *in statu nascendi* was useful for the preparation of a standard since the benzoic acid could be removed with ether, in which our substance was insoluble.

There was, however, a great need for simpler and more efficient purification methods. A considerable step forward in this respect was achieved when it was found that saturation of an aqueous solution, containing the active substance, with ammonium sulphate yielded an active precipitate. This finding suggested that SP might be a peptide, an assumption which was verified by direct tests with trypsin preparations[6].

An important improvement was the application of adsorption chromatography on aluminium oxide[12]. When an extract in 70% methanol was passed through a column of Al_2O_3, SP was retained and could be eluted with decreasing concentrations of methanol. Most of the activity could be recovered in a narrow region and could be further purified by partition chromatography on cellulose and elution with butanol/acetic acid/water, yielding a preparation with an activity of up to 3000 units mg^{-1}. (The unit was defined as 2–4 threshold doses on the isolated rabbit jejunum in a 30 ml bath.) This represented in fact a high degree of purification and made a number of studies possible. Later Franz, Boissonas and Stürmer[8] were able to isolate what appeared to be the pure substance with an activity of 35,000 units mg^{-1}. Some of these highly purified preparations were, however, unstable and lost much of their activity even in 24 h, a circumstance that delayed the full exploitation of their results. Thus, it was not until 1970 that Chang and Leeman[2] succeeded in isolating pure SP, followed by chemical identification and synthesis.

The activity of the extracts was originally assayed against a standard on the isolated intestine and on the blood pressure of the rabbit in the presence of atropine. In later work the most commonly used assay organ was the guinea pig ileum in the presence of atropine, a histamine blocker and a 5-HT antagonist. Other preparations were also used such as the rat duodenum, the guinea pig vas deferens and the chicken rectal caecum. Gaddum also proposed a microtechnique using the goldfish intestine in a 0.05 ml bath, allowing detection of a few milliunits of SP.

By subjecting the extracts to chymotrypsin treatment, which rapidly inactivated SP, or to treatment with acids or alkali, the results could be further secured. The differentiation between related peptides, such as eledoisin and physalaemin was more difficult and required refined differentiation procedures. Unfortunately no SP antagonist was available at the time of the early studies, but some specificity was afforded by the tachyphylaxis appearing after a large dose of SP.

Occurrence and distribution

Some activity of the same kind as that observed in intestinal extracts was also found in the stomach and possibly in the urinary bladder, but in other organs, including uterus, lung, liver, kidney, pancreas, spleen and striated muscle, the amounts were at most very low, and considering the limitations of our assay method it was not possible to state with certainty whether or not these organs contained the active agent.

However, among the organs examined the brain proved to be a rich source of SP. Contraction of the rabbit's isolated intestine after atropine had been shown previously by Jendrassik, with brain extracts (1929), and these extracts may well have owed their effect to SP. The occurrence of a biologically active substance in the intestine and in the brain was at that time a somewhat unexpected finding, and was the first example of a pattern which, many

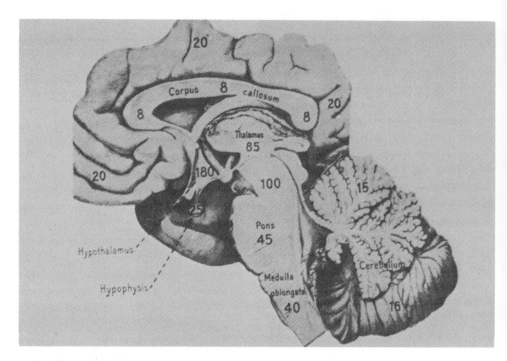

Fig. 2. Mammalian brain. Figures denote SP content (units g^{-1}) in various parts of the dog brain. (From Ref. 12.)

years later, was repeated by a number of peptide hormones.

As to the distribution in the intestine it was only stated in the original work that the muscular coat of the small intestine gave the biggest effects, but later it was shown that large amounts were also present in the mucous membrane (Pernow, 1951). As a general observation the highest activity was noted in the duodenum and jejunum, falling off in the stomach and oesophagus and also in the large intestine and rectum. This seemed to indicate that the SP content was correlated with the degree of motility and led to the suggestion that SP could be an essential factor for gut movement[6]. It may also be added that fish intestine contains SP (Euler and Östlund, 1956). The possibility that the active agent in some way was connected with the intrinsic nervous system in the digestive tract was supported by the finding of Ehrenpreis and Pernow (1952) that the amount of SP was greatly reduced in the aganglionic sections

of intestine in Hirschsprung's disease. It is now firmly established that SP occurs in high concentrations in the Auerbach and Meissner plexa (Hökfelt et al., 1975).

As to the distribution of SP in the brain we found much higher amounts in the basal ganglia than in the brain hemispheres in the horse. Later other groups showed remarkably high concentrations of SP in the hypothalamus, substantia nigra and central gray. The latter finding has become of special interest since it may relate SP to the analgesic opioids. Fig. 2 gives an idea of the distribution of SP in various parts of the human brain. Up to 50 units g^{-1} were found in some parts of fish brain (Euler and Östlund, 1956).

A finding of great significance was the observation by Pernow[12] and by Lembeck[10] that the dorsal roots and the vagus nerve were especially rich in SP, a finding later confirmed by many authors. The difference in SP content between the posterior and the anterior roots became the basis for the hypothesis of Lembeck[10] that SP may serve as transmitter substance of the primary sensory neuron.

Pamela Holton (1958) made the interesting observation that after cutting a peripheral nerve the amount of SP decreased in the peripheral part and increased in the central portion. On analogy with certain neurotransmitters this suggested that SP was bound to particles in the nerve. This seems to have been first observed in the mouse brain (cf. Ref. 11) and was also found in peripheral nerves (Euler and Lishajko, 1963) (Fig. 3).

Early observations on biological actions of SP

Early experiments showed that SP lowered the blood pressure in laboratory animals, mainly due to peripheral vasodilatation. Using purified preparations Pernow and Wahren (cf. Ref. 13), in studies on the human forearm blood flow, found signif-

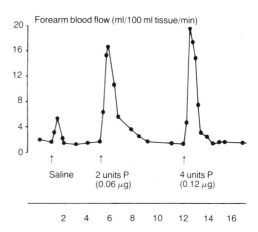

Fig. 4. Effect of single intra-arterial injections of SP on human forearm blood flow. (Modified from Ref. 4.)

icant vasodilatation with amounts as low as 2 units SP intra-arterially (Fig. 4).

The stimulating action of SP on the gut, which led to its discovery, has been studied in detail by several investigators. Gernandt (1942) noted that SP facilitated intestinal peristalsis *in vivo* and *in vitro* (Fig. 5), later confirmed by many studies in man. The contractile action of SP on smooth muscle has also been observed in a number of other organs.

Studies on the mechanism of action of SP on the intestine seemed to indicate that this was of a complex nature. The peristaltic activity is blocked by hexamethonium[1], whereas the effect on longitudinal muscle is not affected. It appears that SP acts in part directly on the smooth muscle fibres and, in addition, by stimulating or inhibiting ganglion cells and also by exciting afferent neurons. Of special interest is the sialogogic effect, since it was this action which led Chang and Leeman to suspect that their active peptide was SP.

The differentiated occurrence of SP in the brain and in the spinal cord suggested actions on central functions. Euler and Pernow[7] demonstrated various neurotropic effects in the cat and in the rabbit after intra-arterial injections toward the brain and after intracerebroventricular

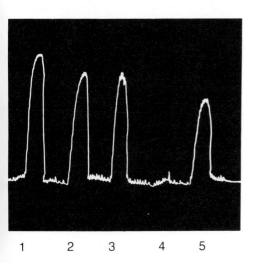

Fig. 3. Contractions of an isolated piece of small intestine from a guinea pig suspended in a bath solution. 1. 0.2 unit SP. 2. Microgranules from bovine vagus nerve obtained by homogenization and differential centrifugation. Granules suspended in water, causing lysis and liberation of SP. 3. same as (2) but granules exposed to HCl at pH 3, causing a release of SP from the granules. 4. Microgranules suspended in iso-osmotic salt solution. No release of SP. 5. 0.16 unit SP. (From Ref. 4.)

injections of SP in unanaesthetized animals. The most constant and characteristic effect was an often long-lasting stimulation of respiration.

Among other findings from the pre-isolation period pointing at neurotropic effects is the enhancement of dorsal root potential IV by SP (Krivoy, 1961), potentiation of the nerve induced a twitch response of the guinea pig vas plus deferens (Sjöstrand and Swedin, 1968) algesic and morphine antagonistic effects[15,16] and inhibitory electrocortical effects (Caspers). SP from the intestine is apparently identical with that from the brain.

run parallel to that of SP.

The properties and actions of SP were reviewed 25 years ago by Pernow (1955) and it can be noted that almost all of these have been verified by later investigations with the chemically pure substance. This is of considerable interest since it shows that the biological characterization was successful even long before the complete purification was achieved, and that SP could be effectively distinguished from a large number of other compounds having superficially similar actions. The reason for this favourable result can be briefly summarized as follows: (a) methods of extraction,

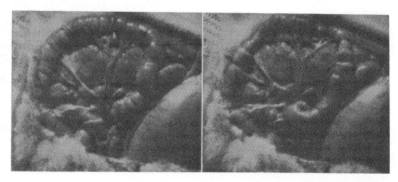

Fig. 5. *Small intestine in an anaesthetized rabbit. In (A) 5 units of SP in 0.5 ml were applied dropwise on the surface causing contraction. (B) 15 s later.* (From Gernaudt (1942) *Acta Physiol. Scand.* 3, 270–274.)

Biological inactivation of SP

If SP plays a role as a neurotropic factor, facilitating or inhibiting neurotransmission or other neural functions, it would be expected that an inactivation mechanism is available as for other transmitters. Early studies indicated that this is the case. Thus, Gullbring (1943) found that extract from muscular coat of horse intestine, as well as from basal ganglia of human brain, inactivated SP, whereas extracts from several other tissues had little or no action. As found by Pernow (1955), chymotrypsin is a very efficient inactivator of SP. He also found that the distribution of the inactivating enzyme in the digestive tract seemed to

purification and inactivation revealing peptide properties; (b) differentiating effects of various blocking agents, by which numerous other compounds could be excluded; and (c) the activity pattern on a variety of test preparations, differentiating SP from many other active substances.

The increasing interest in SP, as demonstrated by the large number of studies (cf. Ref. 14), made it desirable to hold international meetings on the subject. The first Symposium, entirely dedicated to SP, was held in Sarajevo 1961, headed by P. Stern[15] who took a vivid interest in the substance early on. Soon afterwards a second meeting was organized in New York (cf. Ref. 4),

Substance P Symposium, presided by Pavao Stern, Department of Pharmacology, Sarajevo University, 9–10 June 1961

1 E. Stürmer	7 K. Lissák
2 F. Lembeck	8 G. Zettler
3 B. Radmanović	9 B. Pernow
4 Marthe Vogt	10 J. H. Gaddum
5 V. Varagic	11 W. A. Krivoy
6 P. Stern	12 S. Huković

sponsored by the New York Academy of Sciences and which covered other biologically active peptides.

A new era·began in 1970, when the pure substance became available and when radioimmunoassay made it possible to follow its distribution in the organism. Even if it is still too early to make any final statements as to the functional significance of SP there is at least a steady growth of insight in its biological role since the early days in 1930.

References

1 Beleslin, O. and Varagić, V. (1958) *Br. J. Pharmacol.* 13, 321–325

2 Chang, M. M. and Leeman, S. E. (1970) *J. Biol. Chem.* 245, 4784–4790

3 Dale, H. H. and Gaddum, J. H. (1930) *J. Physiol. (London)*, 70, 109–144

4 Erdös, E. G. (ed.) (1963) *Ann. N.Y. Acad. Sci.* 104, 1–464

5 Euler, U. S. v. and Gaddum, J. H. (1931) *J. Physiol. (London)*, 72, 74–87

6 Euler, U. S. v. (1936) *Arch. Exp. Pathol. Pharmakol.* 181, 181–197

7 Euler, U. S. v. and Pernow, B. (1956) *Acta*

Physiol. Scand. 36, 265–275

8 Franz, J., Boissonnas, R. A. and Stürmer, E. (1961) *Helv. Chim. Acta*, 44, 881–883

9 Gaddum, J. H. (1960) in *Polypeptides which affect Smooth Muscles and Blood Vessels* (Schachter, M., ed.), pp. 163–170, Pergamon Press, Oxford

10 Lembeck, F. (1953) *Arch. Exp. Pathol. Pharmakol.* 219, 197–213

11 Lembeck, F. and Zetler, G. (1962) *Int. Rev. Neurobiol.* 4, 159–215

12 Pernow, B. (1953) *Acta Physiol. Scand. Suppl.* 105, 1–90

13 Pernow, B. (1963) *Ann. N.Y. Acad. Sci.* 104, 393–402

14 Skrabanek, P. and Powell, D. (1978) in *Substance P*, Vol. 1, pp. 1–181, Eden Press, Montreal and St. Albans

15 Stern, P. (ed.) (1963) *Symposium on Substance P. Proc. Soc.* Vol. 1, pp. 1–143, Bosnia and Herzogovina, Sarajevo

16 Zetler, G. (1956) *Arch. Exp. Pathol. Pharmakol.* 228, 513–538

U. S. Von Euler is at the Physiology Department, Karolinska Institutet, Stockholm, Sweden.

The tachykinin peptide family

Vittorio Erspamer

Until recently substance P was regarded as the only tachykinin occurring in the vertebrate CNS and intestine. The other known members of the peptide family were confined to the octopod salivary glands and amphibian skin. However, recent studies have shown that substance P may occur even in coelenterates, while an amphibian tachykinin, physalaemin, may be present in mammalian tissues. Thus, there are no phylogenetic barriers between the various members of the tachykinin family. Each of them may occur, alone or in association, in different tissues of different species, where they may subserve a variety of different functions.

Three independent lines of research must be considered when tracing the history of the discovery of peptides belonging to the tachykinins or substance P-like family of peptides.

Half a century ago von Euler and Gaddum[8] described an unidentified substance present in alcoholic extracts of equine brain and intestine which lowered blood pressure and stimulated isolated rabbit duodenum. The substance (referred to as P on tracings and protocols) was found to be distinct from all of the compounds then known to have a stimulatory effect on the gut. Using semi-purified preparations, numerous studies on its biological actions were carried out in von Euler's laboratory and elsewhere, yet, despite its early isolation, the structure of substance P was only determined 40 years later.

In 1947, while investigating the occurrence of biogenic amines, especially 5-HT, in the posterior salivary glands of the Mediterranean octopod *Eledone moschata*, I found an unidentified substance which again lowered blood pressure, stimulated isolated preparations of intestinal smooth muscle and caused profuse salivary secretion[5] Studies on the substance, first called moschatine and then eledoisin, were resumed in 1960, after its peptide nature and its close biological resemblance to substance P were recognized. The structure of elodoisin was established in 1962[6] and in the same year it was found that extracts of the skin of the South American amphibian *Physalaemus bigilonigerus* also contained eledoisin-like activity. Elucidation of the structure of physalaemin[7] was followed by the description of six other tachykinins, all from amphibian skin. At the same time more than 100 physalaemin and eledoisin analogues became available for studies on the structure : activity relationship of these peptides.

The third line of research in the field of substance P was pursued by Leeman et al.[2], who in 1970 isolated a sialagogic peptide from bovine hypothalamic tissue. This seemed to be identical with substance P. The structure of hypothalamic substance P was definitively established in 1971, and 2 years later Studer et al.[18] found that substance P extracted from horse intestine had the same amino acid sequence. At present, a number of natural tachykinins are commercially available and several specific anti-substance P sera have been developed, which are active on both the C- and N-terminal ends of the molecule. In contrast, only one highly specific anti-physalaemin serum has been prepared.

It is beyond the limits of this short article to present even a summary of the large amount of research carried out on substance P, and its analogues. The reader is referred to monographs and symposia proceedings, which have appeared in the past few years[1,9,14,16,17].

In this article I wish to put forward the suggestion that amphibian tachy-kinins should be included in research on substance P since this family of peptides is probably not restricted to invertebrate and lower vertebrate tissues.

Chemistry of the tachykinin peptide family

The amino acid sequences of various peptides belonging to the tachykinin family are shown in Table I. All are deca-, endeca- or dodeca-peptide amides with a Phe residue at position 5 from the C-terminus. In contrast to all other tachykinins, hylambatin has a Met residue replacing the usual Leu at position 2.

Whilst the C-terminal end of the tachykinin molecule is rather similar in all the members of the family, the N-terminal end displays considerable variability in its amino acid composition, and it is this portion of the molecule that accounts for the differences in biological activity.

Tachykinins in invertebrates

Available data on the occurrence of the tachykinin peptide family in invertebrate phylla are rather scanty, but this gap may be shortly filled as a result of the growing interest in invertebrate regulatory peptides.

To date tachykinins have been described in tissues of three inverte-brate species: the posterior salivary glands of *Eledone moschata*, the neu-ral net of *Hydra attenuata* and the nervous system of *Helix aspera* (Piers, personal communication).

The only tachykinin whose chemical structure has been defined is eledoisin, the peptide isolated from *Eledone*. However, nothing is known yet about the immunochemistry and ultra-structure of eledoisin-storing cells or about the possible occurrence of ele-doisin or other tachykinins in the ner-vous system of gastrointestinal tract of octopod molluscs. Eledoisin may be present only in the salivary glands of

TABLE I. The tachykinin peptide family

Molluscan tachykinins	
Pyr-Pro-Ser-Lys-Asp-Ala-Phe-Ile-Gly-Leu-Met-NH$_2$	Eledoisin
Amphibian tachykinins	
Pyr-Ala-Asp-Pro-Asn-Lys-Phe-Tyr-Gly-Leu-Met-NH$_2$	Physalaemin
Pyr-Ala-Asp-Pro-Lys-Thr-Phe-Tyr-Gly-Leu-Met-NH$_2$	Lys^5,Thr^6-Physalaemin
Pyr-Pro-Asp-Pro-Asn-Ala-Phe-Tyr-Gly-Leu-Met-NH$_2$	Uperolein
Pyr-----Asn-Pro-Asn-Arg-Phe-Ile-Gly-Leu-Met-NH$_2$	Phyllomedusin
Asp-Val-Pro-Lys-Ser-Asp-Gln-Phe-Val-Gly-Leu-Met-NH$_2$	Kassinin
Asp-Glu-Pro-Lys-Pro-Asp-Gln-Phe-Val-Gly-Leu-Met-NH$_2$	Glu^2,Pro^5-Kassinin*
Asp-Pro-Pro-Asp-Pro-Asp-Arg-Phe-Tyr-Gly-Met-Met-NH$_2$	Hylambatin*
Mammalian tachykinins	
Arg-Pro-Lys-Pro-Gln-Gln-Phe-Phe-Gly-Leu-Met-NH$_2$	Substance P

*Yasuhara *et al.*, in preparation.

species of the *Eledone* genus, as it has not been found in *Octopus* species, nor in squids, such as *Sepia officinalis* and *Dosidicus gigas*. These negative results may simply be due to inadequacy of the biological methods employed so far, or to the fact that the presence of eledoisin in the *Eledone* salivary glands is an accidental event with no general biological significance. It should be remembered that the amphibian skin peptides are also restricted in their taxonomic distribution.

As far as *Hydra* is concerned, the SP-like material occurring in a specific population of nerve cells in the ectoderm of tentacles and foot of the animal, is most probably authentic substance P (Grimmelikhuijzen and Emson, personal communication), since the *Hydra* peptide separated by high performance liquid chromatography appeared at the same position as substance P and had both N- and C-terminal immunoreactivity corresponding to a substance P-like peptide. Sensory nerve cells in the ectoderm around the mouth of *Hydra* also contain cholecystokinin-like immunoreactivity and nerve cells at the bases of the tentacles and at a site just above the foot contain neurotensin-like immunoreactivity[10].

Coelenterates certainly have the most primitive neurosecretory system of the animal kingdom and the demonstration that substance P or a closely-related peptide occurs in this system suggests that the sequence of amino acids constituting substance P developed in very primitive forms of life and has been conserved during evolution.

Tachykinins in vertebrates

Peptides belonging to the tachykinin family have been detected in epithelial cells of the gastrointestinal tract (enterochromaffin cells of the intestinal type) and in central and peripheral nervous structures of all examined vertebrate species, as well as in the skin of certain amphibian species.

Amphibian skin contains a variety of tachykinins. Until recently only a single form of substance P was known for gastrointestinal tract and brain of mammals, i.e. the endecapeptide isolated by Leeman's group. However, using an antiserum against physalaemin which had negligible cross-reactivity with substance P (< 0.0001), Lazarus et al.[12,13] discovered a substance in mammalian tissues with an immunoreactivity resembling that of amphibian physalaemin. Physalaemin-like immunoreactivity has already been described in the gastrointestinal tract of the guinea-pig, mouse and rabbit and in the guinea-pig spinal chord. In guinea-pigs and rats immunostaining was observed in both epithelial cells and nerve fibres of the gastrointestinal tract.

Most recent advances announced by the group of Lazarus (personal communication) include the occurrence of physalaemin throughout the brain tissue with a distribution different from that of substance P, and throughout the mammalian pulmonary tract, from the trachea (peak content of 114 pmol g^{-1} dried canine tracheal mucosa) to the pulmonary tissue (2.8 pmol g^{-1} in the rabbit lung), where the peptide is probably contained in nerve fibres. According to Lazarus, mammalian physalaemin is not identical with the amphibian peptide.

Biological activity of the tachykinins

Substance P, eledoisin and the seven amphibian tachykinins share the same general spectrum of biological activity with important quantitative differences, however, which permit their distinction by bioassay. While the C-terminal pentapeptide varies little within the family and accounts for the fundamental properties of the tachykinins, the N-moiety does show considerable variability and is responsible for the main differences in potency, efficacy and duration of action. The relative potencies of four typical tachykinins on a variety of preparations are shown in Table II.

In addition, in the rat substance P, physalaemin and eldoisin have been found to excite spontaneously-active

TABLE II. The potency of three typical tachykinins measured in various bioassay systems, relative to that of physalaemin (= 100)

	Eledoisin	Kassinin	Substance P
Dog blood pressure	25–30	3–8	150–250
Rabbit blood pressure	20–40	4–7	150–270
Rat blood pressure	50	10	100
Pigeon blood pressure	50	=	150
Man blood pressure	=	=	450
Hepatic arterial blood flow (dog)	30	=	200
Portal venous blood flow (dog)	100	=	400–500
Femoral blood flow (dog)	1–2	=	=
Rat salivary secretion	30–50	6–7	20–25
Dog pancreatic secretion	3.5	=	=
Rat lower oesophageal sphincter	2000	550	50
Rat stomach	90–135	50–100	50–65
Rat colon	150–300	150–300	20–50
Rat duodenum	500–700	400–600	=
Guinea-pig ileum	30–120	10–40	20–60
Guinea-pig large intestine	50–135	30–45	45–80
Rabbit large intestine	30–80	13–40	30–75
Human stomach	170–215	=	8–12
Human taenia coli	300–600	=	20–35
Guinea-pig gall bladder in situ	100–150	70–150	=
Guinea-pig urinary bladder	40–120	10–18	10–35
Rat urinary bladder in situ	50–100	18–50	25–50
Cat urinary bladder	80–150	30–100	25–50
Hamster urinary bladder	3000	3000	50–100
Dog urinary bladder	1000–5000	400–4000	30
Monkey urinary bladder	2000–3000	2000–4000	20–30
Man urinary bladder	1000–2000	1000–3000	15–30
Guinea-pig seminal vesicles	25–100	=	10–30
Rat vas deferens	1000–2000	=	=
Guinea-pig trachea	100–150	=	15–25
Rat uterus	=	=	50
Human fallopian tube	400	=	=
Electrolyte transport (guinea-pig ileal mucosa)	60	180	50
Spinal motoneurons (frog)	135	=	13
Drinking behaviour*: Antidipsogenic effect (rat)	1000	=	25–50
Dipsogenic effect (pigeon)	100	=	1–2

Unless otherwise stated these results were obtained from isolated smooth muscle preparations. =, not determined; *intracerebroventricular injection.

cortical neurones when applied iontophoretically. Substance P was the most potent, followed by physalaemin and then eledoisin[15]. On the other hand, physalaemin produced excitation of an identified giant neurone in the mollusc *Achatina fulica*, both when applied to the external bath and by microdrop application. Substance P was inactive[19]. It may be seen that whilst parallel bioassay of tachykinins on peripheral test preparations is very extensive, little is known about effects of these peptides in the CNS.

On the basis of data reported in Table II and elsewhere, it is possible to postulate the existence of four different tachykinin subfamilies, each characterized by a set of prominent biological activities: (i) substance P has the most potent action on blood pressure, on vascular smooth muscle, and possibly on certain mammalian cerebral neurones; (ii) physalaemin (uperolein, hylambatin, Lys^5,Thr^6-physalaemin) is the most potent stimulant of salivary, lachrymal and pancreatic secretion and has a powerful action on amphibian and molluscan neurones; (iii) eledoisin (phyllomedusin) potently stimulates intestinal and genito-urinary smooth muscle and, when injected intracerebroventricularly, has the most striking effect on central regulatory mechanisms of drinking behaviour[3,4]; finally (iv) kassinin (Glu^2,Pro^5-kassinin) is characterized by a poor action on blood pressure and salivary secretion, but has a potent action on the smooth muscle of the genito-urinary tract and the gut, and on the ileal electrolyte transport. Kassinin may also be considered the least 'tachy' of the tachykinins, because of the longer latency of its action, yet its duration is more sustained than that of the other peptides of this family.

Looking ahead

Among the tachykinins, substance P has so far received the greatest atten-tion, whilst the amphibian and molluscan tachykinins have been considered little more than curiosities, useful only in discussions on structure–activity relationships. The predominant position of substance P is actually justified by its occurrence in mammalian endocrine cells and various peripheral and central nervous structures and by the fact that its amino acid composition appears to be older, in the evolutionary sense, than that of any other tachykinin.

However, the conventional view that substance P is the only representative of tachykinins in the mammalian organism must be re-examined in the light of recent findings demonstrating the existence of physalaemin-containing cells and physalaeminergic neurones in the mammalian gut, lung and CNS.

It is evident that findings of immunocytochemical and radioimmunoassay studies on substance P are only valid provided highly specific anti-sera are employed. Moreover, the use of exogenous substance P, as the sole representative of the tachykinin family, in studies intended to elucidate the physiological significance of the substance P-ergic system is no longer acceptable. In parallel bioassay with substance P, natural tachykinins should be preferred to synthetic analogues, as the former are the outcome of a delicate evolutionary process, whilst the latter are nothing but very rough and largely arbitrary alterations of natural molecules. Data obtained with non mammalian tachykinins may prove in the long run to be as interesting and illuminating as those obtained with substance P itself, and functions now attributed to this peptide may eventually be ascribed to other members of the tachykinin family.

Reading list

1 Bury, R. W. and Mashford, M. L. (1977) *Aust. J. Exp. Biol. Med. Sci.* 55, 671–735

2 Chang, M. M., Leeman, S. E. and Niall, H. D. (1971) *Nature (London), New Biol.* 232, 86–87

3 De Caro, G., Massi, M. and Micossi, L. G. (1978) *J. Physiol. (London)* 279, 133–140

4 De Caro, G., Massi, M., Micossi, L. G. and Venturi, F. (1978) *Neuropharmacology* 17, 925–929

5 Erspamer, V. (1949) *Experientia* 5, 49–50

6 Erspamer, V. and Anastasi, A. (1962) *Experientia* 18, 58–59

7 Erspamer, V., Anastasi, A., Bertaccini, G. and Cei, J. M. (1964) *Experientia* 20, 489–490

8 von Euler, U. S. and Gaddum, J. H. (1931) *J. Physiol. (London)* 72, 74–87

9 von Euler, U. S. and Pernow, B. (1977) *Substance P,* Raven Press, New York

10 Grimmelikhuijzen, C., Sundler, F. and Rehfeld, J. (1980) *Regul. Peptides,* Suppl. 1, S45

11 Konishi, S. and Otsuka, M. (1974) *Brain Res.* 65, 397–410

12 Lazarus, L. H. and Di Augustine, R. P. (1980) *Anal. Biochem.* 107, 350–357

13 Lazarus, L. H., Linnoila, R. I., Hernandez, O. and Di Augustine, R. P. (1980) *Nature (London)* 287, 555–558

14 Marsan, C. A. and Trazyk, W. Z. (1980) *Neuropeptides and Neural Transmission,* Raven Press, New York

15 Phyllis, J. W. and Limacher, J. J. (1974) *Exp. Neurol.* 43, 414–423

16 Skrabanek, P. and Powell, D. (1978) *Substance P.* Vol. 1, Annual Research Review, Churchill Livingstone, Edinburgh, London

17 Skrabanek, P. and Powell, D. (1980) *Substance P.* Vol. 2, Annual Research Review, Eden Press, Westmount

18 Studer, R. O., Trzeciak, H. and Lergier, W. (1973) *Helv. Chim. Acta* 56, 860–866

19 Takeuchi, H., Yokoi, I. and Mori, A. (1976) *Experientia* 32, 606–608

V. Erspamer is Professor of Pharmacology, Institute of Medical Pharmacology, University of Rome, Città universitaria, 00100 Rome, Italy.

Three tachykinins in mammalian brain

Anthony J. Harmar

Two polypeptide precursors to the neuropeptide substance P have recently been identified. One of them (β-preprotachykinin) contains amino acid sequences corresponding not only to substance P but also to substance K, a novel, related peptide. A third substance P-like peptide, neuromedin K, has recently been isolated from spinal cord. The existence in vertebrates of three members of the tachykinin family of peptides may account for pharmacological observations suggesting the presence of more than one type of substance P receptor in the nervous system.

The tachykinin family of peptides (Fig. 1) is characterized by the common amino acid sequence- Phe-X-Gly-Leu-Met-NH$_2$ at the C terminus, where X is a hydrophobic or aromatic residue[1]. Substance P, the best-known member of the family, was until recently the only tachykinin known to occur in mammals, all the other tachykinins having been isolated from octopod salivary glands or from amphibian skin. However, a number of lines of evidence suggested that there might be other tachykinins present in the vertebrate nervous system.

Using a variety of antisera to the amphibian peptide physalaemin, Lazarus and colleagues[2] were able to demonstrate the widespread occurrence in mammals of material with physalaemin-like immunoreactivity. Immunological, chemical and pharmacological analysis of the physalaemin-like material in a small-cell carcinoma from human lung demonstrated that it was similar or identical in its properties to amphibian physalaemin[3]. Keen and colleagues[4] demonstrated the biosynthesis in dorsal root ganglia of substance P together with a related peptide which was immunoprecipitated by C-terminal but not by N-terminal substance P antisera. Analysis of the incorporation of dif-ferent radiolabelled amino acids into the novel peptide indicated that it differed from substance P in containing no proline residues and in containing the amino acids phenylalanine and methionine in the ratio 1/1 instead of 2/1.

Evidence for the existence of novel tachykinins in mammalian tissue was complemented by evidence for the presence of more than one type of tachykinin receptor in vertebrates. This concept, first suggested by Erspamer[1], was extended by Iversen and colleagues[5] who defined the responses of a variety of pharmacological test systems in terms of two types of tachykinin receptor. All the tachykinins display approximately equal potency at one type of receptor (the SP-P receptor), whereas the second type of receptor (the SP-E receptor) is considerably more sensitive to eledoisin and kassinin than to the other tachykinins. Searching for an endogenous ligand to the SP-E receptor, Maggio *et al.*[6] developed a radioimmunoassay for kassinin, the most potent ligand at SP-E receptors. They found that extracts of spinal cord contained abundant kassinin-like immunoreactivity which they attributed to a novel peptide. This peptide they named 'substance K' to indicate its apparent immunochemical similarity

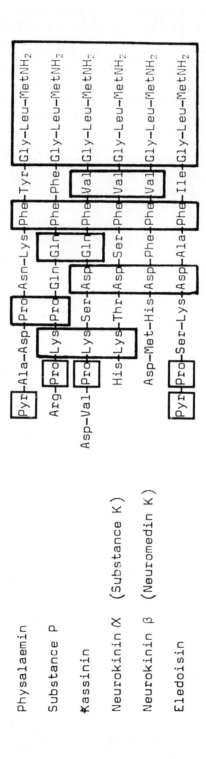

Fig. 1. Structures of the tachykinins referred to in this article showing sequence homologies.

to kassinin.

Kimura et al.[7] were at this time searching for novel neuropeptides in porcine spinal cord, using as an assay their activity on the isolated guinea-pig ileum. Four fractions exhibiting ileum-contracting activity were identified by Sephadex G-15 chromatography: two of the fractions contained substance P and its oxidized derivative; the remaining two fractions contained novel peptides, 'neurokinin α' and 'neurokinin β', which were isolated and sequenced. Neurokinin β proved to be identical in structure to neuromedin K, a spinal cord peptide isolated independently by Kangawa et al. using similar methodology[8]. Neurokinin α proved to be the same as the substance K first described by Maggio et al.[6], and almost certainly corresponds to the substance P-like peptide first described by Keen et al.[4].

At about this time, Nawa et al.[9] conquered one of the great challenges in substance P research by elucidating the nucleotide sequences of cloned cDNAs for two types of bovine substance P precursor.

The techniques used were similar to those which have been successfully employed to identify precursors to a growing number of neuropeptides and hormones[10]. Briefly, mRNA from bovine striatum (a region of the brain especially rich in substance P-synthesizing cell bodies) was isolated and transcribed into cDNA. The cDNA was used to generate a 'library' of bacterial clones containing plasmid DNA into which sequences complementary to striatal mRNA had been inserted. Clones containing substance P-related nucleotide sequences were recognized by the ability of their DNA to hybridize with synthetic DNA probes (oligonucleotides with a sequence predicted by the amino acid sequence of the substance P molecule). A number of positive clones were identified and their cDNA inserts sequenced; two precursor molecules to substance P

– α- and β-preprotachykinin (α- and β-PPT) – were identified.

The structures of α- and β-PPT are illustrated schematically in Fig. 2. α- and β-PPT are identical, except that a 54-nucleotide segment of the cDNA sequence of β-PPT is missing in α-PPT. Thus, β-PPT is a polypeptide of 130 amino acids (mol. wt 15 076), whereas α-PPT lacks 18 consecutive amino acids present in the β-PPT sequence and has a methionine residue in place of the arginine residue at the boundary of the deleted region. The 19-amino acid sequence unique to β-PPT contains the sequence of the substance K molecule. The other structural features of the two PPT molecules are similar to those found in the sequences of other peptide precursors. Like all other polypeptides destined for secretion from the cell, the α- and β-PPT sequences begin with a 15–30 amino acid 'signal sequence' (largely composed of hydrophobic amino acids), which promotes attachment of the newly synthesized polypeptide to the endoplasmic reticulum and its secretion into the intracisternal space[11]. This sequence is cleaved off by a membrane-bound protease during or immediately after synthesis: the exact length of the signal sequence in the PPT molecule has not yet been determined. Immediately preceding the sequence of substance K in the precursor is a pair of basic amino acids (Lys-Arg). A trypsin-like protease is thought to cleave the precursor after the second basic residue to liberate the N terminus of the substance K molecule. The N terminus of the substance P sequence (Arg-Pro) is preceded in the precursor by a single basic amino acid (arginine). Although the double basic amino acid 'signal' for proteolytic processing is again present, the Arg-Pro bond is selectively resistant to trypsin-like proteases and instead the cleavage occurs between the two arginine residues. Immediately following the sequences of substance P and substance

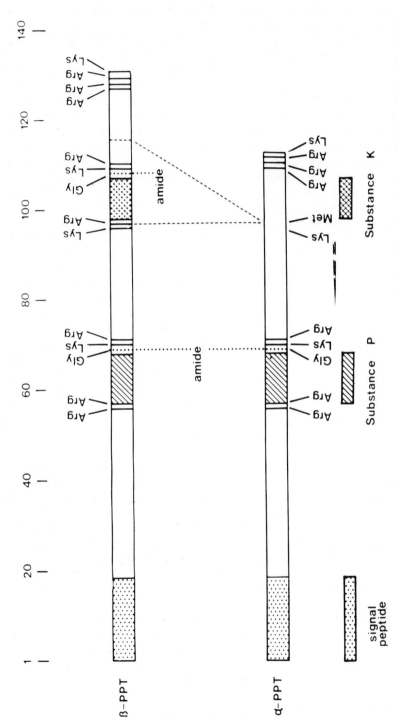

Fig. 2. *Schematic representation of the structures of α- and β-preprotachykinin (α- and β-PPT), showing the locations of substance K, substance P and the putative signal peptide within the two polypeptides. The region of β-PPT which is deleted in the α-PPT sequence is indicated by dashed lines. Basic amino acids corresponding to probable processing sites are shown. 'Amide' represents the sites of amidation for substance P and substance K. (Modified from Ref. 9, with permission.)*

K is the sequence -Gly-Lys-Arg – a pair of basic amino acids indicating a site of proteolytic processing, preceded by a glycine residue which is thought to be the donor of the amide group found at the C terminus of both peptides[12]. Other biologically active peptides may be liberated from the PPT sequences. In particular the sequence -Arg-Arg-Arg-Lys at the C terminus of both precursors could be a processing site, liberating peptides corresponding to residues 72–108 of α-PPT and residues 111–126 of β-PPT. These peptides may possess some, as yet undefined, biological activity.

The presence of two precursors for substance P in brain has exciting implications. The two PPT molecules may arise from two closely similar but separate genes. Alternatively they may arise from a single gene by alternative splicing events. The vast majority of eukaryotic genes consist of precisely defined regions coding for sections of mature mRNA (exons) interspersed with regions (introns) which are either deleted during the synthesis of mRNA precursors or 'spliced' out of the mRNA sequence during its maturation. The portion of the β-PPT mRNA that is missing from α-PPT may correspond to a single exon, and both precursor mRNAs may be generated from a common gene product by different splicing events. A similar variable splicing mechanism enables a single gene (the calcitonin gene) to code for different products (calcitonin and calcitonin gene-related peptide) in the thyroid and hypothalamus, respectively[13]. The origin of the two PPT molecules will finally be understood (no doubt, very soon) when the structure of the PPT gene(s) is established.

Regardless of their origin, the existence of two tachykinin precursors in brain poses intriguing problems for neurobiology. Substance P-containing neurons may express either α- or β-PPT molecules throughout their lifetime, implying the presence of separate groups of 'substance P only' and 'substance P + substance K' neurons in the brain. Alternatively a given neuron may be able to switch its pattern of peptide production between the two states either during development or in response to external stimuli. In this context, it may be particularly worthwhile to examine afresh the effects of nerve growth factor in stimulating substance P synthesis in sensory neurons[14], and the effects of decentralization in increasing – and depolarization in decreasing – SP synthesis in autonomic ganglia[15]. Are the relative amounts of substance P and substance K synthesized also affected?

These questions will doubtless be resolved soon: the production of specific antisera to substance K (and indeed to neuromedin K) will permit the distribution of these peptides in the brain, and any differences between them, to be established. cDNA probes to those parts of the PPT mRNA common to both precursors, and to the region missing from α-PPT, will be used to identify by in-situ hybridization[16] those cells producing each of the two tachykinin mRNAs and to look for plastic and developmental changes in their levels in brain.

This leaves neuromedin K as something of a Cinderella in the substance P family, since we still know nothing of its distribution or biosynthetic origin in the brain. It is attractive to imagine that this peptide, which like substance K is probably a good ligand at SP-E receptors, may exist in a new set of peptidergic neurons in brain. The combined distribution of 'substance P only', 'substance P + substance K' and 'neuromedin K only' neurons might then account for the observed regional differences in substance P receptor subtypes in the nervous system.

Reading list
1 Erspamer, V. (1981) *Trends NeuroSci.* 4, 267–269
2 Lazarus, L. H. and di Augustine, R. P. (1980)

Anal. Biochem. 107, 350–357

3 Lazarus, L. H., di Augustine, R. P., Jahnke, G. D. and Hernandez, O. (1983) *Science* 219, 79–81

4 Keen, P., Harmar, A. J., Spears, F. and Winter, E. (1982) *Ciba Found. Symp.* 91, 145–164

5 Iversen, L. L., Hanley, M. R., Sandberg, B. E. B., Lee, C. M., Pinnock, R. D. and Watson, S. P. (1982) *Ciba Found. Symp.* 91, 186–205

6 Maggio, J. E., Sandberg, B. E. B., Bradley, C. V., Iversen, L. L., Santikarn, S., Williams, D. H., Hunter, J. C. and Hanley, M. R. (1983) *Ir. J. Med. Sci.* 152 (Suppl. 1), 20–21

7 Kimura, S., Okada, M., Sugita, Y., Kanazawa, I. and Munekata, E. (1983) *Proc. Jpn Acad., Ser. B* 59, 101–104

8 Kangawa, K., Minamino, N., Fukuda, A. and Matsuo, H. *Biochem. Biophys. Res. Commun.* 114, 533–540

9 Nawa, H., Hirose, T., Takashima, H., Inayama, S. and Nakanishi, S. (1983) *Nature (London)* 306, 32–36

10 Milner, R. J. (1982) *Trends NeuroSci.* 5, 297–300

11 Blobel, G. and Dobberstein, B. (1975) *J. Cell Biol.* 67, 835–851

12 Maggio, J., Eipper, B., Mains, R. E. and Glembotski, C. C. (1983) *Proc. Natl Acad. Sci. USA* 80, 5144–5148

13 Rosenfeld, M. G., Mermod, J. J., Amara, S. G., Swanson, L. W., Sawchenko, P. E., Rivier, J., Vale, W. W. and Evans, R. M. (1983) *Nature (London)* 304, 129–135

14 Mayer, N., Lembeck, F., Goedert, M. and Otten, U. *Neurosci. Lett.* (in press)

15 Black, I. B., Kessler, J. A., Adler, J. E. and Bohn, M. (1982) *Ciba Found. Symp.* 91, 107–123

16 Gee, C. E., Chen, C.-L., Roberts, J. L., Thompson, R. and Watson, S. J. (1983) *Nature (London)* 306, 374–376

Staff Scientist, MRC Brain Metabolism Unit, University Department of Pharmacology, 1 George Square, Edinburgh EH8 9JZ, UK.

Substance P – the first peptide neurotransmitter?

Masanori Otsuka and Shiro Konishi

This article reviews the evidence for substance P (SP) as a neurotransmitter in primary afferent neurons in the spinal cord and sympathetic ganglia. There is strong evidence indicating that SP released from peripheral branches of visceral primary afferent neurons produces non-cholinergic slow excitatory postsynaptic potentials (EPSPs) in the inferior mesenteric ganglion cells of the guinea-pig. It is also probable that SP released from central terminals of certain primary afferent neurons produces slow EPSPs in the dorsal-horn neurons which are involved in certain types of slow reflex in the neonatal rat spinal cord.

SP is one of the oldest known neuropeptides. It was discovered about half a century ago by von Euler who, together with Gaddum, found that SP exerts a hypotensive action which is not blocked by atropine[11,12]. A glance over the history of SP research shows how long it takes for a substance to be accepted as a neurotransmitter. The case of SP as a putative transmitter needs particularly cautious examination because SP is likely to serve as a model for many other neuropeptides whose functions may in some respects resemble those of SP. The purpose of this article is to examine the evidence for SP as a neurotransmitter. Since the best evidence comes from primary afferent neurons, the main focus will be placed on this type of neuron.

Early history of the pursuit for the sensory transmitter

In his Nothnagel Lecture in 1934, Dale suggested that the chemical transmitter of the axon-reflex vasodilatation might be related to the sensory transmitter at the central synapses because both are liberated from the same sensory neurons, one from peripheral nerve endings and the other from central nerve endings[6]. Since then, much attention has been paid to various vaso-dilator substances in the search for chemical transmitters of primary afferent neurons. Acetylcholine (ACh), a vasodilator agent, was unlikely to be a sensory transmitter because the spinal dorsal roots, consisting of sensory fibers, contain virtually no ACh, as observed by Loewi and Hellauer in 1938[29]. Later, in their search for the sensory transmitter, Hellauer and Umrath in 1947 found that the dorsal-root extract contains a vasodilator agent whose action is resistant to atropine[15]. Around 1953, several groups of investigators found that the dorsal roots contain much more SP than the ventral roots[27,37], and this finding led Lembeck to propose the hypothesis that SP may be a sensory transmitter[27]. Thus, the introduction of SP as a putative sensory transmitter was a consequence of logical and cumulative pursuit from 1931 to 1953. The real exploration of Lembeck's hypothesis, however, was begun in the 1970s.

Determination of the structure of SP

In the 1950s and 1960s progress in SP research was greatly hampered by the lack of knowledge of the structure of SP and the unavailability of pure SP. A breakthrough was made by Leeman and her colleagues when in 1971, 40 years after its discovery, they succeeded in determining the structure of SP as an undecapeptide and then in synthesizing it[4]. In retrospect it is interesting to speculate on the reasons for such a long delay. Possibly the importance of SP was not widely recognized and therefore impetus was lacking. In the early 1960s the Sandoz group made remarkable progress in the purification of SP[3] and we now know that the purity of their preparation was more than 50%, but since authentic SP was still unavailable it must have been difficult for these investigators to assess how close they were to their goal. Leeman used the sialogogic action in the rat for bioassay, which is certainly much more specific than the gut-contracting and hypotensive actions which are commonly used for bioassays of SP, and this certainly must have helped Leeman's group in their pursuit. Erspamer and his colleagues had already in the 1960s succeeded in the chemical characterization of physalaemin and eledoisin, peptides closely related to SP and obtained from rather unusual sources, i.e. South American amphibian skin and octopus salivary gland[10] and synthetic physalaemin and eledoisin had been available long before SP, which could be extracted at any time in large amounts from mammalian brain.

Basic criteria for transmitter identification

Sensory transmitter substances are expected (1) to be present in the dorsal root, probably in larger amounts than in the ventral root, and (2) to exert an excitatory action on spinal neurons. During the search for the sensory transmitters, Otsuka and his colleagues found in 1972 that bovine dorsal roots contain a peptide having an excitatory action on spinal motoneurons of the frog. Subsequent study showed that SP is responsible for this excitatory action, so we tested the action of synthetic SP and found that it was about 200 times more powerful in its action on frog spinal motoneurons than L-glutamate[36] which was then, and still is, a leading candidate as a sensory transmitter. Thus SP appeared at this stage to be a promising candidate as a sensory transmit-

ter, and with the aid of synthetic SP and new techniques such as radioimmunoassay and immunohistochemistry, within a few years SP was proved to fulfil the basic criteria for transmitter identification, as follows. (1) SP is present in the primary afferent terminals in the superficial layers of the dorsal horn as revealed first by bioassay[39], and then by the immunohistochemical studies of Hökfelt's group[19]. At the electron-microscope level SP is present in certain nerve terminals forming axodendritic synapses with spinal neurons in the substantia gelatinosa, and synaptic vesicles are densely stained by SP antibody[8]. (2) SP-like immunoreactivity is released from the spinal cord of the rat and the cat in response to electrical stimulation of sensory nerves in a Ca^{2+}-dependent manner[35,42]. That the SP-like immunoreactivity released from the spinal cord is largely attributable to SP itself was shown by the combined use of high-performance liquid chromatography and radioimmunoassay[2]. (3) When synthetic SP was applied to the isolated spinal cord of the neonatal rat and the response recorded from the motoneurons, SP was found to exert a powerful excitatory action on spinal neurons, being 1000–10000 times more powerful than L-glutamate on a molar basis[34].

Thus by around 1976 the principal criteria for SP as a neurotransmitter in the spinal cord had been fulfilled. But the synapses where SP plays a major role are buried in a tangled jungle of neuron networks containing small cells in the substantia gelatinosa, and it appears extremely difficult to demonstrate the SP-mediated synaptic potential there. However, two lines of study, one in the sympathetic ganglia and the other using a new SP antagonist, suggest that SP produces slow EPSPs in the dorsal-horn neurons.

Studies in the sympathetic ganglia

The presence of SP in peripheral sympathetic nervous tissues was first shown by Pernow (1953). Hökfelt and his colleagues showed that the principal cells in the guinea-pig inferior mesenteric ganglia are surrounded by SP-containing nerve terminals[18]. At the electron-microscope level the SP-containing nerve terminals form axodendritic synapses with the ganglion cells[23,31]. When measured by radioimmunoassay, the inferior mesenteric ganglia of the guinea-pig were shown to contain a remarkably large amount of SP, about 20 times more than the superior cervical ganglia. Furthermore, the SP content in the inferior mesenteric ganglia was reduced by 74% after the severing of the preganglionic nerves, which suggests that the cell bodies are located on the central, not the peripheral, side[25]. In fact a recent immunohistochemical study by Dalsgaard et al. demonstrated that the SP-containing fibers in the inferior mesenteric ganglia represent peripheral branches of visceral primary afferent neurons[7,31] (Fig. 1). The release of SP-like immunoreactivity is evoked by high-K^+ medium from the guinea-pig prevertebral ganglia, i.e. the

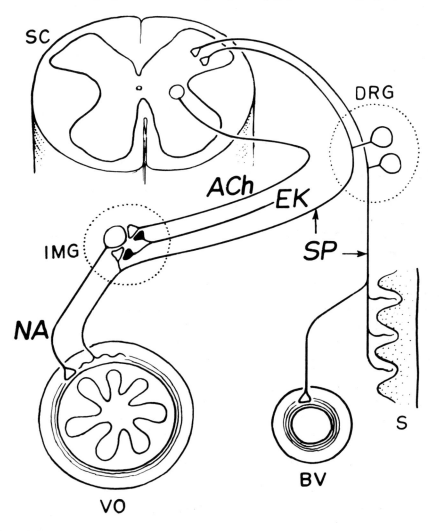

Fig. 1. *Schematic representation of somatic and visceral primary afferent neurons and the sympathetic nervous system. ACh = acetylcholine; NA = noradrenaline; EK = enkephalin; SP = substance P; BV = blood vessel; DRG = dorsal root ganglion; IMG = inferior mesenteric ganglion; S = skin; SC = spinal cord; VO = visceral organ.* (Modified from Ref. 26.)

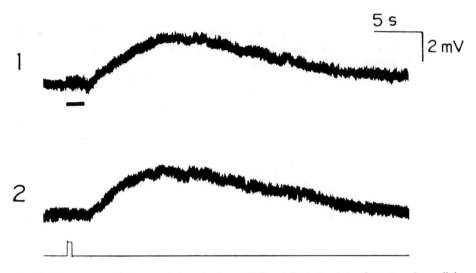

Fig. 2. *Time courses of the non-cholinergic slow EPSP and SP-induced depolarization. Intracellular recordings were made from a neuron of inferior mesenteric ganglion. Cholinergic transmission was blocked by hexamethonium (400 μM) and atropine (4 μM). 1: The non-cholinergic slow EPSP evoked by stimulation of lumbar splanchnic nerves (10 Hz for 2 s). The period of stimulation is marked by a horizontal bar. 2: Depolarization produced by pressure application of SP (5 μM) from a micropipette (upper trace). The period of SP application is indicated by the deflection of pressure monitor (lower trace). (From Ref. 40.)*

inferior mesenteric and coeliac-superior mesenteric ganglia, and the release is Ca^{2+}-dependent[25,40]. When the potential is recorded from the nerve cells of the guinea-pig inferior mesenteric ganglia and single or repetitive stimuli are applied to the preganglionic nerves or to the dorsal roots, a slow EPSP lasting from 20 s to 4 min is elicited, which is not blocked by cholinergic antagonists[5,33] and consequently is referred to as a non-cholinergic slow EPSP. Application of SP produces a depolarization of the ganglion cells, and this action of SP mimics that of the neurotransmitter of the non-cholinergic slow EPSP with respect to the conductance changes and the time course[9,25,40] (Fig. 2). Prolonged application of SP to the ganglion cells produces a sustained depolarization during which the non-cholinergic slow EPSP is occluded, suggesting that both SP and the neural transmitter bind to the same receptors[9,25,40]. Capsaicin, the pungent factor of red pepper, is known to produce a release and a depletion of SP from the ganglia[26,31]. After treatment of the ganglia with capsaicin the non-cholinergic slow EPSP is

abolished[26,40]. Finally, an SP-antagonist, [D-Pro[2], D-Phe[7], D-Trp[9]]SP was reported to block the non-cholinergic slow EPSP[21]. However, this antagonist is known to retain a partial agonist action[14]. In a recent study an improved SP-antagonist, [D-Arg[1], D-Pro[2], D-Trp[7,9], Leu[11]]SP, was shown to block selectively both the SP action and the non-cholinergic slow EPSP[24] (Fig. 3). Together these observations provide compelling evidence that SP is released from axon collaterals of visceral primary afferents and produces the non-cholinergic slow EPSP in the inferior mesenteric ganglion cells.

Slow spinal reflexes

The results obtained in the sympathetic ganglia suggest that SP released from central terminals of certain primary sensory neurons produces similar slow EPSPs in the dorsal-horn neurons. At present it is difficult to record EPSPs from the dorsal-horn neurons which one can confidently assume to be produced by direct action of primary afferent transmitters. However, it may be possible to identify spinal reflexes involv-

ing SP-mediated synapses. Immunohistochemical studies have shown that SP
exists in some (about 20%) of the small-
diameter primary afferents[19]. Therefore one
would expect that the spinal reflexes involving SP action would be evoked by activating the thin primary afferents, which have
slow conduction velocity and high
threshold for activation. When the primary
afferents are stimulated with increasing
intensity in the isolated spinal-cord preparation of the neonatal rat, at a certain level the
slow-conducting and high-threshold primary afferents are activated and at the same
time a slow depolarizing reflex is evoked in
the contralateral ventral root of the same
segment[1]. This slow reflex lasts 20–30 s
and is referred to as the contralateral slow
ventral root potential (VRP). Treatment
with capsaicin either *in vitro* or *in vivo*
abolishes the contralateral slow VRP[1]: this
is expected, since the drug affects the
small-diameter, unmyelinated fibers[32].
Furthermore, the SP-antagonist [D-Arg[1],
D-Pro[2], D-Trp[7,9], Leu[11]]SP depresses the
contralateral slow VRP[43]. These results
strongly suggest that SP-mediated synaptic

excitation is involved in this type of slow
spinal reflex. A likely possibility is that SP
released from central terminals of certain
primary afferents produces slow EPSPs in
the dorsal-horn neurons, which via
polysynaptic pathways produce a depolarizing response in the contralateral
motoneurons. It is noteworthy that the time
course of the contralateral slow VRP is
similar to that of the non-cholinergic slow
EPSP in the sympathetic ganglia.

SP and pain

SP is present in certain small-diameter
primary afferents which probably belong to
the C-fiber group. Since C-fibers are
believed to be important for pain sensation,
it is natural to suppose that SP is a pain
transmitter[16]. Several findings support this
idea. Some SP-antagonists when applied
intrathecally have an analgesic action[38].
Intrathecal injection of SP in mice elicits
behavioral effects suggesting pain sensation[20]. Noxious stimuli given to the skin
of the rabbit evoke a release of SP-like
immunoreactivity from the dorsal spinal
cord as detected by push–pull cannulae[17].

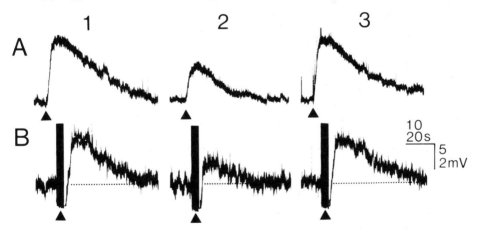

Fig. 3. *Effects of* [D-Arg[1], D-Pro[2], D-Trp[7,9], Leu[11]]SP on the responses to SP and nerve stimulation. Intracellular recordings from an inferior mesenteric ganglion cell. Depolarization is upwards. **(A)** Responses to
pressure applications of SP (0.7 μM, 2 s). **(B)** Cholinergic fast and non-cholinergic slow EPSPs induced by
stimulation of lumbar splanchnic nerves (20 Hz for 5 s). Tops of cholinergic fast EPSPs are cut off. SP and
nerve stimulation were applied at triangles. 1: Control. 2: During perfusion with 10 μM [D-Arg[1], D-Pro[2],
D-Trp[7,9], Leu[11]]SP. 3: After the removal of the antagonist. Voltage scale: 5 mV for **A**; and 2 mV for **B**. Time
scale: 10 s for **A**; and 20 s for **B**. The depolarizing action of the SP-antagonist was eliminated by adding
mepyramine at 3 μM to the perfusion medium throughout the experiment. (From Ref. 24).*

Therefore, SP is probably involved in pain sensation, but this by no means excludes the possibility that other substances might also serve as pain transmitters of primary afferents and that SP conveys other modalities of sensation such as baroception or chemoception to the CNS[13].

SP in other places

Although the distribution and the physiological functions of SP in both central and peripheral nervous systems have been extensively studied, only a few relevant findings can be mentioned because of limited space. In a few places SP appears to be released from axon collaterals of primary afferent neurons and to regulate muscular functions. Namely, in the skin there is evidence that SP acts as a transmitter of axon-reflex vasodilatation[28] and, in the iris, SP probably is released from axon collaterals of sensory trigeminal fibers and causes a contraction of iris sphincter pupillae muscle[38,41]. It is rather pleasing to see that Dale's prediction of half a century ago regarding the intimate connection between the transmitters released from central and peripheral terminals of the sensory neurons[6] appears to be confirmed in various ways in the PNS, i.e. in the sympathetic ganglia, the skin, the iris, and probably also in the heart, as well as in the CNS, i.e. the spinal cord and the brain stem.

The highest content of SP is found in the substantia nigra of the midbrain. Here the major output is dopaminergic neurons and the major excitatory and inhibitory inputs are respectively SP and GABA fibers. In view of the implication of the nigral dopamine system in some neurological disorders, the pharmacological manipulation of its function by SP-related drugs may open up a variety of interesting and useful clinical possibilities.

Conclusion

From the evidence presented here there is little doubt that SP is a neurotransmitter released from peripheral branches of primary afferents and producing a non-cholinergic slow EPSP in the inferior mesenteric ganglia. There is also little doubt that SP is released from central terminals of certain primary afferent neurons and produces an excitatory effect on spinal dorsal-horn neurons. From the observations on both spinal cords and sympathetic ganglia, it is probable that the neurally released SP produces in dorsal-horn neurons EPSPs lasting tens of seconds. In this connection, recent advances in the SP-antagonists[14,38] will be of great help in revealing the SP-mediated EPSPs in the spinal cord as well as in the other places of the CNS. A possibility must be borne in mind, however, that SP might be co-released from certain primary afferent nerve terminals in the dorsal horn together with some unidentified fast-acting transmitter.

The role of SP as a neurotransmitter as revealed in primary sensory neurons will serve as a useful guide for the future studies on other putative peptide neurotransmitters. In particular, the recent studies of Kimura et al.[22] and Maggio et al.[30] have shown in mammalian spinal cords the occurrence of the peptides whose structures are closely similar to that of SP or kassinin. Therefore, the physiological functions of these peptides, called tachykinins, may also be similar to, but at the same time slightly different from, those of SP. The physiological roles of SP-group neuropeptides are probably much more diverse and broader than those we now know for SP.

Reading list

1 Agaki, H., Konishi, S., Yanagisawa, M. and Otsuka, M. (1983) *Neurochem. Res.* 8, 795–796

2 Akagi, H., Otsuka, M. and Yanagisawa, M. (1980) *Neurosci. Lett.* 20, 259–263

3 Boissonnas, R. A., Franz, J. and Stürmer, E. (1963) *Ann. NY Acad. Sci.* 104, 376–377

4 Chang, M. M., Leeman, S. E. and Niall, H. D. (1971) *Nature (London) New Biol.* 232, 86–87

5 Crowcroft, P. J. and Szurszewski, J. H. (1971) *J. Physiol. (London)* 219, 421–441

6 Dale, H. H. (1935) *Proc. R. Soc. Med.* 28, 319–332

7 Dalsgaard, C.-J., Hökfelt, T., Elfvin, L.-G.,

Skirboll, L. and Emson, P. (1982) *Neuroscience* 7, 647–654

8 DiFiglia, M., Aronin, N. and Leeman, S. E. (1982) *Neuroscience* 7, 1127–1139

9 Dun, N. J. and Karczmar, A. G. (1979) *Neuropharmacology* 18, 215–218

10 Erspamer, V. (1981) *Trends NeuroSci.* 5, 267–269

11 Euler, U. S. von (1981) *Trends NeuroSci.* 4, No. 10, IV–IX

12 Euler, U. S. von and Gaddum, J. H. (1931) *J. Physiol. (London)* 72, 74–87

13 Haeusler, G. and Osterwalder, R. (1980) *Naunyn-Schmiedeberg's Arch. Pharmakol.* 314, 111–121

14 Hanley, M. R. (1982) *Trends NeuroSci.* 5, 138–140

15 Hellauer, H. F. and Umrath, K. (1947) *J. Physiol. (London)* 106, 20P

16 Henry, J. L. (1980) *Trends NeuroSci.* 3, 95–97

17 Hirota, N., Kuraishi, Y., Sugimoto, M., Satoh, K. and Takagi, H. (1983) *Jpn. J. Pharmacol.* 33, Suppl. 208P

18 Hökfelt, T., Elfvin, L.-G., Schultzberg, M., Goldstein, M. and Nilsson, G. (1977) *Brain Res.* 132, 29–41

19 Hökfelt, T., Kellerth, J. O., Nilsson, G. and Pernow, B. (1975) *Brain Res.* 100, 235–252

20 Hylden, J. L. K. and Wilcox, G. L. (1981) *Brain Res.* 217, 212–215

21 Jiang, Z. G., Dun, N. J. and Karczmar, A. G. (1982) *Science* 217, 739–741

22 Kimura, S., Okada, M., Sugita, Y., Kanazawa, I. and Munekata, E. (1983) *Proc. Jpn Acad. Ser. B* 59, 101–104

23 Kondo, H. and Yui, R. (1981) *Brain Res.* 222, 134–137

24 Konishi, S., Otsuka, M., Folkers, K. and Rosell, S. (1983) *Acta Physiol. Scand.* 117, 157–160

25 Konishi, S., Tsunoo, A. and Otsuka, M. (1979) *Proc. Jpn Acad. Ser. B* 55, 525–530

26 Konishi, S., Tsunoo, A., Yanaihara, N. and Otsuka, M. (1980) *Biomed. Res.* 1, 528–536

27 Lembeck, F. (1953) *Naunyn-Schmiedebergs Arch. Exp. Pathol. Pharmakol.* 219, 197–213

28 Lembeck, F. and Gamse, R. (1982) in *Substance P in the Nervous System* (Porter, R. and O'Connor, M., eds), pp. 35–54, Pitman, London

29 Loewi, O. and Hellauer, H. (1938) *Pfluegers Arch. Gesamte Physiol. Menschen Tiere* 240, 769–775

30 Maggio, J. E., Sandberg, B. E. B., Bradley, C. V., Iversen, L. L., Santikarn, S., Williams, D. H., Hunter, J. C. and Hanley, M. R. (1983) *Ir. J. Med. Sci.* 152, Suppl. 1, 80

31 Matthews, M. R. and Cuello, A. C. (1982) *Proc. Natl. Acad. Sci. USA* 79, 1668–1672

32 Nagy, J. I. (1982) *Trends NeuroSci.* 5, 362–365

33 Neild, T. O. (1978) *Brain Res.*, 140, 231–239

34 Otsuka, M. and Konishi, S. (1976) *Cold Spring Harbor Symp. Quant. Biol.* 40, 135–143

35 Otsuka, M. and Konishi, S. (1976) *Nature (London)* 264, 83–84

36 Otsuka, M., Konishi, S. and Takahashi, T. (1972) *Proc. Jpn Acad.* 48, 747–752

37 Pernow, B. (1953) *Acta Physiol. Scand.* 29, Suppl. 105, 1–90

38 Rosell, S. and Folkers, K. (1982) *Trends Pharmacol. Sci.* 3, 211–212

39 Takahashi, T. and Otsuka, M. (1975) *Brain Res.* 87, 1–11

40 Tsunoo, A., Konishi, S. and Otsuka, M. (1982) *Neuroscience* 7, 2025–2037

41 Ueda, N., Muramatsu, I., Sakakibara, Y. and Fujiwara, M. (1981) *Jpn. J. Pharmacol.* 31, 1071–1079

42 Yaksh, T. L., Jessell, T. M., Gamse, R., Mudge, A. W. and Leeman, S. E. (1980) *Nature (London)* 286, 155–157

43 Yanagisawa, M., Otsuka, M., Konishi, S., Akagi, H., Folkers, K. and Rosell, S. (1982) *Acta Physiol. Scand.* 116, 109–112

Masanori Otsuka and Shiro Konishi are at the Department of Pharmacology, Faculty of Medicine, Tokyo Medical and Dental University, Bunkyo-ku, Tokyo 113, Japan.

Substance P antagonists

Michael R. Hanley

For over 25 years, the high levels of substance P (SP) in primary afferent terminals stimulated speculation that SP might function as a sensory neurotransmitter in the spinal cord[14]. Indeed, SP has been closely correlated with the sensory modality of nociception[9]; attracting considerable interest to antagonists as potential new analgesics. SP has also been considered for other physiological roles, such as neurogenic inflammation[16]. Consequently, the ability to block SP actions is a crucial part of evaluating proposed physiological functions of endogenous SP. Unfortunately, the lack of SP-specific antagonists has been a source of continuing frustration.

Over the years, SP antagonists have been sought largely in screening efforts. Baclofen (Lioresal, beta-(chlorophenyl)-gamma-aminobutyric acid) briefly surfaced as a candidate[20], but then disappeared when a flurry of reports questioned its specificity for SP (Ref. 6). It became evident that screening could go on indefinitely without success, so attention shifted to programs of modification of the parent SP structure. Folkers and his colleagues claimed promising results in 1979[13, 18, 23] using an approach that had successfully generated LHRH antagonists; namely, replacing residues with D-amino acids, pinpointing the key positions which, when replaced, gave analogues with antagonistic activity, and then optimizing the substitutions. One of the first generation of antagonists, [D-Phe[7]]-SP, gave equivocal results as an SP antagonist on the guinea pig ileum[5]. Nonetheless, these first analogues were used for the design of the next generation of analogues, and a triply-substituted variant, [D-Pro[2], D-Phe[7], D-Trp[9]]-SP, was introduced last year as the first viable antagonist. On the guinea pig ileum, [D-Pro[2], D-Phe[7], D-Trp[9]]-SP gave a dose-dependent specific competitive antagonism of the SP-induced contraction[4], and importantly, had no agonist activity at up to 1 mM, unlike previous analogues.

One of the first problems to which the new antagonist was applied was the significance of SP in nociception. Not unexpectedly, perhaps, the antagonist offered up a few surprises. Piercey *et al.*[17] injected the antagonist into the intrathecal space of mice and found no effect on two frequently used analgesia tests, the tail-flick, and hot-plate reflex tests. However, the antagonist blocked the scratching and biting behaviour, a presumptive nociceptive response, elicited by either cutaneous irritation with capsaicin or intrathecal injection of SP. In the latter case, the authors showed the blocking to be dose-dependent, requiring approximately a 100-fold excess of the antagonist over SP to fully block. The blocking was specific for SP as scratching induced by intrathecal somatostatin was unaffected. Similar results were reported by Lembeck *et al.*[15] for the antagonism of scratching behaviour, but they also demonstrated in a tail withdrawal latency test that intrathecal SP shortened the withdrawal time whereas the antagonist lengthened it. Taken together, these observations link SP to the responses to some types of noxious stimulation. As has been proposed from other lines of evidence, SP may be associated with chemosensitive primary afferents[10] and not with afferents responding to thermal pain[22]. It should also be considered that the antagonist may not have been applied yet to the most interesting sensory tests. For example, does the antagonist alter somatotopic maps of the skin as does destruction of a subpopulation of afferent fibres, including those containing SP, by neonatal capsaicin treatment[21]?

Closely related to these experiments is a historical pharmacological problem. In 1935, Sir Henry Dale noted that when sensory nerves are antidromically activated, there is a peripheral vasodilation[2], presumably due to the release of the same mediator that functions centrally. He suggested that an ideal way to identify the mediator would be to find a naturally-occurring compound that mimicked the effects of antidromic sensory nerve stimulation. SP fulfils the criteria for the endogenous mediator since it not only causes vasodilation, but it also causes the peripheral inflammatory response (known variously as neurogenic inflammation, oedema, or plasma extravasation) seen with antidromic stimulation[16]. Both Rosell's[19] and Lembeck's[15] groups demonstrated that systemic administration of [D-Pro^2, D-Phe^7, D-Trp^9]-SP blocked antidromic vasodilation, completing the catalogue of evidence supporting Lembeck's original suggestion[14] that SP is the sensory mediator of this effect. The significance of the neurogenic inflammation has never been clear – is it purely a pharmacological phenomenon, or is it part of the normal inflammatory response? Rosell, Folkers and their collaborators[8] have explored the physiological function of neurogenic inflammation in the model system of the rabbit eye. Irritation of the eye causes a reactive miosis (reduction in pupil diameter) and a breakdown of the blood-aqueous barrier, as does local application of SP (Ref. 1). The newest SP antagonist, [D-Pro^2, D-Trp^{7,9}]-SP, not only blocked the inflammatory responses to SP, but it also blocked the responses to infrared radiation trauma, supporting the idea that a mediator of inflammation might be SP released locally from sensory nerves. The authors raise the intriguing point that since the antagonist was topically active, it might be useful in treatment of the symptoms of eye inflammation.

There is more to a nervous system than a spinal cord, and the antagonists have been applied to problems in the central and peripheral nervous system. An important point is whether the antagonists are useful blockers in iontophoretic experiments *in vivo* or *in vitro*. Engberg et al.[3] tested the [D-Pro^2, D-Trp^{7,9}]-SP analogue as an antagonist of micro-iontophoretic application of SP to locus coeruleus neurones, a site where SP has been shown to give a dose-dependent excitation. Application of the antagonist did not alter the spontaneous firing rate of single neurones, but abolished the increased firing rate provoked by iontophoretic SP, and not the stimulations by iontophoretic acetylcholine or glutamic acid. Thus, the [D-Pro^2, D-Trp^{7,9}]-SP analogue appears to be a selective SP antagonist in a supraspinal site. It is interesting to note that the electrodes were loaded with matched concentrations of SP and the antagonist, and that for an ejection current of 10 nA for SP, the excitation was fully blocked by a 10 nA ejection current for the antagonist electrode. Although the transport numbers for the two peptides might be very different, a more interesting possibility is that the antagonist may be very potent at some CNS sites.

In recent years, peptides have been put forward as candidates for excitatory and inhibitory non-cholinergic, non-adrenergic mediators in the peripheral nervous system. Leander et al.[12] used the [D-Pro^2, D-Trp^{7,9}]-SP antagonist to test for a role for SP. In the guinea pig taenia coli and the rabbit iris pupillary sphincter, the antagonist specifically blocked the actions of exogenous SP as well as the non-cholinergic, non-adrenergic excitatory responses to electrical stimulation. The group also reported that in the guinea pig urinary bladder, although the antagonist blocked the activity of exogenous SP, it had no effect on the contraction elicited by nerve stimulation. Thus, the antagonist results suggest that SP might be one, but not the only, excitatory non-cholinergic, non-adrenergic transmitter in the periphery.

In a short period of time, Folkers, Rosell and their collaborators have dramatically increased our knowledge about the possible roles of SP. Nevertheless, it is important to recognize that there are several problems with the current generation of antagonists. First, on some systems, they act as partial agonists[12]. Second, they are low in potency, requiring concentrations from 10 to 100 μM to block SP actions. This combination of characteristics means that in some systems, as the guinea pig urinary bladder, the antagonists cannot be used except at concentrations where their partial agonist action is maximal. Inevitably, desensitization by the agonist action introduces a problem of interpretation of the results, as had been noted for the [D-Phe[7]]-SP analogue[5]. Lastly, a new but very intriguing problem has appeared. When injected into the brain, [D-Pro[2], D-Trp[7,9]]-SP appears to have neurotoxic actions on neurones[7]! It is unclear to what extent this may be a problem for in-vivo experiments, but Piercey et al.[17] reported motor dysfunctions and partial paralysis after intrathecal injection of [D-Pro[2], D-Phe[7], D-Trp[9]]-SP analogue. This may prove to be either an unselective toxicity arising from the structural modifications or perhaps it may be a direct consequence of the blockade of some SP receptors. Other work has shown that SP can exert a partial protective effect against neonatal neurotoxin damage[11]. One speculation is that SP, in addition to the roles suggested above, may be a trophic agent which influences the survival of some populations of neurones. Even though we may learn about completely unexpected actions of SP through this toxic effect, it must certainly be regarded as an ominous sign for the design of clinically useful analgesics based upon the antagonists.

Reading list

1 Bill, A., Stjernschantz, A., Mandahl, A., Brodin, E. and Nilsson, G. (1979) *Acta Physiol. Scand.* 106, 371–373

2 Dale, H. H. (1935) *Proc. R. Soc. Med.* 28, 319–332

3 Engberg, G., Svensson, T. H., Rosell, S. and Folkers, K. (1981) *Nature (London)* 293, 222–223

4 Folkers, K., Hörig, J., Rosell, S. and Björkroth, U. (1981) *Acta Physiol. Scand.* 111, 505–507

5 Growcott, J. W. and Petter, N. N. (1980) *J. Pharm. Pharmacol.* 32, 376–377

6 Hanley, M. R. and Iversen, L. L. (1980) *Neurotransmitter Receptors Part I. Amino Acids, Peptides, and Benzodiazepines* (Enna, S. J. and Yamamura, H. I., eds), pp. 71–103, Chapman and Hall, London

7 Hökfelt, T., Vincent, S., Hellsten, L., Rosell, S., Folkers, K., Markey, K., Goldstein, M. and Cuello, C. (1981) *Acta Physiol. Scand.* 113, 571–573

8 Holmdahl, G., Håkanson, R., Leander, S., Rosell, S., Folkers, K. and Sundler, F. (1981) *Science* 214, 1029–1031

9 Iversen, L. L., Nagy, J., Emson, P. C., Lee, C. M., Hanley, M. R., Sandberg, B., Ninkovic, M. and Hunt, S. (1981) *Chemical Neurotransmission. 75 Years* (Stjärne, L., Hedqvist, P., Lagercrantz, H. and Wennmalm, A., eds), pp. 501–512, Academic Press, London

10 Janscó, G., Király, E. and Janscó-Gábor, A. (1977) *Nature (London)* 270, 741–743

11 Jonsson, G. and Hallman, H. (1982) *Science* 215, 75–77

12 Leander, S., Håkanson, R., Rosell, S., Folkers, K., Sundler, F. and Tornqvist, K. (1981) *Nature (London)* 294, 467–469

13 Leban, J. J., Rackur, G., Yamaguchi, I., Folkers, K., Björkroth, U., Rosell, S., Yanaihara, N. and Yanaihara, C. (1979) *Acta Chem. Scand.* 33, 664–668

14 Lembeck, F. (1953) *Naunyn-Schmiedebergs Arch. Pharmakol. Exp. Pathol.* 219, 197–213

15 Lembeck, F., Folkers, K. and Donnerer, J. (1981) *Biochem. Biophys. Res. Commun.* 103, 1318–1321

16 Lembeck, F. and Holzer, P. (1979) *Naunyn-Schmiedebergs Arch. Pharmacol.* 310, 175–183

17 Piercey, M. F., Schroeder, L. A., Folkers, K., Xu, J.-C. and Hörig, J. (1981) *Science* 214, 1361–1363

18 Rackur, G., Yamaguchi, I., Leban, J. J., Björkroth, U., Rosell, S. and Folkers, K. (1979) *Acta Chem. Scand.* 33, 375–378

19 Rosell, S., Olgart, L., Gazelius, B., Panopoulos, P., Folkers, K. and Hörig, J. (1981) *Acta Physiol. Scand.* 111, 381–383

20 Saito, K., Konishi, S. and Otsuka, M. (1975) *Brain Res.* 97, 177–180

21 Wall, P. D., Fitzgerald, M., Nussbaumer, J. C., Van der Loos, H. and Devor, M. (1982) *Nature (London)* 295, 691–693

22 Yaksh, T. L., Farb, D. H., Leeman, S. E. and Jessell, T. M. (1979) *Science* 206, 481–483

23 Yamaguchi, I., Rackur, G., Leban, J. J., Björkroth, U., Rosell, S. and Folkers, K. (1979) *Acta Chem. Scand.* 33, 63–68

Michael R. Hanley is lecturer at the Department of Biochemistry, Imperial College, London SW7 2AZ, U.K.

Sir Thomas Lewis's nocifensor system, histamine and substance-P-containing primary afferent nerves

F. Lembeck

Among the most fascinating papers in the British Medical Journal *are those describing two lectures on 'The nocifensor system of nerves and its reactions' by Sir Thomas Lewis*[31,32] *in 1937. His work, based on careful observations of human skin, led to the conclusion that a neurogenic system existed in skin – independent of the CNS – that controlled elements of defence such as inflammation. Considerable support for this theory has emerged recently based on the function of substance P present in a group of small-diameter primary afferent fibers.*

Sir Thomas Lewis described five main sets of observations upon which his 'nocifensor system' hypothesis was based (see Table I).

1. The spreading hyperalgesia around the skin injury was shown to be due to a local nervous mechanism since it could be delayed for some time by the injection of procaine. Nerves emerging via the posterior root system were shown to play a role in the reaction which was independent of activity arising in the central or sympathetic nervous systems. Tissue factors released as a result of the injury, and not the pain of injury *per se*, were regarded as being responsible.

2. Hyperalgesia arising from the stimulation of cutaneous nerves in a distal (antidromic) direction also demonstrated the neurogenic origin of a slowly developing and long-lasting (up to 15 min) tenderness in an area of approximately 20 cm^2 around the point

of injury. The release of 'a pain-producing substance' which acted on overlapping endings of neighbouring sensory nerves was suggested. Clinical observations were described such as the tenderness extending from a tooth in the upper jaw to the whole territory of the maxillary nerve.

3. The flare from local injury, extensively described in his papers on the 'triple response', was shown to coincide with the spreading hyperalgesia. It too was shown to depend on the function of the posterior root system. The release of two neurogenic substances was thought to be involved because of the differences in the duration of the flare caused by histamine and that caused by local injury.

4. The 'antidromic' flush was reviewed with regard to its relation with the posterior root system and to the experimental steps taken to determine its neurotransmitter, which was

TABLE I. Sir Thomas Lewis (1937): Nocifensor system of nerves

	Observation in man	Posterior root nerve system	Vasodilatator reaction	Histamine involved	Substance P involved	Experiments in animals
1. Spreading hyperalgesia from local injury	+	+	?	?	?	+
2. Hyperalgesia from distal stimulation of cutaneous nerves	+	+	?	?	?	+
3. Flare from local injury	+	+	+	+	+	?
4. The 'antidromic' flush	+	+	+	+	+	+
5. Reaction to cold	+	+	+	+	?	?

known to have a delayed action[1,2,22,23].

5. The reaction of human skin to cold was analysed. A distinction between the initial sympathetic vasoconstriction and the subsequent vasodilatation was emphasized; the latter was described as having a neurogenic mechanism. The importance of this neurogenic vasodilator reaction as a protective mechanism against over-cooling was also emphasized. This view is reminiscent of that of Breslauer[5], who first suggested that neurogenic vasodilatation in the skin, via the posterior root system, was an essential mechanism for the protection of skin against damage by any kind of injury. Lewis also discussed various older views on 'trophic nerves'.

On the basis of these observations, Lewis postulated the existence of a 'nocifensor system' mediated by nerves coursing peripherally via the posterior roots. He was aware of the close relation between this system and that sending nociceptive information to the CNS. Although he attributed all five reactions described above to the same system of nerves, he hesitated to suggest that both functions, the peripheral nocifensor response and the centripetal nociceptive transmission, could be localized in one system.

The nocifensor system was finally conceived 'as a system of nerves capable of effecting changes in the skin locally and without reference to the CNS, though very possibly also capable of excitation from brain or cord'. In a truly prophetic way, he regarded 'the nerves as liberating potent substances from cellular elements of the skin into surrounding space thus controlling partly or wholly within the skin, important elements of defence, including inflammation'.

These early observations of Sir Thomas Lewis can be linked to the recent knowledge about the presence, release and functions of substance P located in small-diameter primary afferent fibers. The neurotoxin capsaicin, introduced to pharmacology by Nikolaus Jancsó, was of major importance for these investigations because of its specific and selective actions on these fibers. A small dose of capsaicin immediately stimulates substance-P-containing fibers and causes them to release substance P; a large dose initiates a delayed, long-lasting or even irreversible depletion of substance P in these nerves and the extinction of their function[36].

Several groups of peptidergic sensory neurons with small-diameter unmyelinated fibers (C-fibers) have been described in the dorsal root ganglion. Some populations contain substance P or somatostatin, peptides which can be released and depleted by capsaicin, while others contain CCK-8 or bombesin which cannot be released or depleted by capsaicin[13,34,35]. Neurons containing an enzyme, fluoride-resistant acid phosphatase, constitute a fifth population of nerve cells; they are also depleted by capsaicin[37]. Other neurons contain vasoactive intestinal polypeptide (VIP) and it is likely that other populations of neurons will be defined based on the presence of these or other markers. To date, the substance-P-containing primary afferents are by far the best understood and will be referred to exclusively in the following discussion.

The central terminal – the link to the CNS

Ample evidence exists that substance P transmits impulses of primary afferent neurons carrying nociceptive information[9,26,27,39] and sensations from peripheral heat receptors[42]. Nociceptive information is conveyed in somatic and visceral nerves via substance-P-containing neurons and gives rise to viscerosomatic, viscerovisceral[8], circulatory[15,30] and thermoregulatory

reflexes[43]. All these afferent and reflex events seem to have a much longer duration than those mediated by aminergic mechanisms.

The peripheral terminal – the link to the skin

In a variety of mammals stimulation of dorsal roots or of peripheral sensory nerve fibers causes a slowly rising and sustained cutaneous vasodilatation, exceeding the duration of nerve stimulation by several minutes. Only C-fibers are involved in this antidromic effect[16] and the vasodilatation is confined to cutaneous vessels[1,2]. In addition to the antidromic vasodilatation, plasma extravasation also occurs[19,25,34]. The neurogenic vasodilatation and plasma-extravasation result from peripheral release of substance P which has been measured directly[4,38]. Comparable vascular reac-

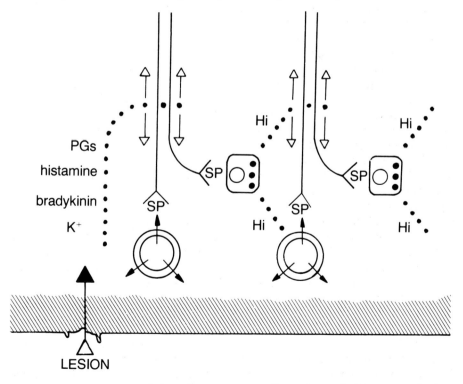

Fig. 1. *Suggested mechanism underlying the axon response. SP = substance P; PGs = prostaglandins; Hi = histamine.* (From Lembeck and Gamse, 1982, with permission of Pitman, London.)

tions have been shown following anti-dromic stimulation of the trigeminal nerve[7]. The finding that a small, nerve-stimulating dose of capsaicin causes plasma extravasation in innervated, but not in sensory denervated, areas of skin suggests that capsaicin acts via peripheral release of a neuro-mediator[6,28,36,40].

If the vasodilatation by antidromic sensory nerve stimulation is of phy-siological relevance, possible modes of its stimulation must be considered. The antidromic vasodilatation does not seem to be part of the central regula-tion of the circulation. Only the peripheral stimulation of these neurons initiates vasodilatation. One such event is the anoxic stimulation of sensory nerves by arterial occlusion; after its release cutaneous reactive hyperemia is observed[24].

A sequence of events may be ini-tiated whenever a nerve terminal is stimulated by various means such as mechanical, thermal or chemical injury in the skin (Fig. 1). Such an injury initiates potassium release from dam-aged cells, histamine release from mast cells and activation of kallikrein result-ing in the formation of bradykinin. All these compounds, especially bradyki-nin which is more powerful than the others, stimulate nociceptors[20]. In addition, they all induce the release of prostaglandins which facilitates their action on nociceptors.

Stimulation of the nociceptors does not necessarily lead to the sensation of pain. Pain is initiated only by the simul-taneous stimulation of many neurons. Below this pain threshold the stimula-tion of nociceptors – or better, the ter-minal region of polymodal nociceptive fibers – is capable of releasing sub-stance P from the peripheral terminals which elicits cutaneous vasodilatation by its action on vascular smooth mus-cle. This effect would, however, be limited to the small area of skin sup-plied by each fiber. In the rat the area supplied by one C-fiber was estimated to be 6 mm^2 (Ref. 21). In human skin the area supplied by a single nocicep-tive fiber seems to be about 1 cm^2 whereas the flare which develops around a small injury encompasses an area of up to 30 cm^2 within several minutes.

Auxillary action of histamine

Lewis suggested a possible role of histamine in the 'triple response' of injured skin (see above), but only recently has the role of substance P been demonstrated. Substance P stimulates the release of histamine from cutaneous mast cells of the rat paw and in human skin (Refs 10, 11, 14, 41). Assuming that some sub-stance-P-containing neurons terminate close to mast cells (a possibility which still needs to be substantiated histologi-cally), an antidromic volley of impulses in substance-P-containing fibers would induce histamine release from mast cells. In addition to the direct vasodila-tor effect of substance P, the released histamine would also (1) contribute to the vasodilator effects of substance P released by antidromic stimulation and (2) stimulate other neighbouring nociceptors. This process would ini-tiate a repetition of this cycle by the terminals of adjacent neurons. As the area of the flare increases, the number of nociceptors reaching threshold gradually decreases and the reaction fades. It is a process requiring much more time than a purely neurogenic reaction. The contribution of histamine to the antidromic vasodilatation was demonstrated by the use of anti-hist-amine drugs and compound 48/80 which inhibit both vasodilatation and plasma-extravasation caused either by infusion of substance P, by antidromic saphe-nous nerve stimulation, or by arterial occlusion[25,29,40]. Following oral pre-treatment with antihistamine drugs, findings relevant to human skin have also been made[11].

Axon 'reflex' or axon 'response'?

In the generally accepted mechanism for the axon reflex, the initial stimulus induces afferent volleys which spread through the terminal ramifications of the axon causing vasodilatation in the surrounding area. This concept of the axon-reflex would, however, explain an immediate vasodilatation but it does not explain the well-known slowly spreading vasodilatation which occurs over a duration of several minutes.

The findings with regard to histamine release from mast cells by substance P suggested a new concept of the axon-reflex which, I believe, is better called an 'axon response'. It would explain the earlier conclusion of Lewis that probably two compounds are needed to explain the flush. The joint functions of neurogenically released substance P and histamine released from mast cells can only happen in a tissue rich in mast cells such as the skin.

A new basis for the nocifensor system

The suggested process, depending on a neurogenic component and on a second component in the tissue, finally leads to vasodilatation. Cutaneous vasodilatation was already regarded by Breslauer[5] in 1919 as an important protective mechanism in the skin against injury of any kind. I think that vasodilatation, because of the increased blood flow, would serve to facilitate the removal of endogenous or exogenous irritants or toxic substances. Increased plasma extravasation could, in addition, allow a faster elimination of larger molecules by the lymph flow. It is an old observation that skin, whenever it is injured, responds by hyperemia. This is seen when the skin is damaged by stroking, radiant heat, ultraviolet irradiation, irritating chemicals, following inten-

sive cold or short-term anoxia. It may also be the mechanism underlying cutaneous antigen–antibody reactions such as occur in various infectious diseases. The result is always a more or less pronounced reddening of the skin for various lengths of time. It seems quite reasonable to associate these observations with the 'nocifensor system' of Lewis. An experimental basis for the antidromic flush now seems to be well established. The flare arising from local histamine injection or local injury also fits fairly well into this concept because blockade of the function of substance-P-containing nerves by capsaicin interrupts the development of the flare around an intradermal injection of histamine[3,11].

The spread of hyperalgesia around skin injury was recently investigated in the rabbit by Fitzgerald[12]. She concluded that the spread of sensitization of polymodal nociceptors from a nearby injury might occur 'by a local, activity-dependent release of such agents which spread into the surrounding inactive area'. The reaction to cold is, however, not so easily incorporated into this concept since a sympathetic vasoconstrictor release may be involved.

Thus, recent findings bring much support to Lewis's idea of a nocifensor system. He doubted whether this nocifensor system and the afferent transfer of nociceptive messages could be attributed to a single neuron of the posterior root system. But recent findings permit the conclusion that both the afferent transfer of nociceptive messages and the peripheral neurogenic 'nocifensor system' can be mediated by the same neuron. Convincing evidence in favour of this was recently reported by Jancsó[18] who demonstrated that intracisternal injection of capsaicin caused selective impairment of the central terminals only (shown by the loss of nociceptive reactions) while the peripheral function of the neuron (shown by neurogenic plasma extravasation) remained intact. The main support for this theory is based on the recent knowledge of the functions of substance P and its presence in neurons as well as on the effects of capsaicin and substance-P-antagonizing peptides.

The nocifensor system has been shown to exist in cutaneous tissue; recent experiments suggest that a similar mechanism is also present in the mucosa of the respiratory tract[33]. A sensory-mediated response to laser irradiation in the eye may also indicate the existence of the nocifensor system there[7,17]. Further exploration of these findings is needed to bring the present experimental achievements within range of possible clinical and therapeutic applications.

Reading list

1 Bayliss, W. M. (1901) *J. Physiol. (London)* 26, 173–207
2 Bayliss, W. M. (1902) *J. Physiol. (London)* 28, 276–299
3 Bernstein, J. E., Swift, R. M., Soltani, K. and Lorincz, A. L. (1981) *J. Invest. Dermatol.* 76, 394–395
4 Bill, A., Stjernschantz, J., Mandahl, A., Brodin, E. and Nilsson, G. (1979) *Acta Physiol. Scand.* 106, 371–373
5 Breslauer, F. (1919) *Dtsch. Z. Chir.* 150, 50–81
6 Buck, S. H., Walsh, J. H., Yamamura, H. I. and Burks, T. F. (1982) *Life Sci.* 30, 1857–1866
7 Butler, J. M., Unger, W. G. and Cole, D. F. (1980) *Q. J. Exp. Physiol.* 65, 261–272
8 Cervero, F. and McRitchie, H. A. (1982) *Brain Res.* 239, 283–288
9 Dobry, P. J. K., Piercey, M. F. and Schroeder, L. A. (1981) *Neuropharmacology* 20, 267–272
10 Erjavec, F., Lembeck, F., Florjanc-Irman, T., Skofitsch, G., Donnerer, J., Saria, A. and Holzer, P. (1981) *Naunyn-Schmiedebergs Arch. Pharmakol.* 317, 67–70
11 Foreman J. and Jordan, C. (1983) *Agents and Actions* 13, 105–116
12 Fitzgerald, M. (1979) *J. Physiol. (London)* 297, 207–216
13 Gamse, R. (1982) *Naunyn-Schmiedebergs Arch. Pharmakol.* 320, 205–216
14 Hägermark, O., Hökfelt, T. and Pernow, B. (1978) *J. Invest. Dermatol.* 71, 233–235
15 Häusler, G. and Osterwalder, R. (1980) *Naunyn-Schmiedebergs Arch. Pharmakol.* 314, 111–121
16 Hinsey, J. C. and Gasser, H. S. (1930) *Am. J. Physiol.* 99, 679–689
17 Holmdahl, G., Håkanson, R., Leander, S., Rosell, S., Folkers, K. and Sundler, F. (1981) *Science* 214, 1029–1031
18 Jancsó, G. (1981) *Neurosci. Lett.* 27, 41–45
19 Jancsó, N., Jancsó-Gábor, A. and Szolcsányi, J. (1967) *Br. J. Pharmacol.* 31, 138–151
20 Juan, H. and Lembeck, F. (1974) *Naunyn-Schmiedebergs Arch. Pharmakol.* 283, 151–164
21 Kenins, P. (1981) *Neurosci. Lett.* 25, 137–141
22 Langley, J. N. (1923). *J. Physiol. (London)* 57, 428–446
23 Langley, J. N. (1932) *J. Physiol. (London)* 58, 70–73
24 Lembeck, F. and Donnerer, J. (1981) *Naunyn-Schmiedebergs Arch. Pharmakol.* 316, 165–171
25 Lembeck, F., Donnerer, J. and Barthó, L. (1982) *Eur. J. Pharmacol.* 85, 171–176
26 Lembeck, F., Donnerer, J. and Colpaert, F. C. (1981) *Neuropeptides* 1, 175–180
27 Lembeck, F., Folkers, K. and Donnerer, J. (1981) *Biochem. Biophys. Res. Commun.* 103, 1318–1321
28 Lembeck, F. and Gamse, R. (1982) in *Substance P in the Nervous System* (Porter R. and O'Connor, M., eds), pp. 35–54, Pitman Books Ltd, London
29 Lembeck, F. and Holzer, P. (1979) *Naunyn-Schmiedebergs Arch. Pharmakol.* 310, 175–183
30 Lembeck, F. and Skofitsch, G. (1982) *Naunyn-Schmiedebergs Arch. Pharmakol.* 321, 116–122
31 Lewis, T. (1937) *Br. Med. J.* 194, 431–435
32 Lewis, T. (1937) *Br. Med. J.* 194, 491–494
33 Saria, A., Lundberg, J. M., Skofitsch, G. and Lembeck, F. (1983) *Naunyn-Schmiedebergs Arch. Pharmakol.* 324, 212–218
34 Marley, P. D., Nagy, J. I., Emson, P. C. and Rehfeld, J. F. (1982) *Brain Res.* 238, 494–498
35 Moody, T. W., Thoa, N. B., O'Donohue, T. L. and Jacobowitz, D. M. (1981) *Life Sci.* 29, 2273–2279
36 Nagy, J. I. (1982) *Trends NeuroSci.* 5, 362–365
37 Nagy, J. I. and Hunt, S. P. (1982) *Neuroscience* 7, 89–97
38 Olgart, L., Gazelius, B., Brodin, E. and Nils-

son, G. (1977) *Acta Physiol. Scand.* 101, 510–512

39 Piercey, M. F., Dobry, P. J. K., Schroeder, L. A. and Einspahr, F. J. (1981) *Brain Res.* 210, 407–413

40 Rosell, S., Olgart, L., Gazelius, B., Panopoulos, P., Folkers, K. and Hörig, J. (1981) *Acta Physiol. Scand.* 111, 381–382

41 Skofitsch, G., Donnerer, J., Petronijevic, S., Saria, A. and Lembeck, F. (1983) *Naunyn-Schmiedebergs Arch. Pharmakol.* 322, 153–157

42 Petsche, U., Fleischer, E., Lembeck, F. and Handwerker, H. O. (1983) *Brain Res.* 265, 233–240

43 Donnerer, J. and Lembeck, F. (1983) *Br. J. Pharmac.* 79, 719–723

F. Lembeck is at the Institute of Experimental and Clinical Pharmacology, University of Graz, A-8010 Graz, Austria; and with the Pain Research Commission of the Austrian Academy of Sciences.

Capsaicin's action on the nervous system

J. I. Nagy

Over the past several decades capsaicin, a natural product of certain species of red pepper, has been found to have a broad range of physiological effects in adult animals. Recent findings indicate that many of these effects result from a selective action of the compound on a certain population of primary sensory neurons, namely those giving rise to unmyelinated fibres. When administered under appropriate conditions to neonatal rats, capsaicin selectively destroys this same population of neurons. Animals receiving this treatment and raised to adulthood are virtually depleted of unmyelinated primary afferents. These observations have clearly demonstrated capsaicin's potential to aid investigations in the area of sensory physiology. Despite the growing recognition and use of capsaicin as a chemical tool, many details of its actions remain to be elucidated. The present article is a summary of capsaicin's effects with an emphasis on the key problems yet to be confronted.

Capsaicin (see Fig. 1) is the parent molecule of a number of structually related compounds which give a variety of red peppers their pungent flavour[21]. The substance has an influence on a range of physiological processes stretching far beyond those involved in creating its gustatory appeal. For example, neuroanatomical and biochemical investigations have shown that capsaicin exerts effects on specific populations of primary sensory neurons located in sensory ganglia at virtually all cranial and spinal levels. Although investigation of the effects of capsaicin on the nervous system have attracted considerable attention in recent years, the notion that this compound is new to the laboratory is incorrect. The physiological effects of oily extracts from red peppers have been studied for over one hundred years.

The most incisive early contributions were made by the late N. Jancsó and his wife, A. Jancsó-Gábor, through work they initiated in the late 1940s and continued for the subsequent two decades. They established that in adult animals the immediate

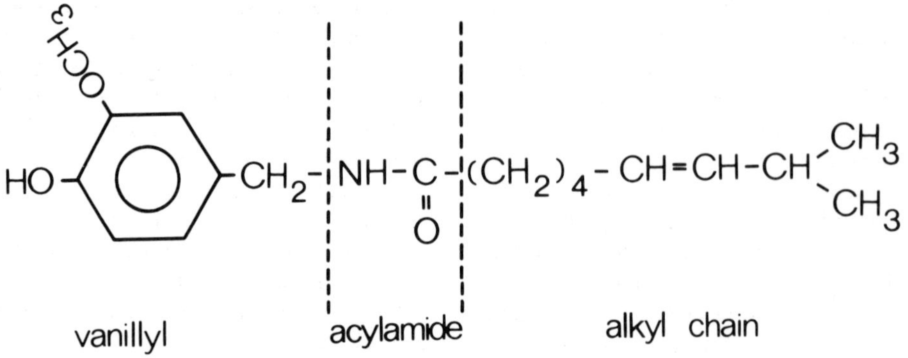

Fig. 1. *The structure of capsaicin showing the three moieties which are important in contributing to the activity of the compound.*

effects of acute low doses of capsaicin are distinguishable from those of larger, chronic doses[12, 13]. In the early 1970s G. Jancsó and his colleagues began studies of the effects of capsaicin in neonatal rats. Their work culminated in a report demonstrating that capsaicin caused rapid degeneration of a specific population of neurons in the dorsal root ganglia (DRG)[10].

These findings indicate that a general account of capsaicin's actions must consider three separate issues, namely its acute and chronic actions in adult animals and its neurotoxic actions in neonates.

Acute actions

Capsaicin's ability to interfere with a large number of biological processes is matched by the plethora of experimental paradigms in which its effects have been studied[17] (Table I). For example, electrophysiological studies have shown it to be remarkable in its selectivity for activating certain unmyelinated (type 'C') primary afferent fibres[19, 20], and its cardiovascular and respiratory reflex function can be traced in part to the excitation of a distinct population of these fibres in the vagus nerve[2, 15]. The importance of particular groups of sensory fibres has been further demonstrated indirectly in studies showing that an intact sensory supply is required for certain effects of capsaicin. For example, chronic sensory deafferentation of skin areas and the guinea-pig ileum abolishes capsaicin-induced inflammatory responses and smooth muscle contraction, respectively[1, 13, 14, 22]. Many of capsaicin's acute effects are extremely potent, with measurable responses being achieved at micromolar concentrations in vitro and microgram quantities in vivo.

Some of the classes of unmyelinated sensory fibres susceptible to capsaicin's acute actions contain the neuropeptides substance P or somatostatin[18]. Although the exact function of substance P and somatostatin in sensory ganglia is unclear, they may have a role as primary afferent neurotransmitters. Both in-vitro and in-vivo experiments have

shown that capsaicin has the ability to cause the release of substance P and somatostatin from the central and peripheral terminals of these primary afferent neurons[4, 6, 26]. Thus, some of capsaicin's acute actions in vivo may result from the release of these peptides.

Chronic actions and desensitization

During prolonged exposure there is a gradual diminution of capsaicin's acute effects[17, 21]. N. Jancsó and his colleagues first observed that animals receiving repeated topical application of capsaicin became insensitive to its irritant properties. They also found that the parenteral administraton of large doses of capsaicin abolished both the induction of hypothermia and the inflammatory response to subsequent doses of capsaicin and other agents which are ordinarily capable of producing an inflammation reaction[12, 13] (Table I).

In in-vitro systems desensitization to capsaicin occurs in the order of minutes and can be achieved using relatively low doses[1, 4, 22]. In contrast, several days may be required for desensitization to occur in vivo and here, the loss in efficacy to capsaicin's acute actions is gradual[12, 13]. Could desensitization be due to the depletion of substance P and somatostatin from primary afferent neurons[3, 6, 7]? While this may be true in certain cases, some of the physiological characteristics of desensitization could equally well be due to capsaicin's inactivation of voltage-sensitive mechanisms in the unmyelinated fibres. An additional problem concerns the demonstration that when capsaicin is applied locally to peripheral nerves, it causes inhibition of the axonal transport of substance P and somatostatin[5], and this produces effects similar to capsaicin desensitization, i.e. it abolishes inflammatory responses to irritant chemicals and produces thermal analgesia in the skin areas supplied by the treated nerve[11].

In early studies, the terms 'capsaicin desensitization' and 'sensory neuron blocking agent' were chosen to describe phenomena associated with chronic treat-

TABLE I. Some of the effects capsaicin has in adult animals after its acute or chronic administration, and in mature animals which have received capsaicin neonatally. Also included are observations using *in-vitro* preparations; in these cases the effects of a single application of capsaicin are listed under acute treatment, and those of repeated applications under chronic treatment. The peptides referred to in the Table are substance P and somatostatin. For more detailed information on the individual observations see Ref. 17.

Effects	Adult acute treatment	Adult chronic treatment	Neonatal treatment
Cardiovascular and respiratory	Increases or decreases: heart rate, blood pressure, respiratory rate, (depending on route of administration)	Reduces effects on heart rate, blood pressure and respiratory rate	
Inflammatory	Promotes inflammatory response	Abolishes inflammatory responses	Abolishes inflammatory responses
Thermoregulatory	Produces hypothermia	Abolishes hypothermic effect, hyperthermia ensues at elevated ambient temperatures	Reduces hypothermic effect, hyperthermia ensues at elevated ambient temperatures
Intestinal *in vitro*	Contracts isolated guinea-pig ileum	Guinea-pig ileum tachyphylactic after repeated exposures	
Neurophysiological	Stimulates unmyelinated primary afferents	Fibres refactory to stimulatory effects	Abolishes 'C' compound action potential in stimulated peripheral nerves
Neuroanatomical		Perturbs morphology of sensory ganglia neurons	Causes degeneration of primary afferent fibres
Biochemical *in vitro*	Releases peptides from primary afferents	Tachyphylaxis to peptide release effect	Abolishes release of peptides contained in primary afferents
in vivo	Releases peptides from primary afferents	Depletes peptides from primary afferents	Destroys peptide-containing primary afferent neurons
Noxious	Produces burning sensation in man and irritation in animals	Reduces responsiveness of animals to noxious chemical and mechanical stimuli	Reduces responsiveness of animals to noxious chemical, mechanical and thermal stimuli

ment because its action was not thought to involve degeneration of primary sensory neurons, despite the long periods of desensitization that persisted after such treatment. While the bulk of available evidence supports the lack of capsaicin-induced neuronal degeneration in adults, this point needs to be further substantiated.

Neurotoxic action

Neuroanatomical studies have shown that administration of capsaicin to neonatal rats causes massive degeneration of primary afferent neurons[9,10,18]. These changes are precipitated with remarkable rapidity – the first signs appear 30 minutes after treatment. Adult animals given capsaicin neonatally have reduced numbers of sensory ganglia neurons and suffer a depletion of fibres in peripheral nerves and dorsal roots. Work by L. L. Iversen's group in Cambridge, U.K., indicates that the degree of fibre depletion in dorsal roots and the type of fibres affected are highly dependent on the dose of capsaicin administered. At high doses a profound depletion of unmyelinated fibres occurs concomitant with a smaller but significant loss of myelinated fibres. In a lower dose range the depletions are restricted to unmyelinated fibres, again in a dose-dependent manner, and depletions as great as 80% can be obtained with negligible loss of myelinated fibres. Thus, under proper conditions the neurotoxic action of capsaicin in the neonate provides the opportunity to dissect out chemically a significant and selective population of primary afferent neurons, namely those giving rise to unmyelinated fibres. As shown in Table I, this fibre loss produces some effects similar to those seen after chronic capsaicin treatment of adult animals. It should be emphasized, however, that a strict correspondence between the effects of the two treatments may not always occur.

Specificity and site of action

None of capsaicin's effects on sensory neurons, e.g. stimulation of peptide release

in vitro, the depletion of peptides *in vivo*, the inhibition of axonal transport or the neurotoxic action in neonates, have been observed for sympathetic or parasympathetic neurons or neurons in the CNS. Thus, capsaicin appears to elicit the release of only substance P or somatostatin and only from primary afferent neurons[4]. Furthermore, with one exception, no other physiological effects of capsaicin have been reported which could be interpreted unequivocally as resulting from a direct action of the compound on the autonomic or central nervous system. The one puzzling exception which has yet to be reconciled with the other findings is that intrahypothalamic injection of capsaicin has the same effect on thermoregulation as other routes of capsaicin administration[8]. Thus, acute subcutaneous, intravenous or intrahypothalamic injections of capsaicin all produce a prompt fall in body temperature. Sustained treatment by these routes all result in the remarkable inability of animals to maintain their normal body temperature when placed into an environment kept at 30 or 37°C (Ref. 8).

Although an action directly on axon terminals seems likely, most of the present experimental paradigms (other than the inhibition of axonal transport) do not allow a distinction to be made between the anatomical locus of action on axons, terminals and cell bodies of sensory neurons.

Mechanism of action

The compelling conclusion to be drawn from capsaicin's specificity is that its actions do not involve perturbation of neuronal membrane-associated secretion-coupling or action-potential generator mechanisms which may be common to all neurons, but rather involve sites which may be unique to certain primary afferent neurons.

The depletion of substance P and somatostatin from primary afferent neurons *in vivo* could be the result of their release as observed *in vitro*. However, caution should be exercised in assuming causality.

While inhibition of axonal transport could explain substance P and somatostatin depletion in the periphery, it is not immediately obvious how such a site of action on axonal transport could give rise to the acute actions of capsaicin; e.g. the *in-vitro* evoked release of these peptides. The structure–activity studies discussed below also force distinctions to be made between the mechanisms of capsaicin's acute and chronic actions.

It is not known how capsaicin induces the degeneration of sensory ganglia neurons. Furthermore, susceptibility of neurons in the neonate may only partially be related to the mechanisms underlying capsaicin's specificity in the adult. This notion is prompted by the selectivity of its action on unmyelinated fibres in the adult while in the neonate it causes, at high doses, the degeneration of both unmyelinated and myelinated primary afferent fibres. Capsaicin's broader spectrum of actions in the neonate may be due to the immature or undifferentiated state of neurons at this stage of development. Developing neurons are known to be more susceptible to a variety of disturbances. When neonatal rats are injected subcutaneously with capsaicin they stop breathing for several minutes. Could anoxia contribute to the degeneration of sensory neurons, perhaps in conjunction with a more direct and selective action of capsaicin on these cells?

Structure–activity relationships

Work by Szolcsányi and Jancsó-Gábor has provided some clues regarding capsaicin's molecular site of action[23, 24]. They have established the nociceptive or pain-producing potency of a large number of capsaicin congeners and found that certain structural requirements are necessary to maintain potency. These requirements are as follows (see also Fig. 1): a free hydroxyl group on the aromatic ring is essential; a critical distance linking the acylamide and vanillyl moieties must be maintained; conversion of the nitrogen from a secondary to a tertiary amine abolishes activity; and the alkyl chain has an optimal length of 8–10 carbon atoms. These findings suggest that capsaicin interacts with a molecular recognition site which is able to discriminate subtle changes in ligand structure.

Preliminary evidence from a number of sources indicates that the nociceptive potencies of compounds which are structurally related to capsaicin correlate with their potencies to elicit peptide release *in vitro*, to cause sensory ganglia neurons degeneration in the neonate, and to exert effects on the cardiovascular system in the adult[9, 21]. By contrast, there is less of a correlation between capsaicin's desensitizing and nociceptive activities[23, 24]. While nociceptive potency is retained by substitution of the acylamide with an inverted (relative to the vanillyl and alkyl groups) alkyl ester moiety, this substitution abolishes desensitizing activity. Moreover, the optimal alkyl chain length for desensitizing potency appears to be 10–12 carbon atoms. Thus, desensitization may involve mechanisms in addition to or different from those producing its other effects.

Experimental applications of capsaicin

A number of groups have employed capsaicin as a chemical tool in the study of the function and organization of primary afferents. A few of the many examples of these are: (1) the electrophysiological investigations by Coleridge and co-workers who used sensitivity to capsaicin as one means of classifying functionally vagal fibres innervating the cardiovascular and pulmonary systems[2, 15]; (2) the recent work by Lembeck's group and Jancsó's own early contributions involving capsaicin to investigate the neurogenic components of inflammatory responses[12, 13, 14, 16]; (3) the studies by Wall and co-workers who have analysed alterations in receptive field properties of CNS neurons after capsaicin-induced depletions of unmyelinated primary afferent neurons. On the basis of their findings, they suggested that unmyelinated primary afferents may orchestrate the synaptic connections of myelinated prim-

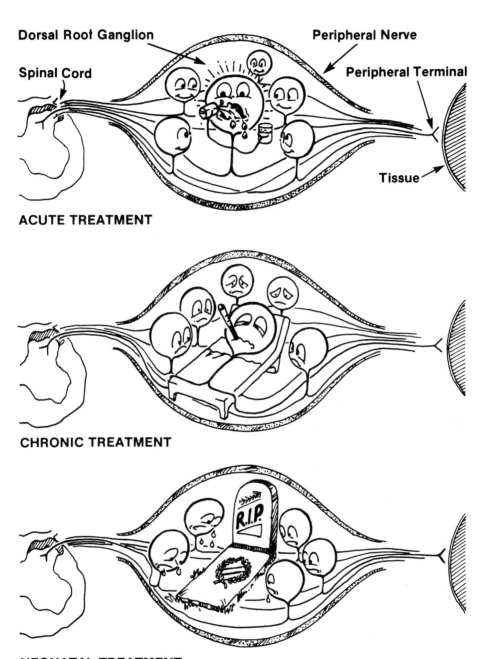

Fig. 2. *Illustration of the three modes of action of capsaicin on certain populations of primary afferent neurons. The acute action is excitation, chronic treatment leads to what has been defined as desensitization, and neonatal treatment results in degeneration.*

ary afferents in the dorsal horn[25]; (4) the work by Iversen and colleagues who, by comparing normal with capsaicin-treated animals, have studied the organization of substance P-containing primary afferents in the periphery and in the dorsal horn[18]; and (5) the work of Gamse and collaborators who, in a sense, have employed capsaicin in a diagnostic fashion by showing this compound to have effects on substance P in sympathetic ganglia similar to those of its effects on substance P elsewhere[6]. Given the specificity of capsaicin for primary afferents, this finding has provided evidence for an innervation of certain sympathetic ganglia by substance P-containing neurons of sensory ganglia.

Conclusion

In this brief review a simple description of capsaicin's actions was given priority over a more detailed consideration of the information already provided by the use of capsaicin, concerning the nature of certain primary afferent neurons. It is hoped that the provision of the current state of knowledge on capsaicin may encourage a quick resolution of the major questions surrounding the actions of this compound. Knowledge of capsaicin's mechanism of action would benefit investigations along three directions. First, this may facilitate the design of active capsaicin analogues which may be better suited for applications in studies where capsaicin is now widely used. Second, such knowledge would help to settle whether the selectivity of capsaicin towards a certain population of primary afferent neurons indicates the existence of, and capsaicin's interaction with, specific biochemical processes intrinsic to these and no other neurons. If such processes exist, then capsaicin and its analogues may prove invaluable as tools to achieve their elucidation. Finally, further details of how capsaicin exerts its actions would enable decisions to be made regarding the possible benefits of the clinical use of capsaicin. It is not inconceivable that eventually 'capsaicin-like' compounds may find therapeutic applications in cases where it would be desirable to neutralize physiological processes mediated by certain classes of unmyelinated primary afferent fibres.

Reading list

1 Barthó, L. and Szolcsányi, J. (1978) *Naunyn-Schmiedeberg's Arch. Pharmacol.* 305, 75–81
2 Coleridge, J. C. G. and Coleridge, H. M. (1977) *Am. Rev. Respir. Dis.* 115, 251–260
3 Gamse, R., Leaman, S. E., Holzer, P. and Lembeck, F. (1981) *Naunyn-Schmiedeberg's Arch. Pharmacol.* 317, 140–148
4 Gamse, R., Molnar, A. and Lembeck, F. (1979) *Life Sci.* 25, 629–633
5 Gamse, R., Petsche, U., Lembeck, F. and Jancso, G. (1982) *Brain Res.* (in press)
6 Gamse, R., Wax, A., Zigmond, R. E. and Leeman, S. E. (1981) *Neuroscience* 6, 437–441
7 Gasparović, I., Hadzović, S., Huković, S. and Stern, P. (1964) *Med. Exp.* 10, 303–306
8 Jancsó-Gábor, A., Szolcsányi, J. and Janscó, N. (1970) *J. Physiol. (London)* 208, 449–459
9 Jancsó, G. and Király, E. (1981) *Brain Res.* 210, 83–89
10 Jancsó, G., Király, E. and Jancsó-Gábor, A. (1977) *Nature* 270, 741–743
11 Jancsó, G., Király, E. and Jancsó-Gábor, A. (1980) *Naunyn-Schmiedeberg's Arch. Pharmacol.* 313, 91–94
12 Jancsó, N. (1960) *Bull. Millard Fillmore Hosp.* 7, 53–77, Buffalo, N.Y.
13 Jancsó, N. (1968) in *Pharmacology of Pain* (Lim, R. K. S., ed.), pp. 33–55, Pergamon Press, Oxford
14 Jancsó, N., Jancsó-Gábor, A. and Szolcsányi, J. (1968) *Brit. J. Pharmacol.* 32, 32–41
15 Kaufman, M. P., Baker, D. G., Coleridge, H. M. and Coleridge, J. C. G. (1980) *Circ. Res.* 46, 476–484
16 Lembeck, F. and Holzer, P. (1979) *Naunyn-Schmiedeberg's Arch. Pharmacol.* 310, 175–183
17 Nagy, J. I. (1982) in *Handbook of Psychopharmacology* (Iversen, L. L., Iversen, S. D. and Snyder, S. H., eds), Vol. 15, Plenum, N.Y. (in press)
18 Nagy, J. I., Hunt, S. P., Iversen, L. L. and Emson, P. C. (1981) *Neuroscience* 6, 1923–1934
19 Szolcsányi, J. (1977) *J. Physiol. (Paris)* 73, 251–259
20 Szolcsányi, J. (1980) *Proc. Int. Physiol. Soc.* 14, 734
21 Szolcsányi, J. (1982) in *Handbook of Experimental Pharmacology, Pyretics and anti-*

pyretics (Milton, A. S., ed.), Springer, Berlin (in press)

22 Szolcsányi, J. and Barthó, L. (1978) *Naunyn-Schmiedeberg's Arch. Pharmacol.* 305, 83–90

23 Szolcsányi, J. and Jancsó-Gábor, A. (1975) *Arzneim. Forsch.* 25, 1877–1881

24 Szolcsányi, J. and Jancsó-Gábor, A. (1976) *Arzeim-Forsch.* 26, 33–37

25 Wall, P. D., Fitzgerald, M., Nussbaumer, J. C.,

van der Loos, H. and Devor, M. (1982) *Nature* 295, 691–693

26 Yaksh, T. L., Jessell, T. M., Gamse, R., Mudge, A. W. and Leeman, S. E. (1980) *Nature* 286, 155–157

J. I. Nagy is at the Department of Physiology, Faculty of Medicine, University of Manitoba, 770 Bannatyne Avenue, Winnipeg, Manitoba, Canada, R3E 0W3.

Multiple endogenous opioid peptides

Volker Höllt

All endogenous opioid peptides isolated belong to one of three peptide families, each deriving from a distinct precursor molecule: pro-opiomelanocortin is the common precursor for β-endorphin and ACTH; pro-enkephalin A is the common precursor for Met-enkephalin and Leu-enkephalin, as well as for several opioid peptides such as peptide E, BAM-22P, -20P, -12P and peptide F; pro-enkephalin B is another precursor for Leu-enkephalin and for a variety of opioid peptides such as dynorphin 1-17 and α-neo-endorphin. This article provides a short overview of our present knowledge of processing, distribution and receptor selectivity in these three opioid peptide systems.

Since the discovery of the enkephalins in 1975, numerous larger opioid peptides, such as β-endorphin, dynorphin 1-17 and peptide E, have been isolated which contain the sequence of either Met-enkephalin or Leu-enkephalin at their N-terminus. Recently it has become clear that all opioid peptides derive from three different precursor proteins. While the existence of common precursors for ACTH and β-endorphin, in the pituitary (pro-opiomelanocortin–POMC, Refs 9, 16), and for Met-enkephalin and Leu-enkephalin in the adrenal medulla (pro-enkephalin – Ref. 15) has been known for some time, the precise structure of each has only been determined recently using recombinant DNA techniques[4,11,20,22]. Fig. 1 shows the structures of bovine pre-POMC, bovine pre-pro-enkephalin A and a third precursor, porcine pre-pro-enkephalin B, and the peptides derived from them in schematic form.

There are several similarities between the three precursors: they are composed of similar numbers of amino acids (between 257 and 265); they contain repetitive structures, for example, in pre-POMC there are 3 melanocyte stimulating hormone (MSH) sequences, in pre-pro-enkephalin A there are six copies of Met-enkephalin and one of Leu-enkephalin, and in pre-pro-enkephalin B there are three sequences of Leu-enkephalin; and all three precursors possess a cysteine-containing amino terminal sequence, preceded by a signal peptide which consists predominantly of hydrophobic amino acids and is required for vectorial transport of the precursor across the membranes of the endoplasmic reticulum. Subsequently, the signal peptide (or 'pre' sequence) is cleaved and the 'pre-pro-peptide' becomes the 'pro-peptide'.

The majority of the repeated Met- and Leu-enkephalin sequences, as well as the biologically active domains in the pre-POMC, are flanked by pairs of basic amino acids, which appear to be 'processing signals' for a trypsin-like enzyme.

The gene encoding pre-pro-enkephalin A has been analysed[21,23]. There is a close resemblance between the structural organizations of the POMC gene and the pro-enkephalin A gene. Both genes contain two introns (intervening sequences), one of which is inserted in the protein coding sequence near the signal peptide region at an almost equivalent position in the two genes. Moreover, all repeating enkephalin or MSH sequences are encoded by a single large exon (DNA which codes for the final mRNA).

The POMC system

POMC and its processing have been the subject of several reviews (for example, see Ref. 9). In this article some aspects of the processing of the β-endorphin domain in the molecule will be discussed.

POMC is a glycopeptide with sugars attached towards the N-terminal end of the molecule (see Fig. 1). Recently, evidence for phosphorylation of rat POMC at a serine within the ACTH domain has been reported[2]. Whether these post-translational modifications might play a role in processing, by exposing or masking cleavage sites, remains to be elucidated.

Biosynthetic experiments on isolated rat pituitary cells indicate that POMC is processed into β-endorphin with β-lipotropin as an intermediate[16]. Further processing of β-endorphin into α-endorphin and γ-endorphin and Met-enkephalin has not been demonstrated. On the other hand, β-endorphin in the rat intermediate pituitary is further cleaved into β-endorphin 1–27. This and β-endorphin are then α-N-acetylated, a modification step which completely abolished the opiate-like activity of the peptides[30]. Another end product in the processing appears to be α-N-acetyl-β-endorphin 1-26 (Ref. 6).

Processing of POMC appears to be tissue specific. In the adenohypophysis, the predominant precursor products are the larger peptides β-lipotropin and ACTH; only a small proportion of β-lipotropin is further processed into β-endorphin, which is not further cleaved or α-N-acetylated in the adenohypophysis[6]. The processing of POMC in the brain resembles that in the intermediate pituitary, although the precise processing of POMC in the brain, into its fragments as well as the α-N-acetylation of these peptides, still remains to be determined by biosynthesis experiments.

The pro-enkephalin A system

Assuming that paired basic amino acids are obligatory processing signals, the structure of pro-enkephalin A indicates it will be cleaved into four copies of Met-enkephalin and one copy each of Leu-enkephalin, the heptapeptide Met-enkephalin-Arg^6-Phe^7 and the octapeptide Met-enkephalin-Arg^6-Gly^7-Leu^8. These peptides have been isolated and sequenced from bovine adrenal medullary tissues. In addition, a wide variety of larger intermediate peptides have been isolated by Udenfriend's and Matsuo's group[13, 15, 19] (for a review, see Ref. 25). The peptides with demonstrated opiate-like activity are shown in Fig. 1.

Initially, pro-enkephalin A was thought to be the unique common precursor for Met-enkephalin and Leu-enkephalin and was called simply pro-enkephalin (Ref. 15). However, after the recent discovery of the common precursor for dynorphin and the neo-endorphins, which contains three copies of Leu-enkephalin, Numa's group proposed the name pro-enkephalin A for the common precursor of Met-enkephalin and Leu-enkephalin, and pro-enkephalin B for the precursor of the neo-endorphins and dynorphins (Ref. 11).

Pro-enkephalin A contains a potential carbohydrate attachment site in the middle of the molecule[22]. To date however, no glycosylated forms of pro-enkephalin A and/or its intermediates have been isolated. The structure of both bovine and human pre-pro-enkephalin A have been elucidated by recombinant DNA techniques[4, 21, 22]. The human sequence contains four additional amino acids. Moreover, there are several differences in the respective amino acid sequences. For example, the human sequence of peptide F differs by five amino acids from that of the bovine sequence. On the other hand, the complete sequence of peptide E (Ref. 13) is conserved between the two species, indicating that peptide E and/or its fragments, the bovine adrenal medulla peptides (BAM-P), BAM-22P, BAM-20P and BAM-12P, might have important physiological functions[4]. The existence of fragments of peptide E, like BAM-22P, and -12P, suggests the involvement of cleaving enzymes of specificity different from trypsin-like enzymes and thus it has been suggested that these

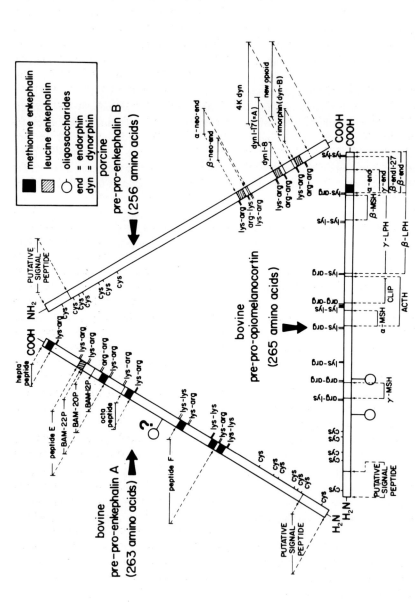

Fig. 1. *Schematic representation of bovine pre-pro-opiomelanocortin, bovine pre-pro-enkephalin A and porcine pre-pro-enkephalin B. The figure is based on the data from Refs 11, 20 and 22. The heptapeptide is Met-enkephalin-Arg⁶-Phe⁷; the octapeptide is Met-enkephalin-Arg⁶-Gly⁷-Leu⁸; BAM-P = bovine adrenal medulla peptides (see Ref. 19).*

peptides are artificially generated by the extraction procedure[13]. However, there is increasing evidence that enzymatic processing does not necessarily involve pairs of basic amino acids as signals. Radioimmunoassays used in combination with chromatographic techniques, have shown BAM-12P and BAM-22P to exist in bovine brain and adrenal medulla[1, 10].

The pro-enkephalin B system

Porcine pre-pro-enkephalin B contains three Leu-enkephalins flanked on both sides by pairs of basic amino acids (Fig. 1). The peptide is the common precursor for a series of intermediate peptides discovered during the past 3 years: α-neo-endorphin (Ref. 12), β-neo-endorphin, dynorphin 1-8; dynorphin 1-17 (dynorphin A; Refs 7, 8) and rimorphin (Ref. 14) (dynorphin B; Ref. 7). In addition, two larger dynorphins have been isolated: mol. wt 4 000 dynorphin (= dynorphin-32) comprising dynorphin 1-17 and rimorphin and dynorphin-32-(1-24) which contains the structure of dynorphin 1-17 and that of Leu-enkephalin (Ref. 7). On the basis of the pro-enkephalin B structure, Kakidani et al.[11] proposed the existence of a new opioid peptide containing the N-terminal sequence of rimorphin plus 16 additional C-terminal amino acids. The existence of dynorphin 1-8 and rimorphin in the pre-pro-enkephalin B and of BAM 12P in the pre-pro-enkephalin A molecule indicates that the base pair Arg-Arg might not be an obligatory processing signal (Fig. 1).

Distribution of the three opioid peptide systems

Radioimmunoassay and immunohistochemical studies have been undertaken to localize and quantitate several peptides originating from these peptide systems. The peptides belonging to the POMC family are localized in high amounts in the pituitary, from which they are released into the blood stream in response to stress and a variety of endocrine manipulations.

POMC-derived peptides have also been localized in cells within, and adjacent to,

the arcuate nucleus of the hypothalamus. Axons of these cells project to the amygdala nuclei and to the periaqueductal grey of the midbrain[3]. In contrast, peptides derived from pro-enkephalin A and pro-enkephalin B have a much wider distribution. They occur in many brain areas, in addition to the pituitary, the spinal cord, the adrenal medulla, the sympathetic ganglia and the gastrointestinal tract. Although pro-enkephalin A- and pro-enkephalin B-derived peptides have different biosynthetic pathways, a significant overlap in their distribution apparently exists. Areas such as the nucleus accumbens, the median forebrain bundle, the hypothalamus, the hippocampus and the spinal cord contain neurons which stain for both peptides[28].

In view of the striking similarity in the distribution the possibility exists that pro-enkephalin A and pro-enkephalin B might be synthesized by the same neurons. On the other hand, there are a few areas such as the substantia nigra which are rich in peptides deriving from pro-enkephalin B, but which cannot be consistently immuno-stained with antibodies directed against peptides belonging to the pro-enkephalin A family[28]. The bovine adrenal medulla contains the highest amounts of the pre-pro-enkephalin A-derived peptides, but very few, if any, peptides derived from pro-enkephalin B (Ref. 18).

The hypothalamic posterior pituitary pathways are particularly good examples of the fact that peptides belonging to the pro-enkephalin B family occur in different neurons than those of the pro-enkephalin A family. Thus, dynorphin related peptides have been shown to be present in the vasopressin producing magnocellular nuclei, whereas Met-enkephalin appears to be localized in the oxytocin-producing cells[17, 26].

Relationship between the different opioid peptide systems and multiple opiate receptors

There is now general agreement that opiate receptors can be classified into at least three types: μ, κ and δ[5]. The enkephalins, which are the proposed end products in the processing of either pro-enkephalin A or pro-enkephalin B, but not of POMC, have been shown to possess a preferential affinity for the δ receptor. On the other hand, all intermediate peptides in the processing of pro-enkephalin B tested, for example dynorphin 1-8, dynorphin 1-17, α-neo-endorphin and rimorphin, show a selective affinity for the κ receptor[5,7,29]. β-Endorphin, the opioid active end product in the processing of POMC, has high affinity for μ, κ and δ sites. No endogenous peptides with selectivity for the μ receptor have been previously described. Recently, however, in collaboration with H. H. Loh, we found evidence that some of the intermediate peptides in the processing of pro-enkephalin A, such as peptide E and BAM-22P, exhibit a high selectivity for μ receptor sites. In addition, these peptides induce a substantial analgesia after intracerebroventricular (i.c.v.) injection into mice[10]. These findings support the hypothesis that the analgesic action of certain opioid peptides might be mediated by the occupation of μ receptors.

Although certain benzomorphans, which are prototype κ agonists, are also potent antinociceptive agents, the pro-enkephalin B intermediates which are proposed to be endogenous ligands for the κ receptor such as dynorphin 1-17 or α-neo-endorphin, have a very weak analgesic activity when administered into the brain of rats and mice. However, recent evidence indicates that dynorphin 1-17 appears to have a pronounced analgesic action when injected into the spinal cord[24]. The evidence available at present, however, might still be insufficient to allocate different receptors to different physiological functions.

One interesting principle that is emerging from these studies is that a single precursor peptide generates peptides with different receptor selectivities and, moreover, that the selectivity changes as the processing continues. For instance, pro-enkephalin B generates first a set of κ-selective intermediates (e.g. dynorphin

1-17, α-neo-endorphin) which might be further processed into the δ-receptor-specific Leu-enkephalin. This suggests that the processing enzymes might play a key role in determining the relative receptor selectivity of the processed peptides. On the other hand, selectivity for the κ receptor would appear to be retained, if the mol. wt 4 000 dynorphin were processed into dynorphin 1-17 and, still further, into dynorphin 1-8 (Refs 5, 27). The latter peptide is readily degraded by peptidases and its potency in various bioassay systems is considerably less than that of dynorphin 1-17, even if its metabolism is prevented by the addition of enzyme inhibitors[5]. The concentrations of dynorphin 1-8 in various regions of the brain, however, are 2- to 10-fold higher than those of dynorphin 1-17 (Ref. 27). It has thus been hypothesized that the 'small dynorphins' like dynorphin 1-8 might have the properties of short-acting neurotransmitters and/or neuro-modulators, where the larger dynorphins might have the qualities of long-acting neurohormones[5].

Reading list

1 Baird, A., Ling, N., Böhlen, P., Benoit, R., Klepper, R. and Guillemin, R. (1982) *Proc. Natl Acad. Sci. U.S.A.* 79, 2023–2025
2 Bennet, H. P., Browne, C. A. and Solomon, S. (1981) *Proc. Natl Acad. Sci. U.S.A.* 78, 4713–4717
3 Bloom, F. E., Battenberg, E., Rossier, J., Ling, N. and Guillemin, R. (1978) *Proc. Natl Acad. Sci. U.S.A.* 75, 1591–1595
4 Comb, M., Seeburg, P. H., Adelman, J., Eiden, L. and Herbert, E. (1982) *Nature (London)* 295, 663–666
5 Corbett, A. D., Paterson, S. J., McKnight, A. T., Magnan, J. and Kosterlitz, H. W. (1982) *Nature (London)* 299, 79–81
6 Eipper, B. A. and Mains, R. E. (1981) *J. Biol. Chem.* 256, 5689–5695
7 Fischli, W., Goldstein, A., Hunkapiller, M. W. and Hood, L. E. (1982) *Proc. Natl Acad. Sci. U.S.A.* 79, 5435–5437
8 Goldstein, A., Fischli, W., Lowney, L. I., Hunkapiller, M. and Hood, L. (1981) *Proc. Natl Acad. Sci. U.S.A.* 78, 7219–7223
9 Herbert, E. (1981) *Trends Biochem. Sci.* 6, 184–188
10 Höllt, V., Haarmann, I., Grimm, C., Herz, A.,

Tulunay, F. C. and Loh, H. H. (1982) *Life Sci.* 31, 1883–1886

11 Kakidani, H., Furutani, Y., Takahashi, H., Noda, M., Morimoto, Y., Hirose, T., Asai, M., Inayama, S., Nakanishi, S. and Numa, H. (1982) *Nature (London)* 298, 245–249

12 Kangawa, K., Minamino, H., Chino, N., Sakakibara, S. and Matsuo, H. (1981) *Biochem. Biophys. Res. Comm.* 99, 871–877

13 Kilpatrick, D. L., Taniguchi, T., Jones, B. M., Stern A. S., Shively, J. E., Hullihan, J., Kimura, S., Stein, S. and Udenfriend, S. (1981) *Proc. Natl Acad. Sci. U.S.A.* 78, 3265–3268

14 Kilpatrick, D. L., Wahlström, A., Lahm, H. W., Blacher, R., Ezra, E., Fleminger, G. and Udenfriend, S. (1980) *Life Sci.* 31, 1849–1852

15 Lewis, R. V., Stern, A. S., Kimura, S., Rossier, J., Stein, S. and Udenfriend, S. (1980) *Science* 208, 1459–1461

16 Mains, R. E., Eipper, R. A. and Ling, N. (1977) *Proc. Natl Acad. Sci. U.S.A.* 74, 3014–3018

17 Martin, R. and Voigt, K. H. (1981) *Nature (London)* 289, 502–504

18 Maysinger, D., Höllt, V., Seizinger, B. R., Mehraein, P., Pasi, A. and Herz, A. (1982) *Neuropeptides* 2, 211–225

19 Mizuno, K., Minamino, N., Kangawa, K. and Matsuo, H. (1980) *Biochem. Biophys. Res. Comm.* 97, 1283–1290

20 Nakanishi, S., Inoue, A., Kita, T., Nakamura, M., Chang, A., Cohen, S. N. and Numa, S. (1979) *Nature (London)* 278, 423–427

21 Nakanishi, S., Teranishi, Y., Noda, M., Notaka, M., Watanabe, Y., Kakidani, H., Jingami, H. and Numa, S. (1980) *Nature (London)* 287, 752–755

22 Noda, M., Furutani, Y., Takahashi, H., Toyosato, M., Hirose, T., Inayama, S., Nakanishi, S. and Numa, S. (1982) *Nature (London)* 297, 431–434

23 Noda, M., Teranishi, Y., Takahashi, H., Toyosato, M., Notake, M., Nakanishi, S. and Numa, S. (1982) *Nature (London)* 297, 431–434

24 Pierce, M. F., Verner, K. and Schroeder, L. A. (1982) *Eur. J. Pharmacol.* 80, 283–284

25 Rossier, J. (1981) *Trends NeuroSci.* 4, 94–97

26 Watson, S. J., Akil, H., Fischli, W., Goldstein, A., Zimmerman, E., Nilaver, G. and van Wimersma Gredanus, T. B. (1982) *Science* 216, 85–87

27 Weber, E., Evans, C. J. and Barchas, J. D. (1982) *Nature (London)* 299, 77–79

28 Weber, E., Roth K. A. and Barchas, J. D. (1982) *Proc. Natl Acad. Sci. U.S.A.* 79, 3062–3066

29 Wüster, M., Schulz, R. and Herz, A. (1980) *Eur. J. Pharmacol.* 62, 235–236

30 Zakarian, S. and Smyth, D. G. (1979) *Proc. Natl Acad. Sci. U.S.A.* 76, 5972–5976

Volker Höllt is at the Max Planck-Institute für Psychiatrie, Kraepelinstrasse 10, D-8000 München 40, F.R.G.

Multiple endogenous ligands for opioid receptors

Eckard Weber, Christopher J. Evans and Jack D. Barchas

Three separate opioid-peptide precursors have now been characterized from mammalian brain, adrenal and pituitary tissues. Post-translational proteolytic processing at specific sites is required to generate opiate-like activity from these large proteins. The three precursors give rise to multiple opioid peptides which vary in their affinity and interaction with different subtypes of opioid receptors. The relative ratio of the products from a given precursor differs among brain regions or between brain vs. pituitary or brain vs. adrenal, suggesting differential proteolytic processing. Since the different opioids that are generated from each of the precursors have variable receptor characteristics and extracellular stability, the differential processing may be of physiological importance in the function of the endogenous opioid systems.

The first opioid peptides to be fully characterized were the pentapeptides methionine-enkephalin (Met-enkephalin) and leucine-enkephalin (Leu-enkephalin)[12]. Since then some sixteen other opioid peptides have been isolated and characterized from mammalian brain, pituitary and adrenal tissues (Fig. 1). All these opiate active peptides have in common an aminoterminal Met- or Leu-enkephalin sequence, and all eighteen substances have been shown to be derived from only three separate precursors whose amino acid sequence was deduced from recombinant DNA analysis of their respective mRNA (Fig. 1). The three precursors are pro-enkephalin[5,10,25], characterized from the adrenal medulla; pro-opiomelanocortin (POMC), first identified[19] and characterized[24] from pituitary tissues; and most recently, pro-dynorphin[14], sequenced from hypothalamus. There is now substantial evidence derived from measurements of the concentration of various precursor products in different tissues that all three precursors are subject to complex proteolytic processing pathways. Surprisingly, the processing is not uniform among all tissues (neural and non-neural) in which the precursor pro-

ducts can be found and the opioid receptor binding activity of the peptide products from a given precursor can show vast differences.

Differential processing of opioid-peptide precursors

Most endogenous opioid peptides are generated from their respective precursors by proteolytic cleavage at double basic amino acid residues (Lys-Arg, Lys-Lys, Arg-Arg, Arg-Lys)[8], although there are at least two peptides [dynorphin(1–8), dynorphin B] that deviate from this classical pathway in that they are generated by a processing mechanism that involves cleavage at a single basic arginine residue[9,15,21]. Of considerable interest is that not all double basic amino acid residues seem to be equally susceptible processing sites. If the cleavage of every double basic amino acid residue that is present within the three precursors went to completion, then the only opioid peptides generated would be Met- and Leu-enkephalin, Met-enkephalin-Arg^6-Phe^7 and Met-enkephalin-Arg^6-Gly^7-Leu^8, from pro-enkephalin; β-endorphin-(1–27), from pro-opiomelanocortin; and Leu-enkephalin, from pro-dynorphin (Fig.

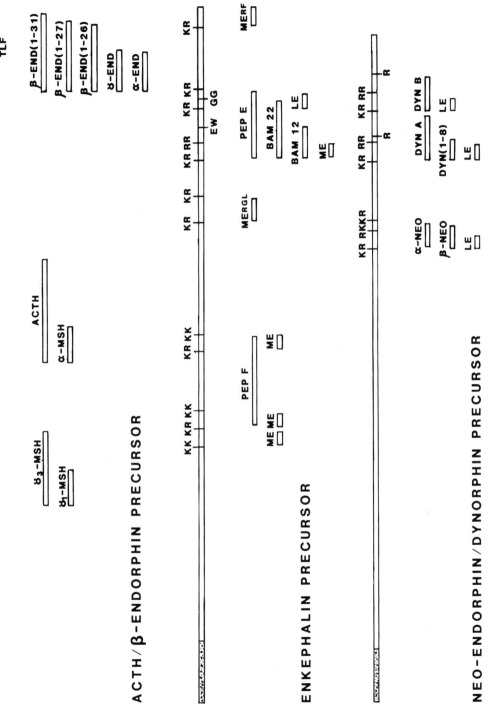

Fig. 1. The three mammalian opioid-peptide precursors that have now been characterized, and which give rise to at least eighteen different opiate active peptides[5, 10, 14, 24, 25]. Abbreviations and symbols:

⬚⬚⬚⬚⬚⬚⬚⬚⬚ = putative signal peptides; MSH = melanocyte-stimulating hormone; ACTH = adrenocorticotropic hormone; END = endorphin; ME = methionine-enkephalin; LE = leucine-enkephalin; NEO = neo-endorphin; DYN = dynorphin; R = arginine; T = threonine; F = phenylalanine; W = tryptophan; K = lysine; L = leucine; E = glutamic acid; G = glycine.

1). However, many of the peptides that are generated from the precursors and that have been isolated from various tissue sources carry one or sometimes even two intact double basic amino acid residues within their primary structure. These peptides are: dynorphin A, dynorphin(1–8), dynorphin B, α-neo-endorphin and β-neo-endorphin, from pro-dynorphin; β-endorphin, from POMC; and Bam 12, Bam 22, peptide E and peptide F, from pro-enkephalin (Fig. 1). The mere existence of these peptides and the fact that they are detectable in either the adrenal medulla, the pituitary or the brain clearly indicates that the cleavage at double basic amino acid residues seems to be incomplete in some tissues.

The extent to which the processing of these higher molecular weight opiate active peptides occurs is highly variable among different tissues. The longer peptides derived from pro-enkephalin carrying double basic amino acid residues (peptide E, peptide F, Bam 22, Bam 12) can be found in significant quantities only in the adrenal medulla[1,27]. There, shorter fragments such as Met- and Leu-enkephalin are not as prevalent as these longer peptides. In contrast to the adrenal medulla, brain tissues contain only very small or negligible quantities of these larger pro-enkephalin products but are abundantly stocked with the Met- and Leu-enkephalins[27]. Recent studies using antibodies that recognized different parts of the pro-enkephalin precursor molecule have indeed shown that the processing of pro-enkephalin in brain is much more complete than in the adrenal medulla[16].

The relative concentrations of β-endorphin and its truncated forms β-endorphin(1–26) and β-endorphin(1–27) in various parts of the brain and in the pituitary indicate that differential processing occurs also with POMC, the precursor molecule giving rise to β-endorphins. β-Endorphin, for example, is much more prevalent in the hypothalamus than in certain midbrain areas, where shorter forms [β-endorphin (1–26), β-endorphin(1–27)] seem to be more prevalent[26]. Similar differential processing occurs in the anterior and intermediate lobes of the pituitary, with β-endorphin(1–31) being the major form in the anterior lobe whereas β-endorphin-(1–26) and β-endorphin(1–27) predominate in the intermediate lobe[18].

The most dramatic differences in region-specific proteolytic processing have been recognized in opioid peptides that are derived from the third mammalian opioid-peptide precursor, pro-dynorphin. First of all it should be noted that it is not clear whether the processing of pro-dynorphin at all double basic amino acid residues goes to completion in any tissue which would result in the generation of Leu-enkephalin. Although Leu-enkephalin is present in high concentrations in most brain regions that contain pro-dynorphin products, many of these regions also contain pro-enkephalin as indicated by the presence of its specific products Met-enkephalin-Arg^6-Phe^7 and Met-enkephalin-Arg^6-Gly^7-Leu^8 (Ref. 13) as well as immunoreactivity related to Bam-22 (Ref. 28). It is therefore possible that all the Leu-enkephalin in these tissues derives from pro-enkephalin rather than from pro-dynorphin. All pro-dynorphin-derived peptides that have been isolated so far are either products of a Lys-Arg double basic residue cleavage or they involve cleavage at a single arginine residue (Fig. 1). Since the three Leu-enkephalin segments in pro-dynorphin are followed by either an Arg-Arg or an Arg-Lys (as opposed to a Lys-Arg) dipeptide sequence, and since these double basic residues remained untouched and are present within the larger isolated peptides, it may be that only the Lys-Arg sequence in pro-dynorphin is cleaved and that the Arg-Arg and Arg-Lys sequences are relatively stable to attack by proteolytic processing enzymes.

However, when one compares the relative distribution in the brain of the major products of pro-dynorphin, one can nevertheless detect dramatic examples of differential proteolytic processing: one of

TABLE I. Differential processing of dynorphin A into dynorphin(1–8) in different regions of rat brain[29]

Immunoreactivity (pmol per g tissue)

Brain region	Dynorphin A	Dynophin(1–8)	Molar ratio D(1–8)/DA
Medulla/pons	3.9 ± 0.4	22.5 ± 0.6	5.7
Midbrain	6.2 ± 1.0	59.6 ± 3.7	9.6
Cerebellum	< 0.2	< 1.2	
Spinal cord	12.1 ± 2.3	22.7 ± 1.6	1.9
Cortex	2.6 ± 0.6	21.0 ± 1.9	8.2
Striatum	7.3 ± 0.7	64.1 ± 4.1	8.8
Hippocampus	3.4 ± 0.7	26.5 ± 2.2	7.9
Hypothalamus	10.3 ± 1.1	65.5 ± 1.8	6.4
Posterior pituitary	503.6 ± 32.9	1 384.0 ± 84.4	2.8

the major products of pro-dynorphin is dynorphin(1–8)[29]. It is apparently derived by cleavage of dynorphin A at a single arginine-residue cleavage site (see below). By comparing the concentrations of dynorphin(1–8) and dynorphin A using highly specific antibodies to each of the peptides, it becomes obvious that the molar ratio of the two peptides is not constant across brain areas (Table I). In the striatum, for example, the processing of dynorphin A into dynorphin(1–8) is much more complete than it is in the spinal cord or in the neural lobe of the pituitary.

One other peptide from pro-dynorphin is the product of differential processing among brain regions. β-Neo-endorphin is identical in amino acid sequence to α-neo-endorphin except that it lacks a lysine residue at the carboxyterminus (Fig. 1). This lysine residue would be relatively stable to removal due to the fact that the preceding amino acid residue is a proline which is extremely resistant to many peptidases[3]. However, significant quantities of β-neo-endorphin are generated in the hypothalamus and neural lobe of the pituitary whereas the striatum has extremely low levels of β-neo-endorphin compared to α-neo-endorphin, again suggesting differential processing[30]. If β-neo-endorphin has any functional significance, it is likely that a specific enzyme is involved in its proteolytic processing from α-neo-endorphin.

Thus, it appears that all three opioid-peptide precursors – pro-enkephalin, POMC and pro-dynorphin – can generate opioids of varying chain length and that the relative concentrations of these products and therefore the proteolytic processing pattern of the precursors is differentially regulated in different tissues.

'Unusual' processing signals in the opioid-peptide precursors

As mentioned earlier, most known opioid peptides are generated from the three precursors by a classical proteolytic cleavage at double basic amino acid residues. The cleavage is thought to occur at the carboxyterminus of the double basic residues followed by subsequent removal of the basic residues by a carboxypeptidase B-like enzyme[8]. However, products from all three precursors have been described that seem to deviate from this conventional processing pathway. These peptides from pro-enkephalin are Bam 12 and Bam 22, and those from POMC are α- and γ-endorphin. The amino acid residues that are part of the cleavage site that generates these peptides have no commonality[22,23] and the cleavage seems to occur randomly. Bam 12 and Bam 22 have been isolated from the adrenal medulla and α-and γ-endorphin are from the pituitary. However, it is not clear whether these four peptides are prevalent products in the brain. Only trace amounts of Bam 12 have been found in the bovine hypothalamus[2] and little is known whether the POMC products α- and γ-endorphin are physiological cleavage products in the brain or even in the pituitary.

The situation is different with the two major 'unusual' cleavage products from pro-dynorphin. Firstly, the cleavage sites that give rise to these two peptides are similar: both dynorphin(1–8) and dynorphin B are generated by proteolytic cleavage at a single arginine residue (Fig. 1). Secondly, both peptides are major products in the brain and in the neural lobe of the pituitary[6,29]. In fact, in rat brain both peptides are more prevalent than their larger parent peptides (dynorphin A and dynorphin B-29) that are precursor products involving cleavage at classical double basic residue sites.

Furthermore, as we have already mentioned, the extent to which dynorphin(1–8) is cleaved from dynorphin A is dramatically different among brain regions (Table I). It remains to be seen whether dynorphin B undergoes a similar differential processing as dynorphin(1–8). Moreover, it will be of great importance to determine whether a specific single arginine-cleavage enzyme is involved in the generation of dynorphin B and dynorphin(1–8) and if this enzyme is different from the enzyme(s) that cleave(s) peptides at the conventional double basic amino acid residues.

Does each precursor produce ligands for only one opioid-receptor subtype?

There is now strong evidence that the brain contains at least three separate opioid-receptor subtypes, namely the μ, δ and κ opioid receptors[17,20]. It appears that the enkephalins that are generated from pro-enkephalin have a good selectivity for interaction with δ receptors, whereas the peptides that are generated from pro-dynorphin can all interact with the κ opioid receptor. Based on this evidence it has been proposed that each of the three precursors produces predominantly ligands to one of

the three receptor subtypes with pro-enkephalin being the δ-ligand precursor, pro-dynorphin the κ-ligand precursor, and POMC the μ-ligand precursor. However, this is by no means certain. β-Endorphin, for example, the main opioid from POMC, interacts equally well with the μ and δ receptors[17]. While the enkephalins are predominantly interacting with the δ receptor, it is not clear what the receptor selectivity is of the larger peptides that are derived from pro-enkephalin (Bam 12, Bam 22, peptide E, peptide F). All of them produce a potent analgesia when injected into the brain[11] and it is therefore possible that they can interact with the μ receptor since analgesia is thought to be mediated by this receptor subtype, in which case pro-enkephalin would be a μ/δ-ligand precursor.

Likewise, it is not clear whether pro-dynorphin is a pure κ-ligand precursor. If significant quantities of Leu-enkephalin are generated from pro-dynorphin (which is not precluded by the structure of the precursor), then the δ receptor for which Leu-enkephalin possesses good selectivity may well be a target of this precursor. Moreover, some of the smaller peptide products of pro-dynorphin, such as β-neo-endorphin and dynorphin(1–8), while having a high affinity for the κ receptor also show some affinity for the μ receptor[7]. We therefore favor the idea that each of the precursors can produce ligands for more than one opioid-receptor subtype, and specificity and selectivity may then be determined by: (1) the relative number of either δ, μ or κ receptors that are present at the site of release, i.e. in the synaptic vicinity of a given opioid-peptide neuron; and (2) by the extent to which the processing occurs in a certain neuron. For example, it is conceivable that certain pro-dynorphin neurons cleave the precursor predominantly in such a way that they produce mainly the δ ligand Leu-enkephalin, whereas other neurons may produce mainly the longer Leu-enkephalin-containing peptides such as dynorphin(1–8), dynorphin A and α-neo-endorphin that have a high affinity to the κ receptor and do not bind to the δ receptor at all[4,7].

Further functional implications of differential processing of opioid-peptide precursors

Given the striking difference of precursor processing patterns among different tissues and brain regions, it is important to relate these findings to a possible function of processing as a regulating mechanism for opioid activity. We have already mentioned that processing may affect receptor selectivity. However, there are certain other indications that processing may be of functional importance. From observations made in opioid bioassays on peptide products derived from any of the three precursors, it appears that the small molecular weight opioids are less potent than their respective parent peptides of higher molecular weight. This feature has been observed in *in-vivo* analgesia assays as well as in assays that measure the potency of opioids to inhibit electrically induced contractions of certain smooth-muscle preparations *in vitro*. For example, β-endorphin is much more potent in analgesia assays than β-endorphin(1–27) which lacks only four amino acid residues at the carboxy-terminus, and the adrenal peptides Bam 22 and peptide E are much more analgesic than Bam 12, and aminoterminal fragment of Bam 22 and peptide E[11].

Striking differences in opioid-activity characteristics were also observed when different fragments of dynorphin A were tested in the guinea-pig ileum/myenteric plexus smooth-muscle preparation[7]. In this assay, dynorphin(1–8), the predominant dynorphin-like opioid in brain, had a very rapid onset and short duration of action whereas the longer dynorphin A [the putative 'parent peptide' of dynorphin(1–8)] had a slow onset of action with an extremely long-lasting activity. This long-lasting mode of action was shown to be due to a better stability of the longer dynorphin A to digestion by peptidases that are ubiquitously present throughout the nervous system[7].

Similarly, the larger peptides derived from pro-enkephalin (peptide E, Bam 22, Bam 12, peptide F) have a much higher potency in all *in-vitro* bioassays than the shorter enkephalins that are contained within and apparently can be generated from these peptides[27]. Thus by studying the differential processing of the opioid-peptide precursors in different tissues and brain regions and by combining this information with studies on receptor distribution, detailed receptor interactions, potencies, and mode of action of the opioid-peptide products, one may be able to obtain a better insight of how opiate activity within certain neuronal populations is regulated. Once this has been established, it will be of the utmost importance to determine whether external stimuli can alter the processing pattern and whether functionally significant processing pathways are accessible to pharmacological manipulations.

Conclusion

The three opioid-peptide precursors that have now been characterized give rise to at least eighteen different opiate active peptides. The proteolytic processing of each of the three precursors seems to be differentially regulated in different tissues and brain regions. The various products from a given precursor show vast differences in receptor selectivity and opioid potency, suggesting that post-translational proteolytic processing may be a primary factor for regulating opioid activity in different tissues and brain regions. Much information regarding this issue has accumulated over the last few years and it is likely that the opioid peptides will serve as a model system which will help us to determine how proteolytic processing regulates peptide neurotransmitters in general.

Acknowledgements

We thank Sue Poage for preparing the manuscript. The authors' research is supported by a grant from the National Institute on Drug Abuse

(DA 01207). Eckard Weber is the recipient of a Potamkin-Lerner Fellowship in the Neurosciences.

Reading list

1 Alessi, N., Taylor, L. and Akil, H. (1982) *Life Sci.* 31, 1875–1878

2 Baird, A., Ling, N., Bohlen, P., Benoit, R., Klepper, R. and Guillemin, R. (1982) *Proc. Natl Acad. Sci. USA* 79, 2023–2025

3 Barrett, A. J. (ed.) (1977) *Proteinases in Mammalian Cells and Tissue*, North-Holland Biomedical Press, Amsterdam

4 Chavkin, C. and Goldstein, A. (1981) *Proc. Natl Acad. Sci. USA* 78, 6543–6547

5 Comb, M., Seeburg, P. H., Adelman, J., Eiden, L. and Herbert, E. (1982) *Nature (London)* 295, 663–666

6 Cone, R. I. and Goldstein, A. (1982) *Neuropeptides* 3, 97–106

7 Corbett, A. D., Paterson, S. J., McKnight, A. T., Magnan, J. and Kosterlitz, H. (1982) *Nature (London)* 299, 79–81

8 Docherty, K. and Steiner, D. F. (1982) *Annu. Rev. Physiol.* 44, 625–638

9 Fischli, W., Goldstein, A., Hunkapillar, M. W. and Hood, L. E. (1982) *Proc. Natl Acad. Sci. USA* 79, 5435–5437

10 Gubler, U., Seeburg, P. H., Gage, L. P. and Udenfriend, S. (1982) *Nature (London)* 295, 206–208

11 Hollt, V., Tulunay, F. C., Woo, S. K., Loh, H. H. and Herz, A. (1982) *Eur. J. Pharmacol.* 85, 355–356

12 Hughes, J., Smith, T. W., Kosterlitz, H. W., Fothergill, L. A., Morgan, B. A. and Morris, H. R. (1975) *Nature (London)* 258, 577–579

13 Ikeda, Y., Nakao, K., Yoshimasa, T., Yanaihara, N., Numa, S. and Imura, H. (1982) *Biochem. Biophys. Res. Commun.* 107, 656–662

14 Kakidani, H., Furutani, Y., Takahashi, H., Noda, M., Morimoto, Y., Hirose, T., Asai, M., Inayama, S., Nakanishi, S. and Numa, S. (1982) *Nature (London)* 298, 245–249

15 Kilpatrick, D. L., Wahlstrom, A., Lahm, H. W., Blacher, R. and Udenfriend, S. (1982) *Proc. Natl Acad. Sci. USA* 79, 6480–6483

16 Liston, D., Vanderhaegen, J. J. and Rossier, J. (1983) *Nature (London)* 302, 62–65

17 Lord, J. A H., Waterfield, A. A., Hughes, J. and Kosterlitz, H. W. (1977) *Nature (London)* 267, 495–499

18 Mains, R. E. and Eipper, B. A. (1981) *J. Biol. Chem.* 256, 5683–5688

19 Mains, R. E., Eipper, B. A. and Ling, N. (1977) *Proc. Natl Acad. Sci. USA* 74, 3014–3018

20 Martin, W. R., Eades, C. G., Thompson, J. A., Huppler, R. E. and Gilbert, P. E. (1976) *J. Pharmacol. Exp. Ther.* 197, 517–532

21 Minamino, N., Kangawa, K., Fukuda, A., Matsuo, H. and Igarashi, M. (1980) *Biochem. Biophys. Res. Commun.* 95, 1475–1481

22 Mizuno, K., Minamino, N., Kangawa, K. and Matsuo, H. (1980) *Biochem. Biophys. Res. Commun.* 95, 1482–1488

23 Mizuno, K., Minamino, N., Kangawa, K. and Matsuo, H. (1980) *Biochem. Biophys. Res. Commun.* 97, 1283–1290

24 Nakanishi, S., Inoue, A., Kita, T., Nakamura, M., Chang, A. C. Y., Cohen, S. N. and Numa, S. (1979) *Nature (London)* 278, 423–427

25 Noda, M., Furutani, Y., Takahashi, H., Toyosato, M., Hirose, T., Inayama, S., Nakanishi, S. and Numa, S. (1982) *Nature (London)* 295, 202–206

26 Smyth, D. G. and Zakarian, S. (1981) *Nature (London)* 288, 613–615

27 Udenfriend, S. and Kilpatrick, D. L. (1983) *Arch. Biochem. Biophys.* 221, 309–323

28 Watson, S. J., Khachaturian, H., Akil, H., Coy, D. H. and Goldstein, A. (1982) *Science* 218, 1134–1136

29 Weber, E., Evans, C. J. and Barchas, J. D. (1982) *Nature (London)* 299, 77–79

30 Weber, E., Evans, C. J., Chang, J.-K. and Barchas, J. D. (1982) *Biochem. Biophys. Res. Commun.* 108, 81–88

Eckard Weber, Christopher J. Evans and Jack D. Barchas are at the Nancy Pritzker Laboratory of Behavioral Neurochemistry, Department of Psychiatry and Behavioral Sciences, Stanford University School of Medicine, Stanford, CA 94305, USA.

The case for multiple opiate receptors

R. Suzanne Zukin and Stephen R. Zukin

As recently as ten years ago the opiate receptor was demonstrated biochemically for the first time and it was assumed that opiate drugs produced their psychotropic actions through a unique opiate receptor. Today compelling evidence from behavioral, pharmacological and biochemical studies indicates the existence of at least four receptor classes, μ, δ, κ and σ. The constellation of neuropharmacological actions of opiates as well as those of the three major classes of opioid peptides (β-endorphin, the enkephalins and dynorphin-related peptides) are now thought to occur by an interaction with a combination of these sites.

A wide body of biochemical, pharmacological and behavioral evidence indicates that opiates exert their wide spectrum of psychotropic actions by interaction with μ, δ and κ opiate receptors. The μ receptor is operationally defined as the high-affinity site at which morphine-like opiates produce analgesia and a variety of other classical opiate effects. The δ receptor is defined pharmacologically as the receptor which is found in peripheral tissues such as the mouse vas deferens[1], as well as in the CNS (Ref. 2), and which exhibits a higher affinity for the naturally occurring enkephalins (a class of shorter opioid peptides) than for morphine. The κ receptor is that at which keto-cyclazocine-like opiates produce analgesia, as well as their unique ataxic and sedative effects[3,4]. More recently it has been defined as a receptor highly selective for dynorphin (a 17 amino acid opioid peptide)[5]. Actions at all three of these sites are reversible by the opiate antagonist naloxone, with increasing doses required going from μ to δ to κ receptors. In addition, certain of the benzomorphan opiates such as SKF-10,047 (*N*-allylnorcyclazocine) and cyclazocine produce their stimulant and psychotomimetic effects through a fourth class of receptor, the σ receptor[3,4,6].

This site is not considered an opiate receptor by some because actions mediated here are not naloxone-reversible. This receptor appears to represent the same entity as the phencyclidine (PCP) receptor which is proposed to mediate the psychotomimetic effects of PCP and related drugs[6,7]. Many opioids interact with more than one of these receptors. Thus, the constellation of pharmacological actions of a given opioid appears to reflect its various potencies at a combination of μ, δ, κ and σ receptors.

Ligand selectivity

The μ, δ, κ and σ receptors differ with respect to their ligand selectivity patterns (Table I). The μ receptor exhibits highest affinity for morphine and related morphine-like alkaloids (normorphine, dihydromorphine, levorphanol), as well as for certain synthetic enkephalins which have been modified so as to confer μ-like character. The latter include D-Ala², *N*-Phe⁴-Met(O)ol⁵-enkephalin (FK 33824)[8] which exhibits somewhat higher affinity for μ than for δ receptors[9]; and D-Ala², *N*-Phe⁴-Gly-ol⁵-enkephalin (DAGO)[10] which exhibits 220:1 preference for μ:δ receptors. The δ receptor exhibits highest affinity for the naturally occurring Met⁵- and Leu⁵-

enkephalins and their congeners. Highest selectivity for the δ receptor is exhibited by D-Ala[2]-D-Leu[5]-enkephalin (DADLE)[2] and by D-Ser[2], L-Leu[5]-enkephalyl-Thr (DSLET)[11]. Thus, although most μ and δ ligands cross-react with μ and δ receptors, highly selective μ and δ ligands have been designed. Neither μ nor δ opioids exhibit significant affinity for the κ or σ receptors. The prototypic κ ligands, ketocyclazocine and ethylketocyclazocine (EKC), do exhibit high affinities for both μ and κ receptors[12,13]. More recently, U-50,488 has been reported to be a highly selective κ ligand essentially devoid of μ or δ activity[14]. Prototypic σ agonists (SKF-10,047 and cyclazocine) exhibit potent affinities at μ and, in the case of cyclazocine, κ receptors[3,6]. We have demonstrated that phencyclidine and (+) SKF-10,047 are specific ligands for the σ receptor[6,15] and exhibit no detectable affinity for μ, δ or κ receptors.

Tissue distribution of receptor types

An important criterion used to demonstrate the existence of multiple opiate receptors is the presence of tissues highly specific for a given receptor type (Table II). A variety of studies indicate that the three major opiate receptor classes have somewhat different distributions throughout the central and peripheral nervous systems. For example, the thalamus and hypothalamus of rat brain appear to have a higher proportion of μ than δ

receptors, whereas rat frontal cortex and striatum show more selective localizations of δ receptors[2]. In the periphery, the guinea-pig ileum appears to have mainly μ and κ receptors, as shown by the twitch or other bioassays (see below), in contrast to the mouse vas deferens which has a high concentration of δ receptors in relation to the other two types[1]. Of particular importance has been the finding that the neuroblastoma cell line N4GT1 is a homogeneous source of δ receptors[16].

The most selective localization of putative κ receptors occurs in the deep layers V and VI of the cerebral cortex, thought to play a role in emotional processes[17]. Two tissues, the rabbit vas deferens[18] and human placenta[19], appear to be essentially 'pure' sources of κ receptors. Interestingly, the pigeon appears to lack this receptor altogether. We (by binding studies)[7,12] and Pert and co-workers (by autoradiography)[20] have mapped the σ/PCP receptor in the brain. This site exhibits a unique distribution quite unlike that of the μ, δ or κ receptors. Highest distributions of PCP/σ receptors occur in the hippocampus and frontal cortex; moderate density is found in the cerebellum, a tissue devoid of either μ or δ sites.

Peptide families as ligands

The question arises as to whether μ, δ and κ receptors subserve distinct transmitter or modulator molecules. It is now

TABLE I. Ligand selectivity patterns of brain opioid receptors

Ligand	Receptor specificity	Ratio	Refs
Dihydromorphine	μ > δ	29:1	51
Normorphine	μ > δ	72:1	52
D-Ala[2], Gly-ol[5]-enkephalin (DAGO)	μ >> δ	220:1	10
D-Ala[2], D-Leu[5]-enkephalin (DADLE)	δ > μ	12:1	2
D-Ser[2], L-Leu[5]-enkephalyl-Thr (DSLET)	δ >> μ	24:1	11
U-50,488	κ > μ	5.5:1	14
(+) SKF-10,047	σ >> μ	200:1	53
Phencyclidine	σ >> μ	200:1	15

TABLE II. Distribution of opioid receptor classes in the central and peripheral nervous systems

Tissue	Receptor classes	Refs
1. CNS		
Rat brain		
thalamus, hypothalamus	$\mu > \delta$	2
striatum	$\delta > \mu$	2
hippocampus	$\kappa, \sigma > \mu$	15, 17, 20
Guinea-pig brain		
frontal cortex, layers V and VI	$\kappa > > \mu$	17
Toad brain	κ	54
2. PNS		
Guinea-pig ileum	μ, κ	1
Mouse vas deferens	μ, δ, κ	1
Rabbit vas deferens	κ	18
3. Neuronal cell lines		
N4 GT1	δ	16
NCB 20	δ, κ, σ	50

well established that there are three major classes of opioid peptides: β-endorphin, the enkephalins and dynorphin-related peptides. These arise from three different precursor molecules in three independent biosynthetic pathways (for a review see Ref. 21). The first, β-endorphin, occurs together with adreno-corticotrophic hormone (ACTH), a peptide which stimulates the adrenal cortex, in the 31 000 mol. wt precursor molecule pro-opiomelanocortin (POMC)[22] (Table III). POMC, β-endorphin and ACTH are found in highest concentrations in the pars intermedia and pars distalis of the pituitary. Under conditions of severe stress, β-endorphin and ACTH are co-released.

The second class includes Met- and Leu-enkephalin[23] pentapeptides that arise from pro-enkephalin, an approximately 50 000 mol. wt protein that has been identified in the adrenal medulla and in the striatum[24]. The pro-enkephalin molecule contains six copies of Met-enkephalin and one of Leu-enkephalin. The distribution of the enkephalins differs from that of β-endorphin in that they appear to be much more widely distributed throughout the brain.

Dynorphin A, a 17 amino acid peptide that contains the sequence of Leu-enkephalin at its N-terminal end, is the most recently discovered opioid peptide[25]. It arises together with dynorphin B, its 1–13 counterpart, from a 4 000 mol. wt peptide which in turn is found in the much larger pro-dynorphin molecule[26]. Dynorphin A and its (1–8) fragment occur in approximately equal concentrations in the brain. Whereas β-endorphin displays equipotency at μ and δ receptors, the enkephalins show a much greater affinity for the δ receptor. It has been speculated that the more stable β-endorphin molecule functions as a neuro-hormone in both pathways, whereas the enkephalins play a more specific role, acting as neurotransmitters or neuro-modulators over shorter distances[1]. The longer dynorphin forms (1–13 and 1–17) appear to be more κ-selective and are more stable, whereas the shorter fragments (for example 1–8) are potent at both κ and δ receptors, are less stable, and are more likely candidates for trans-mitter-like function[27].

Receptor molecular properties

What is the molecular basis of opiate receptor heterogeneity? Models which have been proposed are: (1) that μ, δ and κ receptors are distinct proteins of different molecular weights; (2) that these represent interconvertible forms of the same protein (as has been suggested by Pert and co-workers[28]); (3) that the receptor types may arise from the same polypeptide chain by post-translational modification or by coupling to a guanyl nucleotide binding protein. Studies from our laboratory[29] indicate that μ and κ receptors differ significantly in their macromolecular properties including size, as estimated by gel filtration analysis. Lee and Smith[30] have advanced an intriguing model in which a single opiate receptor provides a proteinaceous binding site for enkephalin and a lipid binding site for alkaloids, with β-endorphin interacting at both sites. Solubilization of the receptor species and its partial purification and characterization have begun to provide the size, subunit composition, and structural information to distinguish among these and other possibilities.

Although opiate receptor subclasses have been shown to differ with respect to ligand specificity, their interrelationships at the cellular level and possible functional distinctions have not been determined. Preliminary studies by ourselves[31,32] and others[33] suggest that μ receptor binding may be significantly more sensitive to negative regulation by guanyl nucleotides than is δ receptor binding. Thus, μ receptors could be functionally coupled to adenyl cyclase but δ receptors could not. Recent in-vitro electrophysiological studies of isolated myenteric neurons[34] and of isolated dorsal root ganglia[35], and tests of isolated vas deferentia[36,37], have provided suggestive evidence for the coexistence of μ and δ receptors on the same cell.

Validation for the existence of the major classes of opiate receptors comes from behavioral, pharmacological and biochemical studies. Historically, the first suggestion of multiple opiate receptors was made by Martin and his co-workers[3,4] on the basis of animal behavioral studies. In particular, κ and σ opiates were shown to produce effects through mechanisms which must involve receptors distinct from the 'classical' (μ) receptor. κ-Drugs failed to suppress morphine abstinence, nor did they precipitate abstinence in morphine-dependent monkeys. These drugs produced a more pronounced sedation than do other opiates and have been evaluated as anesthetic agents. SKF-10,047 (N-allyl-norcyclazocine), cyclazocine and related drugs of the benzomorphan group differ from classical opiates in displaying psychotomimetic effects in humans and unique behavioral effects in animals[38]. At low doses many of these drugs clinically antagonize the analgesic and respiratory-depressant effects of classi-

TABLE III. The opioid peptide systems and their receptor specificities

Peptide system	Structure	Receptor specificity	Refs
1. β-Endorphin		μ, δ	1
2. The enkephalins		δ >> μ	1
Met-enkephalin	Tyr-Gly-Gly-Phe-Met		
Leu-enkephalin	Tyr-Gly-Gly-Phe-Leu		
3. Dynorphin-related peptides			
Dynorphin A (1–17)	Leu^5-enkephalyl-Arg-Arg-Ile-Arg-Pro-Lys-Leu-Lys-Trp-Asp-Asn-Gln	κ > μ, δ	25, 27
Dynorphin B (1–13)	Leu^5-enkephalyl-Arg-Arg-Gln-Phe-Lys-Val-Val-Thr	κ > μ, δ	25
Dynorphin (1–8)	Leu^5-enkephalyl-Arg-Arg-Ile	κ, μ, δ	25, 27

cal opiates. At higher doses such benzomorphans produce a combination of sedation, 'drunkenness' and psychosis differing from any morphine effect. In animal behavioral studies these drugs also produce both classical opiate[39] and unique effects, including canine delirium, tachycardia and tachypnea ('σ' effects)[3,4]. Certain of the effects of SKF-10,047 or cyclazocine in animals cannot be reversed by the pure opiate antagonists naloxone or naltrexone[38]. The distinctive behavioral effects of δ ligands are less well understood, probably because most of these peptides cross-react quite well with μ receptors and are in many cases unstable, thus being unsuitable for systemic administration. β-Endorphin and Met-enkephalin injected centrally have been shown to produce a number of behavioral effects in common with morphine, including analgesia, activation at low doses, sedation at high doses, and euphoria[40].

An important unresolved question is whether, in the CNS, morphine, enkephalin and EKC produce analgesia by an interaction with the same or with different opiate receptors. In the case of morphine and EKC, data in support of a common receptor are: (1) the similar pA2 values for naloxone-reversal of both morphine- and EKC-induced analgesia in the tail-flick nociceptive test[41]; and (2) the ability of the irreversible ligand naloxazone to reduce morphine and EKC-induced analgesia by the same extent[42]. On the other hand, several lines of evidence argue for separate receptors. Morphine and EKC (or dynorphin) do not produce complete cross-tolerance[4,41,43], and EKC (or dynorphin) and morphine produce analgesia through receptor sites that differ somewhat in their neuroanatomical distributions[44,45] and appear at different ages of the young rat (Barr, Paredes, Erickson and Zukin, unpublished observations). One possible explanation is that at the spinal level, κ receptors are functional, whereas at the level of the brain (which has fewer κ receptors), analgesia is mediated primarily by μ receptors.

In pharmacological studies, two interesting experiments that have been carried out are those of 'selective tolerance' and 'selective protection'. In these studies, isolated peripheral tissue preparations are used, for example the guinea-pig ileum myenteric plexus-longitudinal muscle which has been shown to be enriched in μ receptors. Other useful preparations include the mouse vas deferens which has a higher relative proportion of δ receptors, and the rabbit vas deferens which appears to be a source of κ sites exclusively[17]. In all of these systems, opiates produce a dose-dependent inhibition of electrically induced contractions of the tissue. Long-term exposure to an opiate agonist such as morphine (μ ligand) renders the tissue tolerant; that is to say, a much higher dose of the same agonist will be required to produce a given effect. Herz and co-workers[36,43] reasoned that if all opiate effects were mediated by one receptor, then chronic exposure of the mouse vas deferences to sufentanyl (μ-selective opiate) should produce tolerance not only to normorphine but also to Leu-enkephalin (δ opiate). Instead, they observed tolerance to normorphine only. Similarly, chronic exposure to D-Ala^2, D-Leu^5-enkephalin (DADLE, δ ligand) produced selective tolerance to Leu-enkephalin but not to normorphine. Chronic simultaneous infusion with DADLE and sufentanyl reduced significantly the efficacy of Leu-enkephalin, β-endorphin and sufentanyl itself, while essentially not affecting the efficacy of dynorphin (putative κ peptide). These results provide strong evidence for a multiplicity of opiate receptors in the peripheral nervous system.

In a second set of experiments, additional pharmacological evidence has been provided using the irreversible opiate antagonist β-chlornaltrexamine

$(\beta\text{-CNA})^{46}$. Pretreatment of guinea-pig ileum myenteric plexus with β-CNA makes the preparation insensitive to opioid agonists. If, however, a reversible opioid is included during the β-CNA treatment, this agent will 'protect' the receptors with which it interacts from the irreversible ligand; the preparation will retain opioid sensitivity after the reversible drug is washed out. Goldstein and co-workers[47,48] carried out 'selective protection' experiments using μ or κ ligands in order to study homogeneous populations of these receptors. They found that the selective κ agonists dynorphin A (1–13) and dynorphin A (1–17) protect against inactivation of κ sites but not μ sites. In contrast, protection with sufentanyl (μ opiate) preserves the function of μ sites but not of κ sites. Even after several hours, the activity of the destroyed receptors does not return (C. Chavkin, unpublished observations). Together these studies may provide further evidence for distinct μ and κ receptors.

A great deal has also been learned from biochemical studies. Ideally, in order to study the molecular properties of μ, δ, κ and σ receptors one would like tissue sources highly enriched in a specific receptor type or type-specific ligands. In the absence of these, it has been necessary to develop strategies to target each of the receptor types in biochemical studies. For example, we have been able to show that $[^{3}\text{H}]\text{SKF-}$10,047 binds to μ and σ receptors. We were able to reveal binding of this radioligand specifically to the μ receptor by using low concentrations of $[^{3}\text{H}]\text{SKF-}$10,047 and by using the selective μ opioid normorphine as the displacing ligand. On the other hand, we were able to direct $[^{3}\text{H}]\text{SKF-}10,047$ binding specifically to σ receptors by including selective μ and δ ligands to block binding of the radioligand to μ and δ receptors. The high- and low-affinity binding sites for this ligand have been identified as

the μ and σ receptors, respectively, by three findings: (1) the rank order of potencies of a series of opiates in the displacement of $[^{3}\text{H}]\text{SKF-}10,047$ to these sites; (2) the brain regional distribution of the two sites; and (3) their differential sensitivities to protein-modifying reagents[49]. Similar 'receptor-targeting' experiments have been carried out for $[^{3}\text{H}]\text{EKC}$ (Ref. 50).

This type of blocking experiment has been used in autoradiography experiments as well. Thus, Snyder and his co-workers[17] used $[^{3}\text{H}]\text{ethylketocyclazocine}$ (κ drug) and $[^{3}\text{H}]\text{bremazocine}$ (κ drug) binding to slide-mounted sections of frozen brain in the presence of μ and δ blockers to elucidate a unique κ receptor distribution. Our laboratory has used $[^{3}\text{H}]\text{SKF-}10,047$ in the presence of these same blockers to map σ receptors (Zukin et al., unpublished observations). Using such a tactic, we were able to show that these sites are distributed much like the PCP receptors mapped by Pert and her co-workers using $[^{3}\text{H}]\text{PCP}$ (Ref. 20).

Conclusions

We have reviewed research which shows that opiates produce their actions on nervous tissue by an interaction with at least four sites: the μ, δ, κ and σ receptors. The μ, κ and possibly the δ receptor are thought to mediate analgesia. In addition, these four receptors are thought to mediate distinct behavioral syndromes. Particularly striking are: (1) the κ syndrome which includes ataxia and pronounced sedation; and (2) the σ syndrome which includes hallucinations and dysphoria. Most of the known opiate drugs and opioid peptides interact with more than one of these receptor sites. Thus, the complex neuropharmacological actions of a given opioid would appear to reflect its interaction with varying potencies at a combination of these sites.

At present a controversy surrounds the issue as to whether μ, δ and κ opiate receptors are different entities or inter-convertible forms of the same receptor. Results of selective tolerance and selective protection experiments would appear difficult to reconcile with an interconverting model of these sites. On the other hand, the rather similar distribution of the receptors in many areas of the brain argues for the 'interconvertible' hypothesis. Ultimately, the resolution of these issues lies in the purification and sequencing of all the receptor forms.

Acknowledgements

The authors' research is supported by grants from the National Institute on Drug Abuse (DA 01843 to R. Suzanne Zukin, and DA 02587, to Stephen R. Zukin) and from the National Science Foundation (BNS 8308634). R. Suzanne Zukin is the recipient of Research Career Development Award from the National Institute of Drug Abuse (DA 00069).

Reading list

1 Lord, J. A. H., Waterfield, A. A., Hughes, J. and Kosterlitz, H. W. (1977) *Nature (London)* 267, 495–500

2 Chang, K.-J., Cooper, B. R., Hazum, E. and Cuatrecasas, P. (1979) *Mol. Pharmacol.* 16, 91–104

3 Gilbert, P. E. and Martin, W. R. (1976) *J. Pharmacol. Exp. Ther.* 198, 66–82

4 Martin, W. R., Eades, C. G., Thompson, J. A., Huppler, R. E. and Gilbert, P. E. (1976) *J. Pharmacol. Exp. Ther.* 197, 517–532

5 Chavkin, C., James, I. F. and Goldstein, A. (1982) *Nature (London)* 299, 79–81

6 Zukin, R. S. and Zukin, S. R. (1981b) *Mol. Pharmacol.* 20, 246–254

7 Zukin, S. R. and Zukin, R. S. (1979) *Proc. Natl Acad. Sci. USA* 76, 5372–5376

8 Romer, D., Buscher, H. H., Hill, R. C., Pless, J., Baur, W., Cardinaux, F., Closse, A., Hauser, D. and Huguenin, R. (1977) *Nature (London)* 268, 547–549

9 Kream, R. M. and Zukin, R. S. (1979) *Biochem. Biophys. Res. Commun.* 90, 99–109

10 Handa, B. K., Lane, A. C., Lord, J. A., Morgan, B. A., Rance, M. J. and Smith, C. F. C. (1981) *Eur. J. Pharmacol.* 70, 531–540

11 Garcel, G., Fournie-Zaluski, M.-C. and Roques, B. P. (1980) *FEBS Lett.*118, 245–247

12 Zukin, R. S. and Zukin, S. R. (1981a) *Life Sci.* 29, 2681–2690

13 Kosterlitz, H. W., Paterson, S. J. and Robson, L. E. (1981) *Br. J. Pharmacol.* 73, 939–949

14 Vonvoigtlander, P. F., Lahti, R. A. and Ludens, J. H. (1983) *J. Pharmacol. Exp. Ther.* 224, 7–12

15 Zukin, S. R., Fitz-Syage, M. L., Nichtenhauser, R. and Zukin, R. S. (1983) *Brain Res.* 277–284

16 Chang, K.-J., Miller, R. J. and Cuatrecasas, P. (1978) *Mol. Pharmacol.* 14, 961–970

17 Goodman, R. R. and Snyder, S. H. (1982) *Proc. Natl Acad. Sci. USA* 79, 5703–5707

18 Oka, T., Negishi, K., Suda, M., Sawa, A., Fujino, M. and Wakimasu, M. (1982) *Eur. J. Pharmacol.* 77, 137–141

19 Valette, A., Porthe, G., Audigier, Y., Pontonnier, G. and Gros, J. (1981) in *Advances in Endogenous and Exogenous Opioids* (Takagi, H., Simon, E. and Kodansha, J., eds), pp. 30–32, Proceedings of the 12th International Narcotic Research Conference, Tokyo

20 Quirion, R., Hammer, R., Herkenham, M. and Pert, C. B. (1981) *Proc. Natl Acad. Sci. USA* 78, 5881–5885

21 Weber, E., Evans, E. J. and Barchas, J. D. (1983) *Trends NeuroSci.* 6, 333–336

22 Mains, R. E., Eipper, B. A. and Ling, N. (1977) *Proc. Natl Acad. Sci. USA* 74, 3014–3018

23 Hughes, J., Smith, T. W., Kosterlitz, H. W., Fothergill, L. A., Morgan, B. A. and Morris, H. R. (1975) *Nature (London)* 258, 577–579

24 Gubler, U., Seeberg, P. H., Gage, L. P. and Undenfriend, S. (1982) *Nature (London)* 206–208

25 Goldstein, A., Fischli, W., Lowney, L. I., Hunkapiller, M. and Hood, L. (1981) *Proc. Natl Acad. Sci. USA* 78, 7219–7223

26 Kakidani, H., Furutani, Y., Takahashi, H., Noda, M., Morimoto, Y., Hirose, T., Asai, M., Inayama, S., Nakahishi, S. and Numa, S. (1982) *Nature (London)* 298, 245–249

27 Corbett, A. D., Paterson, S. J., McKnight, A. T., Magnan, J. and Kosterlitz, H. W. (1982) *Nature (London)* 299, 79–81

28 Bowen, W. B., Gentleman, S., Herkenham, M. and Pert, C. B. (1981) *Proc. Natl Acad. Sci. USA* 78, 4818–4822

29 Chow, T. and Zukin, R. S. (1983) *Mol. Pharmacol.* 24, 203–212

30 Lee, N. M. and Smith, A. P. (1980) *Life Sci.* 26, 1459–1464

31 Zukin, R. S. and Gintzler, A. R. (1980) *Brain Res.* 186, 486–491

32 Zukin, R. S., Walczak, S. and Makman, M. H. (1980) *Brain Res.* 186, 238–244

33 Pert, C. B. and Taylor, D. (1980) in *Endogenous and Exogenous Opiate Agonists and*

Antagonists (Way, E. L., ed.), pp. 87–90, Pergamon Press, New York

34 Egan, T. M. and North, R. A. (1981) *Science* 214, 923–924

35 Werz, M. A. and McDonald, R. L. (1982) *Nature (London)* 299, 730–733

36 Schulz, R., Wuster, M., Krenss, H. and Herz, A. (1980) *Mol. Pharmacol.* 18, 395–401

37 Schulz, R., Wuster, M., Krenss, H. and Herz, A. (1980) *Nature (London)* 285, 242–243

38 Holtzman, S. G. (1979) in (Brand, M. C., ed.), pp. 371–382, Raven Press, New York

39 Killam, K. F., Jr, Brocco, M. J. and Robinson, C. A. (1976) *Ann. NY Acad. Sci.* 281, 331–335

40 Koob, G. F. and Bloom, F. E. (1983) *Br. Med. Bull.* 39, 89–94

41 Tank, A. S. and Yaksh, T. L. (1982) *Brain Res.* 247, 75079

42 Pasternak, G. W. (1980) *Proc. Natl Acad. Sci. USA* 77, 3691–3694

43 Wuster, M., Schulz, R. and Herz, A. (1980) *Eur. J. Pharmacol.* 62, 235–236

44 Wood, P. L. and Rackham, A. (1980) *Neurosci. Lett.* 23, 75–80

45 Yaksh, T. L., Yeung, J. C. and Rudy, T. A. (1976) *Brain Res.* 114, 83–88

46 Portoghese, P. S., Larson, D. L., Ting, T. B., Caruso, T. P. and Takemori, A. E. (1979) *J. Med. Chem.* 22, 168–173

47 Chavkin, C. and Goldstein, A. (1981) *Proc. Natl Acad. Sci. USA* 78. 6543–6547

48 James, I. F., Chavkin, C. and Goldstein, C. (1982) *Life Sci.* 31, 1331–1334

49 Zukin, R. S. (1983) in *Methods in Neurobiology* (Marangos, P., Campbell, I. and Cohen, R. M., eds), Academic Press, New York (in press)

50 West, R. E., McLawhon, R. W., Dawson, G. and Miller, R. J. (1983) *Mol. Pharmacol.* 23, 486–492

51 Gillan, M. G. C., Kosterlitz, H. W. and Paterson, S. J. (1980) *Br. J. Pharmacol.* 70, 481–490

52 Kosterlitz, H. W. and Paterson, S. J. (1981) *Br. J. Pharmacol.* 73, 299P

53 Zukin, R. S. and Zukin, S. R. (1983) in *Phencyclidine and Related Arylcyclohexylamines: Present and Future Applications* (Kamenka, J. M., Domino, E. F. and Geneste, P., eds), NPP Books, Ann Arbor, MI

54 Ruegg, U. T., Hiller, J. M. and Simon, E. J. (1980) *Eur. J. Pharmacol.* 64, 367–368

R. Suzanne Zukin is at the Departments of Biochemistry and Neuroscience, and Stephen R. Zukin is at the Department of Psychiatry, Albert Einstein College of Medicine, Bronx, NY 10461, USA.

Metabolism of enkephalins and the inactivating neuropeptidase concept

Jean-Charles Schwartz

The potentiation of the effects of enkephalins on target cells by selective peptidase inhibitors raises the possibility that peptidergic signals are turned off not only by diffusion but also by hydrolysis by 'neuropeptidases'. Two recently identified peptidases are likely to play such a role in enkephalinergic neurotransmission, and their inhibition constitutes an important experimental tool for analysing the physiological functions of the opioid pentapeptides.

Although an increasing number of neuropeptides have been identified and localized within the CNS in the last few years, little is known about the mechanisms of peptidergic neurotransmission. For instance, to understand the roles of neuropeptides, it is necessary to determine how the transmission of signals by these substances compares with that accomplished by classical neurotransmitters, i.e. amines and amino acids. A specific example is the mechanism of termination of transmitter action. The millisecond duration and high frequency of the signals conveyed by classical neurotransmitters requires their rapid removal from the synaptic cleft. This is achieved by re-uptake processes or by metabolism into inactive compounds since diffusion of the intact messenger from the cleft is too slow. In contrast, neuropeptides seem responsible for signals with much longer durations and it may be argued that diffusion processes alone may be adequate for their termination. However, the 'sluggish' character of signals transmitted by peptides may be due not to their slow inactivation but rather to factors such as their slow dissociation from receptors (for which many peptides display

affinities 10 000 times greater than those typical for classical neurotransmitters). Hence it is still possible that the termination of these signals depends on 'neuropeptidases', e.g. enzymes uniquely fitted to the hydrolysis of synaptically released peptides either because of their highly selective substrate specificity or their strategic localization. This article considers the evidence for this last possibility in the case of enkephalins, whose simple chemical structure has made it relatively easy to determine their metabolic pathways.

Multiple enkephalin-hydrolysing peptidases in brain

Shortly after the enkephalins were discovered it was noticed that they were almost immediately hydrolysed into their constituent amino acids when brought into contact with brain tissues either *in vivo* by local injection or *in vitro* with tissue extracts. Such experiments do not tell us much about the enzymes involved, but their activities have been studied by determining which fragments of the enkephalin molecule appear first in the presence of brain tissues. Other approaches have been to assess the effects of the few selective peptidase inhibitors available, and to determine whether the enkephalins are substrates for previously purified cerebral peptidases. The peptidases identified by these various approaches and their hydrolysis products are shown in Fig. 1.

Aminopeptidases were the first enkephalin-hydrolysing enzymes to be identified when it was realized that large amounts of tyrosine were released by breakdown of the pentapeptide *in vivo* and *in vitro*. The heterogenous pattern of inhibition by several reagents on different subcellular fractions[13] suggests that the enkephalin-hydrolysing aminopeptidase activity from brain is not a single enzyme species. In addition enkephalin-hydrolysing aminopeptidases partially purified from either soluble or particulate brain fractions in various laboratories seem to differ from one another in their substrate specificity[9-11,23]. These enzymes all seem to be metallopeptidases and the most potent inhibitor presently available is bestatin[2], a compound of bacterial origin[26]. Its structure suggests that it chelates the metal (probably Zn) in the active sites. Puromycin, a drug generally used for other purposes, also inhibits enkephalin-hydrolysing aminopeptidases from several brain preparations[9-12,16,23] but is generally less potent than bestatin and seems to be almost inactive on a membrane-bound enzyme partially purified from rat brain[10].

Dipeptidyl aminopeptidases hydrolysing the Gly^2-Gly^3 amide bond of enkephalins are also present in brain[8] in membrane-bound form but no selective inhibitor for these enzymes is known. In particular it is important to stress that the inhibitors of the other enkephalin-hydrolysing enzymes do not prevent the hydrolysis of enkephalins by dipeptidyl aminopeptidases.

Angiotensin-converting enzyme (peptidyldipeptide hydrolase, EC 3.4.15.1) (ACE), which catalyses the formation of the octapeptide angiotensin II from the decapeptide angiotensin I, was detected in brain tissue several years ago[27]. However, its functional role is not clear because the presence of a renin-angiotensin system in brain is still a matter of controversy[21]. In 1979 Erdös *et al.* showed that purified ACE hydrolyses the enkephalins at the level of the Gly^3-Phe^4 amide bond, an action potently inhibited by compounds like captopril[6].

Enkephalin dipeptidylcarboxypeptidase (commonly designated 'enkephalinase') activity was first detected by Malfroy *et al.*[15] in cerebral membranes used for opiate-receptor-binding assays. Like ACE, 'enkephalinase' is a metallopeptidase which cleaves the Gly^3-Phe^4 amide bond but it clearly differs in its substrate specificity, its regional distribution, and the effect of inhibitors[1,24,25]. Thus captopril is 1 000 times less potent on 'enkephalinase' than on ACE, whereas the recently discovered inhibitor thiorphan is about 50 times more potent (nanomolar affinity) on 'enkephalinase' than on ACE[22]. 'Enkephalinase' is found not only in brain but also in a variety of peripheral tissues and has recently been almost completely purified[17]. It appears to be identical or very similar to a 'neutral endopeptidase' identified 10 years ago in

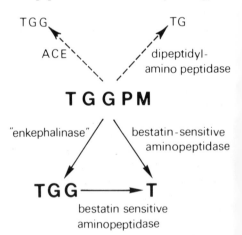

Fig. 1. *Pathways for the metabolism of enkephalins.*

The various peptidases involved in the metabolism of both exogenous (broken arrows) and endogenous enkephalins (full arrows) are indicated. The amino acid abbreviations are: T = tyrosine; G = glycine; P = phenylalanine; M = methionine.

rabbit kidney but whose function had since remained obscure[7,17].

This short summary (for a more complete review see Ref. 25) of the various cerebral peptidases able to hydrolyse the enkephalins into inactive fragments (the whole pentapeptide sequence being necessary for recognition by opiate receptors) illustrates that the CNS is richly endowed with these enzymes. This does not automatically mean that any of them plays a physiological role in turning off enkephalinergic signals since additional criteria have to be met to establish a 'neuropeptidase' function.

Substrate specificity of peptidases and biological inactivation of exogenous enkephalins

The mechanisms responsible for the synaptic inactivation of classical neurotransmitters have been rather easy to identify because they generally display a high degree of chemical specificity. For instance acetylcholine is probably the sole neurotransmitter hydrolysed by acetylcholinesterases, and catecholamines are taken up in a unique fashion by the high-affinity transport systems in the neurones. The identification of a physiologically relevant inactivating 'neuropeptidase' is much more difficult because peptidases generally display a broad substrate specificity which depends only on the amino acids engaged in the scissile amide bond and on one or two adjacent amino acids. Consequently, a given neuropeptide can be hydrolysed by a variety of enzymes (as illustrated above in the case of enkephalins) and, as a corollary, a given peptidase can act on several neuropeptides (ACE hydrolyses angiotensin I, bradykinin, enkephalins, etc.). Clearly none of the hitherto-identified enkephalin-hydrolysing enzymes recognize the opioid pentapeptides in a unique fashion, and additional factors must be taken into consideration in identifying specific 'neuropeptidases'.

One starting point is to identify which bonds in the enkephalin molecule have to be protected in exogenous enkephalins to enhance their biological activity. Even when enkephalins are injected into the brain in very large doses, they elicit only marginal and very short-lasting biological effects. Indeed under these circumstances the half-life of ^{3}H-enkephalins is in the minute range[18] – one reason why their analgesic action is difficult to demonstrate. This is similar to the action of exogenous acetylcholine which can be properly demonstrated only when the substance is protected from acetylcholinesterase either by modifying the hydrolysable ester bond (as in compounds like carbamylcholine) or co-administering a suitable enzyme inhibitor. Similar approaches may provide some clues to identifying the enzymes responsible for the inactivation of exogenous enkephalins.

Several of the synthetic enkephalin analogues have markedly enhanced opioid activity *in vivo*, an effect attributed not to increased affinity for the receptor but to resistance to hydrolysing enzymes[19]. Thus substitution of the Gly^2 residue by D-amino acids, such as D-Ala or D-Met, increases analgesic activity (after local administration) by about tenfold, an observation suggesting that aminopeptidases or dipeptidyl aminopeptidases have a critical role, as their action is prevented by such substitutions. In the same way, various chemical modifications which give increased resistance to hydrolysis by either ACE or 'enkephalinase' (methylation of the Gly^3–Phe^4 amide bond, replacement of the C-terminal amino acid by proline, amidification of the carboxylate group) have strongly enhanced biological activity[24]. Although combinations of these various 'manipulations' of the enkephalin molecule have led to compounds up to 10 000 times more active *in vivo*, unfortunately these observations do not provide definitive identification of the relevant peptidases.

When (Met^5) enkephalin is injected intracerebroventricularly in mice, its half-life and its anti-nociceptive activity are both significantly increased by inhibition of either 'enkephalinase' by thiorphan or aminopeptidase(s) by bestatin. The effect is particularly dramatic when activities of the two enzymes are simultaneously inhibited[5]. Interestingly, neither puromycin, an aminopeptidase inhibitor, nor captopril, an ACE inhibitor, elicit such a potentiation. Taken together these observations suggest that both 'enkephalinase' and bestatin-sensitive aminopeptidase(s) participate in the biological inactivation of exogenous enkephalins but it may well be that different enzymes are responsible for the inactivation of the synaptically released enkephalins (Table I).

Localization of enkephalin-hydrolysing peptidases

Although the various enkephalin-hydrolysing peptidases do not appear to display unique chemical specificity towards the opioid pentapeptides, selective action of one (or several) of these enzymes could still result if they were strategically located close to the sites of enkephalin release and action. Again classical neurotransmitters offer a parallel, as it is well established that the crucial role of acetycholinesterases is

attributable not only to highly efficient catalytic properties but also to the location of the enzymes within membranes of cholinoceptive cells and cholinergic neurons. Also it should be realized that the specific role of the high-affinity uptake systems in the inactivation of several amines and amino acids is due less to their (limited) chemical specificity than to their location in the nerve-terminal membrane edging the synaptic clefts into which these transmitters are released.

Is this the case for any of the enkephalin-hydrolysing peptidases? Although this is probably the critical question to be answered before any of these enzymes can be considered as a true 'neuropeptidase' it cannot be assessed without histochemical localization, particularly at the electron microscope level.

Nevertheless this problem is being attacked by comparing the regional and subcellular distributions of these enzymes with markers of enkephalinergic neurones, and by determining the effect of selective lesions. In particular, localization of the candidate enzyme in membranes seems most compatible with a 'neuropeptidase'

TABLE I. Properties of various enkephalin-hydrolysing peptidases

	Enkephalinase	Aminopeptidases	Dipeptidyl-aminopeptidases	Angiotensin-converting enzyme
Localization				
Subcellular	Neuronal membranes	Cytoplasm and membranes	Membranes	Neuronal membranes
Regional	Somewhat parallel to enkephalinergic	Homogenous	Homogenous	Heterogeneous not parallel to enkephalinergic markers
Selective inhibitors	Thiorphan	Puromycin, bestatin	?	Captopril
Effects of inhibitors				
Protection of exogenous enkephalins	Yes	Yes		No
Protection of endogenous enkephalins	Yes	Yes		No
Anti-nociception	Yes	Yes		No

function.

The bulk of enkephalin-hydrolysing aminopeptidase and dipeptidylaminopeptidase activity in brain is in soluble form and its regional distribution does not correlate with that of enkephalinergic markers[8,16,18]. There is, however, a membrane-bound aminopeptidase activity, which seems to correspond to several enzymes species[10]. This can even be detected in a subcellular fraction enriched in synaptic membranes[1,13]. Cerebral ACE activity is found in synaptic membrane fractions and is reduced by lesions with kainate (a neurotoxin selective for perikarya), but its regional distribution differs greatly from that of enkephalinergic markers[27].

On the other hand 'enkephalinase' distribution correlates strikingly well at the subcellular level with that of opiate receptors[4] and reasonably well at the regional level with enkephalin content[14]. Furthermore 'enkephalinase' activity in striatum is reduced following administration of the neurotoxins kainate and 6-hydroxydopamine. With 6-hydroxydopamine, there is also a decrease in opiate-receptor binding, suggesting that at least dopaminergic nerve terminals bear both the receptor and the enzyme[16].

Finally the location of these enzymes in cell membranes in contact with the extracellular space can be assessed indirectly by identifying ³H-enkephalin fragments formed when the opioid peptide is left in contact with brain slices in a physiological medium with no detectable peptidase activity. Together with the assessment of ³H-enkephalin protection afforded by selective inhibitors, this leads to the conclusion that the hydrolysis occurs along two major and approximately equivalent pathways (Fig. 1): 'enkephalinase', and aminopeptidase(s) sensitive to bestatin but largely insensitive to puromycin[5]. In this model only a marginal amount of ³H-Tyr-Gly is formed by dipeptidylaminopeptidases which are not affected by thiorphan and bestatin, and ACE inhibition does not clearly result in decreased ³H-enkephalin hydrolysis.

Protection of synaptically released enkephalins by peptidase inhibition

All the data discussed above indicate that the metabolism of exogenous enkephalins occurs mainly along the two major pathways depicted in Fig. 1. The metabolism of endogenous enkephalins may well be qualitatively and quantitatively different: the various experimental devices used could allow exogenous enkephalins to come into contact with enzymes which the endogenous pentapeptides never encounter under physiological conditions.

To settle this point we first evaluated the effect of peptidase inhibitors on the recovery of endogenous enkephalins released by depolarization of brain slices. This model has the important advantage of maintaining the tissue organization, namely the spatial relationship between neuronal stores of the peptides and their potential synaptic inactivation systems. In the absence of any peptidase inhibitor only a small fraction (16%) of radioimmunoassayed (Met⁵) enkephalin released from the tissue is recovered from the incubation medium in intact form, even though the medium has no detectable peptidase activity (Table II). The presence of

TABLE II. Effects of various peptidase inhibitors on recovery of (Met⁵) enkephalin released from potassium-depolarized slices of rat striatum

Inhibitors	Recovery of released (Met⁵) enkephalin
None	16 ± 2%
Captopril (1 μM)	15 ± 2% (not significant)
Puromycin (0.2 mM)	21 ± 2% (not significant)
Thiorphan (0.1 μM)	29 ± 5%[a]
Bestatin (20 μM)	40 ± 5%[a]
Thiorphan (0.1 μM) + bestatin (20 μM)	98 ± 8%[a]

[a] $p < 0.05$

After preincubation in the presence of peptidase inhibitors, the slices were exposed for 5 min to 50 mM potassium and then removed from the medium. The levels of (Met⁵) enkephalin were radioimmunoassayed in tissues and medium before and after depolarization. The recovery represents the ratio of amounts of intact pentapeptide found in medium to amounts released from tissues by the potassium stimulus. *Data from Patey et al.[20] and De la Baume et al.[5]*

either thiorphan or bestatin enhances recovery by about twofold but it is only when both inhibitors are present that the recovery is complete[5,20]. Neither the aminopeptidase inhibitor puromycin nor the ACE inhibitor captopril significantly enhances recovery. These crucial experiments indicate that a major fraction of (Met[5]) enkephalin released from endogenous stores is hydrolysed by 'enkephalinase' and a bestatin-sensitive aminopeptidase(s) before diffusing into the external medium. Other peptidases do not participate in this inactivation process.

These conclusions are fully confirmed by studying the effects of peptidase inhibitors on the behavioral responsiveness of mice to nociceptive stimuli[3,5]. Endogenous opioid peptides seem to participate in the control of some (but not all) nociceptive reflexes. For instance, naloxone, an opiate-receptor antagonist, decreases the response latency to noxious stimuli (pro-nociceptive activity). It decreases the latency of the jump response in mice placed on a hot-plate and of vocalization in rats submitted to a noxious stimulus, and increases the number of writhing episodes in mice injected intraperitoneally with an irritant solution. In these various test situations, captopril has no effect, but thiorphan and bestatin produce an apparent analgesia which is markedly increased when both peptidase inhibitors are administered together. The effects of these compounds are blocked by naloxone, so it can be inferred that the inhibitors are protecting endogenously released opioid peptides from hydrolysis.

Interestingly the antinociceptive properties of these two peptidase inhibitors are displayed only in behavioral tests where naloxone has pro-nociceptive activity. All three compounds are inactive in other tests, like hot-plate paw licking or tail-flick, which are often used by pharmacologists to study the action of synthetic opiates (P. Chaillet, H. Marçais-Collado and J. Costentin, unpublished observations).

These observations not only confirm that the two peptidases have a key role in the metabolism of endogenous enkephalins. They also indicate that only some responses to nociceptive stimuli are controlled by a concomitant release of the opioid pentapeptides. Hence the selective peptidase inhibitors provide us with important new tools, in addition to opiate antagonists, for investigating the involvement of enkephalins in various physiological control mechanisms.

Conclusion

The apparent protection of enkephalins released from their endogenous stores by the peptidase inhibitors thiorphan and bestatin, supports a variety of other data which indicate that they are inactivated enzymatically and not by diffusion alone. In fact, it suggests that two enzymes ('enkephalinase' and a bestatin-sensitive aminopeptidase) both act as 'neuropeptidases'. This is similar to the situation for several other neurotransmitters, such as the catecholamines, which are inactivated in the synaptic cleft by at least two independent mechanisms. It remains to be established whether these putative inactivating 'neuropeptidases' are restricted to enkephalinergic synaptic complexes or if they are distributed in a more diffuse manner among cerebral cells, as is the case for enzymes like catechol-O-methyltransferase or histamine-N-methyltransferase.

Reading list

1 Alstein, M. and Vogel, Z. (1980) in *Neurotransmitters and their Receptors* (Littauer, U. Z., Dudai, Y., Silman, I., Teichberg, V. I. and Vogel, Z., eds), pp. 497–507, John Wiley and Sons

2 Barclay, R. K. and Phillipps, M. A. (1980) *Biochem. Biophys. Res. Commun.* 96, 1732–1738

3 Chaillet, P., Marçais-Collado, H., Costentin, J., Yi, C., de la Baume, S. and Schwartz, J. C. (1983) *Eur. J. Pharmacol.* 86, 329–336

4 De la Baume, S., Patey, G. and Schwartz, J. C. (1981) *Neuroscience* 6, 315–321

5 De la Baume, S., Yi, C. C., Schwartz, J. C., Chaillet, P., Marçais Collado, H. and Costentin, J. (1983) *Neuroscience* 8, 143–151

6 Erdös, E. G., Johnson, A. L. and Boyden,

N. T. (1978) *Biochem. Pharmacol.* 27, 843–848

7 George, S. G. and Kenny, A. J. (1973) *Biochem. J.* 134, 43–57

8 Gorenstein, C. and Snyder, S. H. (1979) *Life Sci.* 2, 2065–2070

9 Hayashi, M. (1978) *J. Biochem. (Tokyo)* 84, 1363–1372

10 Hersh, L. B. (1981) *Biochemistry* 20, 2345–2350

11 Hersh, L. B. and McKelvy, J. G. (1981) *J. Neurochem.* 13, 171–178

12 Knight, M. and Klee, W. A. (1978) *J. Biol. Chem.* 253, 3843–3847

13 Lane, A. C., Rance, M. J. and Walters, D. S. (1977) *Nature (London)* 269, 75–76

14 Llorens, C., Malfroy, B., Schwartz, J. C., Gacel, G., Roques, B. P., Roy, J., Morgat, J. L., Javoy-Agid, F. and Agid, Y. (1982) *J. Neurochem.* 39, 1081–1089

15 Malfroy, B., Swerts, J. P., Guyon, A., Roques, B. P. and Schwartz, J. C. (1978) *Nature (London)* 276, 523–526

16 Malfroy, B., Swerts, J. P., Llorens, C. and Schwartz, J. C. (1979) *Neurosci. Lett.* 11, 329–334

17 Malfroy, B. and Schwartz, J. C. (1982) *Biochem. Biophys. Res. Commun.* 106, 276–285

18 Meek, J. L., Yang, H. Y. J. and Costa, E. (1977) *Neuropharmacology* 16, 151–154

19 Morley, I. S. (1980) *Annu. Rev. Pharmacol. Toxicol.* 20, 81–110

20 Patey, G., De la Baume, S., Schwartz, J. C., Gros, C., Roques, B. P., Fournié-Zaluski, M. C. and Soroca-Lucas, E. (1981) *Science* 212, 1153–1155

21 Ramsay, D. J. (1979) *Neuroscience* 4, 313–321

22 Roques, B. P., Fournié-Zaluski, M. C., Soroca, E., Lecomte, J. M., Malfroy, B., Llorens, C. and Schwartz, J. C. (1980) *Nature (London)* 288, 286–288

23 Schnebli, H. P., Phillipps, M. A. and Barclay, R. K. (1979) *Biochim. Biophys. Acta* 569, 89–98

24 Schwartz, J. C., De la Baume, S., Malfroy, B., Patey, G., Perdrisot, T., Swerts, J. P., Fournié-Zaluski, M. C., Gacel, G. and Roques, B. P. (1980) *Adv. Biochem. Psychopharmacol.* 22, 219–235

25 Schwartz, J. C., Malfroy, B. and De la Baume, S. (1981) *Life Sci.* 29, 1715–1740

26 Umezawa, H., Aoyagi, T., Suda, H., Hamada, M. and Takeuchi, T. (1976) *J. Antibiot.* 29, 97–99

27 Yang, H. Y. T. and Neff, N. H. (1973) *J. Neurochem.* 19, 2443–2450

Jean-Charles Schwartz is at the Unité de Neurobiologie U 109, Centre Paul Broca de l'INSERM, 2ter, rue d'Alésia, 75014 Paris, France.

How do opiates act?

Richard Miller

Little is known about the biochemical mechanisms involved in the action of opiates. It is thought that cAMP may be involved. However, recent observations suggest that effects on Ca^{+2} distribution rather than cAMP may subserve the acute effects of opiates.

The pharmacology of opiates and endogenous opioid peptides has been particularly intensively studied over the last few years. A very large number of opiate induced actions have been identified, both in the central and peripheral nervous systems. Two of the most commonly observed effects of opiates are a depression of neuronal firing and an inhibition of neurotransmitter release. This latter effect has been used as the basis for several bioassays of opiate activity (e.g. guinea pig ileum, mouse, rat and rabbit vas deferens, frog neuromuscular junction). In addition to their acute effects on neuronal function, opiates have certain chronic effects associated with the production of tolerance and dependence. It is clear that specific cellular receptors exist for opiates. Through the use of biochemical receptor binding assays and isolated tissue pharmacology, a variety of opiate receptor subtypes have been defined (μ, δ, κ, ϵ and σ)[1]. What are the biochemical events that occur subsequent to the activation of such receptors by opiate agonists and how are these translated into effects on neuronal firing? Surprisingly little is known about exactly how opiates produce their effects at a cellular level. However, some recent observations have helped to shed some light on this area.

It is well known that cAMP acts as a second messenger for many extracellular stimuli. Thus, cellular membrane receptors for many agents may either stimulate or inhibit adenylate cyclase and so regulate cellular cAMP concentrations. This is probably true in the case of several neurotransmitters. It is now well established that a variety of membrane ionic channels can be modulated by cAMP-mediated phosphorylation events[2]. Such systems have been clearly demonstrated in a number of invertebrate neurons and also seem to occur in the nervous system of higher animals. Until recently, the prevailing view as to the biochemical events occurring subsequent to opiate receptor stimulation was that they involved adenylate cyclase[3]. This view was essentially the result of studies on cultured neuroblastoma related cell lines that possess opiate receptors. In these cell lines, stimulation of the receptors leads to an inhibition of adenylate cyclase and a reduction in cell cAMP concentrations. Moreover, inhibition of brain adenylate cyclase by opiates has also been demonstrated[4]. Are the acute effects of opiates on neuronal firing and transmitter release produced by this mechanism? Unfortunately there is really no evidence that this is the case. In a study of the depressant effects of opiates on myenteric neurones, it was observed that cAMP and its analogues actually produced the same effects on firing as did opiates[5]. Clearly, if opiates act by reducing neuronal cAMP concentrations then the opposite result would have been anticipated.

Another recent approach to this problem has been to try and utilize agents which interfere with the interaction of the opiate receptor with the cyclase *in situ*. This may be achieved by treating cells with pertussis toxin. This toxin has the property of causing the covalent modification of the guanyl nucleotide regulatory protein (Ni) that 'couples' adenylate cyclase to inhibitory receptors. Another toxin, cholera toxin, produces similar effects on the regulatory protein (Ns) that couples adenylate cyclase to stimulatory receptors. Indeed, it can be demonstrated that in NG108-15 cells the inhibition of cyclase by opiate agonists can be completely blocked by pretreatment of the cells with pertussis toxin[6]. Normally opiate agonists decrease the electrically-stimulated contractions of the guinea pig ileum. This is a result of their ability to inhibit evoked release of transmitter from cholinergic neurones in the myenteric plexus. A recent study has examined the effects of pertussis toxin on this process[7]. It was observed that toxin treatment did not block the ability of opiates to reduce transmitter output. This implies that an inhibition of adenylate cyclase by opiates in myenteric neurones is not responsible for their acute effects in this system. However, one interesting observation was that toxin treatment did block the ability of opiates to induce long term changes in neuronal excitability (dependence). Interestingly, cholera toxin treatment had a similar effect[8]. Thus it remains possible that the opiate effect on adenylate cyclase mediates some of the chronic actions of opiates even though it does not appear to mediate the acute effects.

If adenylate cyclase does not mediate the acute effects of opiates, are there any clues as to the possible biochemical events involved? Moreover, is stimulation of all opiate receptor subtypes linked to the same effector system? With the cholinergic or adrenergic systems where receptor subtypes have been recognized, different biochemical mechanisms are certainly linked to different receptors.

Some recent observations suggest that this may also apply to opiate receptors.

Some evidence as to the mechanism of opiate action has come from recent electrophysiological studies. Three systems have been particularly useful in this respect. These are the myenteric plexus, the locus coeruleus (LC) and sensory neurones (dorsal root ganglion cells). In each of these cell types, some population of neurones possesses opiate receptors and activation of such receptors causes an inhibition of transmitter release. The transmitters utilized by these neuronal populations are acetylcholine (among others), norepinephrine and substance P respectively. In the case of the sensory neurons, at least three types of opiate receptors (μ, δ and κ) have been shown to be present[9-13]. How is this inhibition of transmitter release produced? One possibility is that activation of the opiate receptor somehow leads to a decrease in the influx of Ca^{+2} via voltage sensitive calcium channels required for stimulus/secretion coupling of transmitter release. Indeed, a direct modulation of voltage-sensitive calcium channels by opiates has been suggested (*vide infra*). Another possibility is that opiates could enhance some K^+ conductance in neurones, possibly hyperpolarizing the cell. Depending on the region of the neuron in which this occurred, such an action could lead to reduced action potential duration and subsequent voltage-dependent Ca^{+2} influx presynaptically or an inhibition of action potential propagation into nerve terminal varicosities[14]. There is also evidence for this type of mechanism.

In locus coeruleus neurones, opiates clearly hyperpolarize cells[15]. This effect is associated with an increase in membrane conductance which appears to be due to K^+ ions[16]. Opiates also depress Ca^{+2}-dependent spikes in these neurones[17]. This action is prevented when CsCl electrodes are used instead of KCl or by addition of extracellular Ba^{+2}, both manipulations which block cellular K^+ conductances. This indicates that in these neurones the effects of opiates on voltage-dependent Ca^{+2} influx is secondary to an opiate-induced outward K^+ conductance. Similar effects of opiates have been noted in cultured mouse dorsal root ganglion (DRG) cells. In this case μ and δ specific opiates also depress Ca^{+2}-dependent spikes[12,13,18]. Again, this effect is blocked by the intracellular injection of Cs^+ indicating that it is the result of an increased K^+ conductance[10]. The question now arises as to the nature of the opiate-induced K^+ conductance. One interesting observation common to mouse DRG cells[10], LC neurones[16] and myenteric neurones[19] is that opiates prolong the after-hyperpolarization (AHP) that follows action potential generation. This AHP has been shown to be a reflection of a Ca^{+2}-activated K^+ conductance, $I_{K(Ca)}$. Moreover this effect of opiates is still observed on removal of extracellular Ca^{+2}. Thus it might be hypothesized that opiates are able to 'mobilize' Ca^{+2} from intracellular stores, resulting in an enhancement of $I_{K(Ca)}$. Such Ca^{+2}-mobilizing mechanisms clearly exist in a number of cell types. It is known that in several cases, the cellular effects of various agents are mediated by Ca^{+2} that is liberated from some intracellular store subsequent to receptor stimulation rather than obtained from extracellular sources. This type of action has now been confirmed in many instances by the use of the new Ca^{+2} specific fluorescent dye, quin-2 (Ref. 20). It would not be surprising if such mechanisms also occurred in neurones. Clearly, however, if this is one of the effects of opiates in neurones, it must occur at some region of the cell where the liberated Ca^{+2} would not be accessible to transmitter release sites.

Although there is evidence that opiate actions on neurones are mediated by activation of a K^+ conductance, other data suggest that opiate effects on transmitter release are due to direct actions on voltage-sensitive calcium channels. Workers investigating the opiate-induced depression of the Ca^{+2}-dependent portion of spikes in Rohon-Beard neurones[21] or chick DRG cells[22] or the inhibition of transmitter release from chick DRG cells[22] or at the frog neuromuscular junction[23] have suggested this type of mechanism. A close perusal of these results, however, reveals that these studies do not in general totally rule out a stimulation of a K^+ conductance as being the primary action of opiates. One exception to this is in the study of Mudge et al.[22] who observed that the effects of opiates were not reduced by extracellular Ba^{+2} at concentrations at which a block of K^+ conductances might have been expected. Although there appears to be a discrepancy between these results and those discussed above using DRG cells, it should be noted that cells from different species were used (mouse and chick). Clearly the effects produced by opiates may be dependent on species or even on the time of neuronal development. More recently, more conclusive evidence has been obtained suggesting a direct modulation of voltage-sensitive calcium channels by opiates. In mouse DRG cells μ, δ and κ opiate receptor subtypes are all present[9–13]. In the experiments discussed above, it was pointed out that the actions of μ and δ opiate agonists in these cells were blocked by intracellular Cs^+. However, similar effects on DRG action potentials are observed with κ-opiate agonists, such as dynorphin. The effects of these agents are not blocked by Cs^+. Certain other agents that block Ca^{+2} spikes in these cells such as α_2-adrenergic agonists also act in a Cs^+-resistant fashion. Moreover, all these agents reduce rather than enhance the AHP in these neurones.

Thus we are left at an interesting point. It appears that cAMP may be more concerned with the chronic rather than the acute effects of opiates. With respect to the latter actions, opiates seem ultimately to reduce transmitter release either subsequent to a mobilization of intracellular Ca^{+2} (μ and δ agonists) or by directly modulating voltage-sensitive calcium channels (κ agonists). The biochemical details of these actions remain to be elucidated. Moreover, it has also recently been shown that more than one type of voltage-sensitive calcium channel occurs in DRG cells[24]. It will be interesting to see which of these is specifically modulated by κ-opiates.

Reading list

1 Miller, R. J. (1982) *Med. Biol.* 60, 1–6
2 Siegelbaum, S. A. and Tsien, R. W. (1983) *Trends NeuroSci.* 6, 307–313
3 Sharma, S. K., Nirenberg, M. and Klee, W. A. (1975) *Proc. Natl Acad. Sci. USA* 72, 590–594
4 Gentleman, S., Paranti, M., Neff, N. and Pert, C. (1983) *J. Cell. Mol. Neurobiol.* 3, 17–23
5 Karras, P. and North, R. A. (1979) *Br. J. Pharmacol.* 65, 647–652
6 Burns, D. L., Hewlett, E. L., Moss, J. and Vaughan, M. (1983) *J. Biol. Chem.* 258, 1435–1438
7 Collier, H. O. J., Plant, N. T. and Tucker, J. F. (1983). *Eur. J. Pharmacol.* 91, 325–326
8 Lux, B. and Schulz, R. (1983) *Eur. J. Pharmacol.* 96, 175–176
9 Fields, H. L., Emson, P. L., Leight, B. K., Gilbert, R. F. T. and Iversen, L. L. (1980) *Nature (London)* 284, 351–353
10 Werz, M. A. and MacDonald, R. L. (1983) *Neurosci. Lett.* 42, 173–178
11 Werz, M. A. and MacDonald, R. L. *Neurosci. Lett.* (in press)
12 Werz, M. A. and MacDonald, R. L. (1982) *Nature (London)* 299, 730–733
13 Werz, M. A. and MacDonald, R. L. (1983) *J. Pharmacol. Exp. Ther.* 227, 394–402
14 North, R. A. and Williams, J. T. (1983) *Trends NeuroSci.* 6, 337–340
15 Pepper, C. M. and Henderson, G. (1980) *Science* 209, 394–396
16 Williams, J. T., Egan, T. M. and North, R. A. (1982) *Nature (London)* 299, 74–76
17 North, R. A. and Williams, J. T. (1983) *Br. J. Pharmacol.* 80, 225–229
18 Werz, M. A. and MacDonald, R. L. (1982) *Brain Res.* 239, 315–321
19 Tokimasa, T., Morita, K. and North, R. A. (1981) *Nature (London)* 294, 162–163
20 Tsien, R. Y. (1981) *Nature (London)* 290, 577–578
21 Bixby, J. L. and Spitzer, N. C. (1983) *J. Neurosci.* 3, 1014–1018
22 Mudge, A., Leeman, S. E. and Fischbach, G. D. (1979) *Proc. Natl Acad. Sci. USA* 76, 526–530
23 Bixby, J. L. and Spitzer, N. C. (1983) *Nature (London)* 301, 431–433
24 Nowycky, M., Fox, A. P. and Tsien, R. W. (1984) *Biophys. J.* 45, 36a

Richard Miller is at the Department of Pharmacological and Physiological Sciences, University of Chicago, 947 East 58th Street, Chicago, Illinois, IL 60637, USA.

How do opiates inhibit neurotransmitter release?

R. Alan North and John T. Williams

Opiates and opioid peptides inhibit the discharge of nerve cells. This action has been considered to result from 'postsynaptic' inhibition of cell firing, or from a 'presynaptic' reduction in the release of excitatory transmitters. In cells of the myenteric plexus and locus coeruleus, opiates directly inhibit cell firing by opening membrane potassium channels and hyperpolarizing the membrane. A hyperpolarization also occurs on nerve cell processes; this can lead to a reduction in transmitter release by blocking action potential propagation and by reducing the entry of calcium during the action potential. Thus both forms of inhibition may result from a single ionic mechanism – an increase in membrane potassium conductance.

Man has used opiates for at least two thousand years, but only in the last decade has the realization emerged that these drugs usurp the role of endogenous opioid peptides. Thus, the search for the mechanism of action of opiates at the cellular level has also become a study of the likely actions of endogenous opioids within the nervous system. Our first clue to the mechanism of action was the finding of Trendelenburg in 1917[19] that the peristaltic reflex of the guinea-pig isolated ileum was exquisitely sensitive to inhibition by opiates. Paton[13] and Schaumann[16] showed that this resulted from a reduction of acetylcholine (ACh) release, and in an elegant series of experiments[4] Kosterlitz's group demonstrated that the receptor involved in this effect was pharmacologically indistinguishable from that which mediated antinociception in animals and analgesia in man. The myenteric plexus of the guinea-pig ileum also contains an abundance of enkephalin[1], where it appears to exert a tonic inhibitory influence on peristaltic movements[5]. However, the mechanism whereby opiates inhibited peristalsis and depressed the release of ACh evoked by electrical stimulation of the myenteric plexus remained a mystery. One possibility was a simple membrane hyperpolarization which could result in failure to excite neurons with a given electrical current. A second possible mechanism was a block of propagation of the action potential before it reached release sites on the varicose nerve processes. A third was a direct interference with depolarization–secretion coupling at the varicosities from which ACh is released. The relative contribution of these three mechanisms has now been investigated electrophysiologically, and the rest of this review will be devoted to a discussion of the results that have been obtained.

Enteric neurons – activation of potassium conductance

Intracellular recording from myenteric neurons isolated from guinea-pig ileum has shown that a proportion of the cells are hyperpolarized by opiates[11]. This action has the hallmarks of a receptor-mediated event; for example, it occurs at concentrations in the nanomolar to micromolar range, is mimicked by levorphanol but not by dextrorphan, and is reversed or prevented by naloxone. The hyperpolarization results from an increase in the membrane potassium conductance, since the direction of the opiate action is reversed when the membrane is polarized beyond the potassium equilibrium potential[8]. Considerable evidence supports the idea that the potassium conductance affected is one which is sensitive to the intracellular calcium concentration. The action potential in one type of myenteric neuron carries calcium ions into the cell and this triggers a very long-lasting (several seconds) increase in potassium conductance of the membrane (after-hyperpolarization). Low concentrations of opiates prolong this after-hyperpolarization, as though opiates may inhibit the process by which the neuron reduces the free intracellular calcium concentration close to the plasma membrane[18].

The morphine hyperpolarization and conductance increase recorded in the soma of myenteric neurons is quite variable from cell to cell, suggesting that it might result from a primary action on the membrane of the cell processes. Fortunately, the myenteric plexus is a flat tissue with cell processes laid out in a two-dimensional lattice work. Therefore it was possible to show that application of opiates to cell processes (by iontophoresis) could result in a hyper-

polarization in the soma, even when equivalent application to the soma is without effect[12].

What might be the functional significance of such an action? The myenteric neurons have long processes which propagate action potentials, but which bear varicosities containing the ultrastructural features associated with transmitter release. The propagation of the action potential was studied directly by initiating it with an extracellular stimulating electrode, and recording its arrival in the soma with an intracellular electrode (Fig. 1). Opiates applied to the site of stimulation prevented the action potential, but this could often be overcome by increasing the stimulus strength. Opiates applied along the course of the cell process prevented propagation of the action potential into the soma. These experiments demonstrated that the hyperpolarization occurred on the processes of many cells even when it was not detectable with an electrode in the soma[7].

These electrophysiological findings sug-

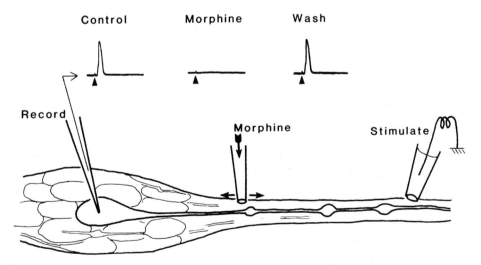

Fig. 1. *Morphine blocks action potential propagation in myenteric neurons. An intracellular recording is made from a neuron in a guinea-pig myenteric ganglion. The process of the neuron can be electrically stimulated by a focal electrode placed on the strand of fibres entering the ganglion. Morphine is then applied by iontophoresis to various points along the cell process. Top trace shows intracellular recordings. Black triangles mark stimulus artefacts. Action potentials are about 2 ms in duration and 70 mV in amplitude; resting potential is −55 mV. Iontophoresis of morphine blocks propagation of the action potential. This action is mimicked by morphine perfusion (100 nM) and blocked by naloxone perfusion (not shown). (Modified from Ref. 7.)*

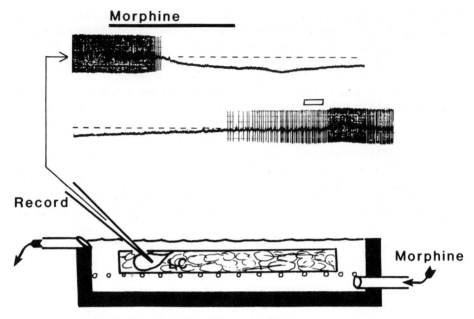

Fig. 2. *Morphine increases potassium conductance in locus coeruleus neurons. A slice of brain tissue cut from rat pons is supported on a net in a shallow bath and continuously perfused from below. Top trace is an intracellular recording from a spontaneously firing LC neuron (action potentials truncated). When the perfusing solution was changed to one containing morphine (3 μM) (solid bar) the membrane hyperpolarized and firing stopped (apparent delay in onset is artefactual due to the time required for the solution to pass through a heating coil). Morphine application was for 2 min and this hyperpolarized the cell by 16 mV. Bottom and top traces are continuous. After washout of morphine, a brief (20 s) application of γ-aminobutyric acid (GABA) (1 mM) was made (open bar). GABA depolarizes LC neurons when recording with a KCl electrode. (Unpublished work of authors.)*

gested that opiates would inhibit transmitter release from myenteric neurons by the first two of the three mechanisms mentioned above. The membrane hyperpolarization would simply prevent excitation of some neurons where electrical field stimulation is used. The propagation block would prevent recruitment of release sites. There is other indirect evidence for these actions. First, the depression by opiates of ACh release evoked by field stimulation is greater when the strength of electrical stimulation is reduced. Second, Szerb[17] found that morphine reduces the size of the releasable pool of ACh in the guinea-pig ileum. By contrast, a reduction of calcium concentration reduces the amount of ACh released from a pool of fixed size. This also suggests that opiates depress transmitter release by preventing excitation of neuron or recruitment of varicosities.

Locus coeruleus – activation of potassium conductance

One of the difficulties in working on the myenteric plexus is the heterogeneity of the cell types – both in terms of functional role and transmitter content. The rat nucleus locus coeruleus (LC) provides a homogeneous population of cells all of which contain noradrenaline and its synthesizing enzymes. It is known that the firing of nerve cells in the LC is inhibited by local or systemic administration of opiates in analgesic doses[3]. Henderson and colleagues developed a brain-slice preparation which permitted intracellular recordings and found that opiates hyperpolarized LC neurons[14] (Fig. 2). The preparation should also be well suited for study of the possible function of endogenous opioids, since enkephalin is contained within nerve terminals making synaptic contacts with LC dendrites[15]. We found that all rat LC neurons are hyperpolarized by morphine; indeed the amplitude of the hyperpolarization is remarkably consistent from cell to cell. For example, 100 nM hyperpolarized by 6.3 ± 1.0 mV (mean ± SE), 1 μM hyperpolarized by 19.3 ± 1.2 (n = 12) mV, and 10 μM hyperpolarized by 27.3 ± 1.7 (n = 8) mV. Such reproducible and dose-dependent agonist actions allowed us to use antagonists to determine the receptor type involved. This receptor has a K_e* for naloxone (determined by the pA_2 method) of between 1 and 2 nM, indicating that we

teric neurons, the potassium activation occurs not only on the cell soma but predominately on the processes. It seems likely that the processes of the LC neurons are also hyperpolarized by opiates. The evidence for this does not come from the slice preparation, in which the distal processes are severed, but from electrophysiological experiments *in vivo*. Nakamura and colleagues[10] used an extracellular electrode to stimulate the processes of LC neurons close to their terminals in the frontal cortex (Fig. 3). They judged whether or not the terminal was

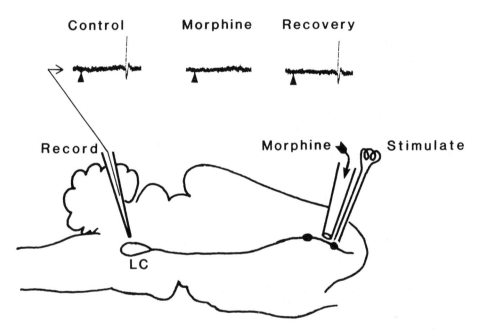

Fig. 3. *Morphine reduces excitability of terminals of locus coeruleus neurons in rat frontal cortex. Extracellular recordings were made from single LC neurons while electrically stimulating their terminal region in the frontal cortex. Morphine was applied by local infusion. Upper trace illustrates experimental results. Stimulus (triangle) is followed in about 50 ms by antidromic action potential in LC. Antidromic action potential disappears during morphine infusion. This most probably results from hyperpolarization of nerve terminals. (Figure is based on the experiments of Groves and colleagues, Ref. 10.)*

are dealing with a μ-receptor. The hyperpolarization of LC neurons also results from opening of membrane potassium channels[21].

We mentioned above that in the myen-

excited by recording the action potential after it propagated to the cell soma in the LC. The excitability of the LC nerve terminal could be measured by increasing the intensity of the stimulus current applied until 50% of stimuli resulted in action potential initiation. Local application of opiates to the region of stimulation reduced

* K_e is the equilibrium dissociation constant for the antagonist.

the excitability of the fibres, indicating a hyperpolarization of the terminals.

We argued above that a hyperpolarization of cell processes in the myenteric neurons would result in inhibition of transmitter release, because fewer varicosities would be invaded by the action potential. Could a similar mechanism apply in the CNS? Opiates inhibit noradrenaline release from slices of cortex which contain the nerve terminals of LC neurons[6]; this is also mediated by a μ-receptor (Hughes, unpublished observations). However, in those experiments transmitter release is evoked by high-potassium solutions and it remains to be seen whether an increase in potassium conductance could account for the inhibition of potassium-evoked release.

The third mechanism mentioned by which opiates could inhibit transmitter release was a reduction in the inward calcium current at the release site. Unfortunately such an action can only be investigated with electrodes in the cell soma, since intracellular recordings cannot be made from mammalian nerve terminals. Cell somata of primary afferent fibres from immature chicken[9] or neonatal mice[20] have a calcium action potential which is depressed by enkephalin, We have found that opiates inhibit a calcium action potential in the cell bodies of LC neurons. However, this results from the increase in potassium conductance because it does not occur after intracellular caesium injection or extracellular barium application (Williams and North, unpublished observations). Kandel[2] distinguishes between direct modulation of calcium entry by transmitters and indirect modulation, in which an effect on potassium channels changes the duration of the action potentials. In LC neurons calcium entry is indirectly modulated.

Conclusions

We have reviewed research which shows that opiates open potassium channels in myenteric and locus coeruleus neurons and thereby inhibit action potential discharge.

This effect results from occupancy of μ-receptors, and the concentrations of morphine required are relevant to those found in brain following systemic administration. Clearly such an action of morphine on neurons in a nociceptive pathway would result in pain relief. This same ionic mechanism is entirely appropriate for a neurotransmitter role for endogenous opioids, although as yet no hyperpolarizing synaptic potentials have been reported which are blocked by naloxone.

The hyperpolarization occurs not only on cell soma but also on the more distant cell processes. What might be the significance of such an action? We propose that this may lead to the inhibition of transmitter release which is a widely observed feature of both opiate and α_2-agonist action. The precise mechanism by which potassium activation in nerve processes inhibits transmitter release is likely to involve blockage of action potential propagation and indirect modulation of calcium entry.

It is worth mentioning that the potassium activation produced by the opiates and opioid peptides are not unique to them. Agonists acting on α_2-receptors produce effects which are identical to those described above in both the myenteric plexus and the LC. The parallels between opioid peptides and α_2-agonists are not limited to this identity of the ionic mechanism of their action. They have a similar distribution in the nervous system, they both inhibit adenylate cyclase in certain tissues, they both inhibit ACh release from myenteric neurons and noradrenaline release from cortical slices, and they both produce signs of physical dependence with long-term administration.

Acknowledgements

Work in the authors' laboratory is supported by grants from the US Department of Health and Human Services.

Reading list

1 Costa, M. and Furness, J. B. (1982) *Br. Med. Bull.* 38, 247–252

2 Kandel, E. R. (1981) *Nature (London)* 293, 697–700

3 Korf, J., Bunney, B. S. and Aghajanian, G. K. (1974) *Eur. J. Pharmacol.* 25, 165–169

4 Kosterlitz, H. W. and Waterfield, A. (1975) *Annu. Rev. Pharmacol.* 15, 29–45

5 Kromer, W. and Pretzlaff, W. (1979) *Naunyn-Schmiedebergs Arch. Pharmakol.* 309, 153–157

6 Montel, H., Starke, K. and Weber, F. (1974) *Naunyn-Schmiedebergs Arch. Pharmakol.* 283, 357–369

7 Morita, K. and North, R. A. (1981) *Neuroscience* 6, 1943–1951

8 Morita, K. and North, R. A. (1982) *Brain Res.* 242, 145–150

9 Mudge, A. W., Leeman, S. E. and Fischbach, G. D. (1979) *Proc. Natl Acad. Sci. USA* 76, 526–530

10 Nakamura, S., Tepper, J. M., Young, S. J., Ling, N. and Groves, P. M. (1982) *Neurosci. Lett.* 30, 57–62

11 North, R. A., Katayama, Y. and Williams, J. T. (1979) *Brain Res.* 165, 67–77

12 North, R. A. and Tonini, M. (1977) *Br. J. Pharmacol.* 61, 541–549

13 Paton, W. D. M. (1957) *Br. J. Pharmacol.* 12, 119–127

14 Pepper, C. M. and Henderson, G. H. (1980) *Science* 209, 394–396

15 Pickel, U. M., Joh, T. H., Reis, D. J., Leeman, S. E. and Miller, R. J. (1979) *Brain Res.* 160, 387–400

16 Schaumann, W. (1957) *Nature (London)* 178, 1121–1122

17 Szerb, J. C. (1982) *Neuroscience* 7, 320–347

18 Tokimasa, T., Morita, K. and North, R. A. (1981) *Nature (London)* 294, 162–164

19 Trendelenburg, P. (1917) *Arch. Exp. Pathol. Pharmakol.* 81, 55–129

20 Werz. M. A. and MacDonald, R. L. (1982) *Brain Res.* 239, 315–321

21 Williams, J. T., Egan, T. M. and North, R. A. (1982) *Nature (London)* 299, 74–77

R. Alan North and John T. Williams are at the Neuropharmacology Laboratory, 56-245, Massachusetts Institute of Technology, Cambridge, MA 02139, USA.

Peptide hormone gene expression in heterogeneous tissues

The pro-opiomelanocortin system

James L. Roberts, Ching-Ling C. Chen, France T. Dionne and Connie E. Gee

The pro-opiomelanocortin (POMC) gene which codes for a polyhormone protein is regulated differentially in the lobes of the pituitary. The expression of the POMC gene can be modulated at the level of transcription, processing of heteronuclear RNA, and stabilization of messenger RNA. With recombinant DNA technology and the newly developed in-situ hybridization histochemistry, this system can be used advantageously in the study of peptide hormone gene regulation. Data obtained thus far point out two different types of regulation: gene activation or inactivation in corticotrophs and/or the change in number of POMC-producing cells. This paper will focus on the new approaches which may enable one to distinguish between the regulation of gene expression and the differentiation of cells due to hormonal induction.

Until recently, interest has been focused primarily on the synthesis and processing of neuropeptide hormones, not regulation of peptide hormone gene expression. With the development of recombinant DNA technology, a better understanding of the regulation of the genes coding for these neuromodulators will be forthcoming. The pathway of expression of a peptide hormone gene involves many steps. Under

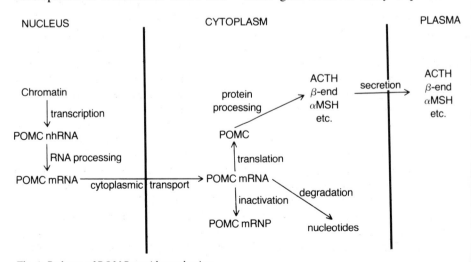

Fig. 1. *Pathway of POMC peptide production.*

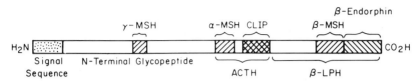

Fig. 2. *Protein structure of pro-opiomelanocortin. Peptide hormones in the precursor are separated by pairs of basic amino acids. Abbreviations used: ACTH, adrenocorticotropin; MSH, melanocyte stimulating hormone; CLIP, corticotropin-like intermediate lobe peptide; LPH, lipotropin.*

appropriate hormonal and environmental conditions, the gene is transcribed into heteronuclear RNA (hnRNA) which is then processed to the mature mRNA within the nucleus (Fig. 1). After transport to the cytoplasm, the mRNA is either translated into protein, stored or degraded. This protein undergoes tissue specific co- or post-translational modifications, or both, as glycosylation and proteolysis, to give the individual mature peptide hormone. The hormones are then stored in secretory granules to await the proper stimulus to signal secretion.

In neural and endocrine tissues, the same peptide hormone may be expressed in multiple cell types, even in the same tissue. Therefore, it is often necessary to look at individual cell types within a given tissue to determine if there is a similar or differential pattern of gene expression.

The POMC peptide hormone system is an excellent model for studying neural/endocrine gene regulation. POMC is a polyhormone protein which can be processed post-translationally to β-endorphin, adrenocorticotropin (ACTH), corticotropin-like intermediate lobe peptide (CLIP), β-lipotropin, and the melanocyte stimulating hormones (α- , β- and γ-MSH, see Fig. 2, Ref. 2). It is expressed in a variety of tissues, the primary sites being the intermediate and anterior lobes of the pituitary and the arcuate nucleus of the hypothalamus. Although it appears that the pituitary and the hypothalamus are producing a similar if not identical POMC protein, the post-translational modifications in these tissues vary, resulting in different sets of hormones. For example, in the anterior pituitary, ACTH is produced while the intermediate lobe processes all of the ACTH to α-MSH and CLIP. The POMC neurons of the arcuate region appear to produce a mixture of ACTH, α-MSH and CLIP[6]. These alternate pathways in processing of POMC peptides and the resultant biological activities may necessitate the differential regulation of gene expression seen in these tissues, which will be discussed in detail in the following section.

Hormonal and environmental factors modulating the synthesis and secretion of pituitary POMC peptides have been extensively described. Less is known about those factors which regulate hypothalamic POMC synthesis and secretion. However, it has only been within the last several years that we have learned anything about regulation of POMC gene expression, i.e. those factors which modulate POMC gene transcription or cytoplasmic POMC mRNA levels. Using recombinant DNA technology, reliable assays have now been developed for easy measurement of levels of specific hnRNAs and mRNAs. In these experiments, a DNA molecule complementary to the POMC mRNA or gene, or both, is used to quantitate through specific hybridization to the POMC RNAs in extracts of an expressing tissue. Similar to many other neuropeptides, POMC is expressed in various cell types of heterogeneous tissues. Thus, the study of RNA levels in tissue extracts may not reflect the actual pattern of gene expression. A more refined technique called *in-situ* hybridization histochemistry has been developed to visualize the specific mRNAs in individual cells[1]. Using this technique along with the RNA quantitation assays of tissue extracts, a more accurate pattern of the regulation of gene expression may now be obtained.

Regulation of POMC gene expression in the pituitary

A variety of hormonal and environmental factors have been identified which affect POMC peptide secretion in the intact animal and in primary cultures of the pituitary (Fig. 3). In general, it has been found that when a compound has an effect in one lobe of the pituitary, it does not have a similar effect in the other lobe. For example, glucocorticoids inhibit POMC peptide secretion from the anterior lobe but have no effect on POMC peptide secretion in the intermediate lobe. The recently characterized hypothalamic hormone, corticotropin releasing hormone (CRH), is a potent stimulator of anterior lobe POMC release while it has no apparent effect on intermediate lobe POMC secretion[17]. Dopamine

at physiological concentrations inhibits the release of POMC peptide from the rat intermediate lobe, presumably mediated through the dopamine axons innervating this tissue[16]. The release of anterior lobe POMC peptide does not seem to be affected by dopaminergic compounds (although one group of investigators have reported a stimulation of ACTH release in primary cultures of rat anterior pituitary). Other factors, such as light cycle, estrogens, vasopressin and mineralocorticoids, have also been shown to regulate the POMC peptide secretion in one lobe or another[16].

Unlike the peptide data, very little is known about the modulation of the gene expression of POMC in these two tissues. So far, only glucocorticoids and dopaminergic compounds have been shown to affect the cytoplasmic POMC mRNA levels in the pituitary.

Using either indirect cell-free protein translation/immunoprecipitation or

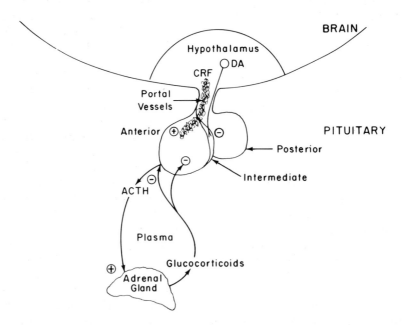

Fig. 3. *Hypothalamic/pituitary/adrenal axis. ACTH is released into the bloodstream from the anterior pituitary in response to hypothalamic factors (CRH, vasopressin) which travel down the portal vessels. ACTH then causes an increase in glucocorticoid production by the adrenal gland. The glucocorticoids, in turn, elicit a negative (feedback inhibitory) effect on both ACTH production and secretion from the anterior pituitary. POMC production in the intermediate lobe, in contrast, is negatively regulated by direct dopaminergic (DA) innervation from the hypothalamus.*

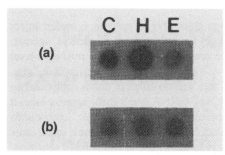

Fig. 4. *Regulation of POMC mRNA by dopaminergic compounds. Rats were injected with haloperidol (H, 2 mg kg⁻¹ day⁻¹), 2-Br-α-ergocryptine (E, 1 mg kg⁻¹ day⁻¹), or without treatment (C) for 4 days.* **(a)** *Intermediate and* **(b)** *anterior lobes of the pituitary were dissected and RNAs were isolated from the two tissues by proteinase K/phenol–chloroform extraction. Equal amounts of RNAs were spotted on nitrocellulose paper and POMC mRNA was determined by hybridization to a specific POMC cDNA probe. The intensity of the spot on the autoradiogram correlates with the level of POMC mRNA.*

DNA:RNA hybridization assays, several groups have demonstrated that glucocorticoids lower the POMC mRNA level in rat pituitary. Nakanishi and colleagues[10] have reported a two-fold increase in total pituitary POMC mRNA after adrenalectomy and a four-fold decrease following dexamethasone treatment of adrenalectomized rats. The half-time of this deinduction was 24 h. Schachter *et al.*[15] assayed POMC mRNA in separated anterior and neurointermediate lobes (the intermediate lobe with the posterior lobe still attached) from pituitary of dexamethasone treated adrenalectomized rats. They found that glucocorticoids decreased by 30–50-fold the level of anterior lobe POMC mRNAs induced by 7-day adrenalectomy. This same treatment has resulted in only a three-fold suppression of the level of POMC mRNAs in the intermediate lobe. Herbert and colleagues[4] obtained similar data with the exception that they saw no change in the level of intermediate lobe POMC mRNA. They also demonstrated that adrenalectomy, after a lag period of 6–10 h, progressively increased POMC mRNA levels in the anterior lobe to ten-fold. The response

of POMC mRNA levels to different steroids at various concentrations has also been studied in rats and the POMC-producing AtT20 tumor cells[10, 11, 13]. Based on these results, it is believed that the inhibitory effect of dexamethasone is mediated by the classical cytoplasmic/nuclear glucocorticoid receptor.

These observations raise an important point in the study of gene expression in a heterogeneous tissue. Since two different regions of the pituitary express the POMC gene, it is important to analyse them separately to see if they are differentially regulated. By treating the pituitary as a homogeneous tissue, Nakanishi and his colleagues' data could not be clearly interpreted.

It has also been shown that dopaminergic compounds exert an inhibitory effect on POMC gene expression in the rat pituitary. Chen, Dionne and Roberts (unpublished observations), using a dopamine antagonist, haloperidol, were able to show a four–six-fold time- and dose-dependent increase in the intermediate lobe POMC mRNA (Fig. 4). This stimulatory effect was detectable as early as 6 h after injection. Ergocryptine, a dopamine agonist, decreased the POMC mRNA level two–three-fold in the intermediate lobe. There was no effect of either compound on POMC mRNA levels in the anterior lobe. It appears that dopaminergic compounds modulate POMC mRNA levels in the same way as they do POMC peptide secretion. However, as with glucocorticoids, there is a time lag before the change in POMC mRNA levels is observed.

The mechanism of dopaminergic modulation of POMC mRNA levels has not been elucidated, but a possible mechanism has been described recently for another peptide hormone. Using nuclear transcription assay *in vitro*, Maurer has shown that dopamine inhibits the synthesis of prolactin hnRNA in primary cultures of rat anterior pituitary[8]. The maximal effect was observed within 45 min of treatment with ergocryptine. This effect was mimicked by a rise in the intracellular cAMP levels. Therefore, he suggests that the dopamine effect on PRL gene transcription is mediated through a rise in the intracellular cAMP level. It is conceivable that dopaminergic compounds may regulate the POMC mRNA levels in the intermediate lobe by a similar mechanism. Dopamine receptors have been identified in the cells of the intermediate lobe, but appear to be associated only with the lactotrophs in the anterior pituitary[3, 12]. This may explain why dopamine has no effect on POMC gene expression in anterior lobe corticotrophs.

Analysis of POMC gene expression in individual cells

In the previous sections, we have discussed various considerations involved in the study of peptide hormone gene regulation

in heterogeneous tissues. One obvious problem is the presence of a gene coding for identical proteins in two different cell types. Hybridization histochemistry, a technique developed to visualize specific mRNAs at the cellular level, can be used to study the expression of this specific gene in a single cell within a large cell population.

In this technique, thin sections of tissue are incubated with a radioactive DNA probe complementary to the mRNA of interest. The resulting cDNA:mRNA hybrids are visualized by autoradiography. An initial screening of tissues containing the specific mRNAs can be obtained rapidly with [32P]-labeled cDNAs[5]. A higher resolution study requiring longer exposure times can be done using [3H]- or [35S]-labeled cDNA probes. A newly developed technique for synthesizing biotin-derivitized

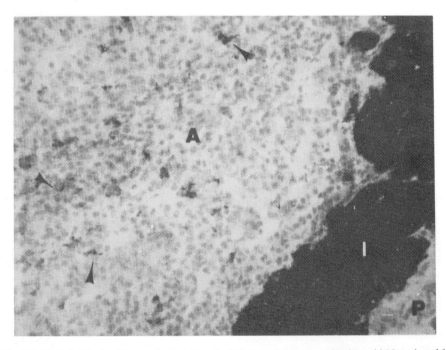

Fig. 5. In situ *hybridization. Frozen sections (6 μm) of adult rat pituitary were fixed in cold 95% ethanol for 1 h. They were rehydrated through graded alcohols and equilibrated in hybridization buffer consisting of 450 mM sodium chloride, 45 mM sodium citrate (pH 7.2), 50% formamide, 0.02% each of polyvinyl pyrolidine, bovine serum albumin and ficoll. Each section was incubated with 30,000 cpm of tritium-labeled single-stranded mouse endorphin DNA probe in hybridization buffer at 28°C for 40 h. The sections were then washed with 300 mM sodium chloride and 30 mM sodium citrate for 4 h to remove nonhybridized probes. The slides were coated with Kodak Ilford L4 nuclear emulsion and exposed at 4°C for 12 weeks. P = pars nervosa; I = pars intermedia; A = pars distalis; arrows are identifying some corticotrophs.*

DNA combines the use of molecular hybridization and immunocytochemistry, yielding single cell resolution[7].

Fig. 5 shows an example of a hybridization experiment *in situ* using a [³H]-labeled POMC cDNA hybridized to a thin section of normal rat pituitary. As shown by the distribution of the silver grains, the anterior lobe corticotrophs represent a few percent of the anterior lobe cell population, while the intermediate lobe consists mainly of POMC producing cells. There are no POMC mRNA-positive cells in the posterior pituitary. These observations are in agreement with the classical histological data. At higher magnifications, silver grains can be seen to localize primarily in the cytoplasm, implying that the POMC cDNA is hybridized to POMC mRNA. Thus, it is possible to identify individual cells expressing a specific gene product using this technique.

It is not yet possible to measure the POMC mRNA levels from grain densities quantitatively, but one can obtain qualitative information on the amounts of hybridizing mRNA after hormonal manipulation of the animal. For example, studies *in situ* by Gee and Roberts (unpublished observations) using pituitaries from adrenalectomized and normal rats showed an approximate five-fold difference in grain densities over the corticotrophs. It was also observed that there was a two–three-fold increase in positive POMC cell number in the anterior pituitary of the adrenalectomized rat. Thus, this technique may be useful for observing changes in mRNA levels in individual cells as well as changes in the number of cells synthesizing peptide hormones.

Differential gene regulation in heterogeneous tissues

The data presented in this paper suggest that the POMC gene in heterogeneous neurotissues is modulated differently. There are two obvious interpretations. A simple explanation may be that there are several POMC genes coding for identical

POMC mRNAs, and each of these is regulated by different hormones. There is precedence for families of genes in the haploid mammalian genome; a prime example is that of the human growth hormone. The structure of the POMC gene has been determined in the bovine, human and rat genomes. In these cases, there was no solid support for multiple POMC genes. In the mouse genome, initial evidence showed that there were at least two copies of the POMC genes. Further work by Euler and Herbert (unpublished observations) has identified the second POMC gene to be non-functional.

Another theory for the differential regulation of POMC genes in heterogeneous tissues may be that the various POMC expressing cell types differ in their ability to respond to the modulating hormones. The modulation of POMC peptides by glucocorticoids and CRH has been well documented. CRH stimulates the secretion of POMC peptides from the anterior corticotrophs. Glucocorticoids block this stimulatory effect via the classical steroid receptor system. Several investigators have shown by autoradiographic studies with labeled steroids that there is no localization of glucocorticoids in the nuclei of POMC-producing cells of the intermediate lobe. This observation suggests that there are no functional glucocorticoid receptors in the intermediate lobe. A similar example is the dopaminergic effects on the POMC system which has been discussed in the regulation section.

These data support the concept of an identical POMC gene being expressed in heterogeneous tissues and being regulated by various hormonal factors rather than the multiple gene theory[14].

Finally, we would like to stress the distinction between changes in the number of expressing cells and changes in the level of gene expression in the individual cells of a given tissue. For example, the corticotrophs in the anterior pituitary account for about 5% of the total cell population. A two–three-fold increase in the number of

POMC producing cells in response to adrenalectomy (Ref. 9; Gwen Childs, personal communication), could also be seen as an increase in POMC gene expression, if the tissue is assayed as a whole. All measurements done in tissue extracts are normalized to total RNA or DNA, and even if there is no change in POMC mRNA levels in individual cells, one would still see a three-fold increase in the POMC mRNA. Thus, the 30–50-fold increase in the level of POMC mRNA in the anterior lobe represents a combination of POMC gene induction in corticotrophs and appearance of more POMC-producing cells.

The *in-situ* hybridization histochemistry technique measures both aspects; changes in gene expression and cell number. This technique has resolution at the cellular level. It will be possible to determine if there are subpopulations of expressing cells which are differentially regulated. *In-situ* hybridization histochemistry is particularly applicable in the study of neural tissues where specific peptide hormone producing cells are few in number.

Acknowledgements
We would like to thank Edith Kupsaw for her time and patience in helping us to prepare this manuscript for print.

Reading list
1 Brahic, M. and Haase, A. T. (1978) *Proc. Natl Acad. Sci. U.S.A.* 75, 6125–6129
2 Eipper, B. A. and Mains, R. E. (1980) *Endocrinol. Rev.* 1, 1–27
3 Gudelsky, G. A., Nansel, D. D. and Porter, J. C. (1980) *Endocrinology* 107, 30–34
4 Herbert, E., Birnberg, N., Lissitsky, J. C., Civelli, O. and Uhler, M. (1981) *Neurosci. Newslett.* 12, 16–27
5 Hudson, P., Penschow, J., Shine, J., Ryan, G., Niall, H. and Coghlan, J. (1981) *Endocrinology* 108, 353–356
6 Krieger, D. T. and Liotta, A. S. (1979) *Science* 205, 366–372
7 Langer, P. R., Waldrop, A. A. and Ward, D. C. (1981) *Proc. Natl Acad. Sci. U.S.A.* 78, 6633–6637
8 Maurer, R. A. (1981) *Nature (London)* 294, 94–97
9 Moriarty, G. C., Halmi, N. S. and Moriarty, C. M. (1975) *Endocrinology* 96, 1426–1436
10 Nakanishi, S., Kita, T., Taii, S., Imura, H. and Numa, S. (1977) *Proc. Natl Acad. Sci. U.S.A.* 74, 3283–3286
11 Nakamura, M., Nakanishi, S., Sueoka, S., Imura, H. and Numa, S. (1978) *Eur. J. Biochem.* 86, 61–66
12 Nansel, D. D., Gudelsky, G. A. and Porter, J. C. (1979) *Endocrinology* 105, 1073–1077
13 Roberts, J. L., Budarf, M., Baxter, J. and Herbert, E. (1979) *Biochemistry* 18, 4907–4915
14 Roberts, J. L., Chen, C.-L. C., Eberwine, J. H., Evinger, M. J. Q., Gee, C., Herbert, E. and Schachter, B. S. (1981) *Recent Progress in Hormone Research*, Springer-Verlag, Berlin
15 Schachter, B. S., Johnson, L. K., Baxter, J. D. and Roberts, J. L. (1982) *Endocrinology* 110, 1442–1444
16 Thody, A. J. (1980) *The MSH Peptides*, Academic Press, London
17 Vale, W., Spiess, J., Rivier, C. and Rivier, J. (1981) *Science* 213, 1394–1397

James L. Roberts, Ching-Ling C. Chen, France T. Dionne and Connie E. Gee are from the Center for Reproductive Sciences and Department of Biochemistry, Columbia University, New York, NY 10032, U.S.A.

The mesocortico-prefrontal dopaminergic neurons

J. Glowinski, J.P. Tassin and A.M. Thierry

The mesocortico-prefrontal dopaminergic neurons represent a dopaminergic sub-system which is distinct from other ascending dopaminergic pathways. Via their inhibitory modulatory influence on cortical efferent neurons, they can indirectly regulate DA transmission in subcortical structures and hence may participate in the control of motor activity, emotional responses and cognitive processes.

For several years, it was believed that the dorsal noradrenergic (NA) system was the only catecholaminergic pathway innervating the cerebral cortex. However, experiments involving the destruction of this NA system lead to the discovery of an additional dopaminergic (DA) input. In 1973 we observed that cortical DA levels were unaltered or even increased in rats in which the ascending NA fibers had been destroyed by electrolytic or 6-hydroxydopamine (6-OHDA) lesions. In addition [3H]DA synthesis from [3H]tyrosine could be demonstrated in both cortical slices and synaptosome preparations taken from lesioned animals[1]. Following this a benztropine-sensitive specific affinity [3H]DA uptake mechanism and a DA receptor type coupled to adenylate cyclase (D_1 receptor) were identified in the cerebral cortex[2]. The existence of the cortical DA innervation has now been confirmed by histochemical studies[3,4,5]. In contrast to the widespread distribution of NA nerve terminals, DA fibers are found mainly in deep layers of the frontal, cingulate, piriform and enthorhinal cortices. In addition, lesion experiments have revealed that the DA cell bodies responsible for the cortical DA innervation are distributed in both the ventral mesencephalic tegmentum (VMT) and substantia nigra (SN). Since these earlier investigations, numerous studies have been devoted to mesocortical DA neurons – which have now been identified in several species, including man[6,7,8].

These mesocortical DA neurons are of particular importance because their discovery has provided new insight into the DA hypothesis of schizophrenia. As originally formulated, this placed emphasis on overactive DA transmission to subcortical structures innervated by the mesolimbic system. Thus it was generally thought that the antipsychotic effects of neuroleptics were linked mainly to their ability to block DA transmission in limbic areas, while their extrapyramidal and endocrine side effects were believed to be due to drug action on DA receptors in the striatum and median eminence respectively. Yet functional deficits induced by lesions to prefrontal cortex are reminiscent of some of the symptoms seen in schizophrenic patients; these include disruption of higher cognitive functions, attention deficits, increased and stereotypic motor behavior, disturbance in affective response and withdrawal from interaction with other people[6]. Thus an abnormality in the function of the mesocortico-prefrontal DA neurons might also explain some of the characteristics of this disease.

Intrinsic properties of the mesocortico-prefrontal DA neurons
Anatomy

In the rat and other mammals, DA innervation of the frontal lobe is restricted to the prefrontal cortex. This neocortical field receives direct projections from the medio-dorsal nucleus of the thalamus and is divided into a medial region corresponding to the pregenual part of the anteromedial cortex and a lateral region limited to the dorsal bank of the rhinal sulcus[3,5].

The anteromedial DA system, which has been investigated particularly extensively, originates mainly in the medio-rostral part of the A10 group of DA cell bodies, located in the ventral tegmental area (VMT)[5,9]. In an electrophysiological study, Deniau et al.[10] have shown that most of the DA neurons which innervate the anteromedial cortex project only to this structure. This selectivity applies to other A10 DA cells innervating subcortical limbic areas, implying that very few VMT-DA cells have collaterals. This has been confirmed anatomically since very few double or triple labelled cells are seen in the lateral VMT or the medial SN[11,12] following retrograde transport of fluorescent dyes injected into separate DA projection fields including the prefrontal cortex. In addition to the DA neurons, non-DA VMT cells innervate the anteromedial cortex as well as subcortical limbic structures. Non-DA VMT cells also project to the septum or the nucleus accumbens[11]. Those non-DA VMT cells which are resistant to 6-OHDA are characterized by their high conduction velocity (3.2 ms^{-1}) suggesting that their axons are myelinated. This contrasts with the DA neurons destroyed by 6-OHDA which exhibit a slow conduction velocity (0.55 msec»fb[1])[10,13].

As shown in the rat by Hökfelt et al. a large proportion of VMT cells contains cholecystokinin-8-sulfate (CCK-8) and this peptide coexists with DA in many but not in all DA cells[14]. Some of the DA-CCK-8 neurons innervate the caudal pole of the nucleus accumbens because DA and CCK-8 levels decrease following a 6-OHDA lesion of VMT DA cells. Since in contrast to DA levels, CCK-8 levels are not decreased in the anteromedial cortex of 6-OHDA lesioned rats, the mesocortico-prefrontal DA neurons do not appear to be mixed DA-CCK-8 neurons. However, the non-DA cells innervating the anteromedial cortex could be CCK-8 neurons since cortical levels of CCK-8 are decreased after electrolytic lesions of the VMT[15].

Physiology

Information concerning the activity of mesocortico-prefrontal DA neurons can be obtained by measuring DA decline following inhibition of the transmitter synthesis, dihydroxyphenylacetic acid (DOPAC) levels or the DOPAC/DA ratio. DA turnover in the prefrontal cortex is much faster than in subcortical limbic areas or in the striatum[6,16]. Furthermore, the basal discharge rate as well as the relative degree of bursting activity observed in DA neurons projecting to the rat prefrontal cortex is higher than in other mesocortical DA neurons, a difference which is even more striking when the comparison is made with nigrostriatal DA neurons[6]. DA released from dendrites exerts a tonic inhibition on the activity of nigral DA cells by acting on DA autoreceptors distributed on the soma or the proximal dendrites. DA released from nerve terminals in the striatum down-regulates its own release and synthesis by acting on DA presynaptic receptors. DA autoreceptors and presynaptic receptors which are more sensitive to DA agonists than DA postsynaptic receptors are present on most ascending DA systems. However, recently Bannon *et al.* have reported that the mesocortico-prefrontal DA neurons (as well as those innervating the cingulate cortex) lack DA autoreceptors and DA presynaptic receptors[6,17]. This may partly explain the high firing rate and high DA turnover of these mesocortical DA neurons, but specific interneuronal regulation mechanisms may also contribute to these distinctive properties.

Afferents to the mesocortico-prefrontal DA neurons

A functional distinction between the mesocortical and mesolimbic DA systems, was first suggested by the unusual sensitivity of the mesocortico-prefrontal DA neurons to foot-shock stress and neuroleptic drugs (see below). This has been confirmed in anatomical and electrophysiological studies, and has been studied further by examining the effect of lesioning VMT inputs on DA

Fig. 1. *Effect of VMT stimulation (1 Hz) on the spontaneous activity of a prefrontal cortical cell in the rat. The inhibitory response is shown in oscilloscope records (upper trace, 10 superimposed sweeps) and raster dot-display (lower records)[24].*

utilization (DOPAC/DA ratio) in the anteromedial cortex and the nucleus accumbens[6,7,8]. Thus, following electrolytic lesions of the dorsal or median raphé, DA utilization is selectively enhanced in the nucleus accumbens but is decreased (median raphé) or unaffected (dorsal raphé) in prefrontal cortex. Conversely electrolytic lesions of the habenula or the cerebellar interpositus nucleus do not affect DA utilization in the nucleus accumbens but result in selective increases (habenula) or decreases (cerebellar nucleus) in the cortex. Furthermore, DA utilization decreases at the cortical level and remains unaltered in the nucleus accumbens following 6-OHDA-induced degeneration of NA fibers projecting to the VMT[18]. These results indicate that distinct VMT inputs are involved in the control of the activity of the mesocortical and mesolimbic DA neurons. In fact, Phillipson has observed that distinct neuronal inputs, originating either from the habenula or from the raphé, selectively innervate the anterior medial part (site of origin of the mesocortico-prefrontal DA neurons) or other regions of the VMT[19].

Cortical DA receptors and influence of mesocortico-prefrontal DA neurons on target cells.

Both D_1 and D_2 receptors are present in the rat prefrontal cortex, though the D_2 receptor sites are difficult to demonstrate since a large component of [^{3}H]spiroperidol binding is actually related to 5-HT receptors in this structure[20]. D_1 receptors are located on cortical cells rather than presynaptically, since DA-sensitive adenylate cyclase activity is still present following DA denervation. D_1 receptors supersensitivity is observed following electrolytic lesions to the VMT and this procedure also induces a marked decrease of cortical DA levels. The cortical NA innervation seems to exert a permissive effect on

the D_1 receptor denervation supersensitivity because this does not occur after VMT 6-OHDA lesions which destroy both ascending DA and NA fibers[21]. This would suggest that some prefrontal cortical neurons are innervated by both DA and NA neurons.

Extracellular recordings made by Bunney and Aghajanian have shown that cells in the anteromedial cortex are inhibited by micro-iontophoretic application of DA and that this effect is antagonized by trifluoperazine[22]. Some of the cells sensitive to DA are also inhibited by NA. Recently, Benardi et al.[23], who have succeeded in recording cells intracellularly in the rat prefrontal cortex, reported that DA induces a slow depolarization of the cell membrane decreasing the firing rate without significant change in membrane resistance. Extracellular recordings show that either the spontaneous firing of anteromedial cortical neurons or their excitatory responses evoked by electrical stimulation of the thalamic medio-dorsal nucleus are blocked by electrical stimulation of VMT neurons (Fig. 1). The cessation of spontaneous firing of cortical cells, induced by VMT stimulation, still occurs after the destruction of ascending NA neurons but it disappears in rats injected with α-methylparatyrosine, or in animals with selective lesion of the ascending DA neurons[24]. Therefore, the mesocortico-prefrontal DA neurons exert an inhibitory influence on cells in the antero-medial cortex.

Indirect influence of mesocortico-prefrontal DA neurons on subcortical DA transmission

As shown in the rat[25] or the monkey[26], efferent prefrontal cortical neurons innervate some other ipsi- and contra-lateral cortical areas as well as several subcortical structures. Some of these efferent cells are branched neurons projecting to two or three structures[26,27]. Thus, the mesocortico-prefrontal DA

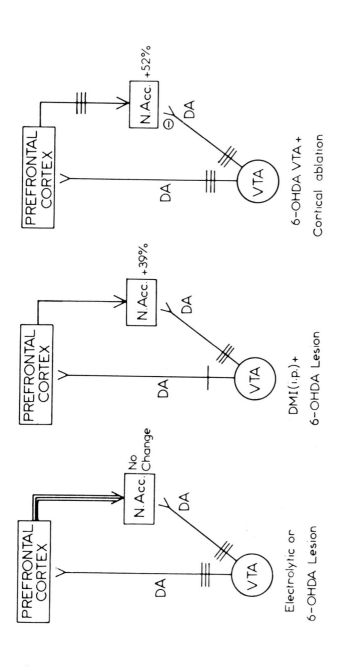

Fig. 2. *Influence of the prefrontal cortex on the development of the denervation supersensitivity of the DA receptors coupled to adenylate cyclase (D_1) in the rat nucleus accumbens.*

Denervation supersensitivity of the D_1 receptors in the nucleus accumbens occurs only when mesocortico-prefrontal DA neurons are partially protected from the 6-OHDA lesion made in the ventrotegmental area (VTA) by pretreatment with desmethylimipramine (DMI) (middle part), or when an electrolytic lesion of the prefrontal cortex is made following the 6-OHDA induced degeneration of the ascending DA neurons (right part). Likely due to an activation of cortico-nucleus accumbens neurons (   ) no change in D_1 receptors supersensitivity is seen in the nucleus accumbens when both mesocortico-prefrontal and meso-nucleus accumbens DA neurons are simultaneously destroyed by VTA 6-OHDA or electrolytic lesions (left part) (for details see Refs. 21 and 29).

neurons, via their action on cortical efferent cells, may control DA transmission in areas containing the cell bodies of ascending monoaminergic pathways or those, such as the nucleus accumbens or the striatum, that are rich in DA nerve terminals. Indeed Pycock *et al.* have reported that both DA turnover and DA receptors are increased in the striatum and nucleus accumbens following selective prefrontal cortical DA lesions[28]. Recently, we have observed that DA utilization is enhanced in the nucleus accumbens of rats with bilateral electrolytic lesions in antero-medial cortex. Such lesions also exert a permissive influence on the appearance of D_1 receptor denervation supersensitivity in the nucleus accumbens while this supersensitivity is prevented by removal of cortical DA innervation[21,29] (Fig. 2). These data may partly explain the potentiation of amphetamine- or apomorphine-increased locomotor activity seen following frontal cortical lesions[6]. More generally, the interactions between mesocortico-prefrontal DA neurons and subcortical DA pathways should be taken into consideration in order to elucidate the mechanisms underlying behaviors elicited by DA agonists or antagonists.

Peculiar reactivity of mesocortico-prefrontal DA neurons to neuroleptics or to perturb environmental conditions

Neuroleptics

When injected acutely, neuroleptics increase DA turnover in all DA innervated structures. For nigrostriatal DA neurons, this effect is mainly due to the blockade of striatal postsynaptic DA receptors. This in turn leads to an increased firing rate of nigral DA cells, mediated by the striato-nigral neuronal loop. The blockade of DA autoreceptors on the soma of the DA neurons, and of the DA presynaptic receptors located

on their dendrites or nerve terminals, also contributes to the acceleration of DA turnover induced by neuroleptics. A tolerance phenomenon is observed following chronic treatment with neuroleptics which has been attributed to the blockade of the activity of nigral DA cells following their excessive depolarization. Interestingly, mesocortico-prefrontal DA neurons are much less sensitive to acute injections of neuroleptics than DA neurons innervating the striatum or other subcortical structures (high doses are required to observe an increased DA turnover in the prefrontal cortex). In addition, as first shown by Scatton *et al.* and then confirmed by other workers, the mesocortico-prefrontal DA neurons do not develop the tolerance phenomenon induced by chronic treatment with neuroleptics and observed in both nigrostriatal DA neurons and, to a lesser degree, in mesolimbic DA neurons[6,7,30]. The lack of auto- and pre-synaptic DA receptors, or the existence of different feedback neuronal loops, could explain this peculiar reactivity of the mesocortico-prefrontal DA neurons to both acute and chronic neuroleptic treatments.

Self-stimulation, stress and isolation

In the rat, mesocortico-prefrontal DA neurons appear to be highly sensitive to self-stimulation induced by electrodes implanted in the VMT. For example, following a 10 minute self-stimulation session DA utilization is much higher in the prefrontal cortex than in the nucleus accumbens[31]. Another feature of mesocortico-prefrontal DA neurons, which suggests their involvement in emotional behavior, is their sensitivity to stress. Indeed, among all DA innervated structures, the antero-medial cortex and, to a lesser extent, the cingulate cortex are the only structures in which DA utilization is increased markedly following foot-shock stress[6,7,8,16,32]. This activation of the mesocortico-prefrontal DA neurons, which is prevented by benzodiazepine pretreatment, seems to be related to the activation of habenulo-VMT substance P neurons. Indeed, substance P levels in the VMT are decreased in stressed rats[8] and the activation of the mesocortico-prefrontal DA neurons can be prevented by injecting substance P antibodies into the VMT[33]. The foot-shock stress-induced activation of meso-cortico-prefrontal DA neurons has also been shown in BALB/C and C57 BL6 mice, the effect being more pronounced in the BALB/C strain which is characterized by its high emotional behavior. Moreover, cortical DA utilization is increased selectively in BALB/C but not in C57 BL6 mice when they were introduced for 2 minutes in an open-field, a response associated with a reduced motor activity[8]. Behavioral disturbances, such as hyper-reactivity in response to a new environment or to stressful stimuli, are observed in rats that have been held in isolation for several weeks. In these animals DA utilization is reduced in the prefrontal cortex and conversely increased in the nucleus accumbens and the striatum. Moreover, prolonged isolation potentiates the responses of the mesocortico-prefrontal DA neurons to foot-shock stress[34]. These various observations emphasize the role of mesocortico-prefrontal DA neurons in emotional responses and further indicate the specificity of this VMT DA subsystem when compared with other ascending DA pathways.

Further roles of the mesocortico-prefrontal DA neurons

Le Moal et al. have shown that in the rat lesions to the VMT induce a permanent syndrome characterized by locomotor hyperactivity, hyper-reactivity, impairment in tests requiring inhibition of a previously learned response, facilitation of approach learning and of active avoidance, impairment of hoarding behavior and hypoemotivity[35,36]. Although less pronounced, similar deficits, as well as enhanced distractibility to environmental stimuli and impairment of delayed alternation responses, were observed following 6-OHDA lesion of the VMT DA neurons[37]. Taking into consideration the role of the prefrontal cortex in cognitive processes and its numerous relations with other cortical areas and subcortical structures several of these deficits can be partly attributed to the destruction of the mesocortico-prefrontal DA systems. In fact, a correlation has been found between the extent of cortical DA denervation and the increased locomotor activity[38]. In addition, impairment in spatial delayed alternation performance has been observed both in the rat and the monkey following selective lesion of prefronto-cortical DA innervation[37,39], suggesting that DA depletion in prefrontal cortex can reproduce some of the deficits that occur in many species following lesions of the prefrontal cortex.

Several of the deficits which follow lesions to the prefrontal DA innervation resemble positive symptoms seen in schizophrenic patients. Therefore, the DA hypothesis of schizophrenia cannot be simply based on an overall excessive DA transmission in the brain and should be revised taking into consideration the complex interactions between the mesocortico-prefrontal DA neurons and other ascending DA pathways innervating subcortical limbic structures. Indeed, although these interactions have still to be understood in detail, it is tempting to suggest that an abnormal decreased activity of mesocortico-prefrontal DA neurons leads to an excessive DA transmission in subcortical structures, and that it is this dysregulation that is responsible for the positive symptoms observed in patients. Conversely, the negative symptoms could be attributed to an abnormal increase in the activity of mesocortico-prefrontal DA neurons if the resulting prolonged inhibition of the cortical efferent neurons were associated with a reduced DA transmission in some subcortical structures. Undoubtedly, further knowledge of the precise role(s) of mesocortical DA neurons in the control of other DA ascending pathways is critical for a better understanding of the antipsychotic effects of neuroleptics.

Reading list

1 Thierry, A. M., Blanc, G., Sobel, A., Stinus, L. and Glowinski, J. (1983) *Science* 182, 499–501

2 Tassin, J. P., Bockaert, J., Blanc, G., Stinus, L., Thierry, A. M., Lavielle, S., Prémont, J. and Glowinski, J. (1978) *Brain Res.* 154, 241–251

3 Berger, B., Thierry, A. M., Tassin, J. P. and Moyne, M. A. (1976) *Brain Res.* 106, 133–145

4 Hökfelt, T., Ljungdahl, A., Fuxe, K. and Johansson, O. (1974) *Science* 184, 177–179

5 Lindvall, O., Björklund, A. and Divac, I. (1978) *Brain Res.* 142, 1–24

6 Bannon, M. J. and Roth, H. (1983) *Pharmacol. Rev.* 35, 53–68

7 Glowinski, J. (1981) in *Psychiatry and the Biology of the Human Brain* (Mathysse, G., ed.), pp. 15–28 Elsevier North Holland

8 Thierry, A. M., Tassin, J. P. and Glowinski, J. (1984) in *Monoamine Innervation of Cerebral Cortex* (Descarries, L. and Jasper, H. H., eds), Alan R. Liss, Inc. New York 229–232

9 Fuxe, K., Hökfelt, T., Johansson, O., Jonsson, G., Lidbrink, P. and Ljundahl, A. (1974) *Brain Res.* 82, 349–355

10 Deniau, J. M., Thierry, A. M. and Féger, J. (1980) *Brain Res.* 189, 315–326

11 Fallon, J. H. (1981) *J. Neurosci.* 4, 1361–1368

12 Swanson, L. N. (1982) *Brain Res. Bull.* 9, 321–353

13 Thierry, A. M., Deniau, J. M., Hervé, D. and Chevalier, G. (1980) *Brain Res.* 201, 210–214

14 Hökfelt, T., Skirboll, L., Rehfeld, J. F., Goldstein, M., Markey, K. and Dann, O. (1980) *Neuroscience* 5, 2093–2124

15 Studler, J. M., Simon, H., Cesselin, F., Legrand, J. C., Glowinski, J. and Tassin, J. P. (1981) *Neuropeptides* 2, 131–139

16 Lavielle, S., Tassin, J. P., Thierry, A. M., Blanc, G., Hervé, D., Barthelemy, C. and Glowinski, J. (1979) *Brain Res.* 168, 585–594

17 Bannon, M. J., Michaud, R. L. and Roth, R. H. (1981) *Mol. Pharmacol.* 19, 270–275

18 Hervé, D., Blanc, G., Glowinski, J. and Tassin, J. P. (1982) *Brain Res.* 237, 510–516

19 Phillipson, O. T. (1979) *J. Comp. Neurol.* 187, 99–116

20 Tassin, J. P., Simon, H., Glowinski, J. and Bockaert, J. (1982) in *Brain Neurotransmitters and Hormones* (Collu, R., Ducharme, J. R., Barbeau, A. and Tolis, G., eds), pp. 17–30, Raven Press, New York

21 Tassin, J. P., Simon, H., Hervé, D., Blanc, G., Le Moal, M., Glowinski, J. and Bockaert, J. (1982) *Nature (London)* 295, 696–698

22 Bunney, B. S. and Aghajanian, G. K. (1976) *Life Sci.* 19, 1783–1792

23 Bernardi, G., Cherubini, E., Merciani, M. G., Mercuri, N. and Stanzione, P. (1982) *Brain Res.* 245, 267–274

24 Ferron, A., Thierry, A. M., Le Douarin, C. and Glowinski, J. (1984) *Brain Res.* 302, 257–265

25 Beckstead, R. M. (1979) *J. Comp. Neurol.* 184, 43–62

26 Schwartz, M. L. and Goldman-Rakic, P. (1982) *Nature (London)* 299, 154–156

27 Thierry, A. M., Chevalier, G., Ferron, A. and Glowinski, J. (1983) *Exp. Brain Res.* 50, 275–282

28 Pycock, C. J., Kerwin, R. W. and Carter, C. J. (1980) *Nature (London)* 286, 74–77

29 Reibaud, M., Blanc, G., Studler, J. M., Glowinski, J. and Tassin, J. P. (1984) *Brain Res.* 305, 43–50

30 Scatton, B., Glowinski, J. and Julou, L. (1976) *Brain Res.* 109, 184–189

31 Simon, H., Stinus, L., Tassin, J. P., Lavielle, S., Blanc, G., Thierry, A. M., Glowinski, J. and Le Moal, M. (1979) *Behav. Neural Biol.* 27, 125–145

32 Fadda, F., Argiolas, A., Melis, M. R., Tissari, A., Onali, P. and Gessa, G. L. (1978) *Life Sci.* 23, 2219–2224

33 Bannon, M. J., Elliott, P. J., Alpart, J. E., Goedert, M., Iversen, S. D. and Iversen, L. L. (1983) *Nature (London)* 306, 791–792

34 Blanc, G., Hervé, D., Simon, H., Lisoprawski, A., Glowinski, J. and Tassin, J. P. (1980) *Nature (London)* 284, 265–267

35 Le Moal, M., Stinus, L. and Galey, D. (1976) *Exp. Neurol.* 50, 521–535

36 Stinus, L., Gaffori, O., Simon, H. and Le Moal, M. (1978) *J. Comp. Physiol. Psychol.* 92, 288–296

37 Simon, H., Scatton, B. and Le Moal, M. (1980) *Nature (London)* 286, 150–151
38 Tassin, J. P., Stinus, L., Simon, H., Blanc, G., Thierry, A. M., Le Moal, M., Cardo, B. and Glowinski, J. (1978) *Brain Res.* 141, 267–281
39 Brozovski, T. J., Brown, R. M., Rosvold, H. E. and Goldman, P. S. (1979) *Science* 205, 929–932

J. Glowinski, J. P. Tassin and A. M. Thierry are at the Chaire de Neuropharmacologie, INSERM U. 114, Collège de France, 75231 Paris Cedex 5, France.

Dopamine receptors explained

Ian Creese

An enormous controversy has arisen concerning the existence, identification and classification of dopamine receptors. In this review I attempt a synthesis which I hope will disentangle you from the morass of confusion. As this task will require a degree of simplification, some pertinent (but not yet conclusive) data will have to be excluded. Hopefully the general reader will be able to use this review as a framework in which to evaluate future research in this complicated area.

It is generally agreed that pharmacological studies indicate the existence of a number of distinct types of dopamine receptor[12]. For example, dopamine agonists and butyrophenone antagonists have micromolar potency in influencing hormone release from the parathyroid glands, while they have nanomolar potency in regulating prolactin release from the anterior pituitary. Controversy has arisen with the attempted biochemical identification of these putative receptors.

The early years

In 1972, Greengard, Makman and later Iversen, initiated biochemical studies of dopamine receptors and identified a dopamine-stimulated adenylate cyclase in the mammalian superior cervical ganglion, retina, and in the striatum (the area of the CNS with the highest dopaminergic innervation)[10]. The dopamine-stimulated adenylate cyclase was proclaimed as *the* dopamine receptor as it had many characteristics expected of a dopamine receptor. Dopamine and dopamine agonists were the most potent stimulators, and archetypal dopamine antagonists (the antipsychotic, neuroleptic drugs such as phenothiazines and butyrophenones) were competitive inhibitors. However, a major inconsistency was skirted around for years. Relative to the phenothiazines, the actions of butyrophenones were far too weak in inhibiting

the dopamine-stimulated adenylate cyclase when compared with their comparative potent antagonism of dopamine-mediated effects *in vivo*. The pharmacokinetic excuses put forward to explain this discrepancy were not convincing, so it is clear that all dopamine receptors cannot be linked to stimulation of adenylate cyclase activity. In fact, it is still not known what biological function the dopamine-stimulated adenylate cyclase-linked receptor in the striatum serves. In contrast, in the parathyroids it is clear that dopamine-stimulated cAMP accumulation promotes parathyroid hormone release. In a recent review, Kebabian and Calne termed the receptor linked to the stimulation of adenylate cyclase activity the D-1 dopamine receptor[12].

The next breakthrough in dopamine receptor research occurred in 1975 when binding sites for the butyrophenone dopamine antagonist [³H]haloperidol were identified in the striatum[4, 16]. The regional distribution of these binding sites is similar to both that of dopamine-containing nerve terminals and neuronal sensitivity to iontophoretically applied dopamine. Most importantly, at these sites, neuroleptic drugs of many chemical classes have nanomolar affinities which correlate closely both with their behavioral effects, as dopamine antagonists in animals and their clinical effectiveness in the treatment of schizophrenia[5, 17]. Thus, although no biochemical response has been directly associated with these striatal binding sites, it is reasonable to suppose that [³H]butyrophenones label antagonist binding sites associated with true post-synaptic dopamine receptors.

Subclassification of potential receptors

These data suggest that there are at least two types of dopamine receptor; the D-1 receptor linked to stimulation of cAMP production and the [³H]butyrophenone binding site which apparently labels the classic pharmacological dopamine receptor in the brain. Further definition of the characteristics of the [³H]butyrophenone

binding site has been made much simpler by the study of the anterior and intermediate lobes of the pituitary. Here, [³H]-butyrophenone sites are the only dopamine receptors found, so their properties can be studied in isolation – unlike the striatum where the presence of multiple receptors complicates the issue.

In the pituitary, butyrophenones potently inhibit the nanomolar efficacy of dopamine in inhibiting prolactin and α-MSH release. Since dopamine does not stimulate cAMP production in this tissue, Kebabian and Calne termed this the D-2 receptor in contrast to the D-1 adenylate cyclase-linked stimulatory receptor whose archetype is found in the parathyroids[11]. Since the

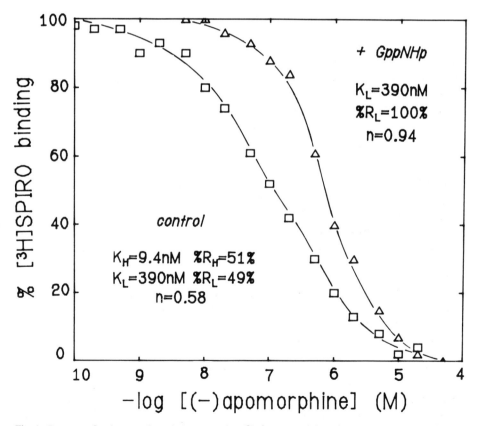

Fig. 1. *Computer fitted curves for a (−)apomorphine/[³H]spiroperidol competition experiment in bovine anterior pituitary membranes. The (−)apomorphine control curve is best fitted by assuming a two site model whereas in the presence of 10⁻⁴ M guanyl-5′-yl-imidodiphosphate (GppNHp) a one site model is sufficient to explain the data. When the two curves are analysed simultaneously and constrained to share the same KL value, there is no worsening of the fit. RH and RL represent the high and low affinity agonist binding states respectively.*

TABLE I. Model of anterior pituitary D-2 receptor

High antagonist affinity R_H High agonist affinity (K_H)	GTP $\rightleftharpoons$	High antagonist affinity R_L Low agonist affinity (K_L)

biochemical mechanism of D-2 receptors was unknown, they were defined by exclusion, a rather poor criterion one must admit. These D-2 receptors can be labeled with [³H]butyrophenones in the pituitary and almost all current evidence indicates that these binding sites are identical to the majority of the [³H]butyrophenone binding sites previously identified in the striatum.

A factor which originally complicated the D-2 picture was the observation that *in*

vitro dopamine agonists have nanomolar potency in regulating prolactin release, whereas in the striatum dopamine agonists were reported to have close to micromolar potency in inhibiting [³H]butyrophenone binding. However, closer observation of both the striatal and pituitary data indicates that the effect of the presence of agonists on [³H]butyrophenone binding does not obey the mass action kinetics typical of a bimolecular reaction. The displacement curves are shallow and span a range of concentrations of many orders of magnitude. The reason for this is that there are both high nanomolar and low micromolar affinity components to agonist displacement of [³H]butyrophenone binding (Fig. 1). By using a weighted, non-linear curve fitting

TABLE II. Characteristics of dopaminergic binding sites

	D-1	D-2 $R_H \rightleftharpoons R_L$		D-3
Usable radioligands				
[³H]Thioxanthenes	+	+	+	?[a]
[³H]Butyrophenones	–	+	+	–
[³H]Agonists	?[b]	+	–	+
Agonist affinity	μM[b]	nM	μM	nM
Butyrophenone affinity	μM	nM	nM	μM
Adenylate cyclase association	stimulatory	inhibitory or unassociated		?[a]
Guanine nucleotide sensitivity	+	+	–	?[c]
Function	(i) parathyroid hormone release (ii) striatum: unknown	(i) inhibition of pituitary hormone release (ii) DA mediated behavioral responses and their antagonism by neuroleptics		(i) autoregulation of DA neurones?
Striatal location	(i) intrinsic neurons	(i) intrinsic neurons (ii) cortico-striate afferents?[d]		(i) intrinsic neurons?[e] (ii) nigro-striatal terminals
Pituitary location	–	+		–

[a] [³H]Flupentixol binding to D-3 receptors has yet to be investigated.

[b] [³H]Agonists may label a high affinity state of D-1 receptors although stimulation of adenylate cyclase requires μM dopamine.

[c] D-3 autoreceptors are definitely not linked to stimulation of adenylate cyclase. However their association with inhibition of adenylate cyclase has not been studied. Post-synaptic D-3 binding sites may be a high agonist-affinity state of D-1 receptors.

[d] [³H]Butyrophenone binding sites on cortico-striate terminals may be a distinct receptor subtype (D-4) as they have low agonist affinity and no guanine nucleotide sensitivity. Alternatively, their lack of guanine nucleotide regulation may be an artifact of the kainic acid lesion used to isolate them.

[e] D-3 binding sites appear to be found both on, and post-synaptic to, dopamine terminals in the striatum.

program to separate these two effects it becomes clear that dopamine agonists inhibit about 50% of [³H]butyrophenone binding with nanomolar affinities which correlate with their pharmacological potencies. Interestingly, in the presence of added guanine nucleotides such as GTP this high affinity component of agonist competition for [³H]butyrophenone binding sites is lost and all [³H]butyrophenone binding is displaced with low affinity by agonists. Yet the total amount of [³H]butyrophenone binding is not altered by guanine nucleotides. This finding is reminiscent of many hormone and neurotransmitter receptors which exist in multiple conformational states differentiated by high and low agonist affinities and sensitivity to GTP, but which have equal high affinity for antagonists (Table I).

In summary, the D-2 receptors in the pituitary can be identified by [³H]butyrophenone labeling and these sites demonstrate a guanine nucleotide regulation of agonist binding. This GTP regulation of agonist binding might suggest that these receptors are linked to stimulation of adenylate cyclase. However, most studies have not demonstrated stimulation of adenylate cyclase activity in the pituitary, nor is inhibition of hormone release related to increased levels of cAMP. Recent exciting studies (Rcf. 2 and Onali and Costa, personal communication) have unexpectedly demonstrated that in the pituitary dopamine inhibits both vasoactive intestinal peptide (VIP) and β-adrenergic-stimulated adenylate cyclase activities which stimulate prolactin and α-MSH release respectively. Thus, these pituitary D-2 receptors can now be characterized biochemically as being linked to inhibition of adenylate cyclase activity as well as being labeled by [³H]butyrophenone antagonists with high affinity. In addition, we have recently demonstrated that the potent aporphine dopamine agonists [³H]apomorphine and [³H]N-propyl-norapomorphine can label the high-affinity agonist binding conformation/state of these

D-2 receptors. However, dopamine's affinity at these sites is a little low for identification of [³H]dopamine binding in normal filtration binding assays.

Importantly, a ligand has been identified which binds to the D-1 receptor. [³H]Flupentixol, a thioxanthene, which in contrast to the butyrophenones antagonizes dopamine stimulation of cAMP formation with high affinity, labels both D-1 receptors in the striatum, as well as D-2 receptors[9]. Conceivably, [³H]dopaminergic agonists may also label a high affinity agonist binding state of D-1 receptors, a feature of other receptors linked to stimulation of adenylate cyclase, but there has been little direct research into this possibility. The substantial loss (70–80%) in [³H]agonist binding under certain assay conditions following kainate lesion of the striatum is consistent with this hypothesis, since these lesions remove almost all of the D-1 receptors[13].

Striatal dopamine receptors

There is little disagreement over the results already discussed. The major controversies are (1) do butyrophenones label other sites besides the D-2 receptor type found in the pituitary and (2) do dopamine [³H]agonists label potential receptor sites in the CNS which are distinct from D-1 and D-2 receptors?

The binding characteristics of the D-2 receptors identified with [³H]butyrophenones predict agonist and antagonist pharmacological potencies in both the pituitary and striatum. They also demonstrate a guanine nucleotide regulation of agonist affinity in both tissues[18,21]. In an attempt to determine their cellular localization in the striatum a number of specific lesion techniques have been employed. 6-Hydroxydopamine can selectively lesion the nigrostriatal dopamine terminals denervating post-synaptic dopamine receptors. This results in a behavioral supersensitivity to dopamine agonists and not surprisingly there is a concomitant increase in D-2 receptor sites labeled by [³H]butyrophenones[6]. This suggests that D-2 receptors are post-synaptic to dopamine terminals in the striatum, a hypothesis which has been confirmed by selective removal of the intrinsic neurons of the striatum by kainate microinjections. This removes about 50% of the [³H]butyrophenone binding sites as well as all the D-1 receptors. Most of the remaining [³H]butyrophenone binding sites are found presynaptically on the terminals of the cortico-striate pathway (demon-strated by surgically lesioning this input)[14]. These two populations of [³H]butyro-phenone binding sites distinguished by their neuronal localization can also be differenti-ated biochemically. Whereas the sites found on the intrinsic neurons demonstrate the guanine nucleotide regulation of agonist affinity, those on the corticostriate termi-nals do not[7]. Agonists demonstrate predomi-nantly low affinity at these presynaptic

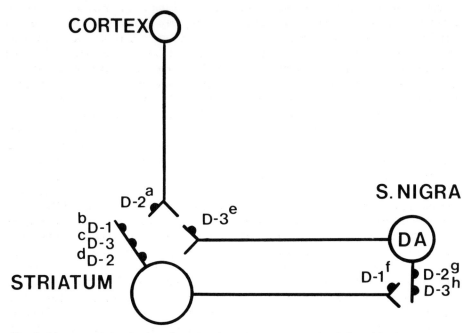

Fig. 2. *Diagrammatic localization of putative dopamine receptors and radioligand binding sites in rat nigrostriatal system.*

(a) *High affinity [³H]butyrophenone binding sites revealed following striatal kainic acid lesion which have low agonist affinity and no GTP regulation. Such sites are lost following cortical lesions. These sites have been termed D-2 or D-4.*

(b) *Dopamine stimulated adenylate cyclase found on intrinsic striatal neurons and lost following striatal kainic acid lesion. These sites have been classified as D-1 receptors.*

(c) *High affinity [³H]agonist binding sites with low butyrophenone affinity lost following striatal kainic lesion. These could represent [³H]agonist labeling of a high affinity agonist binding state of D-1 recep-tors. Also referred to as D-3 sites.*

(d) *High affinity [³H]butyrophenone binding sites with high and low agonist affinity regulated by GTP, lost following striatal kainic acid lesion. Classified as both D-2 or D-4 sites.*

(e) *High affinity [³H]agonist binding sites with low butyrophenone affinity lost following substantia nigra 6-hydroxydopamine lesion. May represent labeling of autoreceptors. Classified as D-3 sites.*

(f) *Dopamine stimulated adenylate cyclase lost following striatal kainic acid lesion or cutting the striato-nigral tracts. Classified as D-1 receptors.*

(g) *High affinity [³H]butyrophenone binding sites lost following substantia nigra 6-hydroxydopamine lesion. Classified as D-2 sites.*

(h) *High affinity [³H]agonist binding sites lost following substantia nigra 6-hydroxydopamine lesion. May represent labeling of autoreceptors. Classified as D-3 sites.*

Sites b, c, d and g, h may or may not share the same neuronal localizations.

binding sites. Thus, the [3H]butyrophenone binding sites on intrinsic neurons appear to be identical to the D-2 receptors in the pituitary, whereas the cortico-striate [3H]butyrophenone binding sites may be a separate class of D-2 receptors distinguished both by lower agonist affinity and lack of guanine nucleotide regulation. Schwartz and colleagues[19] have taken a strong line on this point and termed the receptors on the intrinsic neurons D-2 receptors and those on the cortico-striate terminals D-4 receptors. Seeman, in a recent and extensive review[15], has reversed this terminology referring to receptors on intrinsic neurons with both high agonist and antagonist affinity as D-4 while those on the cortico-striate terminals with high antagonist but low agonist affinity as D-2. This nomenclature, of course, leads to some confusion because, by his definition, D-2 receptors in the CNS will have low agonist affinity in contrast to the D-2 receptors in the pituitary which have a high affinity agonist binding component. It would be less confusing if he had termed the intrinsic neuron receptors D-2 and the cortico-striate receptors D-4. In any case this may be a moot point as I do not yet feel that we can be certain of this division of [3H]butyrophenone D-2 binding sites into two receptor classes. Since in the pituitary guanine nucleotides shift high agonist affinity at D-2 receptors to low agonist affinity it is possible that the cortico-striate receptors may just represent the low agonist affinity (or R_L) binding state of D-2 receptors; this resulting from an indirect, induced phemonenon following kainate lesion. Other confirmatory data will be required to support this subclassification of [3H]butyrophenone bindings sites.

Confusion states

Another major area of confusion concerns labeling of dopamine receptors by [3H]agonists. This has arisen historically because assays have been conducted by different researchers under different conditions in different tissues and species, lead-ing to different sites being labeled by the same [3H]ligand; furthermore different [3H]agonist ligands appear to have differential affinities for these agonist-labeled sites. In 1975, when D-2 sites were first labeled with [3H]butyrophenones, the binding of [3H]dopamine to bovine striatum was also studied[4,16]. [3H]Dopamine binding sites, in contrast to D-2 sites, had high affinity for dopamine and other agonists but low affinity for butyrophenones. However, butyrophenone displacement curves of [3H]dopamine binding were shallow, demonstrating that the sites labeled with high affinity by [3H]dopamine had both high and low affinities for butyrophenone antagonists. Two interpretations were initially made from these data. Seeman felt that [3H]dopamine (and later he found the same results with [3H]apomorphine) was labeling a distinct dopamine receptor subtype termed D-3, while Creese et al. hypothesized that [3H]dopamine may label an agonist high affinity state of D-2 receptors[4]. As it turns out, both interpretations are partially correct. Looking at the interconverting receptor hypothesis, this certainly appears to be true at D-2 receptors in the pituitary where [3H]aporphine agonists label a high affinity conformation of the D-2 receptor. Just as agonist displacement of [3H]butyrophenones at D-2 receptors in the pituitary and striatum is guanine nucleotide-sensitive, so is the high affinity binding of [3H]agonists. [3H]Aporphines also label post-synaptic D-2 receptors in the striatum since 6-hydroxydopamine lesions lead to increases in [3H]apomorphine binding, and kainic acid lesions reduce [3H]apomorphine binding under similar assay conditions[3]. On the other hand, Seeman[15] finds that [3H]dopamine and [3H]apomorphine label sites in rat striatum which are reduced by 6-hydroxydopamine lesions, implying that these binding sites occur on presynaptic dopamine terminals and hence may represent labeling of dopamine autoreceptors (for which there is reasonably good biochemical and electrophysiological evidence). However, even with his best lesions the loss of [3H]agonist binding is not complete, suggesting that [3H]agonists may label post-synaptic D-3 sites (or perhaps D-1 sites) as well.

In recent studies we have clearly demonstrated in bovine striatum that D-3 sites selectively labeled by [3H]dopamine and D-2 ([3H]butyrophenone) binding sites are distinct entities. Phenoxybenzamine treatment alkylates D-2 sites without affecting D-3 sites, whereas a heat pretreatment removes D-3 sites without affecting D-2 binding sites[8]. Interestingly [3H]apormorphine labels both D-2 and D-3 sites. However, in the pituitary where we hypothesize [3H]aporphine agonists only label the high affinity state of D-2 receptors, phenoxybenzamine does not discriminate between [3H]agonist and [3H]antagonist binding. In characterizing the assay conditions required to demonstrate high levels of striatal [3H]dopamine binding we have found that sodium potently inhibits [3H]dopamine binding to both the high affinity state of the D-2 site as well as the D-3 sites. However, divalent cations and chelating agents such as EDTA or EGTA, combined with lower assay temperature increase specific D-2 and D-3 labeling as well as concomitantly decreasing nonspecific binding.

Thus, I can summarize the major reasons for confusion in the identification of [3H]agonist binding sites as being: (1) the presence of at least three distinct classes of dopaminergic binding sites in the most commonly studied tissue – the striatum; (2) [3H]agonist ligands can label both D-2 and D-3 receptors and possibly D-1 receptors as well; but (3) the selectivity of this binding is markedly dependent on ionic composition and temperature of the assay. Like D-1 receptors, the biochemical or physiological function of D-3 agonist binding sites is unclear in the striatum.

One other potential dopamine receptor candidate should be mentioned. Sulpiride is a benzamide antipsychotic agent which demonstrates weak behavioral antagonism of dopamine-mediated behaviors in animals and demonstrates antipsychotic activity in man[11]. It is a very poor antagonist at D-1 receptors and it is also fairly weak at D-2 receptors and D-3 binding sites. However [3H]sulpiride binds to rat brain membranes with high (nM) affinity[20]. Its binding is sodium dependent and demonstrates a pharmacology suggestive of dopamine receptors. Nevertheless it does not, at this point in time, appear to label either D-1, D-2 or D-3 sites. It is too early to determine whether [3H]sulpiride does indeed identify a novel dopamine receptor subtype or what the function of these binding sites might be.

One other major classification of dopamine receptors is detailed in the literature, and it is based on electrophysiological studies in snails and behavioral experiments in cats and rodents[1]. Here, dopamine receptors are classified as either associated with excitation or with inhibition. Whereas the interpretation of the electrophysiological data from the snail is fairly straightforward, the characteristics of invertebrate dopamine receptors may not be of relevance to those in mammals. On the other hand, there are many problems in interpreting behavioral experiments in animals which are based primarily on microinjections of drugs into brain structures such as striatum and nucleus accumbens. These areas have complex anatomical and functional inter-relationships, and a pharmacological analysis is severely compromised by our lack of knowledge of exact drug concentrations at receptor sites or the degree of spread of the injected agents. Thus, the picture arising from these studies is complex and does not clearly correspond with the biochemical studies unless a good deal of data is disregarded in the analysis.

Table II summarizes my present understanding of dopamine receptor classification. The advantage to the terminology used over other classification schemes is that (1) it takes into account the historical development of the field and (2) it attempts to encompass the pharmacological classification of dopamine receptors, association of receptors with adenylate cyclase and identification of binding sites within a common nomenclature. Noted in the table are some points of contention for which there is insufficient data at present to draw firm conclusions. The availability of selective agonists and antagonists is central to receptor classification. The advent of selective D-1, D-2 and D-3 agents in the future may not only allow the resolution of the above questions, but also lead to better pharmacological treatment of disorders such as schizophrenia, tardive dyskinesia, Parkinson's disease, Huntington's chorea, galactorrhea and hyperprolactinemia which certainly involve these receptor subtypes and their regulation.

Acknowledgements

I thank M. Hamblin, D. Sibley and S. Leff for discussion and experimentation, and D. Taitano for manuscript typing. Supported by PHS MH32990. I. Creese is the recipient of a RSDA MH00316.

Reading list

1 Cools, A. R. (1981) *Trends Pharmacol. Sci.* 2, 178–183

2 Cote, T. E., Grewe, C. W. and Kebabian, J. W. (1981) *Endocrinology*, 108, 420–426

3 Creese, I. and Sibley, D. R. (1979) *Communications in Psychopharmacol.* 3, 385–395

4 Creese, I., Burt, D. R. and Snyder, S. H. (1975) *Life Sci.* 17, 993–1002

5 Creese, I., Burt, D. R. and Snyder, S. H. (1976) *Science*, 192, 481–483

6 Creese, I., Burt, D. R. and Snyder, S. H. (1977) *Science*, 197, 596–598

7 Creese, I., Usdin, T. and Snyder, S. H. (1979) *Nature (London)* 278, 577–578

8 Hamblin, M. and Creese, I. (1982) *Mol. Pharmacol.* (in press)

9 Hyttel, J. (1978) *Life Sci.* 23, 551–556

10 Iversen, L. L. (1975) *Science*, 188, 1084–1089

11 Jenner, P. and Marsden, C. D. (1979) *Life Sci.* 25, 479–486

12 Kebabian, J. W. and Calne, D. B. (1979) *Nature (London)* 277, 93–96

13 Leff, S., Adams, L., Hyttel, J. and Creese, I. (1981) *Eur. J. Pharmacol.* 70, 71–75

14 Schwarcz, R., Creese, I., Coyle, J. T. and Snyder, S. H. (1978) *Nature (London)* 271, 766–768

15 Seeman, P. (1980) *Pharm. Rev.* 32, 229–313

16 Seeman, P., Chau-Wong, M., Tedesco, J. and Wong, K. (1975) *Proc. Natl Acad. Sci. U.S.A.* 72, 4376–4380

17 Seeman, P., Lee, T., Chau-Wong, M. and Wong, K. (1976) *Nature (London)* 261, 717–719

18 Sibley, D. R. and Creese, I. (1980) *Endocrinology*, 107, 1405–1409

19 Sokoloff, P., Martres, M. P. and Schwartz, J. C. (1980) *Naunyn-Schmiedebergs Arch. Pharmakol.* 315, 89–102

20 Theodorou, A. E., Hall, M. D., Jenner, P. and Marsden, C. D. (1980) *J. Pharm. Pharmacol.* 32, 441–444

21 Zahniser, N. R. and Molinoff, P. B. (1978) *Nature (London)* 275, 453–455

Ian Creese was born in Bristol in 1949. He studied Psychology at the University of Cambridge where, in 1973, he obtained his Ph.D. with Susan Iversen on studies of the biochemical and anatomical substrates of psychomotor stimulants. After a period as a postdoctoral fellow with Solomon H. Snyder at the Johns Hopkins University Medical School in Baltimore he moved to the USCD Medical School, La Jolla, CA 92093, U.S.A. in 1978 where he is now Professor of Neurosciences.

APPENDIX

As expected for a receptor mediating the stimulation of adenylate cyclase activity, we have found that agonist competition curves for [^{3}H]flupentixol binding to D-1 receptors in the rat are biphasic, with agonists exhibiting both high- (nanomolar) and low- (micromolar) affinity components. The addition of guanine nucleotides appears to lead to a partial conversion of high-affinity to low-affinity sites. Interestingly, the pharmacological potencies of dopamine agonists to stimulate adenylate cyclase activity is better correlated with their affinities in competing for the lower affinity component of agonist/[^{3}H]thioxanthene competition curves. Furthermore, intrinsic activity of agonists in stimulating adenylate cyclase activity correlates highly with their K_L/K_H ratio for displacing [^{3}H]-flupentixol binding. Most importantly, the observation that dopamine agonists compete for D-1 specific [^{3}H]flupentixol binding with high (nano-molar) affinity confirms our previous supposition that the binding of [³H]-agonists should identify D-1 receptors directly.

As we discussed earlier, agonists can label pituitary D-2 dopamine receptors with nanomolar affinity. Such D-2 receptor sites, having nanomolar affinity for both agonists and butyrophen-ones also appear in striatum in addi-tion to 'D-3' binding sites which have nanomolar affinity for [³H]agonists but which demonstrate micromolar affinity for butyrophenones. The num-ber of these 'D-3' binding sites is enhanced by a preincubation of the striatal homogenate at 37°C in the presence of Mg^{2+}.

Binding to both sites can be studied in striata after 6-hydroxydopamine (6-OHDA) lesion of the nigro-striatal tract (Leff and Creese, 1983). 6-OHDA-induced lesions of the nigro-striatal pathway leads to a 60% de-crease in the number of striatal D-3 binding sites as previously reported which led to the suggestion that these sites may identify dopamine autore-ceptors on the nigrostriatal presynap-tic terminals. However, nigrostriatal denervation also produces a concomi-tant depletion of striatal dopamine. Recently, we and others (Bacopolous, 1981; Leff et al., 1983) have seen that acute reserpinization produces de-creases in D-3 binding similar to those produced by 6-OHDA denervation. Twenty hours after an injection of reserpine (4 mg/kg s.c.) the number of D-3 binding sites decreases by $42 \pm 6\%$. Preincubating membranes from reserpine-treated animals with either dopamine (100 nM) or the supernatant from a membrane prepar-ation of a normal striatum reverses the loss in D-3 [³H]agonist binding. Simi-larly, preincubating striatal mem-branes from 6-OHDA denervated striata with dopamine also reverses the lesion-induced loss in D-3 [³H]agonist binding.

In the routine tissue preparation for D-3 binding, the preincubation of striatal membranes must enhance D-3 binding because of the presence of endogenous dopamine in the homo-genate. Following reserpine treatment or 6-OHDA lesion this dopamine is lost, leading to a diminution in the preincubation enhancement of D-3 binding. Thus the 'loss' in D-3 binding seen after these two treatments ap-pears to be an artefact of the depletion of striatal dopamine. Furthermore, D-3 binding must be postsynaptic to the nigrostriatal terminals since the addi-tion of dopamine to 6-OHDA lesioned striata produced normal levels of D-3 binding. Our studies of binding in striata after kainic acid lesion support the hypothesis that D-3 binding is

Appendix Fig. 1. *Radioligand identification of dopamine receptors.*

	D-1		D-2	
	GTP $\rightleftharpoons$ Mg^{2+}		GTP $\rightleftharpoons$ Mg^{2+}	
	R_H	R_L	R_H	R_L
Agonist affinity	nM ('D₃')	μM	nM	μM
Antagonist affinity				
[³H]spiperone	μM	μM	nM	nM
[³H]flupentixol	nM	nM	nM	nM

localized largely on striatal neurons since D-3 binding is decreased by 75% after this treatment which destroys only postsynaptic striatal neurons.

In summary we now feel that, in striatum [³H]agonists label D-2 receptors and D-3 binding sites. As we have shown, D-1 receptor binding sites labeled by [³H]thioxanthenes exhibit a high-affinity state for agonists. We hypothesize that the D-3 binding site represents this high-affinity agonist State of the D-1 dopamine receptor[3]. This hypothesis is supported by our investigation of the potencies of various dopamine antagonists to inhibit both D-1 specific [³H]flupentixol and D-3 specific [³H]dopamine binding in rat striatum. Antagonists inhibit these two binding sites in a highly correlated fashion. Furthermore agonist affinities for D-3 binding sites are closely

correlated with each agonist's high affinity displacement of [³H]flupentixol binding. Figure 1 expresses our current view on how the majority of current dopamine receptor binding data can be accommodated by utilizing only the two dopamine receptor classes D-1 and D-2. It is our hope that such a classification scheme, based on pharmacological and biochemical criteria, may provide a useful conceptual framework around which data dealing with the many types of behavioral, electrophysiological and pharmacological responses may be investigated.

Additional reading list

1 Bacopolous, N. G. (1981) *Life Sci.* 29, 2407–2414

2 Leff, S. E. and Creese, I. (1983) *Nature (London)* 306, 586–589

3 Leff, S. E. and Creese, I. (1985) *Mol. Pharmacol.* (in press)

Recent advances in the study of Parkinson's disease

T. Andreo Larsen and Donald B. Calne

Over the last 5 years there has been increasing recognition of the complications in management besetting parkinsonian patients after several years of levodopa therapy. Notable problems are declining efficacy, increasing dyskinesia, fluctuations in response and deteriorating mental status. These difficulties have provided further motivation for continuing research efforts into the cause, pathophysiology, pharmacology and treatment of Parkinson's disease.

Etiology

The enigma of the etiology of Parkinson's disease remains unsolved, but certain clues are beginning to emerge. Perhaps the first question to be asked is whether Parkinson's disease arises as the result of genetic determination, environmental influences, or both. In an attempt to elucidate this problem, the concordance rate of Parkinson's disease has been studied in identical twins. Out of a series of 32 pairs of monozygotic twins examined by at least one neurologist, definite concordance was found in only one pair, with possible concordance in another (the doubt in this pair deriving from diagnostic difficulty)[5]. This finding indicates that genetic constitution is unlikely to play a critical role in the cause of most cases of Parkinson's disease. Since identical twins usually share a similar environment until they reach late adolescence, there is also an implication that exposure to the causal factors occurs after this period. We know that by the time the clinical features of Parkinson's disease are present, there is already a profound reduction in the concentration of dopamine in the brain[2], so it is likely that etiological mechanisms have been established several years before symptoms develop. We may hence infer that early and mid-adult life may be the major risk periods for exposure to an environmental situation that predisposes to Parkinson's disease. We

have no idea what these risk factors might be. Infective particles or toxic agents (or both) could inflict damage to the nigro-striatal system which only leads to symptoms after the additional neuronal loss that results from normal aging. Infective damage could result from a specific attack on the nervous system by a specialized virus, or it could be consequent upon a series of non-specific viral diseases damaging a selectively vulnerable nigrostriatal pathway.

Pathophysiology

For over a century there have been attempts to formulate a unifying hypothesis of disturbed physiology to explain the major clinical features of Parkinson's disease – tremor, rigidity and bradykinesia. An early opinion proposed that the basic problem was increased neuronal discharge in the motor pathways. This readily explained rigidity, which was interpreted as a direct consequence of the increased activity in motor nerves. Tremor was regarded as interrupted rigidity. Bradykinesia was viewed as deriving from difficulty in passing command signals for movement through pathways that were chronically overactive; an analogy was drawn between the nervous system and a telephone exchange – if all the lines are busy it becomes difficult to place a call. These concepts are now regarded as somewhat naive. It is clear that they are not all tenable; from them one would predict that tremor, rigidity and bradykinesia would generally occur together in whatever part of the body was involved by Parkinson's disease. However, it is quite common clinical experience for these clinical features to appear and progress independently of each other.

Novel physiological approaches have recently been employed in the search for a better understanding of the pathophysiology of the motor deficits in Parkinson's disease. It has been shown that the Parkinsonian tremor, which is undoubtedly caused by a central dysfunction, can be triggered and modulated by peripheral kinesthetic inputs[23]. These findings indicate the importance of peripheral afferent signals, but strict separation of peripheral and central functions is not entirely justified, since these two factors act together. Delivering sudden perturbations to a limb results in a short latency (M1) stretch reflex response in the pertinent muscle, which can be recorded by electromyogram (EMG). Such reflexes are normal in Parkinson's disease. Patients with 'on–off' fluctuations in their clinical state have the same short latency stretch responses in their 'on' and 'off' phases[6]. When the subject is activating the muscle by trying to oppose force during the perturbation, a later component in the response can be often detected in the EMG following the stretch stimulus. This response has been referred to as the long-loop (M2) reflex[11]. Although some earlier investigations indicated a possibility of enhanced long-loop reflexes in Parkinson's disease, the specificity of this finding was questioned on the basis of observations on elderly normal subjects with an elevated background EMG activity, who also showed an increase in the delayed EMG responses to stretch[7]. It was thus suggested that the long-loop reflexes correlated more with the background tension in muscles than with Parkinson's disease *per se*.

Patients with Parkinson's disease have difficulty in making fast movements, but also experience trouble in initiating movements. It is not clear whether the major deficit is in planning or executing the movement. While some observations imply that the major problem is in planning[17], others are more in accord with a defect involving the actual process of movement. For example, when subjects are asked to turn a handle in the direction indicated by a go signal (i.e. they have no prior warning of direction and therefore cannot assemble a plan for movement in readiness for the command), the reaction time for Parkinsonian patients is normal[8]. Similarly, Parkinsonian patients can perform fast eye movements in small saccades with and without visual feedback, which suggests normal integrity of the plan of movement[21].

Parkinsonian patients are not significantly worse than normal subjects in suppressing their vestibulo-ocular reflexes[22], indicating that postural reflexes do not interfere with the initiation of voluntary movement in Parkinsonism. In Parkinson's disease the EMG response to unloading of the muscle, and to passive shortening, is significantly increased[1]. This is an interesting contrast to pyramidal disorders, where these responses are reduced. Both visual[3,9] and auditory[9] evoked responses are delayed and reduced in amplitude in Parkinson's disease. The degree of abnormality in visual evoked responses seems to correlate with the duration of the disease and to be refractory to treatment with dopaminergic drugs. In individual patients, the two eyes are often differently affected. This suggests a prechiasmatic, possibly retinal defect. It is interesting to note that dopaminergic nerve cells have been found in retina and there is indirect evidence that these cells are of D-1 receptor type (see below). From these findings it may be inferred that the pathophysiology of Parkinson's disease is not limited to nigrostriatal interconnections. Because of these diverse observations, the basic pathophysiology of Parkinson's disease still remains an enigma.

Pharmacology

The pharmacology of Parkinson's disease has been an area of spectacular growth of knowledge over the last quarter century. Dopamine has been identified as a neurotransmitter whose depletion plays a major role in the production of bradykinesia and rigidity, with an additional but less profound effect on tremor. Two types of dopamine receptor have been identified (D-1 and D-2), and there is good evidence that stimulation of the D-2 receptor has a therapeutic effect in Parkinson's disease[4]. The role of the D-1 receptor in the striatum is not known. In addition to the central importance of dopamine in extrapyramidal disease, acetylcholine is functionally involved. Prior to the advent of levodopa, drugs which blocked the muscarinic receptors for acetylcholine were the cornerstone of treatment.

While manipulation of synaptic receptors for dopamine and acetylcholine has a definite impact on the clinical features of Parkinson's disease, there is no persuasive evidence that alteration in the activity of any other neurotransmitters or neuromodulators will modify tremor, rigidity or bradykinesia. This general statement can be made in spite of the high concentration of many neurotransmitters and neuromodulators in the basal ganglia (e.g. Substance P, enkephalin), and the known depletion of several neuroregulators other than dopamine in Parkinson's disease (e.g. norepinephrine, serotonin). We have quite detailed neuropharmacological information and yet it is impossible to draw clinical inferences [e.g. we cannot explain the role of gamma-aminobutyric acid (GABA) in motor control, although the inhibitory striatonigral GABA pathway has been analysed in detail]. Part, but not all, of the problem is the lack of stable compounds that will penetrate the blood–brain barrier and achieve reasonably selective activation or inhibition of receptors for such agents as Substance P. Work is currently in progress to develop more compounds that will manipulate the various types of synapse found in the extrapyramidal pathways.

It has recently become possible to infer the number of neurotransmitter receptors and their affinities by measuring the binding of ligands which are thought to become selectively attached at synaptic receptors sites. Studies concerning Parkinson's disease are few so far, but they have already yielded interesting results. Alterations in the binding of labelled ligands to dopamine receptor sites in Parkinson's disease have been observed. There seems to be a trend for the brains of parkinsonian patients on levodopa therapy to have a decreased number of binding sites to drugs which are employed to label dopamine receptors[19]. On the other hand, in the brains of parkinsonians who have never been treated with levodopa, the number of binding sites may be increased (supersensitivity)[10]. A decreased number of spiroperidol binding sites (supposed to represent dopamine receptors) was also observed in lymphocytes from patients with Parkinson's disease[13]. This finding, like the abnormal visual and auditory evoked responses, implies a generalized dysfunction of dopamine function and metabolism in this disease. Alterations in other neurotransmitter receptors have also been found in Parkinson's disease and there have been reports of reduced binding sites for GABA[16] and opioids[20] in the basal ganglia of Parkinsonian patients. Whether the changes inferred in these receptor systems represent a primary dysfunction or secondary changes in response to altered dopamine function remains to be seen. Sodium valproate, an inhibitor of GABA breakdown, does not alleviate Parkinson's disease.

Studies on receptors are opening new insights into Parkinson's disease. However, because of the limited extent of the evidence published so far, no clear picture has yet emerged, and future investigations are needed to elucidate these problems.

Treatment

Since the cause of Parkinson's disease is not known, its treatment can only be palliative. Nevertheless, powerful therapy is available for the most disabling deficits – bradykinesia and rigidity. The story of levodopa is too well known to bear repeating.

Bromocriptine was introduced to the therapy of Parkinson's disease in 1974. Its efficacy as an antiparkinsonian agent exceeds all drugs other than levodopa[24]. Bromocriptine has been especially useful for patients with wearing-off reactions to levodopa. Dyskinesias that are seen as a side effect of levodopa therapy are less prominent with bromocriptine. However, bromocriptine may cause more psychiatric reactions.

New dopaminergic ergot derivatives have recently been introduced for study, notably lisuride[14] and pergolide[15]. These agents lack bromocriptine's peptide moiety and are therefore likely to be less expensive (cost is a significant limitation in the use of bromocriptine). Lisuride closely resembles bromocriptine in its therapeutic profile. In a controlled comparison between bromocriptine and lisuride the side effects were also comparable. Pergolide differs from the two previously mentioned ergot derivatives in that it is claimed to have a longer duration of action, which may result in more stable plasma concentrations. This property may reduce some of the fluctuations in response and make the dosage schedule easier. As dopaminergic agonists, the ergot derivatives may cause side effects by stimulating peripheral dopamine receptors. In an attempt to avoid these actions, domperidone, a dopamine receptor blocker which does not cross the blood–brain barrier, has been given to Parkinsonian patients. Domperidone reduces nausea and vomiting induced by bromocriptine without diminishing the beneficial effects[18].

Another approach to treating Parkinson's disease is inhibition of monoamine oxidase. Deprenyl is a specific inhibitor of monoamine oxidase B, the isoenzyme which breaks down dopamine but not norepinephrine. It is therefore safe to use deprenyl in combination with levodopa (in contrast to non-specific blockers of monoamine oxidase, which induce hypertension when given with levodopa). Clinical studies with deprenyl have yielded conflicting reports and so its potential role in the management of Parkinson's disease remains ill defined[12]. Drugs with antimuscarinic properties (e.g. benzhexol, benztropine) are often helpful, particularly in alleviating tremor, but their actions are less profound than those of dopaminomimetics.

The major challenge now facing physicians managing patients with Parkinson's disease is treatment of advanced pathology, where dopaminergic drugs have already been in use for several years. The main difficulties encountered are declining efficacy, fluctuations in response (on–off and wearing-off reactions), and psychiatric deterioration (confusion, hallucinations and delusions). While the advent of dopaminergic ergot derivatives represents a step forward in reduction of wearing-off reactions, the other problems continue to pose serious dilemmas in management whose resolution may have to await better understanding of the basic mechanisms of Parkinson's disease – its etiology, pathophysiology and pharmacology.

Conclusion

While large strides have been made in our understanding of the pharmacology of Parkinson's disease, treatment is still palliative, knowledge of the physiology of the basal ganglia is scanty, and information on etiology is so sparse that we do not know where to start in the search for environmental risk factors. Much has been learned about Parkinson's disease over the last two decades, but far more continues to elude us.

Reading list

1 Angel, R. W. and LeWitt, P. A. (1978) *J. Neurol. Neurosurg. Psychiatry*, 41, 919–923
2 Bernheimer, H., Birkmayer, W., Hornykiewicz, O., Jellinger, K. and Seitelberger, F. (1973) *J. Neurol. Sci.* 20, 415
3 Bodis-Wollner, I. and Yahr, M. D. (1978) *Brain*, 101, 661–671

4 Calne, D. B. (1981) in *Current Reviews in Biomedicine 1: Towards Understanding Receptors* (Lamble, J. W., ed.), pp. 118–121, Elsevier/North-Holland Biomedical Press, Amsterdam

5 Duvoisin, R. C., Eldridge, R., Williams, A., Nutt, J. and Calne, D. (1981) *Neurology (N.Y.)*, 31, 77–80

6 Dufresne, J. R., Soechting, J. F. and Tolosa, E. S. (1981) *J. Neurol. Neurosurg. Psychiatry*, 44, 315–322

7 Evarts, E. V., Teravainen, H., Beuchert, B. E. and Calne, D. B. (1979) in *Dopaminergic Ergot Derivatives and Motor Function* (Fuxe, K. and Calne, D. B., eds), pp. 45–49, Pergamon, Oxford

8 Evarts, E. V., Teravainen, H. and Calne, D. B. (1981) *Brain*, 104, 167–186

9 Jawel, M. J., Das, P., Vincent, S. and Rose, C. F. (1981) *J. Neurol. Neurosurg. Psychiatry*, 44, 227–232

10 Lee, T., Seeman, P., Rajput, A., Farley, I. J. and Hornykiewicz, O. (1978) *Nature (London)* 273, 59–61

11 Lee R. J. and Tatton, W. J. (1975) *Can. J. Neurol. Sci.* 2, 285–293

12 Lees, A. J., Shaw, K. M., Kohout, L. J., Stern, G. M., Elsworth, J. D., Sandler, M. and Youdim, M. B. H. (1977) *Lancet*, ii, 791–795

13 Le Fur, G., Meininger, V., Baulac, M., Phan, T. and Uzan, K. (1981) *Rev. Neurol.* 137, 89–96

14 LeWitt, P. A., Burns, R. S. and Calne, D. B. (1981) in *Proceedings of Symposium on Experimental Therapeutics of Movement Disorders* (Fahn, S., Shoulson, I. and Calne, D. B., eds), Raven Press, New York (in press)

15 Lieberman, A., Goldstein, M., Leibowitz, M.,

Neophytides, A., Kupersmith, M., Pact, V. and Kleinberg, D. (1981) *Neurology (N.Y.)*, 31, 675–682

16 Lloyd, K. G., Shemen, L. and Hornykiewicz, O. (1977) *Brain Res.* 127, 269–278

17 Marsden, C. D. (1980) *Trends Neurol. Sci.* 3, 284–287

18 Quinn, N., Illas, A., Lhermitte, F. and Agid, Y. (1981) *Neurology (N.Y.)*, 31, 66–67

19 Reisine, T. D., Fields, J. Z., Yamamura, H. I., Bird, E. B., Spokes, E., Schreiner, P. S. and Enna, S. J. (1977) *Life Sci.* 21, 335–344

20 Reisine, T. D., Rossor, R. M., Spokes, E., Iversen, I. L. and Yamamura, H. I. (1979) *Brain Res.* 173, 378–382

21 Teravainen, H. and Calne, D. B. (1980) *Acta Neurol. Scand.* 62, 137–148

22 Teravainen, H. and Calne, D. B. (1980) *Acta Neurol. Scand.* 62, 149–157

23 Teravainen, H., Evarts, E. V. and Calne, D. B. (1979) in *Advances in Neurology: The Extrapyramidal System and Its Disorders* (Poirier, L. J., Sourkes, T. L. and Bedard, P. J., eds), Vol. 24, pp. 161–173, Raven Press, New York

24 Teychenne, P. F., Calne, D. B., Leigh, P. N., Greenacre, J. K., Reid, J. L., Petrie, A. and Bamji, A. N. (1975) *Lancet*, ii, 473–476

T. Andreo Larsen and Donald B. Calne are at the Experimental Therapeutics Branch, National Institute of Neurological and Communicative Disorders and Stroke, National Institutes of Health, Bethesda, MD 20205, U.S.A.

'On–off' effects: the new challenge in parkinsonism

Peter A. Lewitt and Thomas N. Chase

In the past ten years, a virtual epidemic of disabling motor disturbances has emerged among parkinsonians who, in the previous decade, were the grateful recipients of medication which dramatically rescued them from immobility. After several years of L-DOPA therapy, approximately half of parkinsonians will develop 'on–off' effects. Though several clinical syndromes are subsumed under this terminology[10], the disability incurred is best described by analogies that patients commonly offer: 'freezing', 'getting stuck', 'running out of gas'. The problem of akinesia can be sudden and unpredictable, often appearing in patients well-controlled by medication at other times. 'On–off' symptoms may fluctuate from minute to minute as well as on a longer time scale. Frequently, 'on–off' effects appear in the context of other complications common with chronic L-DOPA therapy, such as declining efficacy, involuntary movements, and adverse psychiatric reactions. The 'on–off' syndrome has been the subject of controversy and continuing study, and recent developments in therapeutics hold out promise for its amelioration and, possibly, prevention. Nevertheless, current knowledge of the interaction between parkinsonism and its therapy remains fragmentary and largely descriptive.

Initially, 'on–off' effects were regarded to be the consequence of altered pharmacokinetics with chronic L-DOPA treatment. In symptomatic patients, there may be a great deal of variability in absorption and clearance of L-DOPA, although there has been no clear demonstration that 'on–off' patients differ in blood-level drug profiles as compared to patients with better drug responses[11]. Since the death of nigro-striatal neurons is a major part of parkinsonian pathophysiology, a diminished capacity for residual neurons to take up and metabolize L-DOPA, and to store and release dopamine has been proposed as a factor behind enhanced sensitivity to fluctuations in L-DOPA blood levels[9]. Fahn[3] observed that 'off' symptoms typically develop after peak plasma L-DOPA levels have been reached, and suggested that the

decline *per se* rather than fall below a minimal level triggers 'freezing'. Quinn, Marsden and Parkes have recently demonstrated[13] that patients with seemingly random fluctuations may, in fact, have end-of-dose 'wearing-off' reactions which are identified only from cumulative charting of responses and the oral dosage schedule. Such fluctuations can be reduced when a constant L-DOPA infusion is administered[16]. In clinical practice, prominent 'wearing-off' reactions can be controlled by dividing the daily L-DOPA intake into small, frequent doses.

Deprenyl, a potent monoamine oxidase B (MAO B) inhibitor, has been used in parkinsonian patients in an effort to reduce 'on–off' disabilities. This drug has been proposed to extend the duration of dopamine action, since MAO B activity is one of the major routes of dopamine catabolism. Clinical studies with deprenyl and L-DOPA therapy, have shown that 'wearing-off' reactions may be reduced, although 'on–off' effects of a more random nature have been either unaffected or else increased in frequency[15]. Since deprenyl results in increased brain dopamine levels (with minimal effect for other neurotransmitters), the lack of benefit for the full spectrum of 'on–off' problems may be instructive. The strategy of increasing central dopamine levels or retarding their decline may reduce end-of-dose deterioration ('wearing-off' effects), but is ineffective at preventing random 'on–off' symptoms. Alternative hypotheses for 'on–off' symptoms, such as a 'depolarization block' from peak neurotransmitter levels[4], or interference with L-DOPA by an inactive metabolite, 3-O-methyldopa[14], need further substantiation.

The range of clinical phenomena found with 'on–off' symptoms also suggests that not all fluctuations could be the consequence of periodic decline in L-DOPA levels. For example, patients have been described whose akinetic[4] or tremor[11] symptoms paradoxically worsen when L-DOPA increases. Hardie and colleagues[5] recently reported that during 'off' periods some patients failed to respond to intravenous administration of either L-DOPA or lisuride, a rapid and potent dopaminomimetic agent (to be discussed below). Certain patients demonstrate that 'freezing' phenomena occur under the influence of conditions that cannot be explained by pharmacokinetics. After getting stuck at a doorway, for example, a parkinsonian may be able to move on unhindered by using a 'trick' movement (such as stepping over an imaginary log), only to experience the same arrest of mobility moments later when another impediment is reached[17]. The influences of psychological stress on the 'on–off' effect and variation in behavior are still matters of relative ignorance for clinicians studying the problem, although they are everyday experiences for the patient.

Other pharmacological approaches to the 'on–off' effect may provide clues to the neurochemical disturbances that contribute to the disorder. Dopaminomimetic ergots have been introduced as adjuncts to L-DOPA, anticholinergics and amantadine, drugs that are the mainstay of parkinsonian therapeutics. Dopaminomimetic ergots differ from dopamine in their pharmacological properties[1], and bypass the biosynthetic, uptake, and release mechanisms of presynaptic neurons as utilized by a precursor such as L-DOPA. The ergot derivatives that have had clinical testing, including lergotrile, lisuride, pergolide, and bromocriptine, all have similar therapeutic actions[8]. As solo agents, they probably are less effective than L-DOPA[7]. However, there has been considerable evidence that both fluctuations and severity of parkinsonian symptoms with chronic L-DOPA treatment can be reduced with supplementation by these drugs, and it is probable that longer duration of clinical effect from the ergots is only one part of their benefit.

There are important implications to be gained from a recent prospective study by Lees and Stern[7] and colleagues in the use of bromocriptine monotherapy as an alternative to L-DOPA. After 3 years of bromocriptine treatment, none of eleven patients had 'on–off' symptoms or other fluctuations related to therapy, in contrast to the usual experience in an L-DOPA-treated group. The conclusions from this study are still preliminary but point to alternatives in treatment which may minimize or prevent development of 'on–off' effects. The extent to which avoidance or minimal use of L-DOPA, or co-treatment with ergots might reduce the severity or frequency of fluctuations from chronic therapy is not known. Further studies are needed to learn if ergots lessen 'on–off' symptoms by changing dopamine receptor responses to chronic L-DOPA therapy.

A recent study by Coffey and colleagues[2] describes significant improvement in 'on–off' symptoms from five patients treated with lithium carbonate in a double blind, cross-over trial. In animal studies lithium pre-treatment limits the development of postsynaptic dopaminergic supersensitivity after chronic L-DOPA treatment; but since lithium has a variety of interactions with striatal dopamine synthesis, adenylate-cyclase-linked brain dopamine receptors, acetylcholine receptors, and other neurochemical effects, the basis for clinical improvement is unclear. In two of the patients dyskinetic symptoms worsened, suggesting that enhancing dopaminergic activity may be one action of lithium.

Another strategy for improvement of 'on–off' symptoms has been the use of threo-DOPS, a synthetic precursor of noradrenaline. While threo-DOPS forms noradrenaline exclusively, only a small fraction of L-DOPA is converted to this neurotransmitter. Biochemical pathology of parkinsonism includes deficits in the adrenergic system; symptoms often associated with parkinsonism, such as depression and orthostatic hypotension, may reflect these deficiencies. With threo-DOPS, Narabayashi and colleagues[12] have achieved reversal of symptoms of akinesia and 'freezing' in a group of parkinsonians with long-term, severe symptoms poorly responsive to L-DOPA. An adrenergic deficit may also underlie the exquisite adverse sensitivity of many parkinsonians to stressful situations or fatigue.

In animal models of parkinsonism, an equivalent of 'on–off' effect is not readily found and clinical observations have permitted only the most rudimentary speculations concerning its pathogenesis. Most clinicians would agree that the magnitude of the problem, in both numbers of patients affected and in their individual features of disability, has been related to the chronicity of L-DOPA treatment. Whether the duration of parkinsonism or exposure to particularly high L-DOPA dose enhances the occurrence of these symptoms remains a controversial question. Of interest is a recent report[19] of juvenile parkinsonism acquired from obstructive hydrocephalus

and from encephalitis. 'On–off' effects appeared within weeks of starting L-DOPA therapy in each case, suggesting that neither the long-term use of L-DOPA nor the progression of idiopathic Parkinson's disease are requisite for the development of these symptoms.

The need for effective therapeutics in this disorder is a daily challenge for clinicians, particularly with patients exhibiting 'drug resistant' symptoms. Strategies such as 'drug holiday'[6] and electroconvulsive treatment[8] have not shown consistent benefit for reducing 'on–off' symptoms. Further research into dopaminergic and other neurotransmitter receptor changes with parkinsonism may provide the clues necessary for methods to regenerate a better response to dopaminergic agents. Since fluctuations in motor control are characteristic of untreated parkinsonism as well, an understanding of the pathogenesis of 'on–off' symptoms might also help to explain the still mysterious origins of Parkinson's disease.

Reading list

1 Calne, D. B. (1980) Trends Pharmacol. Sci. 1, 412–414
2 Coffey, C. E., Ross, D. R., Ferren, E. L., Sullivan, J. L. and Olanow, C. W. (1982) Ann. Neurol. 12, 375–379
3 Fahn, S. (1974) Neurology 24, 431–441
4 Fahn, S. and Barrett, R. E. (1979) Adv. Neurol. 24, 451–459
5 Hardie, R. J., Lees, A. G. and Stern, G. M. (1982) Lancet ii, 992–993
6 Koller, W. C., Weiner, W. J., Perlik, S., Nausieda, P. A. and Klawans, H. L. (1981) Neurology 31, 473–475
7 Lees, A. J. and Stern, G. M. (1981) J. Neurol. Neurosurg. Psychiatry 44, 1020–1023
8 LeWitt, P. A. and Calne, D. B. in Lisuride and Other Dopamine Agonists (Calne, D. B., Horowski, R., McDonald, R. J. and Wuttke, W., eds), pp. 473–480, Raven Press, New York (in press)
9 Marsden, C. D. (1980) in Parkinson's Disease: Current Progress, Problems, and Management (Rinne, U. K., Klingler, M. and Stamm, G., eds), pp. 241–254, Elsevier/North-Holland Biomedical Press, New York
10 Marsden, C. D. and Fahn, S., eds (1981) Movement Disorders, Butterworth Scientific, London

11 Muenter, M. D. and Tyce, G. M. (1971) *Mayo Clin. Proc.* 46, 231–239

12 Narabayashi, H., Kondo, T., Hayashi, A., Suzuki, T. and Nagatsu, T. (1981) *Proc. Japan Acad., Ser B* 57, 351–354

13 Quinn, N., Marsden, C. D. and Parkes, J. D. (1982) *Lancet* ii, 412–415

14 Rivera-Calimlim, L., Tandon, D., Anderson, F. and Joynt, R. (1977) *Arch. Neurol. (Chicago)* 34, 228–232

15 Schachter, M., Marsden, C. D., Parkes, J. D., Jenner, P. and Testa, B. (1980) *J. Neurol. Neurosurg. Psychiatry* 43, 1016–1021

16 Shoulson, I., Glaubiger, G. and Chase, T. N. (1975) *Neurology* 25, 1144–1148

17 Stern, G. M., Lander, C. N. and Lees, A. J. (1980) *J. Neural. Transm., Suppl.* 16, 137–141

18 Ward, C., Stern, G. M., Pratt, R. T. C. and McKenna, P. (1980) *J. Neural Transm.* 49, 133–135

Reference added in proof

19 Lang, A. E., Meadows, J. C., Parkes, J. D. and Marsden, C. D. (1982) *J. Neurol. Neurosurg. Psychiatry* 45, 823–825

Peter A. Lewitt and Thomas N. Chase are at the Experimental Therapeutics Branch, National Institute of Neurological and Communicative Disorders and Stroke, Bethesda, MD 20205, U.S.A.

Dopamine-rich transplants in experimental parkinsonism

Stephen B. Dunnett, Anders Björklund and Ulf Stenevi

Advances in techniques for the transplantation of embryonic neural tissue to the brain of host rats, and the demonstrated functional competence of such grafts, have recently led to speculation about the potential clinical use of similar procedures applied to human neurodegenerative diseases. To date, the most widely studied system has been the transplantation of dopamine-rich tissue to the cerebrum of adult rats which have received neurotoxic destruction of the intrinsic forebrain dopamine pathways. This lesion has been widely regarded as an animal model of Parkinson's disease in man. This review seeks to assess what has been achieved by intracerebral grafting so far and the problems which remain unresolved, within the context of this experimental model of parkinsonism.

The history of attempts to transplant neural tissue to the mammalian brain may be traced back to the first decades of this century. However, in these early experiments graft survival was poor, and in those cases where the graft did survive the anatomical techniques were not available for the study of connectivity between the graft and host. Over the last decade the conditions for viable grafting in the CNS have been better characterized, and involve the use of embryonic (or in certain cases neonatal) tissue of a particular developmental age, and graft placement within a milieu which can provide a rapid revascularization of the graft and its incorporation into the host blood and cerebrospinal fluid circulation[40]. With the provision of such conditions, reliable graft survival has now been reported by a number of research groups employing several different transplantation techniques. Moreover, the grafts are generally seen to establish extensive networks of reciprocal axonal connections between the graft and host brain. The newly formed connections are transmitter-specific such that reinnervation into and within target nuclei reflects the pattern of innervation seen in the intact brain. Although the factors which regulate the growth, direction

and terminal distribution of graft-derived reinnervation of the host tissue remain uncharacterized, it has become clear that deafferentation of intrinsic terminals in the target tissue can be an essential component in promoting such growth[3,5].

Since grafted neurons have been seen to be capable of replacing lesioned afferents to a target structure in the host brain and restoring anatomical connectivity, it was of interest to consider whether any parallel functional recovery could be detected in the behavioural impairments induced by the lesion. This issue has been most extensively investigated in rats receiving dopamine (DA)-rich grafts following lesions of the nigrostriatal DA pathway, since the behavioural syndrome induced by DA depletion in the rat is well-characterized and relatively simple to test. This syndrome has been widely regarded as an animal model of Parkinson's disease, and Perlow[32,34] has suggested that intracerebral grafting of dopamine-rich tissue may potentially lead to the development of new clinical treatments that overcome unresolved problems in present pharmacological approaches. The potential clinical importance of this approach is highlighted by the recent report of the first case of treatment of a patient with severe parkinsonism by intracerebral grafting[27].

Dopamine depletion and experimental parkinsonism

Dopamine depletion was first suggested as an animal model for parkinsonism by Carlsson and his co-workers. In a series of studies in the late 1950s, they demonstrated in rodents that reserpine injections, which deplete forebrain catecholamines, produce hypokinesia and sedation and can be reversed by dopa. Based on the high concentration of dopamine in the basal ganglia, the association of basal ganglia disease such as parkinsonism with the loss of motor control, and the psychopharmacological effects of reserpine and dopa, Carlsson[13] hypothesized that dopamine in the basal ganglia might be involved in the control of motor function and that Parkinson's disease, by implication, was due to dopamine depletion. The clinical relevance of this hypothesis was confirmed by the identification of significant dopamine depletions in the post-mortem parkinsonian brain[19,24], which was closely followed by the introduction of L-dopa as an effective clinical treatment in Parkinson's disease[2].

In the development of this animal model, the neurotoxin 6-hydroxydopamine (6-OHDA) has subsequently been used to provide relatively selective and more permanent lesions of dopamine neurons[18,39]. Bilateral lesions placed in the nigrostriatal pathway in the rat produce an akinetic syndrome with characteristic hunched posture and poverty of initiation of voluntary movement similar to the reserpinized rodent, but since the syndrome is longer lasting, severe aphagia and adipsia become a serious problem in keeping the animals alive. Although these rats may show a remarkable capacity for eventual recovery, even after relatively extensive lesions[39,41], in our experience bilateral dopamine depletions exceeding approximately 97% result in the absence of any signs of recovery and the dependence of the rats on permanent tube-feeding for all food and water intake.

In rats, unilateral nigrostriatal lesions using 6-OHDA induce a markedly asymmetrical postural bias to the side of the lesion, which in many respects resembles the scoliosis of hemiparkinsonism. However, the particular attraction of this preparation as an experimental model in the rat lies in the fact that normal regulatory function is maintained by the intact side, and comparison of the two sides provides a within-animal control. Behaviourally, the rat turns spontaneously towards the side of the lesion for 1–2 weeks following surgery, or in response to stress thereafter. Stimulation of dopamine release on the intact side by injection of amphetamine provides strong turning towards the side of the lesion, whereas apomorphine induces turning in the opposite direction, presumably via its action on supersensitive dopamine receptors on the lesioned side. The animals also show sensorimotor impairments, manifested by a profound 'neglect' of all stimuli on the side of the body contralateral to the lesion.

Many aspects of the 6-OHDA syndrome, including the akinesia, aphagia and adipsia in bilaterally lesioned rats and the sensorimotor impairments in rats with unilateral or bilateral lesions, may be temporarily ameliorated or reversed by administration of L-dopa or the dopamine-receptor agonist, apomorphine, although not by drugs that stimulate dopamine turnover or release, such as amphetamine[30,31]. This observation has been taken to suggest that the dopamine system exerts a primarily 'permissive' function: it enables other striatal neuronal processing to take place and regulates the general level of striatal activity, rather than providing a more specific, patterned input[41]. One consequence of this may be seen in the considerably greater advances that have been achieved in the pharmacological treatment of Parkinson's disease as compared with other major neurodegenerative disorders such as Huntington's chorea or Alzheimer's disease. A second consequence is that neuronal grafts of dopamine-rich tissue may achieve functional competence by providing localized and controlled release of dopamine at physiological levels, even if they do not become fully integrated within the neural circuitry of the host brain.

Transplantation in experimental parkinsonism

Several anatomical studies have shown that graft tissue is capable of establishing precise, neurotransmitter-specific, reciprocal connections with the host brain[5, 7, 8, 11, 25]. Moreover, grafts to the de-afferented hippocampus are spontaneously electrophysiologically active, manifest synaptic connections with normal ultrastructural appearance in the host hippocampus, and graft stimulation produces field responses in the host that mimic those seen following activation of the intrinsic innervation[1, 8, 29]. These observations suggest that in certain circumstances grafts may be able to re-establish circuitries damaged by a lesion in such a way as to permit the return of behavioural functions disrupted by the lesion.

Even in the absence of specific patterns of reinnervation, grafts may nevertheless have functional effects on more diffusely organized functions, as revealed by studies on the transplantation of neuroendocrine tissue. Because of its immunologically privileged location, the brain provides a particularly suitable site for the successful grafting of a wide range of endocrine or hormone-secreting cells[33] and such grafts have been shown to be functionally competent. For example hypothalamic grafts placed in the third ventricle secrete vasopressin and can compensate for the polydipsia and polyuria in Brattleboro rats with a genetic vasopressin deficiency[23]. Similarly, intraventricular hypothalamic grafts can also produce compensation in mice with gonadotropin-releasing-hormone deficiency[28]. Although the ependymal lining of the ventricle may provide a barrier to the penetration of axons reconnecting graft and host neuropil, in other respects the lat-

eral, third and fourth ventricles all provide suitable, richly vascularized and relatively non-invasive sites for tissue transplantation[22, 33, 36].

In applying dopamine-rich transplants to experimental parkinsonism, the permissive hypothesis of dopamine function suggests that diffuse dopamine release from intraventricular grafts may be sufficient to reverse at least some aspects of the syndrome. Both the diffuse release of dopamine and specific dopaminergic reinnervation could make dopamine available to denervated striatal receptors, at more stable and localized physiological levels than can be envisaged by pharmacological means.

Intraventricular nigral grafts

The first published report of functional recovery produced by intracerebral transplantation was that of Perlow and coworkers[34]. They grafted pieces of embryonic substantia nigra into the lateral ventricle of rats on the same side as a previously administered unilateral 6-OHDA lesion of the nigrostriatal pathway. The transplantation procedure involved the injection of three pieces of embryonic ventral mesencephalon with 30–40 μl Ringer's solution into the lateral ventricle via a modified lumbar-puncture needle (see Fig. 1B). Such grafts showed long-term survival (monitored up to 10 months) and a rich supply of fluorescent cells and fibers within the graft, but only sparse dopaminergic reinnervation of proximal segments of the deafferented neostriatum[22]. The rats were given repeated tests of apomorphine-induced rotation, and it was observed that those animals with nigra grafts, but not control rats with sciatic nerve implants, showed an average 50% reduction in the rotational response. This compensation of the lesion-induced behavioural asymmetry was attributed to a reduction in supersensitivity of the intrastriatal dopamine receptors on the lesioned side, which has subsequently been confirmed by the DA-receptor binding

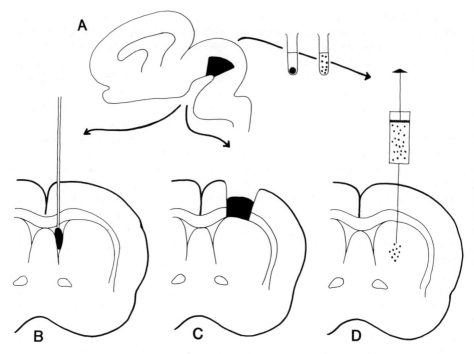

Fig. 1. *Schematic diagram of different experimental procedures for the transplantation of embryonic substantia nigra tissue (A) to the dopamine-depleted caudate-putamen of rat. (B) Insertion of graft tissue via a modified lumbar-puncture needle into the lateral ventricle, medial to the host neostriatum[22,32]. (C) Placement of graft tissue into a previously prepared cortical cavity, dorsal to the host neostriatum[4,6,14,16]. (D) Injection of dissociated cell suspension of graft tissue via a Hamilton syringe directly into the host neostriatum[7,17,35].*

of ^{3}H-spiroperidol[26]. No differences in dopamine fibre ingrowth were seen between the rats that showed the most or the least reduction in the rotational asymmetry, which instead correlated with the completeness of the initial lesion. It was therefore not possible to conclude whether behavioural compensation was attributable to dopamine release from ingrowing fibres, or to a non-specific diffusion of dopamine out of the graft[22].

Intraventricular adrenal grafts

Clearly, a major problem with any clinical application of intracerebral grafting as a treatment of parkinsonism or other neuropathological conditions will lie in the source of donor tissue, in particular if the requirement is for embryonic allograft tissue (i.e. from a human foetus). An alternative approach may be to employ homotypic peripheral neural tissue, since in other experiments adult PNS tissue, unlike adult CNS grafts, has been seen to survive transplantation to the brain. Although there exists no suitable dopamine-secreting peripheral neurons in mammals, the adrenal chromaffin cells which primarily secrete adrenaline and nordrenaline produce dopamine as an intermediary in the synthesis of these other catecholamines. Freed, and co-workers[21] replicated their initial studies but employed adrenal medullary cells taken from young adult rats similarly grafted to the lateral ventricle of host rats ipsilateral to a unilateral 6-OHDA lesion. Again, good graft survival was obtained and fluorescent catecholamine cells gave rise to fine elongated processes, but these fibres were only seldom seen to penetrate the ependymal lining of the ventricle to enter the host[21,35]. Nevertheless, the grafted adrenal tissue was capable of sustaining a 40–50% reduction of apomorphine-induced rotation in these rats, which suggests that functional recovery was mediated by a diffusion of catecholamines from the graft as opposed to dependence on a critical reinnervation.

Nigral grafts to a cortical cavity

We have employed a somewhat different transplantation procedure, in which single pieces of embryonic ventral mesencephalon are placed into a cortical cavity (made 3–6 weeks previously) in direct contact with the dorsal or lateral surface of the neostriatum[3,6,14–16] (see Fig. 1C). Within the grafts dopamine cells become partly organized into layers with perpendicularly extending dendrites, reminiscent of the organization of the intact substantia nigra. Fluorescent axonal bundles are seen to course through the graft and enter the adjacent 6-OHDA-denervated neostriatum where they ramify into a dense terminal plexus which extends to cover up to one-third of the host caudate-putamen. Fluorimetric analysis indicates that dopamine concentrations may attain normal levels proximal to the graft[6] and biochemical measurements reveal a normal rate of dopamine synthesis and metabolic activity in the graft, and normal dopamine turnover in the reinnervated portions of the neostriatum[38].

Our first investigations of graft function also involved rotation measures in rats with unilateral nigrostriatal lesions. The nigral grafts were seen to provide a partial to complete compensation of the spontaneous and amphetamine-induced ipsilateral rotation, and of contralateral apomorphine-induced rotation[4,6,14]. Moreover, rotational compensation was directly correlated with the extent of dopamine fibre ingrowth into the deafferented host neostriatum[6]. Remarkably, replacement of only about 5% of the normal input to the whole striatum was sufficient to provide complete recovery in amphetamine rotational asymmetry. This appears to be attributable, at least in part, to

a topographic organization of function within the striatum. Thus, the spontaneous, amphetamine- and apomorphine-induced rotational asymmetries are only compensated in rats with grafts reinnervating the dorsal striatum, whereas the laterally placed grafts have no ameliorative effect on this asymmetry. Conversely, lateral grafts, which reinnervate ventrolateral segments of the neostriatum, produce extensive recovery of the sensorimotor deficits of rats with unilateral 6-OHDA lesions, which is manifested by a 'neglect' of stimuli of all modalities on the contralateral side of the body[15]. On this measure rats with dorsal grafts remain as impaired as lesioned controls. A further group of functional tests have remained unresponsive to either graft placement – in particular the regulatory impairments in eating and drinking following bilateral lesions, although a partial reduction of the akinesia is seen in the rats with the lateral grafts[6,10,15,16].

Intrastriatal injections of nigra cell suspensions

The studies on the functional effects of different placements of solid grafts indicated that the location of the graft is critical for functional recovery. However, each of the above procedures permits only a limited range of available graft placements adjacent to the medial, dorsal or lateral surface of the neostriatum. A different transplantation procedure has recently been developed which involves the stereotaxic injection of 2–5 μl of a suspension of nigral cells dissociated mechanically after incubation in trypsin[7,37] (see Fig. 1D). This permits graft placement at any site within the host CNS, not only in deep layers of the striatum itself but also cell replacement in the nigra, or injection into the lateral hypothalamus where 6-OHDA lesions have their greatest effect. A further advantage of the procedure is that it enables multiple suspensions to be injected into different forebrain regions with the prospect of attaining more complete recovery of divergent aspects of the 6-OHDA lesion syndrome.

Individual suspensions of nigral cells into the caudate-putamen, on subsequent histological analysis, are seen as clusters of fluorescent dopamine cells at the site of injection, and cells are seen migrating up to about 0.5 mm into the host neostriatum. These cells are surrounded by a sphere of 1–2 mm radius of dense dopamine-containing axonal arborizations and terminal networks, remarkably similar to that seen in the intact neostriatum.

The placement of single or multiple suspension deposits into the 6-OHDA de-afferented caudate-putamen results in a functional recovery of the behavioural impairments parallel to those seen with the solid grafts, but developing more rapidly over 3–6 weeks as opposed to 2–6 months. Thus dorsal placements are essential for compensation of spontaneous or drug-induced rotational asymmetries whereas the lateral placement is the most effective in reversing the contralateral sensory neglect, and only animals with ventral striatum or accumbens placements show significant reductions in apomorphine-induced hyperactivity. Moreover, multiple graft placements appear to be additive, in that rats with suspension injections into all three of these placements (nucleus accumbens, dorsal and ventrolateral neostriatum) recovered on all these measures[17]. The reinnervation of denervated terminal zones by the suspension appears to be a critical factor in the manifestation of behavioural recovery, since viable surviving grafts placed into the substantia nigra or lateral hypothalamus have not been seen to produce any detectable functional effects whatsoever.

Unanswered questions

It might therefore appear that, in particular with respect to suspension grafts, the techniques are available for producing a clinical procedure that could provide a physiologically viable replacement of dopamine cells to counteract the neurological deficiencies of Parkinson's disease. However, a number of unanswered questions remain about several practical, immunological and ethical issues in the clinical application of the model procedure.

(a) How do the grafts function?

It seems likely that the intraventricular grafts described by Perlow, Freed and co-workers function primarily by diffuse release of dopamine into the host cerebrospinal fluid and neuropil. They describe a gradient of biochemically measured dopamine in portions of striatum proximal to the graft even though in many specimens, especially in the case of the adrenal grafts, catecholamine-rich fibre ingrowth is very sparse or absent. Moreover, the functional measure of graft activity (apomorphine-induced rotation) is itself compatible with tonic or diffuse levels of dopamine release over time, reducing receptor supersensitivity in the lesioned striatum, rather than providing a measure of graft function at the time of the test.

By contrast, solid nigral grafts placed in a cortical cavity appear to be dependent upon striatal reinnervation for their functional effects. Functional recovery is directly correlated with the extent of striatal reinnervation, whereas dopamine-rich grafts that fail to reinnervate the caudate-putamen, even with good outgrowth of dopamine fibres into other forebrain areas, fail to show any functional compensation whatsoever. Furthermore, it has recently been found that rats with nigral grafts will 'self-stimulate' by pressing a lever to receive reinforcing electrical stimulation to an electrode implanted in the nigral graft[20]. The rates of self-stimulation of each rat were directly related to the proximity between electrode tip and dopamine cells in the graft, which suggests that the maintenance of the behaviour is dependent upon the axonal transmission of temporally patterned information, rather than by diffuse electrical or neurochemical spread, from the graft into the host. However, self-stimulation involves the presentation of an artificial stimulus directly to the graft. It is not yet clear to what extent the intrinsic dopaminergic activity in the graft is itself regulated by external or internal stimuli to the host brain, and hence which aspects, if any, of graft function may be attributable to its full integration within the host neuronal circuitry.

(b) How many aspects of the syndrome can be restored?

The 6-OHDA-induced dopamine-deficiency syndrome is itself complex. Although dopamine-rich grafts have the capacity for reinstating many of the functional impairments induced by 6-OHDA lesions, this is so far not true for all aspects of the syndrome. At present it is not known whether the continued resistance of the regulatory impairments to graft-induced recovery is attributable to the failure to reinnervate some other critical dopamine-terminal zone in the forebrain, to non-dopaminergic mechanisms disturbed by the lesion, or to the possibility that feeding behaviour requires the more complete integration of dopaminergic neurons within the host neuronal circuitry than has so far been achieved by present grafting procedures.

Therefore, although individual behavioural tests – and particularly those involving pharmacological manipulation – provide powerful experimental procedures for the investigation of various aspects of graft function, any assessment of the clinical potential of individual graft techniques must consider the functional consequences on a wide range of behavioural measures. The importance of this is highlighted by the observation that solid grafts to a dorsal cortical cavity, while restituting both postural asymmetry and spontaneous and drug-induced rotation, exacerbate still further the regulatory impairments when the same animals receive a bilateral 6-OHDA lesion[6,16]. Thus, a graft procedure which is seen to be highly effective in reducing one set of symptoms can actually further impair the experimental animal on a second set of tests.

(c) What is the source for functional graft tissue?

Successful intracerebral grafting in rats has been consistently attained using embryonic tissue from the same inbred strain. At present, the social and medical ethical problems associated with human embryonic donor tissue for clinical transplantation appear restrictive, and three alternatives suggest themselves. Perhaps the ideal solution may lie in the maintenance of permanent tissue or cell cultures which could supply characterized, dopamine-producing neurons for transplantation purposes. However, neither the theoretical nor the technical basis appears to be available yet for the controlled in vitro production and maintenance of such cells.

A second alternative is to seek peripheral neuronal or endocrine tissue, since adult PNS tissue, unlike the CNS, shows good survival when grafted to the brain. This is the rationale behind the use of intraventricular adrenal grafts described above, and may be the closest to direct clinical application[27]. However, the side-effects of central release of large quantities of adrenaline, noradrenaline and various neuropeptides remain unknown and may prove severe. It is also unknown whether grafted adrenal medullary cells can produce sufficient amounts of dopamine for extensive behavioural recovery in the parkinsonism model.

A third alternative, that arises from a consideration of the immunological issues surrounding cerebral transplantation, may be the use of cross-species transplantation.

(d) What are the immunological constraints?

The brain has been described as an 'immunologically privileged site' for transplantation, and recent attempts to transplant between species have had encouraging results. Perlow et al.[33] successfully grafted dispersed cultures of bovine adrenal chromaffin cells to the lateral ventricle of rats, and saw no signs of immunological rejection within the 2-month experimental period. In our own studies[9] solid pieces of embryonic mouse nigra have been grafted to dorsal cortical cavities of rats with unilateral 6-OHDA lesions. Whereas the solid pieces of mouse tissue were rejected, dopamine cells were seen to migrate from the graft into the host striatum in over 50% of the cases to provide an extensive outgrowth into the denervated striatum which was competent to completely compensate the amphetamine-induced turning asymmetries. These grafts remained viable and functional throughout the 6-month observation period. Russian scientists have also recently reported survival and spontaneous electrophysiological activity of embryonic rat septal tissue grafted to the rabbit brain[12].

(e) How good is the animal model?

The interaction over the past two decades between experimental animal models of Parkinson's disease and clinical studies of the neurological condition itself have enhanced our understanding both of dopamine systems in the rat brain and of the disease state in humans. However, the model is not complete – not only does the etiology of Parkinson's disease remain mysterious, but the pathological signs in patients involve a wider spectrum of disorders, both within and beyond the basal ganglia, than a simple decline in the population of dopamine-rich nigrostriatal neurons. Thus, it may be suspected that dopamine cell replacement by transplantation in patients, if eventually possible, may only be able to influence a limited part of the disorder. Moreover, the complex interactions between declining presynaptic dopamine terminals and receptor sensitivity, that appear to limit the duration and efficacy of L-dopa therapy, may suggest that equally complex and unpredictable developments may occur with dopamine-rich transplants.

Conclusions

The recent developments in techniques for neural tissue transplantation in the CNS have enabled the demonstration that such grafts have the capacity to restore functional impairments induced by brain damage. The experimental graft procedure is providing exciting new information about the mechanisms of growth and functional recovery in the CNS. However, it is concluded that much still needs to be understood about these mechanisms before it can be determined whether neural transplantation techniques have any direct clinical application.

Acknowledgements

Our own studies included in the present review have been supported in part by grants from the Swedish and British Medical Research Councils.

Reading list

1 Beebe, B. K., Møllgard, K., Björklund, A. and Stenevi, U. (1979) Brain Res. 167, 391–395
2 Birkmayer, W. and Hornykiewicz, O. (1961) Wien. Klin. Wochenschr. 73, 787
3 Björklund, A. and Stenevi, U. (1979) Physiol. Rev. 59, 62–100
4 Björklund, A. and Stenevi, U. (1979) Brain Res. 177, 555–560
5 Björklund, A. and Stenevi, U. (1981) Brain Res. 229, 403–428
6 Björklund, A., Dunnett, S. B., Stenevi, U., Lewis, M. E. and Iversen, S. D. (1980) Brain Res. 199, 307–333
7 Björklund, A., Schmidt, R. H. and Stenevi, U. (1980) Cell Tissue Res. 212, 39–45
8 Björklund, A., Segal, M. and Stenevi, U. (1979) Brain Res. 170, 409–426
9 Björklund, A., Stenevi, U., Dunnett, S. B. and Gage, F. H. (1982) Nature (London) 298, 652–654
10 Björklund, A., Stenevi, U., Dunnett, S. B. and Iversen, S. D. (1981) Nature (London) 289, 497–499
11 Björklund, A., Stenevi, U. and Svendgaard, N.-Aa. (1976) Nature (London) 262, 787–790
12 Bragin, A. G. and Vinogradova, O. S. (1981) Bull. Exp. Biol. Med. (USSR) 191, 486–489 (in Russian)
13 Carlsson, A. (1959) Pharm. Rev. 11, 490–493
14 Dunnett, S. B., Björklund, A., Stenevi, U. and Iversen, S. D. (1981) Brain Res. 215, 147–161
15 Dunnett, S. B., Björklund, A., Stenevi, U. and Iversen, S. D. (1981) Brain Res. 229, 209–217
16 Dunnett, S. B., Björklund, A., Stenevi, U. and Iversen, S. D. (1981) Brain Res. 229, 457–470

17 Dunnett, S. B., Schmidt, R. H., Björklund, A., Stenevi, U. and Iversen, S. D. (1981) *Neurosci. Lett.* Suppl. 7, 176

18 Duvoisin, R. C. (1976) in *The Basal Ganglia* (Yahr, M. D., ed.), pp. 293–303, Raven Press, New York

19 Ehringer, H. and Hornykiewicz, O. (1960) *Klin. Wochenschr.* 38, 1236–1239

20 Fray, P. J., Dunnett, S. B., Iversen, S. D., Björklund, A. and Stenevi, U. (1983) *Science* 219, 416–419

21 Freed, W. J., Morihisa, J. M., Spoor, E., Hoffer, B. J., Olson, L., Seiger, Å. and Wyatt, R. J. (1981) *Nature (London)* 292, 351–352

22 Freed, W. J., Perlow, M. J., Karoum, F., Seiger, Å., Olson, L., Hoffer, B. J. and Wyatt, R. J. (1980) *Ann. Neurol.* 8, 510–519

23 Gash, D., Sladek, J. R. and Sladek, C. D. (1980) *Science* 210, 1367–1369

24 Hornykiewicz, O. (1963) *Wien. Klin. Wochenschr.* 18, 309–312

25 Jaeger, C. B. and Lund, R. D. (1980) *J. Comp. Neurol.* 194, 571–597

26 Ko, G. N., Freed, W. J., Niehoff, D. L., Cannon-Spoor, E., Morihisa, J. M., Kuhar, M. J., Hoffer, B. J. and Wyatt, R. J. (1982) *Soc. Neurosci. Abstr.* 8, 748

27 Kolata, G. (1982) *Science* 217, 342–344 (reporting work of E. O. Backlund and L. Olson)

28 Krieger, D. T., Perlow, M. J., Gibson, M. J., Davies, T. F., Zimmerman, E. A., Ferin, M. and Charlton, H. M. (1982) *Nature (London)* 298, 468–471

29 Low, W. C., Lewis, P. R., Bunch, S. T., Dunnett, S. B., Thomas, S. R., Iversen, S. D., Björklund, A. and Stenevi, U. (1982) *Nature (London)* 300, 260–262

30 Marshall, J. F. and Gotthelf, T. (1979) *Exp. Neurol.* 65, 389–411

31 Marshall, J. F. and Ungerstedt, U. (1976) *Physiol. Behav.* 17, 817–822

32 Perlow, M. J. (1980) *Peptides* Suppl. 1, 101–110

33 Perlow, M. J. (1981) *Brain Res. Bull.* 6, 171–176

34 Perlow, M. J., Freed, W. J., Hoffer, B. J., Seiger, Å., Olson, L. and Wyatt, R. J. (1979) *Science* 204, 643–647

35 Perlow, M. J., Kumakura, K. and Giudotti, A. (1980) *Proc. Natl Acad. Sci. USA* 77, 5278–5281

36 Rosenstein, J. M. and Brightman, M. W. (1978) *Nature (London)* 276, 83–85

37 Schmidt, R. H., Björklund, A. and Stenevi, U. (1981) *Brain Res.* 218, 347–356

38 Schmidt, R. H., Ingvar, M., Lindvall, O., Stenevi, U. and Björklund, A. (1982) *J. Neurochem.* 38, 737–748

39 Schultz, W. (1982) *Prog. Neurobiol. (Oxford)* 18, 121–166

40 Stenevi, U., Björklund, A. and Svengaard, N-Aa. (1976) *Brain Res.* 114, 1–20

41 Stricker, E. M. and Zigmond, M. J. (1976) in *Progress in Physiological Psychology and Psychobiology* (Sprague, J. M. and Epstein, A. E., eds), pp. 121–188, Academic Press, New York

Stephen Dunnett is a Wellcome Foundation Mental Health Research Fellow at the Department of Experimental Psychology, University of Cambridge, Downing Street, Cambridge CB2 3EB, UK.

Anders Björklund is Docent of Histology at the Department of Histology, University of Lund, Lund, Sweden.

Ulf Stenevi has a joint appointment with the Department of Histology, University of Lund, and the Department of Ophthalmology, Lund University Hospital, Lund, Sweden.

The pathophysiological basis of tardive dyskinesia

Ross J. Baldessarini

In this article Ross Baldessarini introduces the pathology of tardive dyskinesia, and then considers the mechanisms which may be involved in its pathogenesis. There is strong evidence that dopamine receptor supersensitivity may be involved, although not all of the evidence available is compatible with this suggestion. The work in this area is also producing indications for improved medication for the mental disorders treated with neuroleptics.

Antipsychotic agents include phenothiazines and many other compounds which have proven to be effective in the management of a broad range of psychotic symptoms and to be particularly useful in the treatment of schizophrenia and mania. The evidence that this class of substances has real and selective antipsychotic effects, as opposed to merely 'tranquillizing' effects, in schizophrenia and in other disorders marked by abnormalities of thought associations, perceptions, and beliefs, is now overwhelming. Antipsychotic drugs are highly effective in hastening remissions of acute pyschotic illnesses and also seem to prevent later exacerbations of psychotic symptoms, leading to their prolonged use in schizophrenia. Their introduction into European medical practice in 1952 was followed by a virtual revolution in the theory and practice of modern psychiatry.

However, antipsychotic agents in current use regularly produce a variety of presumably extrapyramidal disorders of the control of posture, muscle tone, and movement. A crucial question is whether the almost routinely encountered neurological ('neuroleptic') effects of the antipsychotic drugs are essential to their

actions. The fact that several effective antipsychotic drugs have relatively little tendency to induce acute neurological reactions (dystonias, Parkinsonism, and restlessness) now strongly challenges the inevitability of the association of neurological and antipsychotic effects, and their existence offers some hope that better antipsychotic agents with diminishing neurological side effects can be developed. An important fact (or artifact) is that the methods of screening new substances for potential antipsychotic utility have essentially involved seeking neurological reactions in laboratory animals because there are no satisfactory animal tests for schizophrenia. This impasse, coupled with growing conservatism of the system for development and testing of new agents, has contributed to a repeated 'rediscovery' of agents with very similar actions and limitations over the past 25 years.

Induction of tardive dyskinesia

It is now generally accepted that tardive (late) neurological disorders, including abnormal oral, facial, and tongue movements, as well as choreic (quick, tic-like) and athetotic (slower, writhing) movements of the trunk and extremities, called 'tardive dyskinesia'

(TD) are associated with prolonged clinical exposure to neuroleptic-antipsychotic drugs. While the evidence for this association is mainly epidemiological[4], it is quite compelling. With increased recognition in recent years, prevalence rates are perhaps 10% of patients so treated, including outpatients, as well as those in institutions. This distressing condition challenges the current practice of almost routine prolonged 'maintenance' therapy of chronically psychotic patients – mostly schizophrenics. Its cause is not known. The leading hypothesis is that dopamine (DA) as a synaptic neurotransmitter in the basal ganglia or limbic forebrain may be overactive, either through increased availability, or by increased efficacy, possibly by way of postsynaptic receptor supersensitivity.

Any hypothesis that attempts to explain the pathophysiology of this syndrome (or possibly series of related syndromes varying in their timing, duration, and precise clinical manifestations) must take into account a number of salient clinical observations. These include a late onset after months of treatment with ordinary doses of neuroleptics, usually with some worsening on withdrawal of the drug; more rapid occurrence on abrupt discontinuation of unusually large doses; close similarity to dyskinesias induced during L-DOPA therapy of Parkinsonism, abuse of amphetamines, or the clinical use of stimulants in children with 'minimum brain dysfunction'; worsening of TD by L-DOPA or stimulants, but amelioration by small parenteral doses of the partial direct (possibly selectively presynaptic) DA agonist, apomorphine; at least partial and temporary suppression by DA antagonists, including receptor blockers (potent neuroleptics), storage blockers (reserpine, tetrabenazine), or a synthesis inhibitor (α-methyl-p-tyro-sine); mild and variable effects of cholinergic agents (generally worsening with antimuscarinic-antiparkinson agents, and occasionally partial improvement with eserine, deanol, or choline or phosphatidylcholine, given to enhance the availability of acetylcholine), or agonists of γ-aminobutyric acid (GABA) or serotonin receptors.

In short, the syndrome's differential clinical pharmacology is strikingly *opposite* to that of Parkinsonism, a condition that almost certainly includes DA deficiency of the basal ganglia as an important contributing feature; and, moreover, it is very similar to that of other hyperkinesias such as Huntington's chorea, which is believed to represent a state of relative, and possibly indirect (e.g. by loss of neurones, including GABA-secreting cells that modulate DA neurones) excess of DA function. Moreover, many of the clinical features of severe forms of TD are remarkably similar to those of Huntington's chorea.

Mechanisms of excess of DA function

Such a state of relative excess of DA function in TD, if indeed it is present, could come about through several mechanisms: (a) presynaptic dys-control of DA synthesis and release; (b) decreased availability of other modulating systems (including those using GABA or other neuroinhibitory amino acids, acetylcholine (ACh), serotonin, or substance P or other peptides); or (c) increased quantity or effectiveness of postsynaptic DA receptors of 'effectors' (mechanisms that mediate the postsynaptic effects of DA, possibly including protein-phosphorylating effects mediated by cyclic AMP, the synthesis of which can be stimulated by DA).

Regarding mechanism (a), animal data strongly indicate that an initial increase of DA turnover and metabolite (homovanillic acid, HVA) production induced by neuroleptics is short-lasting. The very 'tolerance' involved in this response to prolonged neuroleptic treatment may be mediated by increased sensitivity to DA transmission postsynaptically or at proposed presynaptic 'autoreceptors' believed to modulate DA synthesis, and possibly also release. Human data on this point are confusing and inconsistent, as increases, decreases, and no change have variously been reported in HVA levels in lumbar CSF of chronic schizophrenics, with a possible trend toward relatively low HVA levels in those with signs of TD. This phenomenon is opposite to the result predicted by the presynaptic hypothesis, but is possibly consistent with a mechanism involving DA receptor supersensitivity. There are also unconfirmed or conflicting reports that the enzyme converting DA to noradrenaline (dopamine β-hydroxylase) may be decreased, or that levels of DA or its metabolites may be increased in the brains of chronic schizophrenic patients (not necessarily with TD) post-mortem.

It is difficult to comment on other neurotransmitters since they have been much less intensively investigated than DA; furthermore, there are few potent and selective agonists or antagonists for many of these, and those which exist have weak or inconsistent clinical effects on TD. Data from recent post-mortem studies of brain tissue of chronic schizophrenics exposed to neuroleptics (but not necessarily showing signs of TD) include increased or decreased activity of choline acetyltransferase (the ACh-synthesizing enzyme), but fairly consistent, if sometimes small and possibly artifactual decreases in glutamic acid decarboxylase (the GABA-synthesizing enzyme) as has also been found in brains of patients with Huntington's disease. These results may possibly suggest neurotoxic effects of neuroleptic drugs on GABA or ACh neurones that may have *indirect* DA-enhancing actions.

DA receptor supersensitivity

Evidence as to the existence of DA receptor supersensitivity in animals is quite compelling. It includes direct (same drug given repeatedly and for final test) and crossed (different drug used to test) tolerance to many

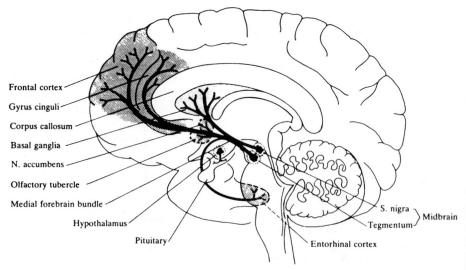

Fig. 1. *The principal dopamine projections in the human brain.*

Frontal cortex
Gyrus cinguli
Corpus callosum
Basal ganglia
N. accumbens
Olfactory tubercle
Medial forebrain bundle
Hypothalamus
Pituitary
S. nigra
Tegmentum
Midbrain
Entorhinal cortex

behavioural (e.g. catalepsy) and biochemical (especially DA-turnover-enhancing) effects of neuroleptics. Such effects are not seen with neuroendocrine responses to neuroleptics (e.g. prolactin release), suggesting differences in the regulation of hypothalamic or pituitary v. forebrain DA systems. In addition, there is striking and consistently increased behavioural sensitivity to DA agonists in many species upon withdrawal from repeated treatment with neuroleptics, but not other central nervous system (CNS) depressants. Nevertheless, these aspects of supersensitivity to DA agonists after neuroleptic treatment are generally short-lived (days to weeks), raising questions about their pertinence to typically long-lasting cases of TD. Another paradox is that some DA *agonists* (including D-amphetamine, apomorphine, ergot alkaloids, and possibly also L-DOPA) may also induce *super*sensitive behavioural responses to themselves or other DA agonists ('reverse tolerance'). Moreover, these paradoxical effects (which may reflect presynaptic DA-turnover *reducing* actions that outlast their acute stimulant actions and so lead to receptor 'disuse supersensitivity'), as well as supersensitivity after neuroleptic treatment, have been described in several laboratories following even a single dose of the agent in question.

Other results that derive from frank denervation of DA projections to the forebrain strongly support the occurrence of DA receptor supersensitivity in laboratory animals. These examples of 'denervation supersensitivity' include strongly enhanced behavioural responses to DA agonists, inconsistent and small increases in the sensitivity of adenylate cyclase in striatal homogenates to DA, increased sensitivity of striatal neurones to iontophoretically applied DA agonists or stimulation of nigrostriatal neurones, and increases in the binding of ligands ([^{3}H]DA and [^{3}H]neuroleptics) proposed to label 'DA receptors' in brain tissue. Moreover, most of these observations have more recently been replicated in brain tissues of animals repeatedly treated with neuroleptic agents and we find that the effect is virtually absent in cerebral cortex, and is not seen after exposure to the rare antipsychotic agents (such as clozapine) devoid of neurological effects. There are even several reports that the post-mortem binding of [^{3}H]neuroleptics is increased in brain tissue of chronic schizophrenics, possibly at least in part as a consequence of prolonged exposure to neuroleptic agents.

Problems extant

Despite all of these impressive scientific findings, a number of serious problems and shortcomings of the DA-receptor-disuse-supersensitivity hypothesis in TD remain. First, the duration of supersensitive responses in most animals is relatively *brief*, usually involving a return to baseline status within a few weeks, at most, after discontinuation of the neuroleptic agent, while clinical TD is typically much more enduring, and sometimes virtually irreversible. On the other hand, newer primate models are more promising in this regard, as long-lasting (months) supersensitivity to DA agonists and spontaneous dyskinesias have been produced, particularly in Cebus monkeys. Secondly, behavioural supersensitivity to DA agonists locally applied to DA-sensitive limbic regions of the forebrain of the neuroleptic-pretreated rat has recently been described. Although these regions are hypothesized to mediate antipsychotic effects of the drugs, increased psychosis following prolonged neuroleptic therapy ('tardive schizophrenia') is unknown clinically.

Thus, this second phenomenon suggests either that DA-sensitive areas (such as the nucleus accumbens septi) that are supposedly limbic in function may actually contribute to extrapyramidal function, or that the popular 'protothesis' that psychoses are mediated by excessive limbic DA function may be invalid or too simplistic. Thirdly, most biochemical and behavioural manifestations of presumed DA receptor supersensitivity involve quantitatively *small* changes (typically 20–30% increases in receptor-ligand binding, and not more than two- or three-fold shifts in values of half-maximally effective doses (ED_{50}) for stimulation of iontophoretic responses, adenylate cyclase activity, or of behaviour by DA agonists). Moreover, these are rapidly reversible, adaptive, and plastic, sometimes developing and fading over times as brief as minutes to hours, and seemingly designed to restore DA function towards normal, that is, to subserve *homeostasis* of neurotransmitter function, rather than to lead to sustained unbalanced increases of function.

For long-lasting or even irreversible changes, one would expect visible neuropathological changes such as frank cell loss, although the available animal and human neuropathological studies following prolonged exposure to neuroleptics do not support that prediction. Possibly other, as yet unknown, functionally important, but histologically so far invisible, toxic metabolic or structural changes in DA-secreting or DA-sensitive cells or their membranes can occur. For example, there is some electron-microscopical evidence of a change in presynaptic vesicles after treatment with the neuroleptic agent, chlorpromazine.

In summary, the DA-receptor supersensitivity hypothesis may help to explain some features of the pathophysiology of TD, and is most likely to contribute to its more rapidly reversible forms, such as acute dyskinesias, that follow abrupt withdrawal of neuroleptic drugs. Furthermore, the entertainment of this hypothesis has shed light on mechanisms only recently appreciated that evidently exert important regulatory effects on central synaptic function and that surely contribute to neuronal 'plasticity' and adaptiveness in the CNS. Moreover, the hypothesis suggests new therapeutic strategies, such as the attempt to suppress supersensitive receptors by the restoration of agonist availability, or through the induction of tolerance to agonists, as a way of moving beyond current attempts to suppress DA availability or function, which seem basically 'antirational' or likely to aggravate the very condition being treated.

Acknowledgements

Supported in part by National Institute of Mental Health Research Scientist Award MH-47370 and Grant MH-31154.

Reading list
1. Baldessarini, R. J. (ed.) (1979) *Task Force Report on Late Neurological Consequences of Antipsychotic Drugs*, American Psychiatric Association, Washington (in press)
2. Baldessarini, R. J. and Tarsy, D. (1976) In: M. Yahr (ed.), *The Basal Ganglia*, pp. 433–466, Raven Press, New York
3. Baldessarini, R. J. and Tarsy, D. (1978) *Int. Rev. Neurobiol.* 1978 (in press)
4. Barnes, T. R. E. and Kidger, T. (1979) *Trends NeuroSci.* 2, 135–136
5. Tarsy, D. and Baldessarini, R. J. (1976) In: H. L. Klawans (ed.), *Clinical Neuropharmacology* Vol. 1, pp. 29–61, Raven Press, New York
6. Tarsy, D. and Baldessarini, R. J. (1977) *Biol. Psychiatry* 12, 431–460

R. J. Baldessarini is Professor of Psychiatry of Harvard Medical School, and Assistant Director of the Mailman Laboratories for Psychiatric Research, McLean Division of Massachusetts General Hospital, Belmont, MA 02178, USA.

Neurobiological substrates of tardive dyskinesia: the GABA hypothesis

Hans C. Fibiger and Kenneth G. Lloyd

Recent observations indicate that the dopamine receptor supersensitivity that occurs after chronic exposure to neuroleptic drugs fails to address or explain many known features of tardive dyskinesia. In contrast, evidence is accumulating which suggests that tardive dyskinesia may be the result of neuroleptic-induced damage to a subpopulation of striatal GABA-containing neurons.

Currently, the most widely quoted hypothesis concerning the pathophysiological substrates of tardive dyskinesia (TD) is based upon the effects of neuroleptic drugs on dopamine (DA) receptors. Goetz and Klawans[1] recently reviewed some of the data from which this hypothesis was formulated and concluded that '. . . there is substantial evidence that tardive dyskinesias are caused by chronic dopamine receptor site blockade, and that the pathophysiology of the disorder is due to the resultant receptor site supersensitivity'. We believe that there is reason to question this conclusion. The purposes of this report are: (1) to review briefly some of the shortcomings of the DA receptor supersensitivity hypothesis which suggest to us that this formulation is no longer tenable; and (2) to propose an alternative hypothesis, namely, that TD is the result of drug-induced destruction of GABA-containing neurons in selected parts of the striatum (caudate nucleus and putamen).

Some shortcomings of the dopamine receptor supersensitivity hypothesis

A major temporal discrepancy between neuroleptic-induced increases in the number of striatal DA receptors and TD is that the former always occurs rapidly (i.e. within one or two weeks) after initiation of neuroleptic administration[2,3] while the latter is by definition observed only after very long-term treatment (typically years). If DA receptor supersensitivity was the cause of TD then it would be predicted that this syndrome should be observed within weeks or a few months after initiation of neuroleptic therapy. A related problem concerns the fact that while TD persists for long periods after cessation of neuroleptic medication and even appears to be irreversible in a significant number of cases[4–6], DA receptor supersensitivity decreases and returns to normal within weeks or at most months after withdrawal from chronically administered neuroleptics[2,3,7,8].

Another failure of the DA receptor supersensitivity hypothesis relates to the fact that spontaneous behavioral changes resulting from DA receptor proliferation are rarely observed in experimental animals that have received neuroleptics for two to four weeks, a period that is sufficient to produce maximal increases in the number of striatal ^{3}H-neuroleptic binding sites[3,7].

Thus, with one exception[9], after two to four weeks of daily injections of neuroleptics no spontaneous behavioral changes have been observed in animals with demonstrated DA receptor supersensitivity as determined by receptor binding methods. In order to demonstrate behavioral consequences of DA receptor supersensitivity it is necessary to administer challenge doses of DA receptor agonists[3,10]. Functionally, therefore, in the absence of DA agonists, the brain appears to be able to compensate quite adequately for the increased numbers of DA receptors that are present after withdrawal from chronic administration of neuroleptics. This situation is clearly different from TD which does not require injections of DA agonists for its manifestation. It is true that spontaneous behavioral changes such as vacuous chewing movements can occur in rats after exposure to chronic neuroleptics for several months or more[8], but there is no evidence that these orofacial dyskinesias are mediated by DA receptor supersensitivity. In fact, Waddington and co-workers[8] found no relation between this syndrome and changes in striatal DA receptors as reflected by the number of specific ^{3}H-neuroleptic binding sites. Clearly DA receptor supersensitivity is not by itself a sufficient condition for the presence of orofacial dyskinesias.

A fourth discrepancy between the DA hypothesis and TD is that while DA receptor supersensitivity is an invariant consequence of chronic neuroleptic treatment in animals, TD affects only a subpopulation of patients on chronic neuroleptic medication. Finally, the DA receptor supersensitivity hypothesis fails completely to account for the fact that the prevalent and core feature of TD is orofacial dyskinesia, or the so-called buccolinguo-masticatory syndrome[6]. The hypothesis provides no explanation for the special vulnerability of the neuronal systems controlling the oral musculature. The above considerations indicate that the DA receptor supersensitivity hypothesis does not address or explain many known features of TD and is in fact at variance with several characteristics of the clinical syndrome. It remains possible that DA receptor supersensitivity is necessary for, and contributes to, the development of TD, although direct evidence for even this limited version of the hypothesis is presently lacking. Clearly, alternative models and hypotheses are required.

The GABA hypothesis of tardive dyskinesia

On the basis of recent information, we propose that TD is the result of neuroleptic-induced destruction of a subpopulation of GABA-containing neurons in the striatum. The striatum is composed predominantly (>95%) of medium-sized, spiny neurons, a significant proportion of which are GABA-ergic[11]. These neurons project to the internal and external segments of the globus pallidus and to the substantia nigra[12,13]. Lesions of these neurons decrease the activity of glutamic acid decarboxylase (GAD), the enzyme that synthesizes GABA from glutamate, in the globus pallidus and substantia nigra[12]. Pakkenberg et al.[14] first demonstrated that there is a significant loss of striatal neurons in rats that received long-term administration of the neuroleptic perphenazine. Subsequently, Nielsen and Lyon[15] confirmed this finding with flupenthixol and found that the neuronal loss was confined to the ventrolateral region of the striatum. As has been pointed out by Mackay[6], 'in the context of tardive dyskinesia, it may be highly significant that the ventrolateral striatum is concerned with the innervation of oral musculature'.

If neuroleptics facilitate the loss of

striatal GABAergic neurons that may occur normally with age[16] or if they damage selected populations of striatal GABA-containing neurons independent of the aging process, then it would be predicted that chronically-administered neuroleptics should decrease the activity of GAD in the globus pallidus and substantia nigra. Recently, Gunne and his colleagues have obtained precisely this result in rats and monkeys subjected to long-term administration of neuroleptics. In the first study it was found that rats that had received eight monthly injections of haloperidol decanoate showed significant (32%) decreases in the activity of GAD in the substantia nigra[17]. Normal GAD activities were obtained in other brain regions (the globus pallidus was not studied). The neuroleptic treated animals also developed vacuous chewing movements, the individual rates of which correlated significantly with the decrease in nigral GAD. In a subsequent study conducted in monkeys, it was found that animals having neuroleptic-induced motor abnormalities that resembled TD had significant and selective decreases in GAD activity in the substantia nigra, the medial segment of the globus pallidus, and the subthalamic nucleus[18]. Most importantly, monkeys that received the same chronic treatment with neuroleptics but which did not develop dyskinesia did not differ from untreated controls in GAD activity. This suggests that the enzyme changes were associated with the dyskinetic symptoms rather than being an invariant consequence of chronic neuroleptic administration.

These data are consistent with the hypothesis that TD is due, at least in part, to neuroleptic-induced degeneration of the striato-pallidal and/or striato-nigral GABAergic systems. The observation that injection of GABA receptor antagonists into the substantia nigra can precipitate oral dyskinesias in rats[19]

tends to emphasize the importance of the striato-nigral projection, although a role for the striato-pallidal projection cannot be excluded at this time. The mechanism by which neuroleptics damage certain striatal GABAergic neurons is not known. It could be by direct actions on the neuronal soma followed by anterograde degeneration of the terminal boutons, or by primary effects on GABAergic terminals and subsequent retrograde degeneration of the striatal perikarya. In addition, why striatal GABA-containing neurons that are involved in the control of the orofacial musculature might be particularly vulnerable to this toxic action of neuroleptic drugs remains completely unknown and is an important priority for future research.

There is indirect evidence which suggests that the dopamine receptor antagonist properties of neuroleptics may not be related to their neurotoxic action on striatal GABA-ergic neurons. For example, 30 days after extensive 6-hydroxydopamine lesions of the ascending dopamine projections the activity of GAD in the striatum and globus pallidus has been shown to be significantly increased[13]. This result is directly opposite to what is found after chronic administration of neuroleptics and indicates that a long-term functional decrease in dopamine input to the striatum does not inevitably lead to a loss of GABAergic neurons. If dopamine receptor blockade and the toxic effects on striatal GABAergic neurons turn out to be unrelated properties of neuroleptics then this would have important implications for the design of new anti-psychotic drugs.

If degeneration of striatal GABA-ergic efferents is related to TD, then it might be anticipated that drugs which enhance GABAergic activity in the brain should be useful in the treatment of TD. It is of considerable interest, therefore, that several GABA receptor agonists have recently been reported to improve TD. Thus, Tamminga *et al.*[20] found that muscimol attenuated involuntary movements in eight neuroleptic-free patients with TD. On the basis of five studies (two open and three double blind) conducted on a total of 57 patients, Morselli *et al.*[21] have concluded that the GABA receptor agonist progabide exerts a significant therapeutic action in TD. Interestingly, in similar studies on L-DOPA-induced dyskinesias in patients with Parkinson's disease, these investigators failed to find a beneficial effect of progabide. The latter finding is consistent with studies in animals indicating that progabide does not attenuate stereotypies and motor abnormalities induced by L-DOPA (see Ref. 22).

The data reviewed above indicate that: (1) the role of the GABAergic striato-nigral and/or striato-pallidal projections in TD is worthy of further detailed investigation; and (2) that pharmacological manipulation of GABA-containing systems may hold considerable promise in the treatment of TD. It is also obvious that the development of neuroleptics that do not damage these GABAergic systems might represent a potentially important clinical advance.

Reading list

1 Goetz, C. G. and Klawans, H. L. (1982) in *Butterworth's International Medical Reviews. Neurology 2: Movement Disorders* (Marsden, C. D. and Fahn, S., eds), pp. 263–276, Butterworth Scientific, London
2 Christensen, A. V., Fjalland, B. and Moller-Nielsen, I. (1976) *Psychopharmacology* 48, 1–6
3 Dewey, K. J. and Fibiger, H. C. (1983) *Naunyn-Schmied. Arch. Pharmacol.* 322, 261–270
4 Crane, G. E. (1971) *Am. J. Psychiatry* 127, 1407–1410
5 Hunter, R., Earl, C. J. and Thornicroft, S. (1964) *Proc. R. Soc. Med.* 57, 758–762
6 Mackay, A. V. P. (1982) in *Butterworth's International Medical Reviews. Neurology 2: Movement Disorders* (Marsden, C. D. and Fahn, S., eds), pp. 249–262, Butterworth Scientific, London
7 Clow, A., Theodora, A., Jenner, P. and Marsden, C. D. (1980) *Eur. J. Pharmacol.* 63, 145–157
8 Waddington, J. L., Cross, A. J., Gamble, S. J. and Bourne, R. C. (1983) *Science* 220, 530–532
9 Pittman, K. J., Jakubovic, A. and Fibiger, H. C. (1984) *Psychopharmacology* 82, 371–377
10 Tarsy, D. and Baldessarini, R. J. (1974) *Neuropharmacology* 13, 927–940
11 Ribak, C. E., Vaughn, J. E. and Roberts, E. (1979) *J. Comp. Neurol.* 187, 261–284
12 Nagy, J. I., Carter, D. A. and Fibiger, H. C. (1978) *Brain Res.* 158, 15–29
13 Fibiger, H. C., Nagy, J. I., Staines, W. A. and Vincent, S. R. (1980) *Brain Res. Bull.* 5, 131–135
14 Pakkenberg, H., Fog, R. and Nilakantan, B. (1973) *Psychopharmacologia* 29, 329–336
15 Nielsen, E. B. and Lyon, M. (1978) *Psychopharmacology,* 59, 85–89
16 McGeer, P. L. and McGeer, E. G. (1976) *J. Neurochem.* 26, 65–76
17 Gunne, L. M. and Haggstrom, J. E. (1983) *Psychopharmacology* 81, 191–194
18 Gunne, L. M., Haggstrom, J. E. and Sjoquist, B. (1984) *Nature (London)* 309, 347–349
19 Arnt, J. and Scheel-Kruger, J. (1980) *Eur. J. Pharmacol.* 62, 51–61
20 Tamminga, C. A., Crayton, J. W. and Chase, T. N. (1979) *Arch. Gen. Psychiatry* 36, 595–598
21 Morselli, P. L., Fournier, V., Bossi, L. and Musch, B. in *Dyskinesia, Research and Treatment* (Casey, D. E., Chase, T. N., Christensen, A. V. and Gerlach, J., eds), Springer-Verlag, Berlin (in press)
22 Lloyd, K. G., Willigens, M. T. and Goldstein, M. in *Dyskinesia, Research and Treatment* (Casey, D. E., Chase, T. N., Christensen, A. V. and Gerlach, J., eds), Springer-Verlag, Berlin (in press)

Hans C. Fibiger is in the Division of Neurological Sciences, Department of Psychiatry, University of British Columbia, Vancouver, B.C. Canada, V6T 1W5. Kenneth G. Lloyd is with LERS – Synthelabo, 31, Av. P.V. – Louturier, 92220 Bagneux, France.

Two syndromes in schizophrenia?

T. J. Crow

Kraepelin's view of dementia praecox was that by contrast with manic-depressive psychosis it was a disease with a poor outcome. However, the range of outcomes is wide – some patients do well, particularly with neuroleptic drugs, and others end up with a defect state which resembles dementia. In some of these cases there is evidence of structural changes in the brain. It is suggested that two syndromes can be distinguished – one, the syndrome of positive symptoms which responds to drugs, is a neurochemical disturbance and associated with an increase in numbers of D2 dopamine receptors; the other, a syndrome of negative symptoms and intellectual impairment, may be a consequence of a degenerative process leading to cell loss.

The concept of functional psychosis – that there are diseases of the mind which are unassociated with a structural change in the brain – originated in the work of Emil Kraepelin[12] at the end of the last century. He thought that such diseases would prove to have a physical basis but suggested they could be distinguished from the organic psychoses including the dementias, and that amongst the functional psychoses two major entities could be discriminated on the basis of outcome: manic-depressive psychosis from which complete recovery could be expected, and schizophrenia which tended to persistence and, in some cases, deterioration. Kraepelin's concept survives but it has defects:

1. It has long been recognized that the distinction between manic-depressive (affective) and schizophrenic psychoses is not clear-cut, there being many intermediate (e.g. schizoaffective) cases.

2. There are many psychotic illnesses with schizophrenic features from which the patient makes a good recov-

ery, at least from the early episodes. Some of these illnesses are associated with prominent affective symptoms leading to the suggestion that they are misclassified cases of manic-depressive psychosis, but this is by no means always the case.

3. At the other end of the continuum are illnesses in which the end state makes the distinction between schizophrenia and dementia difficult to sustain.

Functional v. organic psychosis

An attraction of the concept of functional psychosis is that it is compatible with the plausible view that the fundamental disturbance is a chemical aberration, perhaps a disorder of neurohumoural transmission. This view undoubtedly has been greatly encouraged by the discovery that the symptoms of schizophrenia can be influenced by chemical means, being exacerbated by the amphetamines and ameliorated by neuroleptic drugs.

A neurohumoural theory (the dopamine hypothesis[16]) which can explain

TABLE I. Structural changes in schizophrenia – association with clinical state.

Study	Technique	n	Abnormality	Association
Holden et al., 1973	Echo-encephalo-gram	65	Third ventricle	Treatment resistance
Johnstone et al., 1976	CT scan	18	Lat. ventricle	Intellectual impairment (Withers and Hinton) ? negative symptoms
Rieder et al., 1980	CT scan	17	Lat. ventricle	Intellectual impairment (Halstead–Reitan)
Donnelly et al., 1980	CT scan	15	Lat. ventricle	Intellectual impairment (Halstead–Reitan)
Golden et al., 1980	CT scan	42	Lat. ventricle	Intellectual impairment (Luria–Nebraska)
Weinberger et al., 1980a	CT scan	51	Lat. ventricle	Poor pre-morbid adjustment
Weinberger et al., 1980b	CT scan	20	Lat. ventricle	Treatment resistance
Gross et al., 1981	CT scan	117	Third ventricle	'Pure defect' state
Andreasen, 1981	CT scan	52	Lat. ventricle	Negative symptoms impaired sensorium
Takahashi et al., 1981	CT scan	169	Third ventricle + lat. ventricle + cortex	Blunted affect Uncooperativeness

For references see Crow, T. J. (1981) *Br. J. Psychiatry* 140, 212–213.

these findings is a major contribution of neuroscience to schizophrenic research but leaves unexplained why the response to drugs in many patients is not impressive, and why, as Kraepelin so firmly emphasized, in some cases there is a tendency to progression. It is the nature of this apparently irreversible component of the disease which poses a challenge to neurohumoural theory: an aim of this paper is to suggest that it also undermines the concept of schizophrenia as a functional psychosis.

Intellectual impairments

E. Bleuler[2], who followed Kraepelin in delineating the features of the disease, relabelled what Kraepelin had called dementia praecox as schizophrenia, and went further in asserting that the psychological symptoms differed from those of dementia. Thus, he wrote: 'In contrast to the organic psychoses, we find in schizophrenia . . . that sensation, memory, consciousness . . . are not directly disturbed' and 'the integration of the perceptions concerning spatial and temporal orientation is quite good' and 'memory as such does not suffer in this disease', while Kraepelin himself had asserted that 'the patients are able when they like, to give a correct detailed account of their past life, and often know accurately to a day how long they have been in the institution'. There is little doubt that there is a group of chronic schizophrenic patients for whom these statements do not hold. Thus, approximately 25% of chronic institutionalized schizophrenic patients show severe defects of temporal orientation[6,8] – they do not know how old they are, the current year, or how long they have been in the institution, and the errors they make with respect to each of these questions are consistent. It appears that some of these patients fail to update their concept of their own age with the passage of time; from a certain point in their illness 'time stands still', and they fail to acquire new information. This defect represents an impairment of learning capacity such as is generally held to be characteristic of the organic psychoses. As Heaton, Baade and

Johnson have suggested 'perhaps these patients perform like organic patients on psychological tests because they are organic'[9].

Radiological approaches

The findings of neuroradiological studies reinforce this conclusion. Since the 1930s there have been reports on the basis of air encephalography that some patients with schizophrenia have evidence of ventricular enlargement. These reports have mostly been dismissed on the grounds that they were inadequately controlled although two studies demonstrated a relationship between severity of illness (e.g. as manifest by deterioration) and ventricular change. The introduction of computer-assisted tomography facilitated investigation of this problem and the first CAT scan study[10] demonstrated increased ventricular size in a group of deteriorated institutionalized patients by comparison with age-matched controls. Within the patient group, increased ventricular size was associated with intellectual impairment as in the case of dementia. It was also associated with the presence of negative symptoms (symptoms such as affective flattening, or loss of emotional responsiveness, and poverty of speech which are pathological because a function which is normally present is diminished or absent). A number of subsequent CT studies have replicated the findings of increased ventricular size in some patients. In most studies the change is in the lateral ventricles although in two CT scan studies and one earlier echo-encephalographic study in which the third ventricle was examined an increase in third ventricular width was observed (Table I). Three features have emerged in more than one study as associated with the ventricular changes – intellectual impairment (four studies), resistance to neuroleptic drugs (two studies) and the presence of negative symptoms (three studies). Such findings encourage the view that schizophrenia is nothing other than an organic psychosis of early

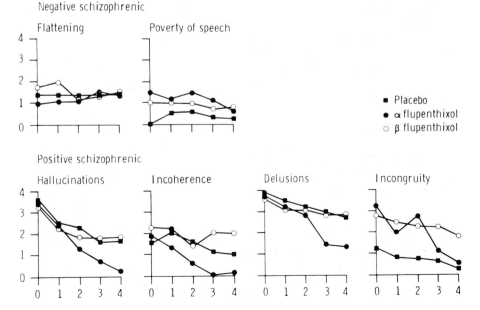

Fig. 1. *The effect of the two isomers of flupenthixol on the positive and negative symptom ratings of schizophrenics measured over a period of 4 weeks.* (Redrawn from Ref. 11.)

TABLE II. Type I and type II syndromes in schizophrenia.

	Type I	Type II
Characteristic symptoms	Hallucinations, delusions, thought disorder (positive symptoms)	Affective flattening, poverty of speech, loss of drive (negative symptoms)
Type of illness in which most commonly seen	Acute schizophrenia	Chronic schizophrenia
Response to neuroleptics	Good	Poor
Intellectual impairment	Absent	Sometimes present
Postulated pathology	? Increased dopamine receptors	? Cell loss and structural changes in brain
Outcome	Reversible	? Irreversible

onset and insidious progression – a true 'dementia praecox'.

The dopamine component

That this cannot be the whole story is demonstrated by the clinical common-place that in some patients the disease remits and in many others it responds to neuroleptic drugs. Such drugs are all dopamine antagonists, and therapeutic activity correlates well with antagonist potency, particularly when this is assessed in the butyrophenone binding assay. The dopamine hypothesis of the antipsychotic effect is further supported by the observation that the antipsychotic effect of the thiaxanthene neuroleptic flupenthixol, like its dopamine antagonist activity, demonstrates sterospecificity[11]. This result is difficult to explain except on the dopamine hypothesis. The findings of this study also revealed that the effects of neuroleptic drugs (as exemplified by α-flupenthixol, the active isomer) were selective to positive schizophrenic symptoms, such as delusions and hallucinations, which are pathological by their presence (Fig. 1). Negative symptoms are more common in chronic states and were infrequent in these patients with acute psychoses; however, when present they showed no response to medication. Thus, those symptoms which are associated with

structural changes in the brain (Table I) do not respond to antipsychotic drugs.

Although CSF and post-mortem studies have not demonstrated increased dopamine neurone activity, there is evidence of increased dopamine receptor numbers[13,14], specifically of the D2 (non cyclase-linked) receptor[3]. Controversy still surrounds the question of whether this change is associated with the disease process or its treatment. There is evidence in favour of the former possibility; if this is the case the efficacy of dopamine antagonists in treatment could be explained.

Two syndromes

The evidence on the one hand for structural changes in the brain associated with intellectual impairment, and on the other for a neurochemical component as manifest by drug responsiveness and perhaps changes in dopamine receptors poses the question of the relationship between these two groups of findings. The solution proposed[4] is that they reflect two separate processes, and that these processes are manifest in the two groups of symptoms identified by the positive–negative dichotomy (Table II).

The type I syndrome is equivalent to the positive symptoms including delusions, hallucinations and probably thought disorder; the type II syndrome includes the negative symptoms, e.g. affective flattening and poverty of speech. The type I syndrome is characteristically seen in acute psychotic episodes, but negative symptoms may also be present particularly when the patient has experienced previous episodes. The type II syndrome (negative symptoms) is commonly seen in chronic schizophrenia (and is roughly equivalent to what is sometimes described as the defect state) and in this situation may or may not be associated with positive symptoms. A practical implication of the dichotomy is that it is the positive symptoms which predict potential response to medication; negative symptoms by themselves predict a poor response. Negative symptoms are associated (at least sometimes, and perhaps commonly) with intellectual impairment; they predict poor long-term outcome, and perhaps represent an irreversible component of the disease process. It is suggested[4] that the two syndromes reflect the presence of two different underlying dimensions of pathology – the type I syndrome reflecting a neurohumoural disturbance (perhaps of dopaminergic processes) and the type II syndrome a degenerative process involving cell loss at some as yet unidentified site and leading to the changes in ventricular size seen neuroradiologically.

The two syndromes cannot represent different diseases since both types of symptom are frequently seen in the same patient. Rather, they represent overlapping constellations as can be represented in a Venn diagram (Fig. 2), which also indicates the changes in symptom pattern which can occur with the passage of time.

Changes with time

Thus, schizophrenic illnesses commonly present with positive symptoms alone. In some cases these remit and the illness may then be described as 'good prognosis schizoprenia', 'schizoaffective psychosis' or 'schizophreniform' psychosis. These labels are applied by various authors to illnesses with schizophrenic symptoms which nevertheless have a good outcome. What must also be included in the pure type I category however are those chronic paranoid illnesses which are characterized only by positive symptoms. In some cases these are resistant to drug treatment; this raises the question of whether in these cases the underlying disturbance is of a different neurochemical nature.

The appearance of negative symptoms (with the passage of time, as indicated by the arrow) indicates a classical Kraepelinian progression to hebephrenic schizophrenia (according to the Bleulerian sub-classification), or to 'non-paranoid schizophrenia' according to the classification of Winokur and Tsuang (who regard only those illnesses which have positive symptoms alone as paranoid schizophrenia). In some of these cases, positive symptoms will persist but in some they may be lost, in which case the patient moves to the righthand segment of Fig. 2, and may be described as suffering from the 'pure defect state'. Also included in this segment are those patients who have developed negative symptoms without ever experiencing positive symptoms. Such patients are described as suffering from 'simple schizophrenia'. Some patients in the group with only negative symptoms may re-acquire positive symptoms, i.e. may move back into the area of overlap. What seems to be unusual however, and if it does occur to be worthy of note, is for patients who have once acquired negative symptoms to lose them. It is suggested that this is because such symptoms are associated with structural change in the brain and represent the irreversible component.

Evidence for two syndromes

A number of findings are consistent with the concept of two overlapping syndromes:

1. As noted in Table I, both negative symptoms and intellectual impairment have been found in some studies to be associated with structural changes.

2. Such structural changes predict non-responsiveness to neuroleptic medication (Table I).

3. In a study of the effects of amphetamine and neuroleptics on schizophrenic symptoms Angrist et al.[1] found positive symptoms to be exacerbated by amphetamine and improved by neuroleptic drugs, while negative symptoms were relatively resistant to both these medications. Thus, the strategies which define the dopaminergic component select out the type I syndrome.

4. In a study of 500 institutionalized patients, Owens and Johnstone[15] found negative symptoms to be significantly associated with intellectual impairment, behavioural disturbance and the presence of neurological signs. These features thus represent the type II syndrome. In this population none of these features were significantly related to the presence of positive symptoms (i.e. the type I syndrome).

5. A post-mortem study[7] of 14 patients who had been assessed in life for the presence of positive and negative symptoms found dopamine receptors (assessed as spiroperidol binding) to be significantly related ($r = 0.72$) to positive but not negative symptoms.

Thus, there is considerable support for the separation of syndromes on the basis of the positive v. negative symptoms dichotomy; the two syndromes appear to be associated with neurochemical and structural changes respectively.

Outstanding questions are the site of the structural changes and the cause both of these changes and the apparent

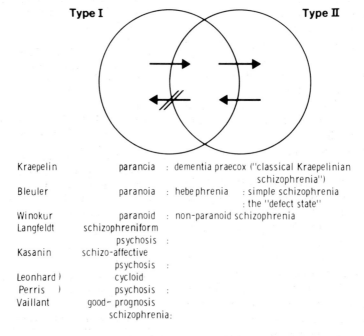

Fig. 2. *The postulated relationship between the type I and II syndromes of schizophrenia. Arrows indicate the possible changes which may occur with the passage of time. Also indicated are the possible correspondences with sub-classification of schizophrenic illness according to various authors.*

perturbation of dopaminergic transmission. Regarding the former there is a case that they may be localized in the temporal lobes. For example, changes in behaviour (e.g. loss of affective response, change in social status) which resemble those seen in chronic schizophrenia have been described following amygdaloid lesions in monkeys. Recently, reductions in cholecystokinin (CCK)-like reactivity in the hippocampus and amygdala, and somatostatin-like immunoreactivity in hippocampus and amygdala have been observed in patients with negative symptoms.

Causation

On the question of causation there is an increasingly cogent case[5] that schizophrenia is a virus disease to which genetically predisposed groups of individuals are susceptible. A genetic factor is established by studies of twins and the adopted off-spring of schizophrenic parents; an environmental factor is demonstrated by the extent to which the concordance rate for monozygotic twins (50–60%) falls short of 100%. Some findings concerning the distribution of the illness within families and the temporal relationship between illnesses in concordant monozygotic twins are compatible with transmissibility[5].

If an infectious agent is involved this could be responsible for both syndromes. In some susceptible individuals the agent could cause a primarily neurochemical disturbance (e.g. by an affinity for the dopamine receptor or a related molecule) but in other individuals could be responsible for a more widespread encephalitis-like disturbance, leading to neuronal degeneration and structural change. In this case, Kraepelin's designation of the disease as dementia praecox is appropriate with the term dementia retaining its contemporary implication of irreversible intellectual impairment; in the former case (the type I syndrome) the disease conforms more closely to the modern interpretation of functional psychosis as a disturbance of neurochemical transmission.

Reading list

1 Angrist, B. M., Rotrosen, J. and Gershon, S. (1980) Psychopharmacology 72, 17–19
2 Bleuler, E. (1950) Dementia Praecox or the Group of Schizophrenias (translated by J. Zinkin), International Universities Press, New York
3 Cross, A. J., Crow, T. J. and Owen, F. (1981) Psychopharmacology 74, 122–124
4 Crow, T. J. (1980) Br. Med. J. 280, 6–8
5 Crow, T. J. (1981) in Epidemiological Impact of Psychotropic Drugs (Tognoni, G., Bellantuono, C. and Lader, M., eds), pp. 33–51, Elsevier/North-Holland
6 Crow, T. J. and Mitchell, W. S. (1975) Br. J. Psychiatry 126, 360–363
7 Crow, T. J., Owen, F., Cross, A. J., Ferrier, I. N., Johnstone, E. C., McCreadie, R. M., Owens, D. G. C. and Poulter, M. (1981) in Transmitter Biochemistry of Human Brain Tissue (Riederer, P. and Usdin, E., eds), pp. 85–96, Macmillian, London
8 Crow, T. J. and Stevens, M. (1978) Br. J. Psychiatry 133, 137–142
9 Heaton, R. K., Baade, L. E. and Johnson, K. L. (1978) Psychol. Bull. 85, 141–162
10 Johnstone, E. C., Crow, T. J., Frith, C. D., Husband, J. and Kreel, L. (1976) Lancet ii, 924–926
11 Johnstone, E. C., Crow, T. J., Frith, C. D., Carney, M. W. P. and Price, J. S. (1978) Lancet i, 848–851
12 Kraepelin, E. (1919) Dementia Praecox and Paraphrenia (translated by R. M. Barclay) Livingstone, Edinburgh
13 Lee, T., Seeman, P., Tourtellotte, W., Farley, I. J. and Hornykiewicz, O. (1978) Nature (London) 274, 897–900
14 Owen, F., Cross, A. J., Crow, T. J., Longden, A., Poulter, M. and Riley, G. J. (1978) Lancet ii, 223–226
15 Owens, D. G. C. and Johnstone, E. C. (1980) Br. J. Psychiatry 136, 384–395
16 Randrup, A. and Munkvad, I. (1967) Psychopharmacologia 7, 416–422

T. J. Crow is at the Division of Psychiatry, Clinical Research Centre, Northwick Park Hospital, Harrow, Middlesex.

Sinistral findings in schizophrenia

High dopamine in the left amygdala

A. V. P. Mackay

While of little immediate practical importance, the quest for the neuroanatomical location of schizophrenic illness has substantial heuristic value. The recent report[1] by Gavin Reynolds, from the Cambridge MRC group, that there is gross asymmetry of dopamine concentrations in the amygdalae of post-mortem brain from schizophrenic patients promises to be a milestone in this process. In itself, the report is nice in its simplicity and, taking a broader view it provides the map reader with a triangulation point, in company with neurological and neuropsychological evidence, to focus attention on the left temporal lobe.

Dopamine (DA) has never been far from centre stage in aetiopathological theories of schizophrenic illness but recently seemed to have run out of steam. Clinical investigation of central DA transmission in unmedicated schizophrenic patients has largely failed to show anything of interest, and results from post-mortem neurochemical investigations – while demonstrating increased DA concentrations and DA receptor densities in limbic and striatal regions – have been devalued somewhat by differences of opinion as to whether the DA receptor abnormalities are due to illness or chronic neuroleptic treatment[2,3]. The special relationship of DA with schizophrenia has also recently been challenged in favour of noradrenaline (NA)[4]. Reynolds simply asked whether there is an imbalance in DA or NA concentrations between left and right amygdalae and caudate nuclei within post-mortem schizophrenic brains? This approach nicely controls out the complicating variables of ante-mortem drug therapy and post-mortem handling, on the reasonable assumption that any such influences would be expected to act symmetrically. On the basis of results from two separate series of brains from the Brain Bank the answer is that left amygdala from schizophrenic brain stands out as having abnormally high concentrations of DA. Otherwise the results from schizophrenic brain are impressively similar to control brain; DA concentrations in right amygdala are normal, DA concentrations in caudate are normal and symmetrical, and NA concentrations are normal and symmetrical in both caudate and amygdala.

This development has not only revived flagging interest in DA, it has made imperative the re-examination of many neurochemical variables in terms of laterality, and it has brought post-mortem neurochemistry into company with a wealth of data from quite unconnected disciplines in pointing to disturbance of the left temporal lobe in schizophrenia. The concept of laterality imbalance in schizophrenia dates back at least to the 1930s in the opinions of Kleist who felt that high-order language dysfunction was central to the illness and that the source lay in the left temporal lobe. Hemispheric imbalance has been implicit in the controversial areas of inter-hemispheric conductance[5] and handed-ness[6] in schizophrenia, but in relation to disorder of the left temporal lobe the work of Flor-Henry is perhaps best known. He and his colleagues have con-sistently postulated a dominant hemi-sphere temporal dysfunction in schizo-phrenic illness, based on extensive studies involving tests of language and detailed EEG records[7]. Similar con-clusions have been reached by Taylor and colleagues who demonstrated left-hemisphere disorder on the basis of linguistic and motor-perceptual tests[8]. Trimble and his group have re-empha-sized and refined the association be-tween schizophrenia and temporal lobe epilepsy by demonstrating that complex partial seizures in the dominant tem-poral lobe are associated with schizo-phrenic phenomena, including auditory hallucinations[9]. Studies of asymmetry in the galvanic skin response (GSR) in schizophrenic patients have likewise been interpreted to reflect dysfunction in deep structures of the left temporal lobe[10], and it may be relevant that amygdala lesions have been specifically linked to GSR abnormalities in experi-ments on primates[11]. The advent of sophisticated radiographic scanning techniques has allowed structural analy-sis of the brain in situ, and recent com-puterized tomography (CT) scan studies show a tendency towards left-hemisphere abnormality[12], left anterior areas in par-ticular[13]. None of these clinical investi-gations can point specifically to the amygdala but it is in the correct neigh-bourhood and is certainly a nodal point in limbic-cortical communication.

If dopaminergic transmission is ab-normal in the left temporal lobe in schizophrenic illness (and the post-mortem DA abnormalities cannot really be interpreted to distinguish between over- or under-activity), it is reasonable to ask whether this might reflect a primary predisposition to abnormal temporal function or an end result of such dysfunction. That is at present impossible to answer but it would seem more likely to be the latter, perhaps a consequence of chronic coarse electrical disturbance whose origins lie in early brain damage. One source of such dam-age might be perinatal birth injury which has been shown to correlate with GSR abnormality and with the likeli-hood of breakdown in the offspring of schizophrenic mothers – representing perhaps one of the environmental insults which can provoke frank illness in the genetically predisposed[14]. Another topical candidate is viral infection[15].

The trouble, of course, with an asym-metric abnormality is finding an aetio-logical model which can allow for the production of a lateralized effect. Altogether an intriguing jigsaw, and the attraction of the report by Reynolds is not just its consonance with data from diverse other sources but also its stimulus to further neurochemical studies of laterality in schizophrenia.

Reading list

1 Reynolds, G. P. (1983) Nature (London) 305, 527–529
2 Mackay, A. V. P., Iversen, L. L., Rossor, M., Spokes, E., Bird, E. D., Arregui, A., Creese, I. and Snyder, S. H. (1982) Arch. Gen. Psychiatry 39, 991–997
3 Crow, T. J. (1982) in Disorders of Neuro-humoral Transmission (Crow, T. J., ed.), pp. 287–340, Academic Press, London
4 Hornykiewicz. O. (1982) Nature (London) 229, 484–486
5 Jones, G. H. and Miller, J. J. (1981) Br. J. Psychiatry 139, 553–557
6 Gruzelier, J. H. (1981) Psychol. Medicine 11, 219–227
7 Flor-Henry, P. (1976) Ann. NY Acad. Sci. 280, 777–780
8 Taylor, M. A., Greenspan, B. and Abrams, R. (1979) Am. J. Psychiatry 136, 1031–1034
9 Perez, M. and Trimble, M. R. (1980) Br. J. Psychiatry 137, 245–249
10 Gruzelier, J. H. and Venables, P. H. (1974) Biol. Psychiatry 8, 55–73
11 Bagshaw, M. H., Kimble, D. P. and Pribram, K. H. (1965) Neuropsychologia 3, 111–119

12 Toone, B. K., Dawson, J. and Driver, M. V.
   (1982) *Br. J. Psychiatry* 140, 244–248
13 Golden, C. J., Graber, B., Coffman, J., Berg,
   R. A., Newlin, P. B. and Bloch, S. (1981)
   Arch. Gen. Psychiatry 38, 1014–1017
14 Parnas, J., Mednick, S. A. and Moffitt, T. E.
   (1981) *Trends NeuroSci.* 4, 262–264
15 Crow, T. J. (1983) *Lancet* i, 173–175

*Angus Mackay is Physician Superintendent,
Argyll and Bute Hospital, Lochgilphead, Argyll
PA31 8LD, UK.*

Antipsychotic drug effects on the electrical activity of dopaminergic neurons

Benjamin S. Bunney

Although antipsychotic drugs have been around for 30 years, the mechanism by which they produce their clinical effects is still unknown. Progress, however, has been made in understanding their cellular site and mechanism of action. In recent years electrophysiological techniques have increasingly made a contribution in this regard. One part of this contribution has come from examining in vivo the effects of antipsychotic drugs on the activity of neurochemically identified neurons, especially those using dopamine as their chemical messenger. Acute and chronic studies have demonstrated specific actions of these drugs on dopaminergic cell firing rate. In addition, chronic studies have revealed time-dependent changes in dopamine cell activity which correlate well with the delayed onset of some of the clinical effects of these drugs. These findings allow one to develop hypotheses concerning the way in which these drugs produce their behavioral effects and suggest ways by which these hypotheses may be tested in man.

Psychosis has probably existed for as long as man has been on earth. Certainly there are descriptions of people exhibiting bizarre behavior in the earliest writings of the earliest cultures. For centuries, people tried to 'treat' psychosis with a remarkable variety of techniques ranging from torture and magic to psychoanalysis and brain surgery; however, none of them have proved particularly efficacious for the majority of patients. Then, in 1953, a treatment was discovered whose impact on the field of mental health was equally as great as the impact of the discovery of penicillin on the treatment of infectious disease. The finding that the phenothiazine, chlorpromazine (Thorazine), could not only help control an agitated patient, but with repeated administration could also diminish hallucinations and delusional thoughts and induce a reintegration of deranged thought processes rapidly revolutionized the treatment of psychosis.

The discovery of other substances with similar effects soon followed and has continued to the present. However, 30 years of experience with these drugs have revealed that they are not quite the miracle drugs we had once supposed. Not only do they ameliorate rather than cure, but they frequently induce unwanted side-effects, some of which are extremely serious. Because of a desire to discover more efficacious antipsychotic drugs which have fewer side-effects, an enormous amount of time, effort and money has been put into trying to find their site and mechanism of action. The first breakthrough in this regard came in 1963 when Carlsson and Lindqvist[1] discovered that these drugs increased the turnover of the chemical messengers, dopamine and norepinephrine, and suggested that they did so by blocking postsynaptic catecholamine receptors. It is now well established that the great majority of antipsychotic drugs, despite diverse chemical structures, all share one property in common – they do, indeed, block catecholamine receptors. Since it was discovered that there exist some antipsychotic drugs which, at pharmacologically relevant doses, only block dopamine receptors, the focus of continued research on the site and mechanism of action has shifted primarily to the dopamine system.

Blockade of dopamine receptors, however, cannot be the whole story of the mechanism of action of these drugs because behavioral, biochemical and electrophysiological evidence suggest that such a blockade can occur immediately after administration of the first dose of an antipsychotic drug. Clinically, however, it often takes several weeks of repeated administration before clinical improvement becomes evident and the neurological side-effects induced by these drugs begin to emerge. Clearly, some time-dependent process must be occurring in the brain which is related to repeated administration of antipsychotic drugs. For this reason, investigators have turned to studying the effects of repeated antipsychotic drug administration on brain function and, particularly, its effects on the functioning of dopaminergic systems. In this review we will focus upon only one aspect of this work, the effects of antipsychotic drugs, administered acutely (single or repeated doses administered in the time span of approximately 1 h) and chronically (repeated administration of the antipsychotic drug over a period of three or more weeks) on the activity of the dopamine cells themselves.

Functional anatomy of forebrain dopamine systems

The electrophysiological studies were made possible by the pioneering work of several Swedish scientists[2–5] who visualized and then mapped in great detail central monoaminergic systems using fluorescence and immunocytohisto-chemical techniques. These investigators found that the majority of dopamine-containing neurons in the CNS are located in the midbrain where they can arbitrarily be divided into two groups: those located in the zona compacta of the substantia nigra (designated A9 by their original discoverers[2]) and those located in the ventral tegmental area (designated A10). The A9 group of cells project primarily to the striatum and, thus, are referred to as the nigro-striatal dopamine pathway. However, intermixed among the dopamine cells projecting to the striatum are cells projecting to the cingulate cortex[6]. Similarly, the A10 neurons form a heterogeneous group, some projecting to various parts of the limbic system while others innervate the prefrontal, piriform and entorhinal cortices[6,7].

Despite this detailed understanding of their anatomy we still know very little about the function of dopamine systems in the brain. What little we do know comes from studies of disease states. The nigro-striatal dopaminergic system appears to be malfunctioning in a variety of neurological disorders characterized by movement abnormalities and, by analogy, is thought to be responsible for mediating many of the neurological side-effects of antipsychotic drugs. Based on the fact that antipsychotic drugs have specific actions on dopaminergic systems and the hypothesized function of some of the limbic and cortical areas innervated by midbrain dopamine systems, the meso-limbic and meso-cortical pathways are suspected of being involved in the pathogenesis of schizophrenia[8]. Evidence in support of this assertion, however, is at present rather meager.

Given these hypotheses concerning the site and mechanism of action of antipsychotic drugs, what can electrophysiological studies of antipsychotic drug action on midbrain dopaminergic neurons tell us which may help test their validity? The first studies of antipsychotic drug effects on the activity of A9 and A10 cells were carried out in the albino rat after the electrophysiological dopaminergic identity of these neurons had been established using a combination of indirect methods[9]. Subsequent *in-vivo* intracellular recording has permitted direct confirmation of the dopaminergic nature of the cells indirectly identified 10 years ago[10,11].

Acute antipsychotic drug effects

The great majority of antipsychotic drugs, when administered intravenously, increase the activity of most A9 neurons tested[9]. In the A10 area responses are more mixed in that a higher percentage show little or no effect. Those cells which respond to intravenously administered antipsychotic drugs not only demonstrate an increase in activity, but, in addition, a concomitant change in firing pattern from slow and irregular to bursting[9]. A burst consists of up to 10 action potentials with progressively decreasing amplitude and increasing duration which is then followed by a quiescent period of approximately 340 ms (Ref. 10). Although this type of firing pattern can be found in untreated animals, the percentage of dopamine

cells possessing it is greatly increased after antipsychotic drug administration. Single doses of many antipsychotic drugs also activate a normally non-firing subpopulation of dopaminergic neurons (Table I)[12–15]. This is true in both the A9 and A10 areas and occurs in both chloral hydrate-anesthetized and gallamine-paralysed animals. In one study this effect was observed for both typical and atypical antipsychotic drugs[13], whereas in another study clozapine, thioridazine, molindone and sulpiride failed to increase the number of active dopaminergic neurons in the A9 area[14].

When administered after A9 and A10 dopamine neurons have been inhibited by systemically administered dopamine agonists (apomorphine, L-DOPA, D-amphetamine, etc.), antipsychotic drugs return activity to baseline levels or above[9,16]. Those neuroleptics which fail to induce a reversal of inhibition to above baseline levels are, again, clozapine and thioridazine[17]. For a while it was thought that dopamine agonist reversal was specific for antipsychotic drugs because the non-antipsychotic phenothiazine analogues, promethazine and diethazine, failed to have such an effect, as did a variety of other com-

Table I. Effect of selected antipsychotic drugs and therapeutically inactive analogues on the number of midbrain dopaminergic neurons firing spontaneously

Drugs tested	Number of cells per track				
	A9		A10		Ref
	Acute	*Chronic*	*Acute*	*Chronic*	
Chlorpromazine[a]	↑	↓	↑	↓	13, 14
Clozapine[a]	↑ , N/C[bc]	↑ , N/C	↑	↓	13, 14
Haloperidol[a]	↑	↓	↑	↓	12–15
Metoclopromide	↑	↓	N/C	N/C	14
Molindone[a]	N/C	N/C	↑	↓	14
Promethazine	N/C	N/C	N/C	N/C	12, 13
Thioridazine[a]	N/C	N/C	↑	↓	14
D Sulpiride	N/C	N/C	N/C	N/C	13
L Sulpiride	↑ , N/C	↓ , N/C	↑	↓	13, 14

[a]Antipsychotic drugs.
[b]N/C = no change.
[c]More than one entry in a column denotes conflicting results from two different studies.

pounds. However, non-antipsychotic drugs such as diazepam and clonidine have now also been shown to be capable of reversing dopamine agonist-induced inhibition[17,18].

Combined, the above findings suggest that antipsychotic drugs have profound effects on midbrain dopamine cell function. Differences between the effects of drugs are intriguing; however, the mechanisms responsible for the differences are unknown. The findings support Carlsson's original hypothesis that antipsychotic drugs increase the activity of dopaminergic neurons. However, since antipsychotic drugs must be administered repeatedly before one observes therapeutic effects (as well as many of the neurological side-effects) one must question whether the findings derived from acute studies are relevant to an understanding of the mechanism and site of action of their clinical effects. For this reason investigators have recently turned to an investigation of the effects of repeated antipsychotic drug administration on the electrical activity of midbrain dopaminergic neurons.

Chronic antipsychotic drug effects

Repeated antipsychotic drug treatment appears to produce profound changes in the functioning of the dopamine system. With a few exceptions (see below), repeated administration of antipsychotic drugs causes a decrease in the number of active dopamine cells in both the A9 and A10 areas (Table I)[12–15]. Glutamic acid (a substance that depolarizes cells and thus activates non-firing hyperpolarized cells), applied to these inactive dopaminergic neurons by means of microiontophoresis, fails to activate them. On the other hand, the hyperpolarizing inhibitory substance GABA when applied to the same neuron, induces activity, presumably by helping the cell to repolarize. Based on these observations, it was concluded that the

inactivity of the dopamine cells is due to the development of a state of tonic depolarization (depolarization block). Intracellular recording from these inactive dopaminergic neurons has confirmed that they are, indeed, in a depolarized state and can be induced to fire either by the injection of hyperpolarizing current or by the i.v. administration of the direct acting dopamine agonist, apomorphine (which also has a repolarizing effect[19]; Grace A. A. and Bunney, B. S. unpublished observations).

The development of depolarization inactivation during repeated administration of antipsychotic drugs can be prevented in the A9 area by lesioning feedback pathways from the caudate nucleus to the substantia nigra prior to the beginning of treatment[12]. This finding would suggest that, for the nigrostriatal dopaminergic system, induction of depolarization block by antipsychotic drugs is not due to a local action of the drug on the cell body, but is rather produced through an action in the innervated area (presumably through chronic blockade of postsynaptic dopaminergic receptors). The importance of feedback pathways in mediating chronic antipsychotic drug effects on A10 cells is less clear. In one study acute transection of the brain anterior to the ventral tegmental area after three weeks of treatment did not reverse the depolarization-induced inactivity of A10 neurons[13]. In another study, destruction of putative feedback pathways from the nucleus accumbens to the A10 area, prior to chronic treatment, significantly increased the number of active dopamine neurons present after four weeks of antipsychotic drug administration[15].

It should be pointed out that not all dopaminergic neurons in the A9 and A10 area become inactive after chronic antipsychotic drug administration. There are always a small number which appear to be unaffected and continue to fire

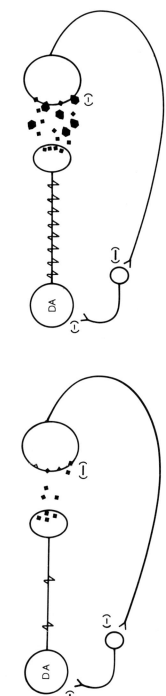

Pre-antipsychotic drug treatment

Acute-antipsychotic drug treatment

■ Dopamine   ◆ Antipsychotic drug   ⋀ Action potential   ▸ Postsynaptic dopamine receptors

Fig. 1. *Schematic representation of feedback pathway mediated antipsychotic drug effects on dopamine cell activity. Only one of many possible configurations for neurons within the feedback pathway(s) is represented. In this model, it is assumed that dopamine is having an inhibitory effect on the first neuron in the pathway and that both neurons forming the pathway are GABAergic and, thus, also have an inhibitory influence on the cells they innervate.*

*(**Left**) Under control conditions activity of the dopaminergic neuron is kept at a slow rate, at least in part, through the action of the feedback pathway.*

*(**Right**) Antipsychotic drug administration results in the blockade of postsynaptic dopamine receptors and, thus, a decrease in the inhibitory influence of the dopaminergic neuron on the initial neuron in the feedback pathway. This results in disinhibition of the dopaminergic neuron with a resultant increase in firing rate and outpouring of dopamine into the synaptic cleft.*

spontaneously even after eight weeks of treatment. Antidromic activation from projection areas and intracellular injection of L-DOPA with subsequent localization by means of fluoresence histochemical techniques[10] have identified these cells as belonging to a specific subpopulation of midbrain dopaminergic neurons which project to either the prefrontal or cingulate cortex[13]. These same cells have recently been shown to lack autoreceptors on both their cell bodies and terminals[20]. Whether or not the lack of autoreceptors is connected with their resistance to antipsychotic drug-induced depolarization block remains to be determined.

Are all antipsychotic drugs the same in regard to their ability to induce depolarization inactivation of A9 and A10 neurons? In the A10 area all antipsychotic drugs tested so far have been found to decrease the number of active dopaminergic neurons when administered for a week or longer[13–15]. However, in the A9 area clozapine, thioridazine, molindone and sulpiride failed to decrease the number of active cells[13,14]. In another study, although clozapine had no effect, sulpiride did decrease the number of spontaneously firing dopaminergic neurons[13]. Preliminary data suggest that the failure of chronic clozapine treatment to induce depolarization inactivation of A9 dopamine neurons may be due to its anticholinergic properties[21]. As in the acute studies, a variety of phenothiazine analogues lacking antipsychotic activity and neurological side-effects, as well as a variety of unrelated compounds (e.g. desmethylimipramine), either failed to have any effect or actually increased the number of active dopaminergic neurons in the A9 and A10 area when administered for three or more weeks.

Clinical speculations

It may be clinically significant that studies which examined the effects of repeated antipsychotic drug administration demonstrated time-dependent changes in midbrain dopamine cell functioning since the time course of those changes matches quite well the time course of the emergence of some of the therapeutic and neurological side-effects of these drugs[22]. What might be the consequences of depolarization inactivation of dopaminergic neuron cell bodies? If the terminals are also tonically depolarized, dopamine release may decrease as this state develops. Preliminary data acquired using voltametric techniques to measure in-vivo dopamine release suggests that this is the case. Could this decreased release be important in the emergence of the time dependent clinical effects induced by these drugs? Based on the biochemical studies of others and the data reviewed here, one could argue in the affirmative. Antipsychotic drugs are competitive dopamine receptor blockers. Acutely, they induce an increase in the number of spontaneously active midbrain dopaminergic neurons, an increase in their firing rate and an increase in the number of neurons exhibiting a bursting pattern of firing. These effects, combined with the demonstrated ability of antipsychotic drugs to block autoreceptors, would lead to a significant increase in dopamine release and thus increase the amount of dopamine available to compete with antipsychotic drug molecules for the postsynaptic dopamine receptor (Fig. 2). Under such circumstances, postsynaptic receptor blockade by an antipsychotic drug may not be very effective. If this is the case, it might explain why one does not see an immediate clinical effect of these drugs. However, if depolarization inactivation develops, with a consequent decrease in dopamine release, the number of dopamine molecules available to compete with the antipsychotic drug molecules would decrease. Conversely, due to repeated administration, the number of

Antipsychotic
drug treatment   Dopamine neuron   Postsynaptic cell

None

Acute

Chronic

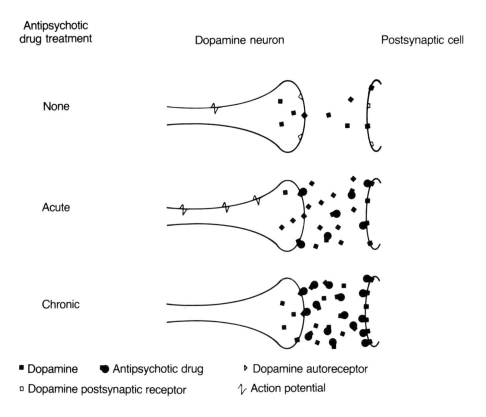

■ Dopamine   ● Antipsychotic drug   ▷ Dopamine autoreceptor
□ Dopamine postsynaptic receptor   ⋎ Action potential

Fig. 2. *Highly speculative schematic representation of synaptic events occurring after the acute and chronic administration of antipsychotic drugs.*

(**Upper**) *Normal dopamine release under no drug conditions.*

(**Middle**) *Acute administration of an antipsychotic drug results in an increase in release of dopamine into the synaptic cleft. The increased release occurs secondary to antipsychotic drug blockade of postsynaptic receptors which leads to a feedback pathway mediated increase in dopamine activity and secondary to blockade of dopamine autoreceptors which leads to an increase in synthesis and release. Due to the consequent flooding of the synaptic cleft with dopamine molecules and their competition with antipsychotic drug molecules for the postsynaptic receptor, postsynaptic receptor blockade is only partial and not very effective.*

(**Lower**) *Repeated antipsychotic drug treatment leads to the development of depolarization block and thus, cessation of impulse flow at the terminal. A decreased release of dopamine results, while, at the same time, the number of antipsychotic drug molecules in the synaptic cleft increases due to repeated administration. The outcome of these two events is an effective blockade of the postsynaptic dopamine receptor.*

antipsychotic-drug molecules would increase.

Combined, these two time-dependent events should result in an increasingly effective blockade of postsynaptic dopamine receptors. If, as has been hypothesized so many times by others, such blockade is the *sine qua non* for many of the clinical effects of antipsychotic drugs, this series of events should lead

to the emergence of neurological side-effects and/or clinical improvement. The fact that a drug such as clozapine, which apparently lacks neurological side-effects, fails to induce depolarization inactivation of A9 cells but shares with the other antipsychotic drugs the ability to induce such a state in A10 cells would support this hypothesis.

All of the above is highly speculative.

Nevertheless, electrophysiological techniques have begun to contribute to our understanding of the mechanism of action of antipsychotic drugs. When combined with anatomical, biochemical and behavioral techniques, they provide a powerful tool for furthering our understanding of the complex action of these drugs in the brain. The fact that we can even begin to formulate hypotheses concerning the clinical actions of these drugs based on observed effects in the brain is an enormous step forward. Whether the hypotheses are right or wrong is perhaps less important than the fact that they may be testable. For example, if it can be determined how antipsychotic drugs produce depolarization block, it may be possible to find or develop drugs which will prevent its development or reverse it. If such drugs acted selectively on nigro-striatal dopamine systems they might constitute a new treatment for these side-effects. Such drugs certainly would make it possible to test the above hypothesis clinically.

Reading list

1 Carlsson, A. and Lindqvist, M. (1963) *Acta Pharmacol. Toxicol.* 20, 140–144
2 Dahlström, A. and Fuxe, K. (1964) *Acta Physiol. Scand.* 62, suppl. 232, 1–55
3 Hökfelt, T., Johansson, O., Fuxe, K., Goldstein, M. and Park, D. (1976) *Med. Biol.* 54, 427–453
4 Lindvall, O. and Björklund, A. (1978) in *Handbook of Psychopharmacology*, Vol. 9 (Iversen, L. L., Iversen, S. D. and Snyder, S. H., eds), pp. 139–231, Plenum Publishing Corp., New York
5 Ungerstedt, U. (1971) *Acta Physiol. Scand. Suppl.* 367, 1–48
6 Lindvall, O. (1979) in *The Neurobiology of Dopamine* (Horn, A. S., Korf, J. and Westerink, B. H. C., eds), pp. 319–342, Academic Press, New York

7 Berger, B., Thierry, A. M., Tassin, J. P. and Moyne, M. A. (1976) *Brain Res.* 106, 133–145
8 Meltzer, H. Y. and Stahl, S. M. (1976) *Schizophrenia Bull.* 2, 19–76
9 Bunney, B. S., Walters, J. R., Roth, R. H. and Aghajanian, G. K. (1973) *J. Pharmacol. Exp. Ther.* 185, 560–571
10 Grace, A. A. and Bunney, B. S. (1983) *Neuroscience* 10, 301–315
11 Grace, A. A. and Bunney, B. S. (1980) *Science* 210, 654–656
12 Bunney, B. S. and Grace, A. A. (1978) *Life Sci.* 23, 1715–1728
13 Chiodo, L. A. and Bunney, B. S. (1983) *J. Neurosci.* 3, 1607–1619
14 White, F. J. and Wang, R. Y. (1983) *Science* 221, 1054–1057
15 White, F. J. and Wang, R. Y. (1982) *Life Sci.* 32, 983–993
16 Bunney, B. S. (1979) in *The Neurobiology of Dopamine* (Horn, A. S., Korf, J. and Westerink, B. H. C., eds). pp. 417–452, Academic Press, New York
17 Bunney, B. S. and Aghajanian, G. K. (1975) *Antipsychotic Drugs, Pharmacodynamics and Pharmacokinetics*, pp. 305–318, Pergamon Press, New York
18 Bunney, B. S. and DeRiemer, S. (1982) in *Advances in Neurology* (Friedhoff, A. J. and Chase, T. N., eds), pp. 99–104, Raven Press, New York
19 Grace, A. A. and Bunney, B. S. (1982) *Neurosci. Abst. I*, 131–137
20 Chiodo, L. A., Bannon, M. J., Grace, A. A., Roth, R. H. and Bunney, B. S. *J. Neurosci.* (in press)
21 Chiodo, L. A. and Bunney, B. S. in *Proceedings of the 5th International Catecholamine Symposium* (Dahlström, A. and Usdin, E., eds), Alan R. Liss, Inc., New York (in press)
22 Klein, D. E. and Davis, J. M. (1969) *Diagnosis and Drug Treatment of Psychiatric Disorders*, p. 95, The Williams and Wilkins Company, Baltimore

Benjamin S. Bunney is Associate Professor in the Departments of Psychiatry and Pharmacology, Yale University School of Medicine, B254 SHM, P.O. Box 3333, New Haven, Connecticut, CT 06150-8066, USA.

Acetylcholine, aging and Alzheimer's disease Implications for treatment

Suzanne Corkin

Normal aging and Alzheimer's disease are characterized by similar morphological, chemical and behavioral changes. These include cell loss, senile plaque formation, the presence of neurofibrillary tangles in the neocortex, amygdala, and hippocampus, deficiency in cholinergic neurotransmission, and impairment of cognitive processes. This article examines the possibility that these features are related to a defect in acetylcholine metabolism and evaluates studies that have tested this hypothesis.

Pre- and post-mortem examinations of patients with dementia have revealed significant correlations not only between increased numbers of senile plaques (see below) and decreases in cortical choline acetyltransferase (CAT) activity, but also between these two variables and scores on behavioral tests sensitive to intellectual deterioration[15]. Moreover, in human subjects the cholinergic abnormality is probably presynaptic in origin. There is no evidence that post-synaptic muscarinic receptors are affected. This suggests that Alzheimer's disease might be treated by augmenting acetylcholine synthesis in the surviving presynaptic neurons thus improving cholinergic transmission[11].

Characteristics of Alzheimer's disease

Alzheimer's disease accounts for approximately 50% of the patients diagnosed clinically as demented. It is more prevalent among women than men.

Historically, the term Alzheimer's disease referred exclusively to pre-senile dementia (progressive dementia in patients under 65 years of age), whereas the term senile dementia was applied to those aged 65 years and over. Because the two conditions are clinically, neurologically, pathologically, biochemically – though perhaps not temporally – alike, they are now believed to be the same disease, and in this article the term Alzheimer's disease will refer to both presenile and senile forms.

The disease begins insidiously, advances in an uneven manner, and limits life expectancy. Its etiology is unknown. Behaviorally, Alzheimer's disease is characterized by marked deficits in cognitive function, including memory, language, complex sensori-motor and perceptual capacities. In some patients behavior deteriorates slowly and in others the change is rapid. The first and most salient symptom is usually loss of recent memory, followed by difficulties with language and constructional tasks. Some patients, however, show a different pattern of symptoms in which either language or constructional skills are affected first. Non-cognitive symptoms comprise affective disorder, agitation, sleep disturbance, poor appetite, decreased sexual activity and unsteadiness of gait. Despite these problems, most patients' social behavior remains appropriate until the late stages of the disease.

The morphological changes in the brain include diffuse degeneration of the neocortex, being most severe in the temporal, parietal and occipital lobes. The posterior cingulate gyrus, amygdala, hippocampus, hypothalamus and certain midbrain and brainstem structures are also involved, yet the anterior cingulate gyrus, caudate nucleus, thalamus and mammillary bodies are affected only minimally, if at all. Electron microscopic examination of biopsied cortex shows the overall cortical organization and most individual neurons to be normal. The pathology is complex and consists of: (1) senile plaques (extracellular clusters of abnormal cell processes in which a central mass of amyloid, a protein, is surrounded by unmyelinated neurites); (2) neurofibrillary tangles (intracellular bundles of paired helical filaments that fill the perikaryal cytoplasm surrounding a normal nucleus); (3) progressive deterioration of dendrites in cortical and hippocampal pyramidal cells and in dentate granule cells; and (4) granulovacuolar degeneration (distinguished by intracytoplasmic vacuoles containing a hematoxyphilic and argyrophilic particle) in hippocampal pyramidal cells, with maximal involvement in areas CA_{1-3} (Ref. 20). These changes usually occur on both sides of the brain but are not necessarily symmetrical, though there is no evidence of a systematic difference.

The neurochemical changes that take place in Alzheimer's disease are presumed to result from these alterations in morphology. Enzymatic markers of five putative neurotransmitters·

have been measured in brain tissue obtained from surgical biopsy and at autopsy both from patients with Alzheimer's disease and from age-matched control subjects. It is now firmly established that there is a significant impairment in central cholinergic function. For example, there is a marked hypoactivity of the enzyme CAT in most areas of the cortex, hippocampus, caudate nucleus and putamen[3,4,7,15,18]. CAT catalyses the synthesis of acetylcholine (ACh) from choline and acetyl coenzyme A and is a specific marker for cholinergic neurons. Acetyl cholinesterase (AChE) activity is also reduced significantly[7,18]. ACh synthesis measured *in vitro* is also reduced in temporal-lobe biopsy samples from patients with Alzheimer's disease[17] but not in specimens from a control group without dementia.

In contrast, the findings for norepinephrine (NE), dopamine (DA), 5-hydroxytryptamine (5-HT) and γ-amino-butyric acid (GABA) are inconclusive. Reports that certain patients with cholinergic deficits also show modest reductions in levels of 5-HT, DA and NE[10] have been discounted on the grounds that the clinical diagnoses of Alzheimer's disease were not checked against autopsy findings. Thus, catecholamine deficiencies might indicate the presence of Parkinson's disease concomitant with Alzheimer's disease, or instead might be secondary to the cholinergic loss.

Cholinergic synapses and memory function

In a series of pharmacological experiments in rats. Deutsch[1] showed that anticholinesterases and anticholinergics have opposite effects on the recall of learned behaviors*. He found the actions of these agents to be consistently complementary, even though the direction of the effect on retention depended upon the particular task. The specificity of these cholinergic drug effects suggests that the substances influence memory processes directly, rather than indirectly, through alterations of such non-specific variables as level of arousal or attention. When centrally-acting cholinergic antagonists, such as scopolamine or atropine, are given to healthy young adults, there is a drop in the subjects' performance on tests of long-term memory capacities, i.e. for periods longer then 30 sec (Ref. 1). When the subjects receive cholinergic agents such as physostigmine and arecoline, the opposite effect is observed. Low doses of physostigmine or arecoline facilitate acquisition and retention of new material, whereas higher ones have a detrimental effect. Furthermore, in young normal subjects the deleterious effects of scopolamine can be reduced considerably by the concurrent administration of physostigmine[9] or choline[14].

In normal elderly and demented subjects, brain areas that show the most marked changes in morphology are the hippocampus, the parahippocampal gyrus and the amygdala[12,19]. These are the same brain structures that have been implicated in amnesic syndromes following head injury, anoxia, or infection. In addition, studies in rats indicate that AChE-positive cells of the medial septal-diagonal band complex project upon all fields in the hippocampal formation[5]. The fact that a particular neurotransmitter clearly involved in memory function is found in brain structures that are known to be compromised in patients with memory dis-

orders suggests a relationship between these behavioral, anatomical and chemical phenomena.

Effects of ACh precursor administration

Significant increases in the concentration of both brain choline and ACh have been observed after rats were given doses of choline chloride that exceeded the normal dietary intake of choline[1]. Similarly, lecithin [phosphatidylcholine (PC)], the usual dietary form of choline, also augments ACh synthesis in the rat.

An increase of brain ACh levels can also be produced by the administration of physostigmine, which retards the degradation of ACh by inhibiting AChE, the enzyme that catalyses this breakdown. The separate actions of choline and physostigmine on cholinergic neurotransmission might explain the finding that when rats are given these two substances in combination, the resulting levels of ACh exceed those obtained when each is given alone.

Use of cholinergic agents to treat Alzheimer's disease

Choline and lecithin have now been tested in 11 clinical studies (Table I). Many of the studies are inconclusive, however, because of flaws in the experimental design or method. An adequate test of the cholinergic hypothesis requires that (1) patients be selected according to rigorous diagnostic criteria; (2) a double-blind treatment protocol be used; (3) drug and placebo be administered for at least 2 weeks and preferably longer; (4) plasma choline levels be obtained as an index of compliance; (5) the measures of behavioral change be quantitative; and (6) the behavioral tests be at levels of difficulty that are suitable for elderly subjects[6]. In addition, the data analyses should take account of

---

* Anticholinesterases are cholinergic agonists that inhibit AChE and thus prolong the lifetime of ACh released at the synapse; anticholinergics are cholinergic antagonists that inhibit muscarinic cholinergic activity by blocking ACh receptor binding sites.

TABLE I. Acetylcholine precursor treatment in Alzheimer's disease

Author and reference*	Severity of dementia Number of cases (N)	Design of study and duration of treatment	Drug and maximum daily dose	Test results
Boyd et al. (1977)	Severe (7)	Open label 4 weeks	Choline chloride 10 g	Cognitive functions unchanged.
Etienne et al. (1978)	Moderate (3)	Placebo control 4 weeks	Choline bitartrate 8 g	Slightly improved performance on block design test in 1/3.
Smith et al. (1978)	Not reported (10)	Placebo control 2 weeks	Choline bitartrate 9 g	Cognitive functions unchanged.
Signoret et al. (1978) Whiteley et al. (1979)	Mild to moderate (8)	Open label 3 weeks	Choline citrate 9 g	Slightly improved relearning and recall in two patients under 65 with recent onset.
Etienne et al. (1978) Etienne et al. (1979)	Mild to moderate (7)	Open label 4 weeks	Lecithin 20% PC, $\bar{X}=75$ g	Improved paired-associate learning in 3/7.
Christie et al. (1979) Yates et al. (1980)	Mild to severe (12)	Open label Choline, 5 days Lecithin, 3 months	Choline 5 g Lecithin 20% PC. 28–100 g	Cognitive functions unchanged. except reduced dyspraxia in 2/12.
Renvoise et al. (1979)	Moderate (18)	Double blind 2 months	Choline chloride 15 g	No differences between drug and placebo groups on crude measures.
Ferris et al. (1979)	Mild to moderate (14)	Open label 4 weeks	Choline chloride 12–20 g	No improvement on 26 cognitive tests.
Fovall et al. (1980)	Mild to moderate (5)	Double blind 6 weeks	Choline bitartrate 8–16 g	Improved auditory and visual word recognition with 12 g day^{-1}
Hu et al. (1980)	8 early 3 late (11)	Double blind crossover 2–3 or 4–6 weeks	Lecithin 53% PC. 35 g	7/11 showed 50–200% improvement in long-term verbal recall on one of several tests.
Sullivan et al. (1981)	Mild to severe (18)	Double blind crossover 6 weeks	Lecithin 55% PC. 30 g 80% PC. 20 g	Cognitive functions unchanged.

practice and any deterioration in the patient's condition.

In the first clinical study with choline, Boyd et al. administered choline chloride to severely demented patients for periods of 4–7 weeks. Some showed less irritability and greater awareness of their surroundings but no change in quantitative measures of cognition. Boyd et al. suggested that precursor treatments might be more effective earlier in the disease when more presynaptic cholinergic terminals are intact. In subsequent trials with choline, most patients were mildly to moderately demented. Even so, the test results in general are not promising (Table I). The report of Foval et al. of a dose-specific improvement in auditory and visual word recognition seemed encouraging but their protocol also had some of the flaws outlined above.

Choline in the form of lecithin was given to patients with Alzheimer's disease in two open-label and two double-blind crossover studies (Table I). Representative of these experiments is one carried out at the Massachusetts Institute of Technology Clinical Research Center. In this investigation, 18 patients with Alzheimer's disease, ranging from mildly to severely demented, completed a double-blind crossover protocol[5]. Although some patients showed improvement on certain memory tests, no patient was more efficient on all measures during lecithin ingestion than during placebo ingestion, and no single test elicited better performance by all patients when they consumed lecithin as compared with placebo. Accordingly, analyses of group data did not reveal significant changes associated with treatment, even in the least demented patients. Most patients, however, did show considerable variability in their test scores across the five sessions. Because of this characteristic, only a substantial treatment effect would have been detectable and minimal benefits might have been masked by the typically erratic performance of patients with Alzheimer's disease. The conclusion, nevertheless, is that in the doses used to date (Table I), lecithin is not by itself an effective treatment for Alzheimer's disease.

More encouraging results come from experiments in which demented patients were given either the cholinesterase inhibitor physostigmine or the muscarinic agonist arecoline (Table II). Gains in memory-test scores were associated with low doses of physostigmine, 0.50 mg or less[8], but not with 1.0 mg doses. A 1.0 mg dose of physostigmine did, however, increase speed and accuracy in copying geometric designs. These data are consistent with previous findings, both in animals and healthy young adults, that the effects of cholinergic manipulation are dose-specific[1].

The fact that positive results can be obtained with a cholinesterase inhibitor, together with the occasional clinical observations that some patients with Alzheimer's disease show a slight benefit from lecithin administration suggest that combining an ACh precursor with the enzyme inhibitor might lead to the benefits expected from cholinergic intervention. Two tests of this hypothesis have been attempted. Following a randomized double-blind protocol, Peters and Levin[16] gave physostigmine (0.25–0.75 mg kg^{-1}) by injection to three patients with moderately severe Alzheimer's disease who had begun lecithin ingestion the previous day. In the second combined-treatment study, 60 g of lecithin and 30 mg of tetrahydroaminoacridine, an oral anticholinesterase agent, were given to ten patients with Alzheimer's disease in a 16-h double-blind trial[5]. In both studies, patients showed a slight improvement in long-term recall of

TABLE II. Effects of cholinomimetics in Alzheimer's disease.

Author and reference*	Severity of dementia [Number of cases (N)]	Design of study	Drug, dose and method of administration	Test results	Comment
Smith *et al.* (1979)	Moderate (1)	Randomized, double blind Saline control	Physostigmine 1.0 mg Injection	No change in number of correct responses on cognitive tests. Decreased number of intrusion errors.	Diagnosis confirmed by brain biopsy.
Muramoto *et al.* (1979)	Severe (1)	Randomized, double blind Saline control	Physostigmine 1.0 mg Injection	Improvement in copies of geometric figures. No change in short-term or long-term verbal recall or manual dexterity.	
Davis *et al.* (1980)	None to moderate (6)	Randomized, double blind Saline control	Physostigmine 0.125 mg 0.25 mg 0.50 mg i.v. infusion	Nondemented improved in verbal recall, demented in picture recognition.	Included two subjects with Alzheimer's disease, one with Huntington's disease, and three nondemented.
Davis *et al.* (1980)	Moderate (9)	Randomized, double blind Saline control	Physostigmine 0.25 mg 0.50 mg i.v. infusion	9/9 showed dose-specific improvement in long-term memory with physostigmine.	Abstract
Christie *et al.* (1981)	Slight to moderate (11)	Randomized, double blind Saline control	Physostigmine 0.25–1.0 mg Arecoline 2 mg or 4 mg i.v. infusion	Picture recognition significantly improved with 0.375 mg physostigmine and 4 mg arecoline.	Marked reproducible gain in two patients, slight in others.

*References cited in Ref. 5.

words. These drug combinations should therefore be tested over longer periods of time and with larger groups of patients.

Defining response to treatment

It has been argued that a positive response to treatment might go unnoticed because the biochemical and behavioral measures used to evaluate such a change are insensitive. For example, it is possible that a significant treatment effect may occur only in certain subgroups of patients with Alzheimer's disease but not in others. In Alzheimer's disease, variables which might be used to subcategorize patients include sex, educational level, previous occupation, age at onset of disease and at time of testing, duration and severity of dementia and biochemical variables, such as CSF levels of peptides, neurotransmitter metabolites and proteins. Work is now in progress to define subpopulations of patients with Alzheimer's disease according to the levels of neurotransmitter metabolites in the cerebrospinal fluid[5]. We also need to have quantitative tools in clinical settings to detect significant alterations in subjects over time[6].

However, treatment success cannot be defined solely in these terms. Statistically significant changes in individual laboratory or behavioral tests are not conclusive by themselves. They must be accompanied by an improvement in the patients' daily behavior that is apparent to the patients or to their relatives and friends. With this consideration as the main criterion of treatment sucess, biochemical and behavioral tests can then be used to confirm and document the benefit. It is unlikely, however, that a satisfactory treatment for dementia would be missed simply because the right test had not been given.

Conclusion

The correlations between the morphological, biochemical and behavioral abnormalities in Alzheimer's disease provided good reason to expect that treatments which enhance central cholinergic neurotransmission should be effective therapy. Yet there is no overwhelming evidence that this is the case. The apparent ineffectiveness of precursor treatment could be due either to inadequate subclassification of patients, improper dosage of precursor, or insufficient duration of treatment; these possibilities are testable. Alternatively, the lack of support for the cholinergic hypothesis might mean that the decreased activity of CAT is an epiphenomenon in Alzheimer's disease, or that one or more non-cholinergic neurotransmitters are involved. These explanations cannot be evaluated until we know more about the neurochemistry of aging and, in particular, about the interaction of different neurotransmitter systems. It is difficult to attribute the failure of precursor therapy in Alzheimer's disease to the fact that large numbers of cholinergic neurons or their neurities have degenerated. Recent treatment efforts have been applied mainly to patients with mild or moderate dementia where cell death is presumably not yet severe. Even in healthy elderly subjects, where cell loss is less marked, the administration of choline and lecithin is ineffective in palliating memory loss. It is possible that more than one aspect of cholinergic neurotransmission is impaired. In the biopsy obtained from one patient who was believed to have Alzheimer's disease, Bowen and Davison[13] found not only a 67% reduction in CAT activity but a 66% reduction in the high-affinity uptake of choline as well. Perhaps the deficiency in the cholinergic mechanism is not in the synthesis of ACh but in its release. Precursor administration might not correct this situation, but any manipulation that would increase the firing rate of cholinergic neurons might. Recently, Wurtman, Magil and Reinstein[5] obtained suggestive evidence that piracetam, a GABA derivative, accelerates septohippocampal release of ACh. Alternatively, piracetam might increase oxidative metabolism, which is known to be deficient in Alzheimer's disease and to affect cholinergic neurotransmission. These chemical findings could have important implications for behavior. Bartus and Dean[2] gave combined doses of piracetam and choline to aged rats in their drinking water for 1 week, and, in addition, gave both substances by injection ½ h before a 24-h retention test. Benefits were not seen in training, but the retention performance of aged rats treated with the choline and piracetam mixture was greatly superior to that of aged rats given saline or either drug alone. This and other safe drug combinations that increase cholinergic tone may soon be tested in patients with Alzheimer's disease. Perhaps, then, we shall witness the improvement in behavioral capacities predicted by the cholinergic hypothesis.

Reading list

1 Barbeau, A., Growdon, J. H. and Wurtman, R. J. (eds) (1979) *Nutrition and the Brain*, Vol. 5, Raven Press, New York
2 Bartus, R. T. and Dean, R. L. (1981) in *Brain Neurotransmitters and Receptors in Aging and Age-related Disorders* (Enna, S., Samoraiski, T. and Beer, B., eds), Vol. 17, pp. 209–224, Raven Press, New York
3 Bowen, D. M., Smith, C. B., White, P. and Davison, A. N. (1976) *Brain* 99, 459–496
4 Bowen, D. M., Spillane, J. A., Curzon, G., Meier-Ruge, W., White, P., Goodhardt,
M. J., Iwangoff, P. and Davison, A. N. (1979) *Lancet* i, 11–14
5 Corkin, S., Davis, K. L., Growdon, J. H., Usdin, E. and Wurtman, R. J. (1981) *Alzheimer's Disease: A Report of Progress in Research*, Raven Press, New York (in press)
6 Corkin, S., Growdon, J. H., Sullivan, E. V. and Shedlack, K. (1981) in *Excerpta Medica New Approaches to Nerve and Muscle Disorders* (Kidman, A. D., ed), pp. 229–249
7 Davies, P. and Maloney, A. J. F. (1976) *Lancet* ii, 1403
8 Davis, K. L., Mohs, R. C. and Tinklenberg, J. R. (1979) *N. Engl. J. Med.* 301, 946
9 Drachman, D. A. (1977) *Neurology* 27, 783–790
10 Gottfries, C. G. (1980) *Trends NeuroSci.* 3, 55–57
11 Growdon, J. H. and Corkin, S. (1980) in *Psychopathology in the Aged* (Cole, J. O. and Barrett, J., eds), pp. 281–296, Raven Press, New York
12 Hooper, M. W. and Vogel, F. S. (1976) *Am. J. Pathol.* 85, 1–13
13 Katzman, R., Terry, R. D. and Bick, K. L. (eds) (1978) *Alzheimer's Disease: Senile Dementia and Related Disorders*, Vol. 7, Raven Press, New York
14 Mohs, R. C., Davis, K. L., Tinklenberg, F. R. and Hollister, L. E. (1980) *Neurobiol. Aging* 1, 21–25
15 Perry, E. K., Tomlinson, B. E., Blessed G., Bergmann, K., Gibson, P. H. and Perry, R. H. (1978) *Br. Med. J.* 2, 1457–1459
16 Peters, B. H. and Levin, H. S. (1979) *Ann. Neurol.* 6, 219–221
17 Sims, N. R., Smith, C. C. T., Davison, A. N., Bowen, D. M., Flack, R. H. A. and Snowden, J. S. (1980) *Lancet* i, 333–336
18 Terry, R. D. and Davies, P. (1980) *Annu. Rev. Neurosci.* 3, 77–95
19 Tomlinson, B. E. (1977) in *Aging and Dementia* (Smith, W. L. and Kinsbourne, M., eds), Vol. 7, pp. 25–89, Spectrum Publications, Inc., New York
20 Wisniewski, H. M. and Iqbal, K. (1980) *Trends NeuroSci.* 3, 226–228

Suzanne Corkin is Associate Professor of Psychology and Senior Investigator at the Clinical Research Center, Massachusetts Institute of Technology, E10-003A, Cambridge, MA 02139, U.S.A.

What is the importance of vasopressin in memory processes?

Don M. Gash and Garth J. Thomas

Vasopressin, a nonapeptide synthesized by neurons in the hypothalamus, has well-defined peripheral actions in regulating fluid and electrolyte balance. Vasopressin is the antidiuretic hormone which permits water resorption in the long collecting tubules of the kidney and, at high physiological titers in the blood, has a significant pressor activity. Based on their studies with rats, DeWied and his associates[5,17] have developed the thesis that vasopressin also plays a major role in the central nervous system's mediation of memory processes. They propose that vasopressin exerts long-term effects on the maintenance of learned responses by facilitating memory consolidation, storage and retrieval. In Hegelian fashion, work from other laboratories has suggested the antithesis; namely, that memory processes are unaffected by vasopressin. The present communication examines recent studies on this controversy and suggests that there is a transition towards a conceptual synthesis regarding our understanding of the role of vasopressin in behavior.

Evidence supporting a role for vasopressin in memory consolidation and retrieval comes primarily from experiments conducted by DeWied and his colleagues on avoidance behaviors. They found that the extinction of shuttle box avoidance behavior was facilitated in rats following neurohypophysectomy but that subcutaneous injections of either pitressin (a vasopressin preparation with a long half-life in the blood) or lysine-8-vasopressin reversed this effect[4]. In normal rats, vasopressin administered either peripherally or centrally has been reported to improve retention of passive avoidance responding (i.e. prolongs extinction)[11,12]. Since intracerebroventricular and intraparenchymal injections of vasopressin in the brain are effective at less than 1/1000th of the dose level required when given peripherally, the CNS appears to be the site of the behavior effects of vasopressin. Studies[10] employing microinjections of antisera to arginine-

vasopressin into the brain of normal rats also support a CNS effect for vasopressin. For example, vasopressin antiserum injected bilaterally into the dentate gyrus of the dorsal hippocampus of Wistar rats immediately after a single learning trial of a passive avoidance response attenuated the retention of the passive avoidance response when it was tested 24 h later[10].

An important animal model for testing the thesis that vasopressin influences memory processes is the Brattleboro rat homozygous for the diabetes insipidus trait (HO-DI rat)[5,6]. These animals show a virtual absence of vasopressin in their blood, pituitary and brain. DeWied and his colleagues have reported[5,6] that HO-DI rats tested for passive avoidance behavior show a severe memory impairment which is alleviated by vasopressin treatment. Experiments conducted by other investigators have yielded quite different results that do not confirm the observations from the preceding studies. Carey and Miller[3] have recently carried out an extensive series of experiments comparing the active and passive avoidance behaviors of HO-DI and normal Long-Evans rats. In their study, which involved over 200 animals and was carefully controlled for such variables as body weight, pre-test handling, and shock intensities, no evidence of learning and memory deficits in HO-DI rats was found. Other groups have even reported contradictory results; for example, Bailey and Weiss[1] who found, using a passive avoidance procedure, the performance of HO-DI rats to be better than that of normal rats. Unless the HO-DI rat shows consistent evidence of memory disturbances that are alleviated by exogenous vasopressin, the hypothesis that vasopressin plays a unique role in memory is of doubtful validity.

There have also been problems in replicating the effects of vasopressin in normal rats. Hostetter, Jubb and Kozlowski[9], using the same experimental design (including the same apparatus, strain and size of rat and the use of lysine-vasopressin) which was reported to demonstrate a positive effect on passive avoidance behavior, found no effects of subcutaneous injections of vasopressin on passive avoidance behavior in Wistar rats.

On the other hand, Sahgal et al.[15] examined the ability of intracerebroventricular injections of vasopressin to enhance the performance of Wistar rats in a passive avoidance task. They found that the post-trial administration of arginine-vasopressin produced a bimodal effect, with some animals showing shortened latencies in re-entering a box where they had previously been shocked (implying impaired memory) while others demonstrated increased latencies (implying enhanced memory). This observation of a bimodal effect may be important, as they suggest, in that it indicates the influence of vasopressin on processes other than memory. Sahgal et al. postulate that exogenous vasopressin increases the animal's state of arousal and,

assuming the Yerkes-Dodson law of a U-shaped function relating arousal and performance, it would be expected that both high and low levels of arousal might result in producing poor avoidance performance. Animals in a low state of initial arousal given vasopressin should show improved behavior while those animals already at the optimal levels of arousal would be raised further with consequent poorer performance.

A study of LeMoal et al.[12] which did demonstrate an influence of vasopressin on active avoidance behavior also provides evidence that the behavioral effects of vasopressin are mediated by other than direct effects on memory processes. First, LeMoal and his colleagues replicated the finding by DeWied's group that subcutaneous injections of arginine-vasopressin could prolong extinction of a pole jump avoidance behavior for as long as 6 h. The protocol followed in these experiments is to select only those animals for further study which make seven or more avoidance responses in the first ten trials. (Clearly if one were dealing with bimodal population, such selection procedures could bias the results.) They then demonstrated that abolishing the pressor effects of vasopressin also abolished the effects of injected vasopressin upon the prolongation of extinction. Le Moal et al. point out that one interpretation of their data is that vasopressin influences avoidance behavior through its visceral effects such as, perhaps, increased blood pressure.

With the extensive utilization of aversive stimuli in testing the behavioral effects of vasopressin, a crucial issue to be addressed is whether a direct causal relationship exists between memory processes and performance in avoidance tasks. The answer may be no. Heise[8] has analysed the problem of inferring memory from passive avoidance behavior and has emphasized its shortcomings. Bolles[2] has also analysed the problem raised by aversive stimulation because of its potential for arousing innate defensive reflexes (called species-specific defense responses) which are unlearned responses. Therefore, the paradigm of using avoidance behavior as a measure of memory must be considered questionable and unproven.

A recent study by Ettenberg et al.[7] emphasizes that vasopressin administration alone may have aversive effects. In a series of experiments they showed that (a) rats avoided an otherwise preferred tasting solution when that solution was previously paired with vasopressin; (b) rats avoided a distinctive environment when previous exposure to that environment was associated with vasopressin; and (c) vasopressin and the aversive agent lithium chloride (a known illness-producing agent) gave similar results in improving performance in an appetitive learning task. Ettenberg and his colleagues, in concordance with the conclusions reached by Sahgal et al.[15], hypothesized that it was the alerting or arousing properties of vasopressin (i.e. visceral or autonomic effects) which accounted for its behavioral effects.

The concept that vasopressin influences behavior through actions involving the autonomic nervous system can be supported by data from several different lines of investigation. Swanson and Sawchenko[16] have recently reviewed the evidence which strongly suggests that oxytocin and vasopressin neurons of the paraventricular nucleus project directly to preganglionic cell groups of both the parasympathetic and sympathetic divisions of the autonomic nervous system and to the principal sensory nucleus of the vagus and glossopharyngeal nerves, the nucleus tractus solitarius. Thus, the anatomical pathways seem to exist for vasopressin to interact directly with the autonomic nervous system and influence such parameters as blood pressure and the level of arousal. Pittman, Lawrence and McLean[14] have recently demonstrated that the intracerebroventricular injection of quantities of arginine-vasopressin ranging from 25 to 5000 pmoles increases the peripheral blood pressure in both Sprague-Dawley and HO-DI rats, thereby providing evidence that endogenous vasopressin plays a role in the central control of blood pressure. Additional evidence comes from Morris and Keller's report[13] that there is a specific deficiency in paraventricular levels of vasopressin and oxytocin, as measured by radioimmunoassay, in the spontaneously hypertensive rat. In summary, it seems that while the thesis that vasopressin directly modulates memory processes is becoming increasingly untenable, evidence is mounting that vasopressin has direct visceral (autonomic) effects which may indirectly influence other behaviors, perhaps by modulating emotional–motivational (arousal) and temperamental factors subserving the specific responses from which higher cognitive functions (like 'memory') are inferred.

Reading list

1 Bailey, W. H. and Weiss, J. M. (1979) Brain Res. 162, 174–178
2 Bolles, R. C. (1978) in Cognitive Processes in Animal Behavior (Hulse, S. H., Fowler, H. and Honig, W. K., eds), pp. 89–107, Erlbaum Press, Hillsdale, NJ
3 Carey, R. J. and Miller, M. (1982) Behav. Brain Res. 6, 1–13
4 DeWied, D. (1965) Int. J. Neuropharmacol. 4, 157–167
5 DeWied, D. (1980) Proc. R. Soc. London, Ser. B 210, 183–195
6 DeWied, D., Bohus, B. and van Wimersma Greidanus, Tj. B. (1975) Brain Res. 85, 152–156
7 Ettenberg, A., van der Kooy, D., LeMoal, M., Koob, G. F. and Bloom, F. E. (1983) Behav. Brain Res. 7, 331–350
8 Heise, G. A. (1981) Trends Pharmacol. Sci. 2, 158–160
9 Hostetter, G., Jubb, S. L. and Kozlowski, G. P. (1980) Neuroendocrinology 30, 174–177
10 Kovács, G. L., Buijs, R. M., Bohus, B. and van Wimersma Greidanus, Tj. B. (1982) Physiol. Behav. 28, 45–48
11 Kovács, G. L., Vécsei, L., Medve, L. and Telegdy, G. (1980) Exp. Brain Res. 38, 357–361
12 LeMoal, M., Koob, G. F., Koda, L. Y., Bloom, F. E., Manning, M., Sawyer, W. H. and Rivier, J. (1981) Nature (London) 291, 491–493
13 Morris, M. and Keller, M. (1982) Brain Res. 249, 173–176
14 Pittman, Q. J., Lawrence, D. and McLean, L.

(1982) *Endocrinology* 110, 1058–1060

15 Sahgal, A., Keith, A. B., Wright, C. and Edwardson, J. A. (1982) *Neurosci. Lett.* 28, 87–92
16 Swanson, L. W. and Sawchenko, P. E. (1983)
   Annu. Rev. Neurosci. 6, 269–324
17 van Wimersma Greidanus, Tj. B. (1982) *Ann.*

NY Acad. Sci. 394, 655–662

*Don M. Gash and Garth J. Thomas are at the
Department of Anatomy and Center for Brain
Research, University of Rochester School of Medi-
cine and Dentistry, Rochester, NY 14642, USA.*

The anatomy of the CNS cholinergic neurons

A. Claudio Cuello and Michael V. Sofroniew

Convincing biochemical and pharmacological evidence of the transmitter role of acetylcholine (ACh) in the CNS has been available for some years, but it is only in recent times that unequivocal tools have been obtained for the demonstration of cellular localization of CNS cholinergic neurons. In this report we summarize aspects of the neuroanatomy of the cholinergic neurons gained through the immunohisto- chemical application of antibodies against the ACh biosynthetic enzyme (choline acetyltransferase).

ACh was the first substance to be recog- nized as a chemical transmitter, but it was not until quite recently that con- vincing morphological evidence of speci- fic cholinergic neurons in the CNS was obtained. In contrast, neurons producing catecholamines or indol- amines, relative newcomers to the ranks of CNS transmitters, were readily visual- ized. Using the Falck and Hillarp tech- nique, various Swedish investigators (notably Dahlstrom, Fuxe, Bjorklund, Hokfelt and others) have elegantly demonstrated a number of defined monoaminergic pathways and this pion- eered the demonstration of the biochemi- cal neuroanatomy of these transmitter substances. Unfortunately, no technique equivalent to the induced fluorescence of the catecholamines has been devel- oped which directly demonstrates ACh in neurons of the central and peripheral nervous systems. The characteristics of cholinergic synapses do not allow the demonstration of cholinergic uptake sites. Choline and acetate are entrenched in many other metabolic pathways and it is therefore difficult to discriminate the specific cholinergic sites from non- specific metabolic sites.

Another potential strategy for reveal- ing cholinergic neurons has been the utilization of histochemical techniques for demonstrating the ACh biosynthetic and inactivating enzymes, choline acetyl- transferase (CAT) and acetylcholin- esterase (AChE). No satisfactory histo- chemical method has been developed for CAT, while the use of AChE sug- gested possible locations of cholinergic cell bodies and fibre networks. In retro- spect, we now know that the AChE methodology has contributed greatly to the clarification of the CNS cholinergic systems. However, the use of AChE histochemistry alone has not made it possible to unambiguously ascertain the cholinergic nature of stained elements, since it has become increasingly clear that AChE activity is not restricted to cholinergic neurons. One of the best- documented cases of this in the CNS is that of the dopaminergic neurons of the substantia nigra which are intensely AChE-positive, as elegantly demon- strated by Butcher and co-workers[1]. In spite of its limitations, the AChE pro- cedure has yielded much information about central cholinergic systems. Shute and Lewis carried out a monumental task studying in detail the neuronal elements which display AChE in the central nervous systems of various mammalian species. In these early studies, they were able to clearly show a number of major cholinergic pathways, confirmed by more recent techniques.

Following the demonstration of catecholamine biosynthetic enzymes it became clear that the best possible strategy for the demonstration of cholinergic elements would be the production and application of specific antibodies against the ACh biosynthetic enzyme, CAT. This enzyme is regarded as being restricted to cholinergic neurons. The purification of CAT and its use as an immunogen proved to be a very difficult task. The results obtained from early attempts at applying antibodies against CAT preparations were unconvincing[2]. In Canada, McGeer and colleagues foresaw the advantage of this strategy and have been working towards this goal for many years. They recently produced a polyclonal anti-CAT antibody which demonstrated some cholinergic elements in the CNS[3,4]. In recent years, initially thanks to the breakthrough of Eckenstein, Barde and Thoenen, highly purified CAT preparations were obtained and applied to the production of polyclonal antibodies[5]. These antibodies satisfied the demand for specific immunological probes made by one of the most critical observers and past participants in this field[6]. Since this communication, several monoclonal antibodies demonstrating CAT in immunocytochemical enzymes have been reported[7–9]. The new antibodies have produced enough information on the major organization of the cholinergic system in the mammalian CNS to form a morphological framework. Our own observations[10,11], using Eckenstein's and Thoenen's antibodies, and the results obtained by others[12,13] are given in the following succinct summary.

Main cholinergic cellular groups in the rat CNS

It is emerging from these studies that the telencephalon has a continuous stream of cholinergic neurons occupying the head of the caudate putamen and being continuous with the nucleus accumbens. This CAT-immunoreactive neuron stream leads to all components of the diagonal band and medial septum and further ventrally to CAT-positive neurons of the olfactory tubercle and islands of Calleja, amygdala and substantia innominata. Cholinergic neurons are prominently concentrated in the nucleus preopticus magnus cellularis, a component of the diagonal band. Although the bulk of the globus pallidus is conspicuously free of cholinergic elements, a rim of cholinergic neurons can be found in the innermost portions bordering the nucleus and in the capsula interna. In the rat, this rim of cholinergic neurons is constituted by somewhat larger cells. This magnocellular group can be considered the rodent equivalent to the primate nucleus basalis (Fig. 1). In the primate, the nucleus basalis is located in a much more ventral position close to the anterior commissure. In the rat, it invades the globus pallidus in caudal parts of the striatum. Also, discrete cholinergic cells are found in the entopeduncular nucleus. A few cholinergic groups can be detected in the diencephalon. There is a conglomeration of CAT-immunoreactive cells which occupies most of the medial habenula and some neurons are found dispersed in the location of the arcuate nucleus and lateral hypothalamus. It is now becoming evident that quite apart from this continuous flow of cholinergic neurons the rat neocortex displays numerous, disperse, cholinergic neurons[11,13,14]. These are mostly small bipolar neurons, possibly aspiny neurons. Using Golgi preparations, similar neurons have been regarded as interneurons. It has been shown recently by Eckenstein and Baughman (unpublished observations) that most if not all of these neurons contain the peptide vasoactive intestinal polypeptide (VIP) in addition to ACh. Some cholinergic elements are detected in the olfactory bulb, anterior olfactory

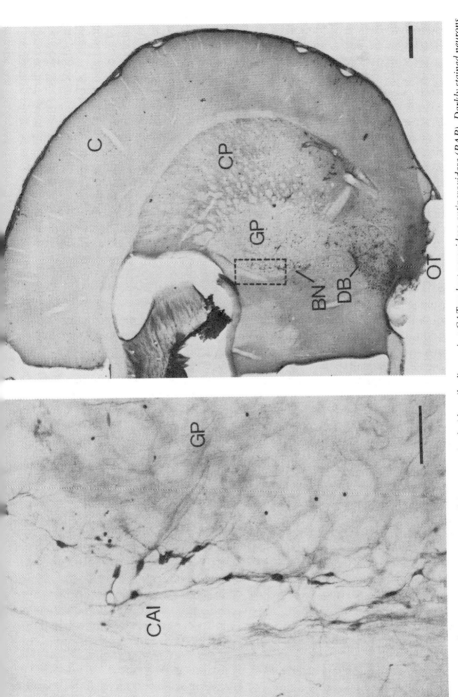

Fig. 1. Micrographs of rat brain section (coronal) immunostained with antibodies against CAT and rat peroxidase-antiperoxidase (PAP). Darkly stained neurons are found prominently in the olfactory tubercle (OT), the horizontal limb of the diagonal band (DB), the cortex (C), and in the caudate putamen (CP). In the rat, the nucleus basalis (BN) is intermingled in the white matter between the capsula interna (CAI) and the globus pallidus (GP). An area of the nucleus basalis is reproduced with enlargement on the left. Scale bars represent 500 μm (right) and 120 μm (left).

nucleus, claustrum and hippocampus.

Immunocytochemical studies in the brain stem have confirmed the cholinergic nature of neurons of the classic motor and preganglionic parasympathetic nuclei of origin of the motor and autonomic nerves. Motor neurons were revealed as large multipolar cells displaying all the features so well described in many classic histological papers. In addition to these motor neurons there is a collection of CAT-positive neurons distributed in large portions of the brain stem. There is a diffuse reticular system medial to the lateral lemniscus in the upper pons, which spreads to the periaqueductal region. Rostrally, this continues with neurons which are in close proximity to the substantia nigra. From the lateral wings of the dorsal raphe in the higher pons, cholinergic neurons spread to parts of the parabrachial nucleus (dorsalis and ventralis) referred to by some authors as the 'pontopeduncular nuclei'. Caudally, this periaqueductal group remains restricted to the lateral dorsotegmental nuclei, as if it were a column continuous with the previous raphe location, spreading further towards the parabrachial complex. Some cholinergic neurons can be found amidst the locus coeruleus neurons. An interesting feature in the medulla oblongata is the loose connection of cholinergic neurons which spread from the facial nucleus, through the reticular formation, towards the nucleus solitarius or caudally from the nucleus ambiguous.

Major cholinergic fibre systems

With the exception of some very conspicuous cholinergic systems, most antibodies so far reported show cell body groups more readily than fibre tracts. This observation revives the question of the possible subcellular localization of CAT in soluble and particulate forms which might be differentially associated to the soma and axons. A diffuse immunoreactive fibre network can be seen in the cortex. Punctate immunoreactivity can be detected throughout the caudate putamen, nucleus accumbens and olfactory tuberculum, which presumably corresponds to cholinergic terminals. Fibres from the medial septum and vertical limb of the diagonal band can be seen running into the fimbria. Other obviously prominent fibre tracts are those originating from the motor nuclei. The nucleus interpeduncularis shows a very intense immunoreaction to CAT which presumably corresponds to cholinergic nerve fibres from the fasciculus retroflexus.

Cholinergic neurons and cholinesterase activity

The analysis of CAT-immunoreactive sites has revealed that not all CNS AChE-positive cells can be regarded as cholinergic[15,16]. Conversely, all cholinergic neurons so far analysed possess AChE activity which ranges from moderate to intense. It has been shown, for example, that the ratio between the numbers of histochemical and immunoreactive sites for the two enzymes is 1/1 in the neostriatum and the nucleus basalis. Examples of non-cholinergic neurons with various degrees of cholinesterase activity are the substantia nigra, the red nucleus, some neurons of the zona inserta, and the nucleus parafascicularis.

Major cholinergic pathways

In the schematic sagittal view of the rat CNS represented in Fig. 2 we have presented the major, best-documented, cholinergic pathways. We have shown, with dots, the localization of the principal groups of CAT-immunoreactive cell bodies (information as discussed in the previous section).

The septal-hippocampal (S, H) projections were first proposed by Lewis and Shute on the basis of their cholinesterase-lesion studies[17]. They have received abundant biochemical confirmation.

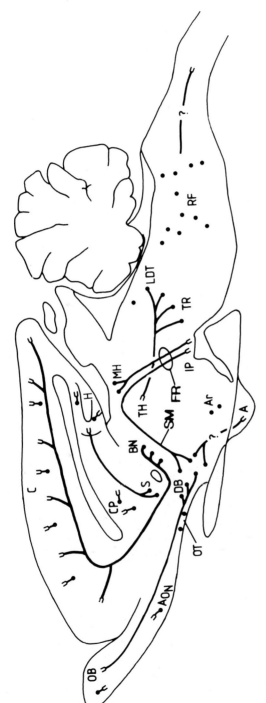

Fig. 2. *Sagittal view of the rat CNS. Schematic representation of principal CNS cholinergic cell groups and major known and probable(?) pathways as discussed in the text. Abbreviations: OB = olfactory bulb; AON = anterior olfactory nucleus; DB = nucleus of the diagonal band; S = septum; CP = caudate putamen; H = hippocampus; BN = nucleus basalis; A = amygdala; TH = thalamus; Ar = arcuate nucleus; TR = tegmental reticular system; LDT = lateral dorsal tegmental nucleus; RF = hindbrain reticular formation; C = cortex; IP = nucleus interpeduncularis; SM = stria medullaris; MH = medial habenula; OT = olfactory tubercle; FR = fasciculus retroflexus. For the sake of clarity, classical motor and autonomic preganglionic neurons are not represented.*

Immunohistochemistry of CAT does indeed show positive fibres from the septum and diagonal band entering into the fimbria. An unanswered point, however, is the relative contribution of the septum versus other possible sources, mainly components of the diagonal band (DB). The hippocampus also contains the local circuit CAT-positive elements which should also be taken into account[11,13].

The cortex (C) receives a widespread distribution of cholinergic fibres, the majority of which seem to originate in the nucleus basalis (BN)[18]. From non-immunohistochemical studies it would appear that a topographic representation exists for this projection[19]. It is now important to establish how extensively basalis cholinergic neurons project to non-cortical areas, a point which deserves to be resolved in view of the retrograde changes suffered by these neurons following decortication (see final section). It is now evident that these fibres are not the only cholinergic cortical component and that a widespread intrinsic cholinergic system exists throughout the cortex via local circuit neurons. This observation is supported by the failure of cortical de-afferentation to produce total cholinergic depletion. It has long been suspected that basal, rostral telencephalic neurons project to the olfactory bulb (OB)[20]. These fibres probably terminate in all layers of the bulb. In addition, some short-axon neurons have been located in the plexiform and internal granular layers. So far, no projections have been described for the cholinergic cells of the anterior olfactory nucleus (AON) that are similar to those produced by interneurons in the cortex[11].

Whilst there is a growing concensus – based on AChE studies – that the large striatal cholinergic neurons of the caudate putamen (CP) are local circuit neurons, there is no information available on projections of cholinergic neurons of the nucleus accumbens.

The nucleus interpeduncularis (IP) receives a substantial cholinergic input via the fasciculus retroflexus (FR). It has been suggested that all these fibres originate from the rostral-basal telencephalic cholinergic neurons via the stria medullaris (SM) (for review, see Ref. 21). However, more recent biochemical studies support the idea that this projection is shared with that of the medial habenula (MH)[22], a large proportion of which contains CAT-positive cell bodies. This requires confirmation by applying combined tract-tracing and immunocytochemistry for CAT.

The amygdala (A) might receive cholinergic fibres from the nucleus basalis, diagonal band and related cholinergic groups in addition to those received from the local circuit elements[23].

There is no indication for the projections of the cholinergic neurons in the arcuate nucleus (Ar) of the hypothalamus. The thalamus, which appears not to contain intrinsic cholinergic cells, receives afferents from CAT-immunoreactive neurons of the tegmental reticular formation (TR) and the lateral dorsal tegmental nucleus (LDT) (Sofroniew, M. V., Priestley, J. V., Consolazione, A., Eckenstein, F. and Cuello, A. C., unpublished observations) (see Fig. 3) and possibly other sources. Losses of CAT activity in the dorsal horn of the spinal cord of patients with lateral amyotrophic sclerosis[24] suggest the existence of descending cholinergic pathways. There is not as yet an immunocytochemical confirmation of this possibility.

In coming years it will be possible to have a more detailed account of 'new' cholinergic pathways, confirmation of 'old' pathways and the extent of the various cholinergic groups branching to more than one area of the CNS. The use of immunocytochemistry combined with retrograde transport of fluorescent dyes and horseradish peroxidase (HRP) will play a decisive role in the clarification of these points. To take a long-term view, a more consistent framework for the pharmacological analysis of CNS ACh will be offered by the synaptic interactions of cholinergic cells with other transmitter-specific neurons. For example, the opposite effects of dopaminergic and cholinergic agonists in Parkinson's disease could be analysed in the light of the biochemical neuroanatomy of the striatum.

Cholinergic receptors and cholinergic neurons

There are a number of extensive studies mapping the cholinergic receptors in the CNS. These studies have been done mainly through the use of the radioautographic procedures pioneered by Kuhar and co-workers, and binding techniques in brain homogenates. Overall, there is a good correlation between the anatomy of the cholinergic innerva-

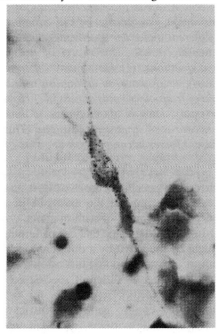

Fig. 3. *Cholinergic neuron double-labelled for retrogradely transported HRP (black dots) and CAT immunoreactivity (diffuse cytoplasmic staining). The double-labelled neuron is located in the lateral dorsal tegmental nucleus and has transported HRP from the thalamus (see text). Scale bar = 20 μm.*

tion of CNS nuclei and the distribution of these receptors (for review, see Ref. 21). It is hoped that future studies will provide more specific information on the transmitter nature of 'cholinoceptive' mechanisms and their share of muscarinic and nicotinic subtypes, as well as their cellular distribution (soma, dendrites, terminals). Cholinergic receptors are probably prominent on motoneurons, as indicated by the loss of muscarinic sites in the hypoglossal nucleus when the cranial nerve has been severed[25]. This aspect of cholinergic autoreceptors has been emphasized by the recent finding of CAT-immunoreactive terminals which establish synaptic contact with cholinergic neurons (Ref. 13; Connaughton, M., Priestley, J. V., Sofroniew, M. V. and Cuello, A. C., unpublished observations).

Cholinergic neurotoxins

It would be of great experimental advantage to find a neurotoxin which could specifically affect cholinergic neurons in the manner analogous to that in which 6-hydroxydopamine and 5',7'-dihydroxytryptamine affect the catecholaminergic and indolaminergic neurons. Attempts have been made recently to produce such a tool by the application of choline mustards[26,27]. These compounds have been reported to diminish CAT activity and reduce choline uptake sites in the hippocampus, cortex and striatum, but confirmation of the specificity of these mustards is not available. These compounds are unstable and do not readily cross the blood–brain barrier. There is a report which indicates that their intracerebral administration in discrete CNS areas leads to non-specific damage[27].

Cholinergic neurons and co-transmission

Good experimental evidence already exists for the coexistence of ACh and peptides in the PNS. This pattern has now been extended to the CNS where CAT immunoreactivity is co-localized with VIP immunoreactivity in the cerebral cortex (Eckenstein, F. and Baughman, R. W., unpublished observations) and with substance P in neurons of the lateral dorsal tegmental nucleus[28]. Synaptic co-operation seems to occur between ACh and the peptide VIP in the PNS and between dopamine and the peptide cholecystokinin (CCK) in the CNS (for review, see Ref. 29). With the many recently discovered neuroactive peptides, these examples are likely to stimulate a search for coexistence in cholinergic neurons. It is conceivable that subsets of cholinergic neurons will be distinguished by the nature of the accompanying peptide or peptides. If confirmed, this will in turn provide further clues to the meaning of co-transmitter synapses in the mammalian CNS.

Cholinergic neurons and senile dementia

There are some indications of an age-dependent decline of CAT activity in the human CNS, but this decline need not necessarily be restricted to cholinergic markers. In the case of senile dementia of the Alzheimer's type, it is clear that severe losses of CAT occur in the cortex and the nucleus basalis[30–32]. There is also a good correlation between the incidence of cortical histopathological features and the degree of loss of cholinergic markers[33] in post-mortem brains of Alzheimer's disease sufferers. As discussed above, the nucleus basalis is the main source of cholinergic fibres to the cortex, in the same way as the substantia nigra gives rise to the majority of dopaminergic fibres to the striatum. On the basis of this analogy it has been suggested that Alzheimer's disease could be a consequence of the loss of cholinergic cells in the nucleus basalis, in the same way that Parkinson's disease is a consequence of the loss of dopaminergic neurons in the substantia nigra.

This idea has been reinforced by the observation that the brains of Alzheimer's patients show a reduction in the number of Nissl-stained large neurons in the nucleus basalis[34]. Nagai and co-workers[35] confirmed the cholinergic nature of these neurons in the human immunocytochemically. We have analysed the number of CAT-immunoreactive cells in the nucleus basalis in the brain of one well-documented case of senile dementia of the Alzheimer type and compared it with age- and sex-matched brains and failed to observe a significant diminution of CAT-immunoreactive neurons in the diseased brain. Nevertheless, the cholinergic neurons appeared significantly smaller than those of the control brain[36]. The shrunken appearance of these diseased cholinergic neurons was similar to the experimental observation that in hemidecorticated rats the CAT-immunoreactive neurons in the rodent equivalent of the nucleus basalis do not disappear but remain in a shrunken state and display distorted processes[37]. The changes observed in the diseased brain are thus open to several interpretations regarding the possible sequence of the cause/effect of this intellectually debilitating disease of the elderly. The shrunken appearance of the diseased neurons is potentially compatible with either a primary effect, or a retrograde effect secondary to a primary cortical lesion. These findings do not contradict the idea of a reduction in the number of large Nissl-stained neurons in the basal nucleus, which though still present in a smaller form might be unrecognizable when conventional histological procedures are being used. Indeed, a disappearance of large Nissl-stained neurons from the human basal nucleus similar to that seen in Alzheimer's disease has been reported following cortical damage[38]. Alternatively, the appearance of cells in the senile dementia of the Alzheimer type might be different from those observed during the presenile onset of Alzheimer's disease.

The precise knowledge of the anatomy of the cholinergic system in man and experimental animals will provide fresh clues to the understanding of any cholinergic involvement in brain diseases.

Acknowledgement

This work was supported by funds from the Medical Research Council (UK), The Wellcome Trust, the E.P. Abraham Cephalosporin Fund (Oxford) and N.I.H. (USA) (NINCOS (NSO6959)).

Reading list

1 Butcher, L. L. and Marchand, R. (1978) *Eur. J. Pharmacol.* 52, 415–417

2 Rossier, J. (1983) *Trends NeuroSci.* 6, 201–202

3 Kimura, H., McGeer, P. L, Peng, J. H. and McGeer, E. G. (1980) *Science* 208, 1057–1059

4 Kimura, H., McGeer, P. L., Peng, J. H. and McGeer, E. G. (1981) *J. Comp. Neurol.* 200, 151–201

5 Eckenstein, F., Barde, Y. A. and Thoenen, H. (1981) *Neuroscience* 6, 993–1000

6 Rossier, J. (1981) *Neuroscience* 6, 989–991

7 Eckenstein, F. and Thoenen, H. (1982) *EMBO J.* 1, 363–368

8 Crawford, G. D., Correa, L. and Salvaterra, P. M. (1982) *Proc. Natl Acad. Sci. USA* 79, 7031–7035

9 Levey, A. I., Armstrong, D. M., Atweh, S. F., Terry, R. D. and Wainer, B. H. (1983) *J. Neurosci.* 3, 1–9

10 Sofroniew, M. V., Eckenstein, F., Thoenen, H. and Cuello, A. C. (1982) *Neurosci. Lett.* 33, 7–12

11 Sofroniew, M. V., Eckenstein, F. and Cuello, A. C. in *The Rat Nervous System* (Paxinos, G. and Watson, C., eds), Academic Press, Sydney (in press)

12 Armstrong, D. M., Saper, C. B., Levey, A. I., Wainer, B. H. and Terry, R. D. (1983) *J. Comp. Neurol.* 216, 53–68

13 Houser, C. R., Crawford, G. D., Barber, R. P., Salvaterra, P. M. and Vaughn, J. E. *Brain Res.* 266, 97–119

14 Eckenstein, F. and Thoenen, H. (1983) *Neurosci. Lett.* 36, 211–215

15 Eckenstein, F. and Sofroniew, M. V. (1983) *J. Neurosci.* 3, 2286–2291

16 Levey, A. I., Wainer, B. H., Mufson, E. J. and Mesulam, M. M. (1983) *Neuroscience* 9, 9–22

17 Lewis, P. R. and Shute, C. C. D. (1966) *Brain* 90, 521–541

18 Mesulam, M. M., Mufson, E. J., Levey, A. I. and Wainer, B. H. (1983) *J. Comp. Neurol.* 214, 170–197

19 Pearson, R. C. A., Brodal, P., Gatter, K. C. and Powell, T. P. S. (1983) *Brain Res.* 261, 321–326

20 Shute, C. C. D. and Lewis, P. R. (1967) *Brain* 90, 497–520

21 Fibiger, H. C. (1982) *Brain Res. Rev.* 4, 327–388

22 Contestabile, A. and Fonnum, F. (1983) *Brain Res.* 275, 287–298

23 Woolf, N. J. and Butcher, L. L. (1982) *Brain Res. Bull.* 8, 751–763

24 Gillberg, P.-G., Aquilonius, S.-M., Eckernas, S.-A., Lundqvist, G. and Winblad, B. (1982) *Brain Res.* 250, 394–397

25 Rotter, A., Birdsall, N. J. M., Field, P. M. and Raisman, G. (1979) *Brain Res. Rev.* 1, 167–184

26 Fisher, A., Mantione, C. R., Abraham, D. J. and Hanin, I. (1982) *J. Pharmacol.* 222, 140–145

27 Asante, J. W., Cross, A. J., Deakin, J. F. W., Johnson, J. A. and Slater, H. R. (1983) *Br. J. Pharmacol.* 80, 573P

28 Vincent, S. R., Satoh, K., Armstrong, D. M. and Fibiger, H. C. (1983) *Nature (London)* 306, 688–691

29 Hokfelt, T., Lundberg, J. M., Skirboll, L., Johansson, O., Schultzberg, M. and Vincent, S. R. (1982) in *Co-Transmission* (Cuello, A. C., ed.), pp. 77–125, Macmillan Press Limited, London

30 Bower, D. M., Smith, C. B., White, P. and Davidson, A. N. (1976) *Brain* 99, 459-496

31 Davies, P. and Maloney, A. J. F. (1976) *Lancet* ii, 1403

32 Rossor, M. N., Garrett, N. J., Johnson, A. L., Mountjoy, C. Q., Roth, M. and Iversen, L. L. (1982) *Brain* 105, 313–330

33 Perry, E. K. and Perry, R. H. (1981) in *Metabolic Disorders of the Nervous System* (Rose, F. C., ed.), pp. 382–417, Pitman, London

34 Whitehouse, P. J., Price, D. L., Struble, R. G., Clark, A. W., Coyle, J. T. and De Longi, M. R. (1982) *Science* 215, 1237–1239

35 Nagai, T., Pearson, T., Peng, F., McGeer, E. G. and McGeer, P. L. (1983) *Brain Res.* 265, 300–306

36 Pearson, R. C. A., Sofroniew, M. V., Cuello, A. C., Powell, T. P. S., Eckenstein, F., Esiri, M. M. and Wilcock, G. R. (1983) *Brain Res.* 289, 375–379

37 Sofroniew, M. V., Pearson, C., Eckenstein,
   F., Cuello, A. C. and Powell, T. P. S. (1983)
   Brain Res. 289, 370–374
38 Pearson, R. C. A., Gatter, K. C. and Powell,
   T. P. S. (1983) *Brain Res.* 261, 321–326

*A. Claudio Cuello and Michael V. Sofroniew are
in the Neuroanatomy/Neuropharmacology Group,
Departments of Pharmacology and Human
Anatomy, University of Oxford, South Parks
Road, Oxford OX1 3QT, UK.*

Monoamines and peptides in cerebral cortex
Contrasting principles of cortical organization

John H. Morrison and Pierre J. Magistretti

Investigators are beginning to define the chemical circuitry of certain elements of the cerebral cortex. In this article we review some of the recent findings on the morphological distribution and cellular effects of monoamines (principally noradrenaline) and peptides (principally vasoactive intestinal peptide) in neocortex. The transmitter-specific anatomical methods establish the morphological constraints of the functional circuits within which the cellular effects must take place. Noradrenaline (NA) and vasoactive intestinal peptide (VIP) are discussed as examples of neurotransmitters which share at least one important cellular effect on cortex (activation of glycogenolysis) but have very different anatomical constraints.

New insights into cortical organization have arisen from neurotransmitter-specific histochemical and pharmacological techniques which have facilitated the study of the cellular localization and postsynaptic actions of neurotransmitters[3,5]. In some instances it has been possible to attach biochemical codes to well-defined elements of cortical circuitry, such as in the identification of GABA as a likely candidate for the neurotransmitter used by cortical basket cells[7]. In other cases this approach prompted re-evaluation of current concepts of cortical organization: for example, the discovery of a direct noradrenaline-containing projection from the brain stem to the cortex challenged the notion that all subcortical afferents originate in the thalamus[28]. In this article we will review the cellular localization and postsynaptic effects of two classes of cortical neurotransmitters, namely the monoamines and the peptides. We will concentrate on NA and VIP as the prototype monoamine and peptide, respectively, because their cellular effects and anatomical organization are more clearly understood than the other monoamines and peptides present in cortex.

Various anatomical studies have demonstrated unequivocally that there are four monoamine projections to neocortex: (a) noradrenergic, (b) serotonergic, (c) dopaminergic, and (d) cholinergic. Lesion and biochemical studies also suggest the existence of a histaminergic projection, for which there is no direct anatomical evidence. Each monoamine projection originates from a separate and distinct nuclear complex at different levels of the neuraxis. The noradrenergic projection originates in the locus coeruleus, a small compact nucleus in the dorsal pons. The serotonergic projection originates from the dorsal and medial raphe, a nuclear complex that occupies the medial portion of the caudal mesencephalon, ventral to the aqueduct. The substantia nigra–ventral tegmental area in the rostral mesencephalon are the nuclei of origin of the dopaminergic projection. The cholinergic projection originates from a nuclear complex in the basal telencephalon that occupies the medial septal nucleus through the diagonal band and further laterally into the nucleus basalis of the substantia innominata. All of the monoamine projections are highly divergent systems. Interestingly, the degree of divergence is correlated with the position in the neuraxis of the nucleus of origin; the two more caudally originating systems, the noradrenergic and serotonergic projections, are among the most divergent projections in the entire central nervous system. The locus coeruleus innervates every major division of the central nervous system, with the notable exception of the caudate-putamen.

Noradrenergic coeruleocortical system

A detailed description of the cortical terminal pattern of each monoamine projection is beyond the scope of this review;

thus, given that the noradrenergic coeruleocortical projection is the best characterized we will base our description of the terminal pattern on this system.

The mode of entry of the fibers into the neocortex is best understood in the rat (see Fig. 1). In the rostral diencephalon the fibers begin to diverge in the mediolateral plane, such that a medial group proceeds through the septal region and provides the noradrenergic innervation of medial cortex. The remaining fibers fan out in the ventral telencephalon, enter the frontal pole ventrally, and proceed caudally, providing the noradrenergic innervation for most of the dorsolateral cortex (see Fig. 1). This intracortical trajectory is clearly demonstrated by the fact that a large area of dor-

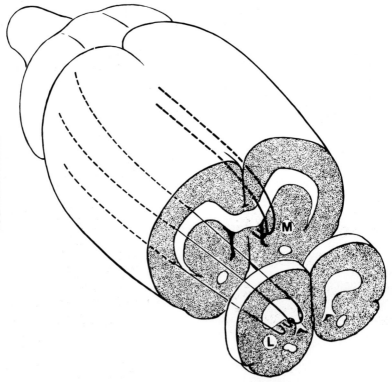

Fig. 1. *Intracortical trajectory of noradrenergic fibers in the rat. The majority of the corticopetal noradrenergic fibers in the medial forebrain bundle follow one of two routes to the neocortex: a medial group (M) ascends through the septal area, and a lateral group (L) continues rostrally through the ventral telencephalon. Once they enter neocortex, these fibers form a continuous sheet of noradrenergic axons, largely within layer VI, that proceeds caudally throughout the longitudinal extent of the medial and dorsolateral cortex, supplying the cortical noradrenergic innervation throughout their trajectory.* (Taken from Morrison, J. H., Molliver, M. E. and Grzanna, R. (1979) *Science* 205, 313–316.)

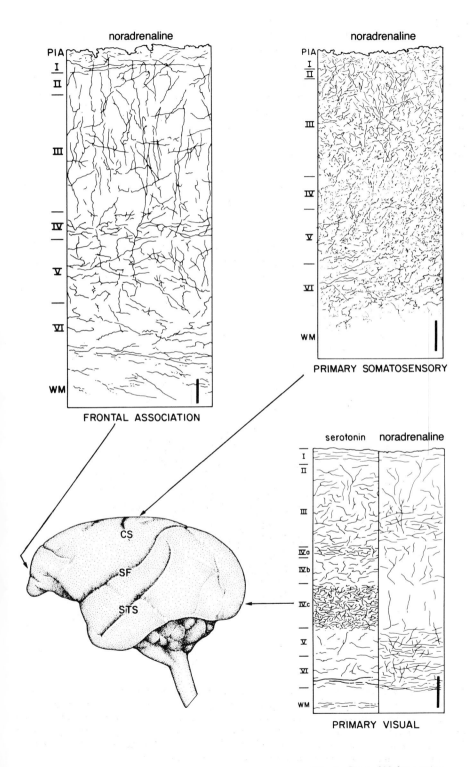

Fig. 2. *See p. 322 for caption.*

solateral cortex can be deprived of noradrenergic innervation by a relatively small lesion of frontal cortex[21].

In the rat, there is a rich network of noradrenergic innervation throughout all layers and regions of the dorsal and lateral cortex[8, 19]. The pattern of noradrenergic innervation is not diffuse, but is characterized by a geometric orderliness which is uniform across cytoarchitectonic boundaries. There appears to be a dense terminal field in layers IV and V, whereas layers II and III are characterized by radial fibers, and I and VI by the presence of tangential fibers[19].

The noradrenergic innervation of primate cortex exhibits a far greater degree of regional heterogeneity than in the rat, in that most major cytoarchitectural regions exhibit distinctive patterns of innervation. The three areas that have been studied in greatest detail are dorsolateral prefrontal cortex (Brodmann areas 9 and 10), the primary somatosensory cortex (areas 3, 1 and 2), and primary visual cortex (area 17) (see Fig. 2)[17, 18]. As in the rat, local damage in the frontal cortex leads to a loss of noradrenergic fibers in more caudal regions. In addition, in the primate cortex, long tangential fibers can be seen crossing cytoarchitectural boundaries (e.g. from primary motor to primary somatosensory). Thus, the tangential intracortical trajectory that is characteristic of the rat brain is also a dominant feature of the noradrenergic innervation of the primate brain[18].

Laminar complementarity

In certain areas of cortex the monoamine terminal fields are restricted to specific layers such that one monoamine projection may terminate in a laminar pattern that is complementary to one of the other monoamine projections. There are two striking cases of laminar complementarity in the monoamine innervation of cortex: (1) noradrenaline and dopamine in the anterior cingulate cortex of the rat[20]; and (2) noradrenaline and serotonin in the primary visual cortex of the monkey[17]. The anterior cingulate cortex has a particularly low density of noradrenergic fibers, and those that are present are found predominantly in layers V, VI, and the deep part of I. A dense plexus of dopamine fibers is present in the superficial half of layer I and in layers II and III (Refs 10, 20), which are the same layers which receive the specific thalamic projection to the anterior cingulate cortex. Thus, the dopaminergic and noradrenergic projections exhibit laminar complementarity such that the dopamine projection terminates in the same layers as the major thalamic projection and the noradrenergic fibers terminate in the remaining layers. In the primary visual cortex, the noradrenergic and serotonergic projections exhibit a high degree of laminar complementarity: the noradrenergic fibers are directed primarily at layers V, VI and deep III, whereas the serotonergic projection is very dense in layer IV (the layer which receives the specific thalamic projection) and sparse in layers V and VI (Ref. 17).

These complementary terminal patterns not only support the notion that monoamine fibers are directed at specific postsynaptic targets, but in addition suggest that in certain regions of cortex, each monoamine projection may engage a different set of cor-

---

Fig. 2. *Noradrenergic innervation of three different regions of primate neocortex. In the case of visual cortex, both noradrenergic and serotonergic innervation patterns are shown. The three areas that are shown are: dorsolateral frontal association cortex, primary somatosensory cortex, and primary visual cortex. The frontal and primary somatosensory regions are similar in that fibers are present in all six layers in both regions. However, these regions differ with respect to specific laminar patterns of fiber distribution and orientation, and in that the primary somatosensory cortex is far more densely innervated than the dorsolateral frontal cortex. The laminar pattern of noradrenergic innervation in primary visual cortex differs fundamentally from both dorsolateral frontal and primary somatosensory cortices, and exhibits a high degree of laminar complementarity with the serotogenic projection. Layers V and VI receive a dense noradrenergic projection and a very sparse serotonergic projection, whereas layer IV receives a very dense serotonergic projection and is largely devoid of noradrenergic fibers. Abbreviations: WM = white matter; CS = central sulcus; SF = sylvian fissure; STS = superior temporal sulcus. Bars represent 200 μm.*

tical neurons. It has been proposed that the noradrenergic and serotonergic afferents to cortex are non-synaptic, releasing their transmitter into the extracellular space, such that the monoamines might diffusely effect all cells with the appropriate recep-

tor[1]. Non-synaptic release of monoamines cannot be definitively ruled out; however, the light-microscope data summarized here and the fact that Molliver and his colleagues have demonstrated that the serotonergic and noradrenergic terminals clearly form

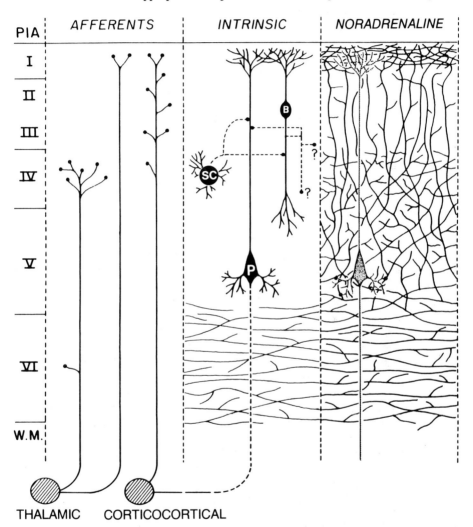

Fig. 3. *Schematic diagram showing three components of cortical circuitry. Left panel: thalamo- and corticocortical fibers terminate in a narrow radial domain with a specific laminar pattern. Middle panel: B = bipolar cell; SC = spiny stellate cell; P = pyramidal cell. These three cells constitute three important links in intrinsic local circuitry. All three receive direct thalamocortical input; SS and B both synapse on pyramidal cells. VIP is present in bipolar cells. Thus, the VIP-containing bipolar cell may be in a position to translate a sustained increase in the local activity of the afferents into an increase in glycogenolysis within the pyramidal cell, whose demand for energy substrates will presumably be increased along with the increased neuronal activity. In contrast, the noradrenergic fibers (right panel) sweep across a vast expanse of cortex and terminate in all layers. Therefore, any homeostatic or metabolic effect that the noradrenergic fibers exert on the postsynaptic targets occurs in many regions simultaneously and is not directly linked to local activity. Anti-VIP prepared by Robert Benoit of the Salk Institute.*

conventional synaptic complexes in neocortex[15] make it unlikely that non-synaptic release is the major mode of action. Furthermore, in the cases where the appropriate laminar analysis has been completed, the distribution of synaptic profiles matches that predicted by the laminar pattern apparent with light microscopy. Several laboratories are engaged in the arduous task of trying to determine which class or classes of cortical neurons are synaptically engaged by the monoamines.

A tangential cortical afferent

The noradrenergic innervation of neocortex – taken in its entirety – may be viewed as a tangential, intragriseal system of afferent fibers whose organization and pattern of termination is different from the well-characterized specific cortical afferents such as the thalamocortical and corticocortical afferents. These afferents project to sharply delineated regions of cortex maintaining strict topographic order, and ramify in the vertical direction with minimal horizontal interaction (Fig. 3). In contrast to the projections from the thalamus and other cortical regions, the coeruleocortical system is not organized radially; the major noradrenergic fibers are oriented and travel longitudinally through the grey matter and branch widely, thus furnishing the coeruleocortical system with the unique capacity to modulate neuronal activity synchronously throughout a vast expanse of neocortex.

Postsynaptic effects

The actions of monoamines on their target cells have been investigated electrophysiologically and biochemically. In the case of NA, iontophoretic studies have shown that the catecholamine has the capacity to enhance evoked activity relative to spontaneous activity, effectively increasing the 'signal-to-noise ratio' in the response of a given cortical neuron to incoming afferent information. Through this process, co-activity between the coeruleocortical system and other

Table I. Various peptide-like immunoreactivies identified in mammalian cerebral cortex

Angiotensin II
Avian pancreatic peptide (APP)
Bradykinin
Bombesin
Corticotropin releasing factor (CRF)
Cholecystokin (CCK8)
Enkephalins
Molluscan cardio-excitatory peptide (FMRF-NH₂)
Neurotensin
Somatostatin [SS28, SS28(1–12), SS14][a]
Substance P
Vasoactive intestinal peptide (VIP)

[a] SS28 (1–12) and SS14 represent the first 12, and last 14 amino acids of the SS28 sequence, respectively. See Refs 30 and 31 for details of characterization and distribution of SS28(1–12).

modality-specific (i.e. auditory, somatosensory, visual) systems converging on the same target neurons leads to more effective synaptic transmission during the period of simultaneous activity. Thus, the coeruleocortical system can adjust the 'state' or 'readiness-to-respond' of cortical neurons in many diverse regions simultaneously (see review by Foote et al.[6] for details).

An important cellular action of monoamines in cerebral cortex is the stimulation of the membrane-bound enzyme adenylate cyclase which results in an increased formation of cyclic adenosine monophosphate (cAMP)[2]. This effect occurs as a consequence of the interaction of the monoamines with specific membrane-bound receptors which are functionally coupled to adenylate cyclase. NA stimulates cAMP formation in the cortex of most species studied. The effects of the other monoamines, in contrast, are more restricted. Thus dopamine promotes cAMP formation only in those cortical areas which receive a dopaminergic input, such as frontal cortex, and the effects of serotonin on the cyclic nucleotide levels are restricted to perinatal animals. NA, serotonin and histamine have also been demonstrated to promote glycogenolysis in rodent cerebral cortex[26]. In the case of NA, this effect on cortical carbohydrate metabolism is linked to an increase in cAMP levels, whereas calcium ions appear to be the intracellular effectors of serotonin and histamine-mediated glycogenolysis.

Peptides

In recent years a number of peptides originally isolated from such diverse tissues as mammalian hypothalamus and gut, or frog skin, have been identified biochemically in extrahypothalamic areas of the CNS, and more specifically, in the cerebral cortex (see Table I). Although in most instances these biochemical data have subsequently been complemented by immunohistochemical localization studies, information about the precise laminar and regional distribution of the majority of cortical neuropeptides is still fragmentary. For example, investigators are just beginning to correlate the morphological characteristics and patterns of connectivity of a particular cell type, as defined by Golgi studies, with those of a neurotransmitter-specified class of cortical neurons. Furthermore, the laminar as well as regional distribution of specific peptide-immunoreactive substances should be evaluated in reference to the termination patterns of known afferent

and efferent cortical pathways in order to determine whether or not any of the long projection systems contain neuropeptides. Very recently some of these questions have been addressed and partially answered for the three cortical peptides present in the highest concentrations, namely VIP, cholecystokinin (CCK) and somatostatin (SS). In Table II we have summarized the morphological characteristics of VIP-, CCK- (in its octapeptide form) and SS-immunoreactive profiles in cerebral cortex. For example, almost all the VIP-positive cells are bipolar, radially oriented neurons[13] (Morrison and Magistretti, unpublished observations) (Fig. 4) and share other morphological features with the 'bipolar cell' described by Peters and Kimerer in Golgi-stained material[22]. Bipolar cells, as demonstrated in Golgi–EM studies, receive direct thalamocortical input and synapse on pyramidal cell apical dendrites[22]. Further immunohistochemical studies at the ultrastructural level are needed; however, it is possible that the VIP-positive neuron possesses identical synaptic connections to those demonstrated for the more general class of bipolar neurons. In contrast, cortical cells containing somatostatin or CCK appear to be far more heterogeneous in

Table II. Morphological characteristics of cells containing VIP-, CCK- and SS-like immunoreactivity in rat cerebral cortex

Peptide	Cell type (morphology and laminar distribution)
VIP $[70-150 \text{ pmoles (g ww)}^{-1}]$	Homogeneous population: bipolar neurons Cell bodies predominantly in layers II and III Dendritic branching in layers I and V Terminals mainly in layers II, III and IV

CCK-8 $[300-600 \text{ pmoles (g ww)}^{-1}]$	Heterogeneous population: bipolar neurons
	    layer I horizontal neurons
	    bitufted and multipolar neurons
	Cell bodies predominantly in layers II and III
	Dendritic branching varies with cell type
	Terminals in layers II–III and V–VI

SS[SS-14, SS-28, SS-28(1–12)] $[140-300 \text{ pmoles (g ww)}^{-1}]$	Heterogeneous population: multipolar
	    modified pyramidal cells
	    pyramidal cells?
	Cell bodies: bimodal distribution, II–III and V–VI
	Dendritic branching varies with cell type
	Terminals: bimodal, I–III and V–VI

their morphological characteristics. Most CCK-containing cells are bipolar, similar to those containing VIP; however, CCK is also present in relatively large horizontally displaced neurons in layer I and multipolar and bitufted stellate cells in layers II and III (Ref. 23). The cells containing somatostatin are also heterogeneous in their morphological characteristics; however, most of the cells are multipolar, bitufted or triangular, with bipolar SS-containing cells being relatively rare[16]. Thus, at the present time, VIP is the only peptide present in cortex which can be equated with a relatively homogeneous cell type.

In addition to the peptidergic systems described in Table II, other peptides have been identified in cortex (see Table I); however, generally they have not been localized to a specific cell type. For example, substance P has been detected by radioimmunoassay and localized in fibers and terminals in rat frontal, piriform, entorhinal, and cingulate cortices[11]. Avian pancreatic polypeptide-containing cell bodies and fibers have been visualized in piriform, entorhinal and neocortex[12]. Met-enkephalin positive cell bodies have been demonstrated in layers V and VI in perirhinal cortex, and the molluscan cardio-excitatory tetrapeptide (FMRF-amide), a peptide related to Met-enkephalin, has also been visualized in cell bodies and fibers in piriform, entorhinal, and frontal cortex[29]. Finally, neurotensin and bombesin have been detected in cortex by radioimmunoassay, and scattered fibers containing bradykinin, angiotensin II and neurotensin immunoreactivity have been visualized. Very recently here at the Salk Institute, the presence of corticotropin releasing factor (CRF) in bipolar and other cortical neurons similar to those that contain VIP and CCK, has been demonstrated.

The actions at the cellular level of cortical neuropeptides are still largely unknown. Electrophysiological experiments have shown inhibitory[25] and excitatory[4] actions of SS-14 and 28; VIP, CCK, substance P and bradykinin appear to be mostly excita-tory on cortical neurons[24].

Cellular actions of cortical neuropeptides detected with biochemical experimental approaches are extremely scarce. In the case of VIP an effect has been demonstrated, namely the stimulation of cAMP formation through specific membrane receptors[27]. The consequences of an increase in intracellular cAMP have been studied in great detail in non-neural tissues; thus it appears that the cyclic nucleotide can induce the phosphorylation of various proteins through an activated cAMP-dependent protein kinase. One such set of phosphorylations initiates the breakdown of glycogen into glucose-1-phosphate while causing the inhibition of glycogen synthesis. This co-ordinated molecular mechanism results in a decrease of intracellular glycogen and in a greater substrate availability for the generation of phosphate-bound energy. Similar mechanisms appear to be operational in the CNS. We have recently demonstrated that VIP promotes glycogenolysis in mouse cortical slices[14]; this effect on glycogen metabolism, which requires only nanomolar concentrations of the peptide, is also observed with NA. Pharmacological and lesion studies have demonstrated that the effects of VIP are independent of noradrenergic neurotransmission[14].

Tangential vs. radial homeostatic control by NA and VIP

It appears that neurotransmitters contained in strikingly different neuronal systems, such as the coeruleocortical noradrenergic projection and the intracortical bipolar VIP neuron, share a common action at the cellular level in cerebral cortex (Fig. 4). The metabolic nature of this cellular action, i.e. glycogenolysis, suggests that VIP and NA may regulate cortical energy metabolism in a complementary fashion. Whereas the VIP-positive cell is a strictly radial intrinsic neuron that is only capable of a highly local effect, the noradrenergic projection from the locus coeruleus is organized tangentially such that the noradrenergic fibers intersect a longitudinal array of columns and may regulate metabolism synchronously throughout a vast expanse of neocortex. Thus, there are at least two independent mechanisms for the regulation of metabolism in cerebral cortex, one very local and closely linked to local and regional variations in neuronal activity, and the other more global, capable of influencing the availability of energy substrates in several functionally distinct regions simultaneously.

Regulation of energy substrate availability may be one of several possible actions of VIP and NA in the cerebral cortex; this cellular action should not be viewed as restrictive, but rather may indicate the existence of other intracellular regulatory processes mediated by VIP and NA through cAMP-dependent phosphorylations or other intracellular effectors. It may be that several of the peptides and monoamines that have specific hormonal effects in peripheral organs exert similar homeostatic functions at the cellular level within the central nervous system; however, within the CNS, the homeostatic cellular effects are integrated into the spatial and temporal constraints that are inherent to central neural circuits.

Given the multitude of neurotransmitters active within the cortex, the interdisciplinary use of neurotransmitter-specific methodologies will be essential in order to define the nature of neuronal interactions within the cortex. This approach allows one to superimpose biochemical codes on the anatomical circuits, and to delineate cortical circuitry in reference to the neurotransmitter-mediated cellular effects. There is evidence that the other monoamine systems, particularly serotonin[9], are also organized tangentially. In addition, the VIP-containing cells represent only one class of bipolar neurons; CCK and CRF are also present in bipolar cells, although they are also present in other cortical cell types. We have very limited information on the synaptic organization and cellular effects of these other systems; however, it is conceivable that a general class of complementary global (tangential) and local (radial) regulatory systems exist which are spatially

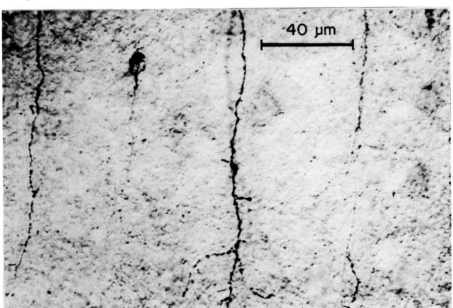

Fig. 4. *Photomicrograph of an anti-VIP immunohistochemical preparation showing VIP-positive cell body and processes in coronal section through layers III and IV of caudolateral cortex. Pial surface at top. Note strict radial orientation of the labelled processes. These processes all emanate from different cell bodies. Each process is approximately 40 μm from the adjacent processes. Bar represents 40 μm.*

and temporally superimposed on the specific afferents and other intrinsic elements that are more directly involved in the modality-linked information-processing that occurs in neocortex.

Acknowledgements

The authors would like to thank Stephen L. Foote and Floyd E. Bloom for helpful advice on the manuscript, and Nancy Callahan for helpful preparation of the manuscript.

Reading list

1 Beaudet, A. and Descarries, L. (1978) *Neuroscience* 3, 851–860
2 Bloom, F. E. (1975) *Rev. Physiol. Biochem. Pharmacol.* 76, 1–103
3 Bloom, F. E. (1981) *The Organization of the Cerebral Cortex* (Schmitt, F. O., Worden, F. G., Adelman, G. and Dennis, S. G., eds), pp. 359–372, MIT Press, Cambridge, MA
4 Dodd, J. and Kelly, J. S. (1978) *Nature (London)* 273, 674–675
5 Emson, P. C. and Hunt, S. P. (1981) *The Organization of the Cerebral Cortex* (Schmitt, F. O., Worden, F. G., Adelman, G. and Dennis, S. G., eds), pp. 325–346, MIT Press, Cambridge, MA
6 Foote, S. L., Bloom, F. E. and Aston-Jones, G. (1983) *Physiol. Rev.* (in press)
7 Hendry, S. H. C. and Jones, E. G. (1981) *J. Neurosci.* 1, 390–408
8 Levitt, P. and Moore, R. Y. (1978) *Brain Res.* 139, 219–231
9 Lidov, H. G. W., Grzanna, R. and Molliver, M. E. (1980) *Neuroscience* 5, 207–227
10 Lindvall, O., Bjorklund, A. and Divac, I. (1978) *Brain Res.* 142, 1–24
11 Ljungdahl, A., Hokfelt, T. and Nilsson, G. (1978) *Neuroscience* 3, 861–943
12 Loren, I., Alumets, J., Hakanson, R. and Sundler, F. (1979) *Cell Tissue Res.* 200, 179–186
13 Loren, I., Emson, P. C., Fahrenkrug, J., Bjorklund, A., Alumets, J., Hakanson, J. and Sundler, F. (1979) *Neuroscience* 4, 1953–1976
14 Magistretti, P. J., Morrison, J. H., Shoemaker, W. J., Sapin, V. and Bloom, F. E. (1981) *Proc. Natl Acad. Sci. U.S.A.* 78, 6535–6539
15 Molliver, M. E., Grzanna, R., Lidov, H. G. W., Morrison, J. H. and Olschowka, J. A. (1982) *Cytochemical Methods in Neuroanatomy* (Chan-Palay, V. and Palay, S. L., eds), pp. 255–277, Alan R. Liss, New York
16 Morrison, J. H., Benoit, R., Magistretti, P. J. and Bloom, F. E. *Brain Res.* (in press)
17 Morrison, J. H., Foote, S. L., Molliver, M. E., Bloom, F. E. and Lidov, H. G. W. (1982) *Proc. Natl Acad. Sci. U.S.A.* 79, 2401–2405
18 Morrison, J. H., Foote, S. L., O'Connor, D. and Bloom, F. E. (1982) *Brain Res. Bull.* 9, 309–319
19 Morrison, J. H., Grzanna, R., Coyle, J. T. and Molliver, M. E. (1978) *J. Comp. Neurol.* 181, 17–40
20 Morrison, J. H., Molliver, M. E., Grzanna, R. and Coyle, J. T. (1979) *Brain Res. Bull.* 4, 849–857
21 Morrison, J. H., Molliver, M, E., Grzanna, R. and Coyle, J. T. (1981) *Neuroscience* 6, 139–158
22 Peters, A. and Kimerer, L. M. (1981) *J. Neurocytol.* 10, 921–946
23 Peters, A., Miller, M. and Kimerer, L. M. (1983) *Neuroscience* (in press)
24 Phillis, J. W. and Kirkpatrick, J. R. (1980) *Can. J. Physiol. Pharmacol.* 58, 612–623
25 Pittman, Q. J. and Siggins, G. R. (1981) *Brain Res.* 221, 402–408
26 Quach, T. T., Rose, C. and Schwartz, J.-C. (1978) *J. Neurochem.* 30, 1335–1341
27 Quik, M., Iversen, L. L. and Bloom, S. R. (1978) *Biochem. Pharmacol.* 27, 2209–2213
28 Ungerstedt, U. (1971) *Acta Physiol. Scand. Suppl.* 367, 1–48
29 Weber, E., Evans, C. J., Samuelsson, S. J. and Barchas, J. D. (1981) *Science* 214, 1248–1251
30 Benoit, R., Bohlen, P., Ling, N., Briskin, A., Esch, F., Brazeau, P., Ying, S. Y. and Guillemin, R. (1982) *Proc. Natl Acad. Sci. U.S.A.* 79, 917–921
31 Benoit, R., Ling, N., Bakhit, C., Morrison, J. H., Alford, B. and Guillemin, R. (1982) *Endocrinology* 111, 2149–2151

John H. Morrison and Pierre J. Magistretti are from the Arthur V. Davis Center for Behavioral Neurobiology, The Salk Institute, La Jolla, CA 92037, U.S.A. Pierre J. Magistretti is now at the Departement de Pharmacologie, Centre Medical Universitaire, Geneva, Switzerland.

Vasopressin and oxytocin in the mammalian brain and spinal cord

Michael V. Sofroniew

The application of immunohistochemical and radioimmunoassay techniques to the study of the distribution of the neurohypophyseal peptides vasopressin and oxytocin has revealed the presence of both peptides throughout the mammalian CNS. Other studies have shown that these peptides exert potent effects on specific central neurons and may be involved in a variety of complex central functions. Recent advances in the concepts surrounding the distribution and possible functions of central vasopressin and oxytocin are summarized in this article.

Since their isolation and chemical characterization 30 years ago, vasopressin and oxytocin have been thought of primarily as the peptide hormones of the posterior pituitary which are produced by hypothalamic neurons, released into the blood vessels of the neurohypophysis, and are responsible for antidiuresis and contraction of the smooth muscle of the uterus and breast. Thus, their functions as hormones have dominated considerations about these peptides for many years. During the past decade it has become clear that neurons throughout the CNS produce a large number of different peptides which upon release are thought to affect the activity of other neurons. Many of these peptides were initially identified on the basis of peripheral effects, but are now known to have central as well as peripheral functions, often in unrelated systems under separate control mechanisms. So too, vasopressin and oxytocin are present, and appear to have functions, in a variety of different regions in the mammalian CNS.

Neurons producing vasopressin and oxytocin

The magnocellular neurons of the hypothalamic supraoptic and paraventricular nuclei have long been recognized as major sources of the vasopressin and oxytocin released from the neurohypophysis[30]. Immunohistochemical studies have now not only confirmed this, but have revealed the presence of vasopressin or oxytocin and their associated neurophysins* in a large number of other neurons located within as well as outside of the hypothalamus (Fig. 1).

Additional magnocellular vasopressin

* Vasopressin and oxytocin are synthesized as portions of large precursor proteins from which the peptides are cleaved. The neurophysins, polypeptides present in neurohypophyseal extracts, are portions of these precursors. There are separate precursors for vasopressin and its associated neurophysin and for oxytocin and its associated neurophysin[16,23]. In immunohistochemical staining, vasopressin and oxytocin can readily be distinguished from one another but the neurophysins usually cannot, unless pretreated species-homologous antisera are used.

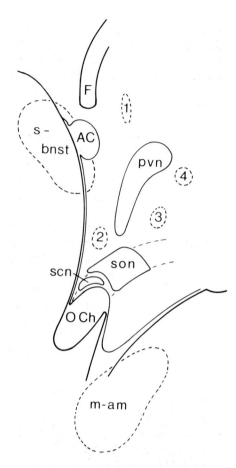

or oxytocin neurons have been identified in a number of so-called accessory nuclei, scattered in various regions of the hypothalamus (Fig. 1). Like the supraoptic and paraventricular nuclei, these accessory nuclei contain intermingled populations of magnocellular (15–35 μm in diameter) vasopressin and oxytocin neurons which for the most part project to the posterior pituitary (see below). The morphology of these neurons, and the input to them, appears to vary somewhat with location, suggesting that functional distinctions may exist (see Refs 26 and 27). Individual neurons appear to produce either vasopressin or oxytocin but not both.

Parvocellular vasopressin and oxytocin neurons have now been identified both inside and outside of the hypothalamus which do not appear to project to the posterior pituitary. Their central projections, where known, are considered below. In the hypothalamic suprachiasmatic nucleus (Fig. 1), a portion of the parvocellular (10–15 μm in diameter) neurons contain vasopressin (but not oxytocin) and its associated neurophysin. These neurons are clearly distinguishable from magnocellular neurosecretory neurons and have been found in all mammals investigated thus far including humans (Fig. 2 a,b) and other primates[29]. In the caudal portion of the hypothalamic paraventricular nucleus, many oxytocin and some vasopressin neurons which are generally smaller than magnocellular neurosecretory neurons give rise to projections to the brain stem and spinal cord rather than to the neurohypophysis[28,30]. These neurons are present in primates as well as rodents. Outside of the hypothalamus, a large number of clearly parvocellular vasopressin- and neurophysin-containing neurons have recently been found following colchicine treatment in the bed nucleus of the stria terminalis, septal region and medial amygdala (Figs 1 and 2 c,d) of the rat[26,32] and mouse (Sofroniew, unpublished

Fig. 1. *Sagittal view of the human hypothalamus depicting the approximate topography of the more prominent groups of vasopressin and oxytocin neurons thus far immunohistochemically identified in mammals. The major commonly known nuclei are the supraoptic (son) and paraventricular (pvn) nuclei, which both contain mixed populations of magnocellular vasopressin and oxytocin neurons. Mixed populations of magnocellular vasopressin and oxytocin neurons are also present in various so-called accessory nuclei in different parts of the hypothalamus. There is no accepted nomenclature for these groups which vary somewhat in location in different species. Here the numbers 1–4 represent groups consistently present in most mammals. In addition, the mammalian suprachiasmatic nucleus (scn) consistently contains a population of parvocellular vasopressin (but not oxytocin) neurons. A large number of parvocellular vasopressin and neurophysin neurons have recently been found in the bed nucleus of the stria terminalis and septum (s-bnst) and medial amygdala (m-am) of rodents treated with colchicine. Other species have not yet been examined. OCh = optic chiasm.*

observations), and smaller numbers in the posterior hypothalamus and a region of the locus coeruleus. Other species have not yet been examined.

Distribution of fibers in the brain and spinal cord

Initially, immunohistochemical techniques were applied to study neuroendocrine aspects of vasopressin and oxytocin neurons, confirming the classical pathway from these neurons to the posterior pituitary (Fig. 3). In addition, a prominent vasopressin projection to the hypophyseal portal capillaries of the median eminence (Fig. 3) was noted by a number of authors. Subsequently, in several laboratories, vasopressin and oxytocin fibers were observed in brain areas not directly associated with neuroendocrine pathways, leading to the discovery of an extensive network of vaso-

pressin and oxytocin fibers distributed throughout the mammalian CNS (Table 1). Fig. 4 schematically depicts the location of some major target areas and known projections. Although initial observations of fibers in various brain areas were made in rodents[5,25,30], the findings have largely been confirmed in other mammalian species including humans and other primates (see Refs 25, 26 and 30). Although quantitative differences in the numbers of fibers present in different areas have been observed in different species, qualitatively the distribution of fibers appears to be quite similar in most mammals examined. The areas containing vasopressin and oxytocin fibers are quite diverse, ranging from autonomic centers or areas involved in nociception in the brain stem and spinal cord to forebrain limbic centers and even to neocortex[26]. However, the

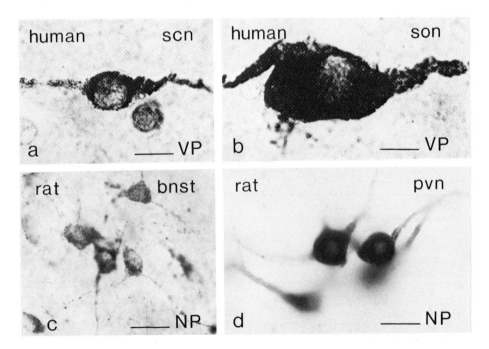

Fig. 2. *Photomicrographs of immunohistochemically stained vasopressin (VP) or neurophysin (NP) neurons.* **(a)** *and* **(b)** *compare a parvocellular VP neuron in the suprachiasmatic nucleus (scn) with a magnocellular VP neuron in the supraoptic nucleus (son) in the human (taken from a routine autopsy specimen). Scale bar = 10 μm.* **(c)** *and* **(d)** *compare parvocellular NP neurons in the bed nucleus of the stria terminalis (bnst) with magnocellular NP neurons in the hypothalamic paraventricular nucleus (pvn) in a colchicine-treated rat. Scale bar = 30 μm.* **(a)** *and* **(b)** *reprinted from Ref. 29 with permission.*

TABLE I. Distribution of vasopressin and oxytocin fibers in the brain and spinal cord

Area	Vasopressin	Oxytocin
I. Forebrain		
Anterior hippocampus		•
Frontal cortex (including piriform, cingulate and entorhinal cortex)	•	•
N. accumbens	•	•
N. tractus diagonalis Broca	+ +	•
Lateral septum	+ + + +	•
N. interstitialis stria terminalis	+	•
Central, anterior, basal, cortical and lateral amygdala	+	+
Medial amygdala	+ +	+
Ventral hippocampus	+	+
Mediodorsal thalamus	+ + +	•
Lateral habenula	+ + + +	
Posterior periventricular hypothalamus	+ + +	
N. supramammillaris	•	+
II. Midbrain		
Substantia nigra pars compacta	+ +	+ + + +
Ventral tegmental area	+	+ +
Central grey area	+	+
N. raphe dorsalis	+	+
N. interpeduncularis	•	+
N. cuneiformis	•	+
N. parabrachialis dorsalis	+	+ +
N. parabrachialis ventralis	•	+
Locus coeruleus	+	+
N. raphe pontis	•	•
III. Hindbrain		
N. raphe magnus	+	+ +
N. raphe obscurus	•	•

N. tractus solitarius	+ +	+ + + +
N. dorsalis nervi vagi	+ +	+ + + +
N. reticularis lateralis	+	+ +
Substantia gelatinosa trigemini	•	+
IV. Spinal cord		
Laminae I–III	•	+
Lamina X	+	+ +
N. intermediolateralis	•	+

⅓ Indicates regular presence of a few fibers and possibly terminals.
+ Indicates regular presence of a number of fibers and/or terminals.
+ +–+ + + + Indicate increasing density of fibers and/or terminals.

density of fibers or terminals within the different areas varies considerably from single isolated fibers as seen in the neocortex to very dense innervation as found in the solitary nucleus and dorsal vagal nucleus in the medulla oblongata. The ratio of vasopressin to oxytocin fibers also varies in different areas (see Ref. 26).

Central distribution of vasopressin and oxytocin as determined by radioimmunoassay

Several studies have examined the distribution of vasopressin and oxytocin in the brains or spinal cords of normal rats[9,11] and humans[12,22] by radio-immunoassay of the peptides in extracted tissue homogenates. Compared with immunohistochemistry, this type of determination allows a more quantitative comparison of different regions or between different groups of specimens in exper-imental studies, but does not allow differentiation of the structures contain-ing the peptides. Thus the results ob-tained with the two procedures can be used to complement each other. In general, the results obtained by radio-immunoassay are very similar to those obtained by immunohistochemistry.

Major areas in which high concentrations of the peptides have been found by radioimmunoassay in the human as well as the rat include the septum, amygdala, hippocampus, medial thalamus, sub-stantia nigra, locus coeruleus, nucleus of the solitary tract, dorsal vagal nucleus, spinal cord and trigeminal substantia gelatinosa and spinal cord intermedio-lateral nucleus.

Nature of the terminals

In neural target areas, immunohisto-chemically stained fibers or terminals can often be seen contacting neuronal cell bodies (counterstained with a Nissl stain) or proximal processes. In fortunate preparations, terminals can clearly be seen lining perikarya or dendrites even in human specimens (Fig. 5). The nature of the contacts thus visualized is in most cases not certain since light microscopy does not provide adequate resolution. However, in some areas vasopressin and oxytocin have been identified in pre-synaptic structures using immunohisto-chemistry at the electron-microscope level[6].

Established projections

Given several types of vasopressin and

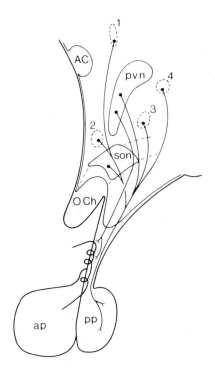

Fig. 3. *Sagittal view of the human hypothalamus and pituitary depicting the vascular projections of hypothalamic vasopressin and oxytocin neurons as established by experimental techniques. As described in detail in the text, most vasopressin and oxytocin neurons in the supraoptic nucleus (son), rostral part of the paraventricular nucleus (pvn) and various accessory nuclei (1–4) project to the posterior pituitary. In addition, some vasopressin neurons in the paraventricular nucleus project to hypophyseal portal capillaries in the infundibulum. OCh = optic chiasm.*

oxytocin neurons in groups distributed in different locations and an extensive network of vasopressin and oxytocin fibers in various vascular and neural target areas, it becomes important to establish which group gives rise to which set of terminals. This has been approached with lesion studies or studies combining immunohistochemistry with tract tracing. Lesion studies have established that the vasopressin terminals contacting the hypophyseal portal capillaries in the median eminence derive from the paraventricular nucleus in both monkeys and rats[1,31]. The vasopressin released from

these terminals may be involved in regulation of adenohypophyseal adrenocorticotropic hormone (ACTH) secretion (see Ref. 26) and thus originates from the same nucleus in which separate neurons producing corticotropin-releasing hormone are located[4]. Immunohistochemistry combined with retrograde tract tracing has been used to examine which vasopressin and oxytocin neurons project to the posterior pituitary, and which project to several brain areas (see Ref. 26). These findings are summarized in Figs 3 and 4. Although much work remains to be done in analysing the projections of various groups of vasopressin and oxytocin neurons, a few basic tendencies can be summarized as follows. Vasopressin and oxytocin neurons in the supraoptic nucleus appear to project primarily if not exclusively to the posterior pituitary. The posterior pituitary also receives vasopressin and oxytocin projections from part of the paraventricular nucleus and from many accessory magnocellular groups. The paraventricular nucleus also sends a vasopressin projection to the hypophyseal portal capillaries in the median eminence as well as oxytocin and vasopressin projections to various areas in the CNS. In the paraventricular nucleus, the vasopressin and oxytocin neurons having vascular or neural projections appear for the most part to be different and located in different parts of the nucleus. The parvocellular vasopressin neurons in the suprachiasmatic nucleus do not project to the posterior pituitary and appear to have no vascular projections since no neurons are labelled in the nucleus following injection of tracer into the vascular system[3]. These neurons do project to at least two neural targets. The exact origin of the vasopressin and oxytocin fibres in many neural target areas is not yet certain, although the newly identified neurons outside the hypothalamus appear likely candidates for some projections. The presence of these neurons strongly sug-

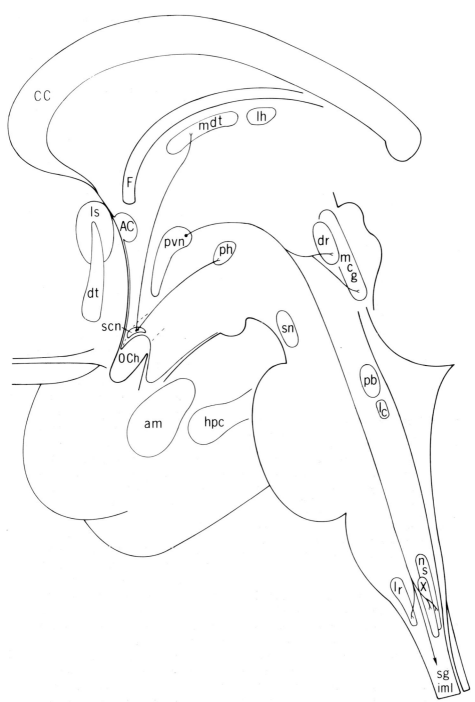

Fig. 4. *Sagittal view of the human brain depicting some of the major nuclear areas containing vasopressin and oxytocin fibers and terminals and showing some pathways established by experimental techniques. The anterior commissure (AC), corpus callosum (CC), fornix (F) and optic chiasm (OCh) are shown only as landmarks. The abbreviations of nuclear areas containing vasopressin and oxytocin fibres are as follows: am = amygdala; dr = dorsal raphe; dt = nucleus of the diagonal tract (Broca); hpc = hippocampus; iml = intermediolateral nucleus; lc = locus coeruleus; lh = lateral habenula; lr = lateral reticular nucleus; ls = lateral septum; mcg = mesencephalic central grey; mdt = mediodorsal thalamus; ns = nucleus of the solitary tract; pb = parabrachial nuclei; ph = periventricular posterior hypothalamus; sg = substantia gelatinosa; sn = substantia nigra; X = dorsal vagal nucleus. In some cases the vasopressin or oxytocin projections have been established as deriving from the paraventricular (pvn) or suprachiasmatic nuclei (scn) as shown. In the other cases it is not yet certain from where the projections derive.*

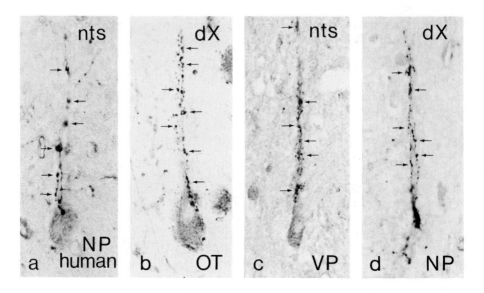

Fig. 5. *Photomicrographs of immunohistochemically stained vasopressin (VP), oxytocin (OT) or neurophysin (NP) terminals which line the dendrites and perikarya of neurons (counterstained with a Nissl stain) in the human nucleus of the solitary tract (nts) and dorsal vagal nucleus (dX) (taken from a routine autopsy specimen).* (a) *and* (b) *reprinted from Ref. 25 with permission.*

gests that not all extrahypothalamic vasopressin fibers are of hypothalamic origin as previously believed.

Functional implications

Although it is not possible in this context to discuss in detail the many possible functional implications presented by vasopressin or oxytocin projections to various areas in the CNS, a few examples are worth noting. Perhaps the most immediate question is what are these peptides doing at the cellular level? There is now good evidence that both vasopressin and oxytocin can specifically alter the electrical activity of neurons in various parts of the CNS where fibers containing these peptides are present[8,17,18]. Nevertheless, these peptides which function as hormones in the periphery might also be involved in influencing other aspects of neuronal activity. Biochemical studies have shown that these peptides can influence cAMP production[24] or can alter catecholamine turnover in specific brain areas[33].

On a broader scale, there is a large amount of experimental evidence that these peptides are involved in a variety of complex central functions. Much attention has been focused on the behavioural effects of administered vasopressin and oxytocin, particularly their effects on memory and learning[7,15] which have also been observed in clinical trials[10,15]. Since this area is of considerable interest it may be pointed out that vasopressin and oxytocin fibers are present in a number of brain areas thought to be involved in memory and other behavioural processes, including the hippocampus, septum, amygdala, neocortex and mediodorsal thalamus. Centrally administered vasopressin has also been shown to alter blood pressure[19], act as an antipyretic[14], and act as an analgesic[2]; there are potential morphological correlates for all of these activities. Thus vasopressin and oxytocin pathways are likely to be involved in functions as diverse as central autonomic regulation, nociception and behaviour. Lastly, it deserves mention that both vasopressin and oxytocin can be detected by radioimmunoassay in cerebrospinal fluid[13,20,21], which may some day find diagnostic application.

In conclusion, there is now ample evidence not only that vasopressin and oxytocin are distributed in specific projections throughout the mammalian CNS, but that these peptides influence the electrical or biochemical activity of local neurons and may be involved in various different centrally regulated functions. Thus, these peptides, which were originally isolated and characterized as circulating hormones, can be viewed as having an additional important role in influencing the activity of central neurons through direct projections to these neurons.

Acknowledgements

The author wishes to thank B. Archer, A. Barclay and J. Lloyd for photographic assistance, and P. Campbell for editorial assistance. Grant support was provided by NINCDS (NS06959).

Reading list

1 Antunes, J. L., Carmel, P. W. and Zimmerman, E. A. (1977) Brain Res. 137, 1–10
2 Berkowitz, B. A. and Sherman, S. (1982) J. Pharmacol. Exp. Ther. 220, 329–334
3 Broadwell, R. D. and Brightman, M. W. (1976) J. Comp. Neurol. 166, 257–284
4 Bugnon, C., Fellmann, D., Gouget, A. and Cardot, L. (1982) Neurosci. Lett. 30, 25–30
5 Buijs, R. M. (1980) J. Histochem. Cytochem. 28, 357–360
6 Buijs, R. M. and Swaab, D. F. (1979) Cell Tissue Res. 204, 355–365
7 De Wied, D. and Versteeg, D. H. G. (1979) Fed. Proc. Fed. Am. Soc. Exp. Biol. 38, 2348–2354
8 Gilbey, M. P., Coote, J. H., Fleetwood-Walker, S. and Peterson, D. F. (1982) Brain Res. 241, 43–48
9 Glick, S. M. and Brownstein, M. (1980) Life Sci. 27, 1103–1110
10 Gold, P. W., Ballenger, J. C., Weingartner, H., Goodwin, F. K. and Post, R. M. (1979) Lancet ii, 992–994
11 Hawthorn, J., Ang, V. T. Y. and Jenkins, J. S. (1980) Brain Res. 197, 75–81
12 Jenkins, J. S., Ang, V. T. Y., Hawthorn, J. and Rossor, M. N. (1983) in The Neurohypophysis: Structure, Function and Control (Progress in Brain Research, Vol. 60) (Cross, B. A. and Leng, G., eds), pp. 123–128, Elsevier, Amsterdam
13 Jenkins, J. S., Mather, H. M. and Ang, V. (1980) J. Clin. Endocrinol. Metab. 50, 364–367
14 Kasting, N. W., Veale, W. L. and Cooper, K. E. (1982) Neurosci. Biobehav. Rev. 6, 215–222
15 Koob, G. F. and Bloom, F. E. (1982) Annu. Rev. Physiol. 44, 571–582
16 Land, H., Schütz, G., Schmale, H. and Richter, D. (1982) Nature (London) 295, 299–303
17 Morris, R., Salt, T. E., Sofroniew, M. V. and Hill, R. G. (1980) Neurosci. Lett. 18, 163–168
18 Mühlethaler, M., Dreifuss, J. J. and Gähwiler, B. H. (1982) Nature (London) 296, 749–751
19 Pittman, Q. J., Lawrence, D. and McLean, L. (1982) Endocrinology 110, 1058–1060
20 Reppert, S. M., Schwartz, W. J., Artman, H. G. and Fisher, D. A. (1983) Brain Res. 261, 341–345
21 Robinson, I.C.A.F. and Jones, P. M. (1982) Neuroendocrinology 34, 59–63
22 Rossor, M. N., Iversen, L. L., Hawthorn, J., Ang, V. T. Y. and Jenkins, J. S. (1981) Brain Res. 214, 349–355
23 Russell, J. T., Brownstein, M. J. and Gainer, H. (1980) Endocrinology 107, 1880–1891
24 Schneider, D. R., Felt, B. T. and Goldman, H. (1982) Pharmacol. Biochem. Behav. 16, 139–143
25 Sofroniew, M. V. (1980) J. Histochem. Cytochem. 28, 475–478
26 Sofroniew, M. V. (1983) in The Neurohypophysis: Structure, Function and Control (Progress in Brain Research, Vol. 60) (Cross, B. A. and Leng, G., eds), pp. 101–114, Elsevier, Amsterdam
27 Sofroniew, M. V. and Glasmann, W. (1981) Neuroscience 6, 619–643
28 Sofroniew, M. V. and Schrell, U. (1981) Neurosci. Lett. 22, 211–217
29 Sofroniew, M. V. and Weindl, A. (1980) J. Comp. Neurol. 193, 659–675
30 Swanson, L. W. and Sawchenko, P. E. (1983) Annu. Rev. Neurosci. 6, 269–324
31 Vandesande, F., Dierickx, K. and De Mey, J. (1977) Cell Tissue Res. 180, 443–452
32 Van Leeuwen, F. and Caffé, R. (1983) Cell Tissue Res. 228, 525–534
33 Versteeg, D. H. G., De Kloet, E. R., Van Wimersma Greidanus, T. and De Wied, D. (1979) Neurosci. Lett. 11, 69–73

Michael V. Sofroniew is at the Department of Human Anatomy, University of Oxford, South Parks Road, Oxford OX1 3QX, UK.

NPY – a new member of the pancreatic polypeptide family

P. C. Emson and M. E. De Quidt

Neuropeptide Y (NPY), a thirty-six amino acid peptide with a characteristic carboxy-terminal tyrosine amide group, is one of the most widespread of neuronal peptides. In the CNS the peptide is found in neurons from cerebral cortex to spinal cord, occurring in cerebral cortical and basal ganglia interneurons, hypothalamic arcuate neurons, and catecholamine neurons of the central adrenergic cell groups. Outside the CNS, NPY-containing neurons constitute a distinct group in the enteric nervous system (PP cells) and throughout the periphery NPY is found in adrenergic nerves innervating both non-vascular and vascular smooth muscle. The effects of NPY on cerebral and peripheral vessels are striking and NPY is among the most potent vasoconstrictor peptides so far isolated. It is likely that NPY and noradrenaline released together contribute to the vasoconstrictor, hypertensive effects of sympathetic nerve stimulation. However, the physiological role of NPY in the majority of non-adrenergic NPY-containing neurons is completely unknown.

Avian pancreatic polypeptide (APP), the first member of the pancreatic polypeptide family, was isolated from chicken pancreas as a by-product of insulin purification[15,16]. Subsequently, homologous peptides were found in the islets of Langerhans of all mammalian species investigated[17] (Table I). Since several gastrointestinal peptides also occur in the brain (for example vasoactive intestinal polypeptide and cholecystokinin), it was logical to look for pancreatic polypeptide-like peptides in the mammalian CNS. Encouraging results were

TABLE I. Amino acid sequences of NPY and related pancreatic polypeptides

	1	2	3	4	5	6	7	8	9	10	11	12	13	14	15	16	17	18
NPY	Tyr	**Pro**	**Ser**	Lys	**Pro**	Asp	Asn	**Pro**	**Gly**	Glu	**Asp**	**Ala**	**Pro**	Ala	**Glu**	**Asp**	**Leu**	Ala
PYY	Tyr	Pro	Ala	Lys	Pro	Glu	Ala	Pro	Gly	Glx	Asx	Ala	Ser	Pro	Glx	Glx	Leu	Ser
APP	Gly	**Pro**	**Ser**	Gln	**Pro**	Thr	Tyr	**Pro**	**Gly**	Asp	**Asp**	**Ala**	**Pro**	Val	**Glu**	**Asp**	**Leu**	Ile
HPP	Ala	Pro	Leu	Glu	Pro	Val	Tyr	Pro	Gly	Asp	Asn	Ala	Thr	Pro	Glu	Gln	Met	Ala
PPP	Ala	Pro	Leu	Glu	Pro	Val	Tyr	Pro	Gly	Asp	Asn	Ala	Thr	Pro	Glu	Gln	Met	Ala

	19	20	21	22	23	24	25	26	27	28	29	30	31	32	33	34	35	36
NPY	**Arg**	Tyr	**Tyr**	Ser	Ala	**Leu**	Arg	His	**Tyr**	Ile	**Asn**	Leu	Ile	**Thr**	**Arg**	Gln	**Arg**	**Tyr**-NH2
PYY	Arg	Tyr	Tyr	Ala	Ser	Leu	Arg	His	Tyr	Leu	Asn	Leu	Val	Thr	Arg	Gln	Arg	Tyr-NH2
APP	**Arg**	Phe	**Tyr**	Asp	Asn	**Leu**	Gln	Gln	**Tyr**	Leu	**Asn**	Val	Val	**Thr**	**Arg**	His	**Arg**	**Tyr**-NH2
HPP	Gln	Tyr	Ala	Ala	Asp	Leu	Arg	Arg	Tyr	Ile	Asn	Met	Leu	Thr	Arg	Pro	Arg	Tyr-NH2
PPP	Gln	Tyr	Ala	Ala	Glu	Leu	Arg	Arg	Tyr	Ile	Asn	Met	Leu	Thr	Arg	Pro	Arg	Tyr-NH2

Abbreviations: NPY = neuropeptide Y; PYY = peptide YY; APP = avian pancreatic polypeptide; HPP = human pancreatic polypeptide; PPP = porcine pancreatic polypeptide. Amino acids common to APP and NPY are in bold.

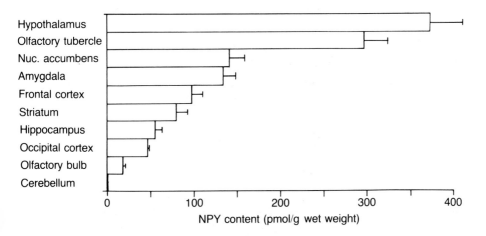

Fig. 1. *Regional distribution of NPY-like immunoreactivity in the forebrain of the rat.*

obtained using an APP-directed anti-serum[18], where a number of positive neurons and their processes were visualized by immunocytochemistry. This was reasonable evidence that the mammalian brain contained peptide(s) belonging to the pancreatic polypeptide family. Thus, following this lead, several groups attempted the characterization of this peptide immunoreactivity using pancreatic polypeptide-directed radioimmunoassays. Unfortunately, despite the striking histochemical staining which suggested an abundant CNS peptide, radioimmunoassays of brain extracts detected at most only trace amounts of immunoreactive material. This problem was fortunately soon resolved when Tatemoto and Mutt[27] reported that porcine brain and gut contained large amounts of a pancreatic polypeptide-like peptide whose amino acid sequence contained an amino-terminal tyrosine residue, and a carboxy-terminal tyrosine amide. The peptide was named PYY (peptide YY, since it has tyrosine at both amino- and carboxy-terminals, Y being the abbreviation for tyrosine in the single letter amino acid code). The carboxy-terminal tyrosine-amide was critical to its chemical identification[26]. Originally, PYY was thought to be present in both brain and gut, but sub-sequent work by Tatemoto and colleagues demonstrated that the brain pancreatic polypeptide-like peptide differed slightly from PYY (see Table I) and was thus called neuropeptide Y (NPY)[25].

Following the availability of pig NPY for the production of antibodies and development of radioimmunoassays, several groups have reported the presence of NPY-like immunoreactivity in many regions of the mammalian nervous system[3,23,24] (Fig. 1). This distribution is in good agreement with previous immunohistochemical observations using APP-directed antibodies[18]. It now seems clear that there was sufficient sequence homology between APP and NPY to allow APP-directed antisera to be used to visualize NPY histochemically, despite the absence of any significant cross-reactivity in radioimmunoassays.

NPY-positive neurons are found throughout the central and peripheral nervous systems (Figs 2 and 3). In the rat visual cortex, NPY neurons constitute approximately 2–3% of the total number of neurons, with the majority being non-pyramidal cell types, including bipolar and multipolar classes (Fig. 2c). In the cerebral cortex and basal ganglia the morphology and distribution of the NPY-containing neurons correspond

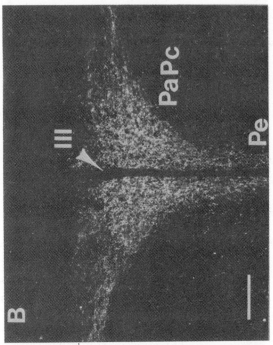

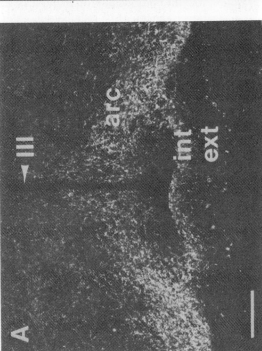

Fig. 2. *Immunocytochemical localization of NPY-like immunoreactivity in the rat brain.* (**A,B**) *Dark-field photomicrographs of the rat hypothalamus to show the localization of reactive terminals in:* (**A**) *the arcuate nucleus – median eminence; and* (**B**) *the paraventricular nucleus.* (**C,D,E**) *Bright-field photomicrographs to show the presence of NPY-like immunoreactivity in:* (**C**) *a visual cortex bipolar neuron (note the major ascending and descending dendrites); and* (**D**) *and* (**E**) *medium-sized neurons of the rat striatum. Cell sections were processed using Sternberger's peroxidase–antiperoxidase technique*[22].

Abbreviations used in (**A**): *III = third ventricle; arc = arcuate nucleus; int and ext = internal and external layers of the median eminence, respectively. Scale bar = 225 μm.*

Abbreviations used in (**B**): *III = third ventricle; PaPc = parvocellular paraventricular hypothalamic nucleus; Pe = periventricular hypothalamic nucleus. Scale bar = 225μm.*

Abbreviations used in (**C**): *III and IV = third and fourth layers of the cerebral cortex, respectively.*

In (**C**), (**D**) *and* (**E**)*, scale bar = 10 μm.*

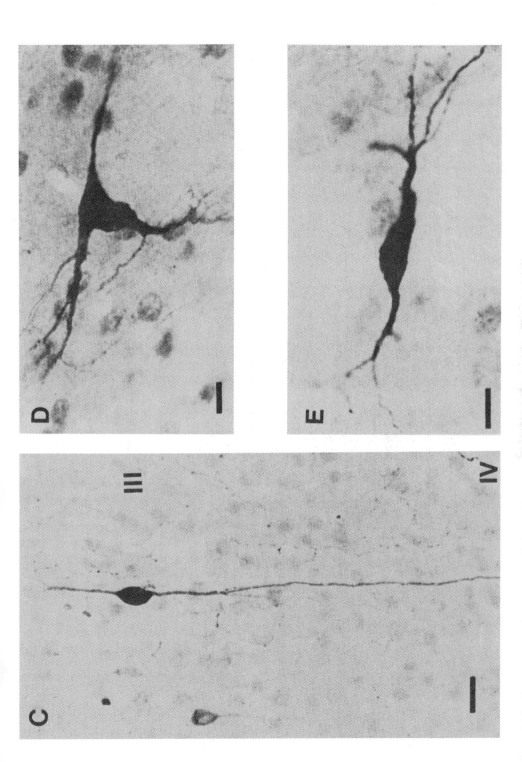

closely to somatostatin-containing neurons, and the coexistence of APP-like immunoreactivity (i.e. NPY) with somatostatin in these regions had already been described[28,29]. At the moment it is not known whether every telencephalic cell that contains NPY also contains somatostatin. In the rat, striatal NPY-containing cells correspond to medium-sized neurons (Fig. 2d,e), and in the human caudate nucleus these cells are relatively preserved in Huntington's disease, so that the NPY content has been found to increase in parallel with that of somatostatin[5], in the caudate nucleus of patients who died with Huntington's disease. In the diencephalon, the hypothalamus is rich in NPY-like immunoreactivity (Fig. 2a,b) including a group of neurons in the arcuate region. The thalamus, by comparison, contains only a few NPY-positive neurons and only a patchy distribution of fibres.

Two major groups of NPY-containing neurons are found in the spinal cord, in the substantia gelatinosa (interneurons, layers I and II) and in the ventral region of sacral cord where NPY may coexist with enkephalin-like immunoreactivity in neurons innervating the pelvic region[14,19]

Of major interest has been the observation of NPY coexistence with catecholamines in both central and peripheral neurons[12,13,21]. Investigation of the sympathetic nervous system using NPY-directed antisera has revealed numerous NPY-positive neurons in superior cervical, stellate and coeliac ganglia[21]. Removal of the appropriate ganglion resulted in a parallel depletion of both NPY and catecholamine-containing terminals from the innervated tissue[21]. This can be demonstrated well in the guinea-pig gut, where a population of noradrenergic fibres contain NPY-like immunoreactivity (Fig. 3a). Treatment of the guinea-pig with the catecholamine neurotoxin 6-hydroxydopamine, or with reserpine which depletes catecholamine stores also depletes NPY-containing

sympathetic fibres of their peptide immunoreactivity (Fig. 3b,c). However, these drugs are without apparent effect on the majority of NPY-containing cells in the gut submucosa, where the peptide does not coexist with catecholamines[9,24] (Fig. 3b,c). It is not known at present whether the reserpine-induced NPY depletion is a secondary depletion of peptide following increased impulse flow in the nerve, or because the peptide is co-stored with the catecholamine in storage granules.

In the myenteric plexus of the guinea-pig NPY-reactive cell bodies constitute approximately 5% of all neurons, whilst in the submucous ganglion, NPY re-activity is found in some 20% of all neurons[9,24] (Fig. 3a,b). The myenteric NPY neurons connect to more caudally situated myenteric ganglia and also innervate the circular muscle, whilst the cells in submucous ganglion innervate the mucosa. No physiological role has yet been ascribed to these NPY-containing gut neurons.

NPY-containing sympathetic neurons innervate heart, gut, the respiratory tract and the urogenital tract, but the greatest interest so far has been in the innervation of vascular smooth muscle (Figs 3 and 4). Two studies have demonstrated a very potent vasoconstriction of vessels following NPY (and PYY) application[7,20]. Cat cerebral vessels responded to NPY with a slow contraction[7], which was abolished in the presence of verapamil, a calcium channel-blocking agent, indicating a calcium dependence (Fig. 5). This NPY-induced slow contraction was in contrast to the rapid contraction produced by potassium depolarization[7]. As predicted from the distribution of NPY-like immunoreactivity, NPY produced a dose-dependent contraction of arteries and arterioles[7,20], but had no effect on veins, which are not innervated. Similarly, Lundberg and Tatemoto[20] demonstrated a slowly developing vasoconstriction in the cat submandibular gland following local

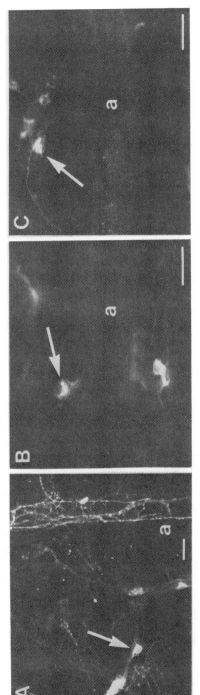

Fig. 3. *Vascular NPY-containing noradrenergic nerves are depleted of NPY by 6-hydroxydopamine (6-OHDA) or reserpine.* (**A**) *Whole-mount of submucosa of normal guinea-pig small intestine, showing NPY nerves with a submucous arteriole (a) and NPY in submucosal nerve cell bodies (for example, see arrow).* (**B**) *After 6-OHDA (doses of 300 and 200 mg kg^{-1} given 7 and 2 days beforehand), NPY nerves with arterioles (a) are depleted, and submucous nerve cell bodies are unaffected (arrow).* (**C**) *2 days after reserpine (4 mg kg^{-1}) there is also depletion of arteriolar nerves (a). Scale bar = 50 μm.* *(Micrographs are from the investigations of J. B. Furness and M. Costa.)*

intra-arterial PYY and NPY infusion, with no effect on salivary secretion. Only combined infusions of noradrenaline and NPY caused a vascular response which was similar to that seen upon sympathetic nerve stimulation. Systemic administration of NPY induced a long-lasting increase in arterial blood pressure, indicating a general vasoconstriction. In the study of Lundberg and Tatemoto[20], NPY and especially PYY were particularly potent in eliciting vasoconstriction with a threshold for response of 10^{-9} M which is of the same order of potency as angiotensin II. In the normal mammal, however, it is unlikely that the NPY levels circulating in plasma are sufficient to cause a general vasoconstriction (although this does not eliminate the possibility of local vascular effects at sites of release), but plasma samples from patients with tumours of the sympathetically derived adrenal medulla cells (phaeochromocytomas), contained greatly elevated NPY levels[1]. In these patients the elevated NPY levels may well contribute to the hypertension characteristic of the condition and measurement of NPY may prove to be of diagnostic value.

In the rat and human CNS, NPY reactivity is also found in some central adrenergic neurons including, in the rat, NPY-containing cells in the locus coeruleus and the dorsal medullary and lateral tegmental cell groups of Dahlström and Fuxe[6 8,20]. These neurons may contain either adrenaline or noradrenaline. However, a recent study demonstrated that NPY is found mainly in those cells containing the noradrenaline-methylating enzyme (PNMT), suggesting that the neurons concerned contain adrenaline[8,13]. These adrenaline-containing cells have been implicated in the central regulation of blood pressure[11]. Investigation of the effects of intracisternal NPY administration showed that NPY had a marked hypotensive action, which mimics that of adrenaline[10].

Further evidence that NPY and adrenergic function may be closely related has come from a study of NPY interactions with adrenergic receptors

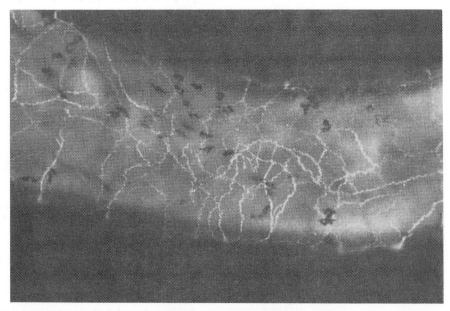

Fig. 4. *Immunocytochemical demonstration of perivascular NPY-containing nerve fibres in the wall of a cat pial artery. Note the dense and delicate network of perivascular fibres, showing a ground plexus. The black cells are melanocytes. Magnification: ×150.* (L. Edvinsson.)

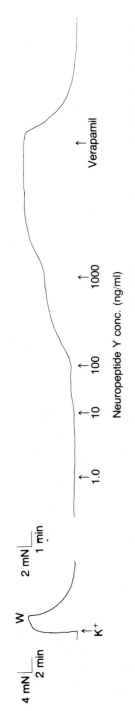

Fig. 5. *Contractile effect of 124 mM potassium (K^+) and NPY in increasing concentrations. The NPY-induced contraction was easily abolished by administration of 10^{-5} M verapamil (a calcium-influx blocker). Abbreviations: W = washout; mN = millinewtons. The experiment was performed in cat middle cerebral artery.* (L. Edvinsson.)

using synaptic membrane binding assays. Initial results indicated an NPY-induced increase in the number of α_2-adreno-receptor sites in membranes prepared from normotensive rats, with no effect on such membranes from spontaneously hypertensive rats[4].

Apart from the vascular smooth muscle sympathetic innervation where noradrenaline and NPY coexist, nor-adrenaline- and NPY-containing fibres innervate smooth muscle in the urino-genital tract including the vas deferens and uterus[21,23]. In both these tissues NPY is able to block electrically induced contraction apparently acting to inhibit acetylcholine (in the uterus)[23] or nor-adrenaline release (in the vas de-ferens)[2,21]. In the vas deferens the potent effects of NPY on noradrenaline release may provide a local inhibitory feedback loop. The effects of NPY on smooth muscle are the best established physiological effects of a widespread and interesting peptide. The presence of the peptide in a variety of interneurons in higher brain regions such as the cerebral cortex may perhaps implicate it in higher cognitive functions, but these remain to be established.

Acknowledgements

We are indebted to Drs John Furness and Marcello Costa for the provision of Fig. 3 and to Dr Lars Edvinsson for Figs 4 and 5. We also wish to thank Dr Kazuhiko Tatemoto for encouraging our work on NPY.

Reading list

1 Adrian, T. E., Terenghi, G., Brown, M. J., Allen, J. M., Bacarese-Hamilton, A. J., Polak, J. M. and Bloom, S. R. (1983) *Lancet* ii, 540–543
2 Allen, J. M., Adrian, T. E., Tatemoto, K., Polak, J. M., Hughes, J. and Bloom, S. R. (1982) *Neuropeptides* 3, 71–77
3 Allen, Y. S., Adrian, T. E., Allen, J. M., Tatemoto, K., Crow, T. J., Bloom, S. R. and Polak, J. M. (1983) *Science* 221, 877–879
4 Battistini, M., Agnati, L. F., Fuxe, K., Benfenati, F., Cavicchioli, L., Härfstrand, A., Mutt, V. and Tatemoto, K. (1983) *Acta Physiol. Scand.* 118, 293–295
5 Copper, P. E., Aronin, N., Bird, E. D.,

Leeman, S. E. and Martin, J. B. (1981) *Neurology* 31, 64

6 Dahlström, A. and Fuxe, K. (1964) *Acta Physiol. Scand.* 62 (Suppl. 232), 1–55

7 Edvinsson, L., Emson, P. C., McCulloch, J., Tatemoto, K. and Uddman, R. *Neurosci. Lett.* (in press)

8 Everitt, B. J., Hökfelt, T., Terenius, L., Tatemoto, K., Mutt, V. and Goldstein, M. *Neuroscience* (in press)

9 Furness, J. B., Costa, M., Emson, P. C., Håkanson, R., Moghimzadeh, E., Sundler, F., Taylor, I. L. and Chance, R. E. (1983) *Cell Tissue Res.* 234, 71–92

10 Fuxe, K., Agnati, L. F., Härfstrand, A., Zini, I., Tatemoto, K., Pich, E. M., Hökfelt, T., Mutt, V. and Terenius, L. (1983) *Acta Physiol. Scand.* 118, 189–192

11 Fuxe, K., Bolme, P., Agnati, L. F., Jonsson, G., Andersson, K., Kohler, C. and Hökfelt, T. (1980) in *Central Adrenaline Neurons (Wenner-Gren International Symposium Series, Vol. 33)* (Fuxe, K., Goldstein, M., Hökfelt, B. and Hökfelt, T., eds), pp. 161–182, Pergamon Press, Oxford

12 Hökfelt, T., Lundberg, J. M., Lagercrantz, H., Tatemoto, K., Mutt, V., Lindberg, J., Terenius, L., Everitt, B., Fuxe, K., Agnati, L. and Goldstein, M. (1983) *Neurosci. Lett.* 36, 217–222

13 Hökfelt, T., Lundberg, J. M., Tatemoto, K., Mutt, V., Terenius, L., Polak, J., Bloom, S., Sasek, C., Elde, R. and Goldstein, M. (1983) *Acta Physiol. Scand.* 117, 315–318

14 Hunt, S. P., Emson, P. C., Gilbert, R., Goldstein, M. and Kimmel, J. R. (1981) *Neurosci. Lett.* 21, 125–130

15 Kimmel, J. R., Hayden, L. J. and Pollock, H. G. (1975) *J. Biol. Chem.* 250, 9369–9376

16 Kimmel, J. R., Pollock, H. G. and Hazelwood, R. L. (1968) *Endocrinology* 83, 1323–1330

17 Lin, T. M. and Chance, R. E. (1974) in *Endocrinology of the Gut* (Chey, W.-Y. and Brooks, F. P., eds), pp. 143–145, C. R. Slack, New Jersey

18 Loren, I., Alumets, J., Håkanson, R. and Sundler, F. (1979) *Cell Tissue Res.* 200, 179–186

19 Lundberg, J. M., Hökfelt, T., Anggard, A., Kimmel, J., Goldstein, M. and Markey, K. (1980) *Acta Physiol. Scand.* 110, 107–109

20 Lundberg, J. M. and Tatemoto, K. (1982) *Acta Physiol. Scand.* 116, 393–402

21 Lundberg, J. M., Terenius, L., Hökfelt, T., Martling, C. R., Tatemoto, K., Mutt, V., Polak, J., Bloom, S. and Goldstein, M. (1982) *Acta Physiol. Scand.* 116, 477–480

22 Sternberger, L. A. (1974) *Immunocytochemistry*, Prentice-Hall, New Jersey

23 Stjernquist, M., Emson, P., Owman, Ch., Sjöberg, N.-O., Sundler, F. and Tatemoto, K. (1983) *Neurosci. Lett.* 39, 279–284

24 Sundler, F., Moghimzadeh, E., Håkanson, R., Ekelund, M. and Emson, P. (1983) *Cell Tissue Res.* 230, 487–493

25 Tatemoto, K., Carlquist, M. and Mutt, V. (1982) *Nature (London)* 296, 659–660

26 Tatemoto, K. and Mutt, V. (1978) *Proc. Natl Acad. Sci. USA* 75, 4115–4119

27 Tatemoto, K. and Mutt, V. (1980) *Nature (London)* 285, 417–418

28 Vincent, S. R., Johansson, O., Hökfelt, T., Meyerson, B., Sachs, C., Elde, R. P., Terenius, L. and Kimmel, J. (1982) *Nature (London)* 298, 65–67

29 Vincent, S. R., Skirboll, L., Hökfelt, T., Johansson, O., Lundberg, J. M., Elde, R. P., Terenius, L. and Kimmel, J. (1982) *Neuroscience* 7, 439–446

P. C. Emson and M. E. De Quidt are at the MRC Neurochemical Pharmacology Unit, Medical Research Council Centre, Medical School, Hills Road, Cambridge CB2 2QH, UK.

Index

A

Acetylcholinesterase (AChE) –
  in Alzheimer's disease; 298, 301
  localisation; 309, 312, 314
  specificity; 211
Acetylcholine receptor –
  channel lifetime; 48, 53
  in vertebrate heart; 75, 79, 121
  localisation; 315, 319
  muscarinic; 49, 55, 59, 65, 79, 114, 254
  nicotinic; 55, 65, 91, 95
Acetylcholine synthesis; 309
Acetylcholine synthesis in Alzheimer's disease; 298
ACTH –
  co-release with β-endorphin; 203
  isolation from pituitary; 27
  peptide precursor; 188, 195, 203, 227
Action potential –
  calcium dependent; 138, 217, 221
  modulation of cardiac potential; 82, 136
Adenylate cyclase –
  dopamine, activation by; 242, 249
  opioids, inhibition by; 216
Adrenergic receptors, activation of second messengers in heart; 78
Alzheimer's disease –
  morphological changes; 298
  neurochemical changes; 298, 316
  treatment; 262, 299, 301
Aminopeptidases; 210
Amnesia –
  see also memory
  in parkinsonism; 262, 271
  morphological changes; 299
Amphetamine –
  parkinsonism and; 262, 271
  schizophrenia and; 279
Analgesia –
  by opiates; 211, 214, 220
  involvement of substance P; 167, 170
Angiotensin metabolism; 211
Antidiuretic hormone, see Vasopressin
Antipsychotic drugs –
  blockade of dopamine receptors; 290
  incidence of remissions; 270
  treatment of parkinsonism; 270, 279, 286
Aplysia –
  effect of peptides on egg laying behaviour; 123
  5-HT sensitive K$^+$ channels; 87
Apomorphine –
  binding sites; 247
  treatment of parkinsonism; 262

ATP, as a transmitter; 119
Atropine –
  block of slow cholinergic excitation; 56, 59, 66
  effect on gut motility; 143
Autonomic ganglia, see also Parasympathetic and Sympathetic ganglia
Autonomic ganglia –
  action of capsaicin; 183
  action of substance P; 147
  slow excitatory cholinergic synapses; 55, 66
Autoradiography –
  demonstration of neurohormones; 136, 231
  determining cDNA nucleotide sequences; 37
  localization of cDNA: mRNA; 229
  localization of opiate receptors; 202, 206
Autoreceptors –
  see also Presynaptic receptors
  cholinergic; 315
  dopaminergic; 246, 244

B

Butyrophenone, binding sites; 246, 244
Bag cells, isolation of peptides; 124
Benzodiazepine, mechanism of action; 52, 239

C

Calcium –
  action potentials; 138, 217, 221, 224
  control by isoproterenol; 89
  regulation of potassium channels; 58, 61, 82
  rôle in cardiac cycle; 75
  regulation of NPY-induced contraction; 342
  voltage-sensitive channels; 217
Capsaicin –
  action on neurons; 166, 171, 174, 180, 181, 183
  action on deafferented skin and ileum; 181
  chemical structure; 180
Cardiac potential –
  ionic basis; 75
  pharmacology; 66, 68, 83
cDNA –
  recombinant DNA techniques; 34, 126, 159, 188, 194, 226
  synthesis; 28, 34, 126, 159, 229
Chromaffin cells –
  neuromodulation; 66
  transplantation in parkinsonism; 264
Cholecystokinin (CCK) –
  amino acid sequence; 27
  biological action; 28, 234
  localisation; 105, 109, 174, 325
  protein precursor; 27, 28, 45

Choline acetyl-transferase –
    decline in dementia; 316
    inhibition by choline mustards; 315
Cloning, recombinant DNA techniques; 34, 126, 159
Co-existence –
    ATP and classical transmitters; 119
    peptides and classical transmitters; 98, 105, 203
Complementary DNA see cDNA
Curare, action of sympathetic neurons; 56, 67
Cyclic AMP –
    action of dopamine; 231, 242
    action of 5-HT; 87, 139
    action of noradrenaline; 324
    action of octopamine; 139
    action of opioids; 216
    action of prolactin; 139
    control of K^+ channels; 62, 87
    dependent protein kinases; 77, 78, 84
    action on the heart; 79

D

Deafferentation –
    of cortex; 233
    of ileum; 181
    of skin; 181
Degeneration –
    of primary afferent neurons; 183
    in the cortex; 262, 277, 298
Dementia –
    decline of CAT; 316
    morphological changes; 299
    similarity to schizophrenia; 279
Denervation supersensitivity, see also Supersensitivity
Desensitisation –
    to ACh; 49
    to capsaicin; 181, 184
Diabetes, levels of vasopressin; 305
Digestion, hormonal control; 27, 28
Dopamine –
    antipsychotic drugs and release; 294
    in tardive dyskinesia; 271
    in schizophrenia; 271, 286
    regulation of gene expression; 229
    regulation of peptide release; 228, 244
    regulation of release; 292, 295
    stimulation of cAMP; 242, 271
    supersensitivity; 238, 253, 263, 272, 275
    synthesis; 233, 271
Dopamine receptors –
    classification; 236, 242, 243
    localization; 242, 246, 290, 319
    in Parkinson's disease; 254, 262, 271
    proliferation in schizophrenia; 282, 286
    stress; 238
    supersensitivity; 238, 254, 263, 273, 275

L-DOPA, treatment of Parkinson's disease; 257
L-Dopa therapy –
    alternatives; 258
    'on-off' effects; 257

E

Electroencephalogram (EEG), in schizophrenia; 287
Electromyogram, in Parkinson's disease; 253
Endorphin –
    co-release with ACTH; 203
    isolation; 43
    protein precursor; 28, 188, 195, 227
Enkephalin –
    biological action; 220, 224
    changes following denervation; 106
    localisation; 32, 43, 105, 108
    metabolism; 209
    protein precursor; 32, 188, 194, 195
Enkephalinase, distribution; 212, 213
Escherichia coli, in production of cDNA clones; 35
EPSP –
    fast nicotinic; 56, 94
    ionic basis; 98
    slow GABAergic; 121
    slow muscarinic; 56, 65, 77,
    slow peptidergic; 59, 60, 71, 95, 129, 138, 163, 166
    slow serotoninergic; 138
Excitatory post-synaptic potentials, see EPSP

F

Fluctuation analysis –
    analysis of neurotransmitter action; 52
    in identification of neurotransmitters; 53

G

GABA –
    action on dopaminergic neurones; 292
    localisation in CNS; 105
    potentiation of response; 52
GABA receptor –
    damage in tardive dyskinesia; 275
    ion channel; 52, 53, 121
Gastrin –
    amino acid sequence; 27
    DNA cloning; 36
Glutamate –
    action on locus coeruleus; 171
    receptor ion channel; 49, 53
Glucagon, localisation; 42
Grafting, intracerebral; 261

H

Heart –
    effect of benzomorphans; 205
    effect of capsaicin; 182

ionic basis of contraction; 75
   regulation of heartbeat; 66, 75, 83, 136, 342
   sensitivity to Ca^{2+}; 66, 75
Histamine –
   localisation in cortex; 319
   mechanism of action; 324
   release by injury; 176
Homarus, see also Lobster
Hormone synthesis; 226
Horseradish peroxidase (HRP) –
   demonstration of cholinergic neurones; 314
   staining of C fibres; 97
5-Hydroxytryptamine, *see* 5-HT
5-HT –
   induction of Ca^{2+} currents; 138
   localisation; 105, 109, 136, 319
   modulation of a K^+ current; 87
   modulation of glycogenolysis; 324
   modulation of posture; 135, 138
Hybridization histochemistry; 229
Hypothalamus –
   detection of gastrin; 28
   detection of opiate receptors; 202
   detection of opioids; 32, 191
Hypothermia, induction by capsaicin; 182

I

Immunohistochemistry, demonstration of amines;
   137, 290
Inhibitory post-synaptic potential, *see* IPSP
Ion channel –
   model; 85
   opening time; 50, 53, 85, 122
   multiple conductance states; 48, 84
IPSP –
   ionic basis; 70
   slow modulatory; 61, 70, 94, 121, 129, 217

L

Lecithin, treatment of Alzheimer's disease; 299,
   301
LHRH-like peptides –
   action of antagonists; 96, 101, 170
   antibody staining; 97
   neuromodulation; 62, 71
Lobsters, role of neurohormones in posture
   control; 135
Locus coeruleus neurones, action of opiates; 217,
   222

M

M currents, potentiation of the EPSP; 59
Melanocyte-stimulating hormone (MSH) –
   dopamine inhibition; 243
   distribution; 27
   protein precursor; 27, 31, 195, 227
Memory –
   determination by avoidance behaviour; 306

in Alzheimer's disease; 298
in schizophrenia; 280
role of vasopressin; 305
Mesocortico-prefrontal dopaminergic neurones;
   233
Messenger RNA –
   modulation by neurotransmitters; 228
   nucleotide sequences; 41
   production via cDNA clones; 34, 159
   translation of; 227
Monoamine oxidase in Parkinson's disease; 255,
   257
Monoclonal antibodies and peptide identification;
   43
Morphine –
   dependence; 204
   receptors; 201, 221, 223
   tolerance; 205

N

Neuroleptics
   action on dopamine receptors; 233, 238,
     273, 276
   neuronal degeneration; 273, 277
   tolerance; 238, 272
Neuromodulation –
   adrenergic; 66, 82, 89, 233
   cholinergic; 49, 56, 59, 66, 82, 94, 271
   dopaminergic; 83, 233
   GABAnergic; 52, 121, 271
   glutaminergic; 49
   purinergic; 121
   serotoninergic; 82, 83, 87, 138
Neuropeptides –
   amino acid sequences; 26, 123, 194, 204,
     338
   evolution of; 25
   localisation; 25, 99, 116, 126, 137, 155, 164,
     191, 325, 339
   metabolism; 209
Neuropeptide y (NPY) –
   amino acid sequence; 338
   localisation; 339
Neurotensin –
   location and isolation; 43, 105
   protein precursor; 27
Noradrenaline –
   action on cortex; 233, 324
   action on heart; 76, 78
   action of opiates on release; 224
   localisation; 105, 319

O

Octopamine, biological action; 135, 138
Opiate receptors –
   classification; 173, 191, 198, 201, 204, 216,
     223
   localization; 136, 202, 206

mechanism of action; 216, 220
molecular basis; 203
Opioids –
biological action; 191, 199, 201, 204, 211,
216, 220
dependence; 216, 217
distribution; 191
protein precursors; 32, 188, 194
Oxytocin –
biological activity; 41
localisation; 29, 329

P

Pain –
effect of opiate antagonists; 173, 192, 205,
214
effect of opioids; 211, 220, 224
rôle of substance P; 167, 170, 174
Pancreatic polypeptide, coexistence with
catecholamines; 115
Parasympathetic ganglia –
location of VIP; 114
synaptic modulation in; 61, 121
Parathyroid dopamine receptors; 243
Parkinson's disease –
pharmacology; 254, 262
treatment; 254, 257, 261, 270, 278
Patch clamp –
cholinergic desensitization; 49
identification of neurotransmitters; 53
neurotransmitter action; 51, 85, 122
Peptidase inhibitors; 210, 213
Peptides –
see also Neuropeptides
biological actions; 27, 28, 124, 147, 154,
166, 171, 201
coexistence with classical neurotransmitters;
98, 104
identification and isolation; 25, 41, 128, 201,
319, 324
mechanisms of action; 54
protein precursors; 27, 44, 123, 161, 188,
210, 226
release by capsaicin; 182
sequence of amino acids; 43
Peptide hormones, synthesis; 227
Phosphatidylcholine, see lecithin
Physalaemin –
chemical structure; 152
localisation; 42
Pituitary –
localisation of ACTH; 27, 188, 203
localisation of dopamine receptors; 244
localisation of endorphin; 203
localization of MSH; 27
localization of POMC; 188, 191, 203, 228,
230

localisation of somatotropin; 42
regulation of POMC gene; 226
regulation of prolactin release; 242, 243, 245
Pro-opiomelanocortin (POMC) –
location; 188
secretion; 228
synthesis; 227
Potassium channels –
calcium-dependent; 58, 61, 82
M currents; 59, 82, 102
regulation by ATP; 121, 122
regulation by 5-HT receptors; 87
regulation by opiate receptors; 217, 218,
221, 224
S current; 62, 87
voltage sensitivity; 55, 61
Presynaptic receptors –
acetylcholine; 315
dopamine; 234, 238, 244, 294
GABA; 139
5-HT; 109, 139
octopamine; 139
opiate; 217, 220
Proctolin –
biological action; 138
localisation; 136
regulation of release; 242, 244
Puromycin, action on aminopeptidases; 210

R

Retina –
defects in Parkinson's disease; 253
dopamine stimulated adenylate cyclase; 242
Recombinant DNA techniques, see cDNA
Reverse transcriptase, role in decoding DNA; 28,
32, 35

S

S currents, reduction by 5-HT; 87
Schizophrenia –
antipsychotic drugs; 270, 279, 286
causation; 285
classification; 283
interaction of dopamine and
cholecystokinin; 109
involvement of dopamine; 109, 233, 239,
243, 271, 282, 286
structural changes; 280, 281, 287
Secretin localisation; 42
Serotonin, see 5-HT
Skin, response to cold and injury; 174
Somatostatin –
coexistence with classical neurotransmitters;
106
influence of capsaicin; 181, 182

isolation; 105
protein precursor; 27
Somatotropin, location and isolation; 43
Striatum –
  damage by neuroleptics; 276
  dopamine stimulated adenylate cyclase; 242
  localisation of AChE; 314
  localization of dopamine receptors; 245,
    246, 250, 266, 290
  localisation of opiate receptors; 202
Stress –
  release of dopamine; 235, 238
  release of endorphin; 203
  release of substance P; 239
  release of POMC; 191
Substance P –
  antagonists; 167, 170, 171
  biological actions; 62, 147
  chemical structure; 163
  effect of capsaicin; 174, 181, 182
  evolution of; 27
  history; 143
  inactivation; 145, 148
  in parkinsonism; 254
  neurotoxicity; 172
  occurrence and distribution; 43, 105, 145,
    155, 174
  polypeptide precursors; 27, 157
  release by injury; 173
  stress and; 239
Supersensitivity –
  denervation; 51, 233, 238, 245, 262, 263,
    273, 275
  disuse; 273

Sympathetic ganglia –
  cholinergic neuromodulation; 56, 65, 70, 94,
    98, 120
  dopamine stimulated adenylate cyclase; 242
  peptidergic neuromodulation in; 59, 71, 94,
    98, 164, 186, 191, 242, 342
  purinergic neuromodulation; 120
Synaptic currents, analysis of channel lifetimes;
  53, 49
Synaptic transmission –
  coexistence of neurotransmitters; 104, 119
  fast nicotinic; 56
  mechanism of transmitter action; 47
  slow muscarinic; 55, 65
  substance P; 163

T

Tachykinins, see also Substance P
Tachykinins –
  biological actions; 153
  chemical structure; 152, 158
  receptors; 157
Tardive dyskinesia pathophysiological basis; 270,
  275

V

Vasoactive intestinal polypeptide (VIP) –
  coexistence with ACh; 110, 114
  dopamine and release; 245
  localisation; 43, 114, 310, 325
Vasopressin –
  localisation; 29, 329
  role in memory; 305
  receptors; 82

The articles in this book have been reprinted
from the monthly review journal

TRENDS IN
NEUROSCIENCES

This journal is available on subscription from
Elsevier Publications (Cambridge)
Department DRP
68 Hills Road
Cambridge CB2 1LA
United Kingdom

Write for details of the personal edition and library edition of
Trends in Neurosciences and our special reduced prices for
students and clinicians.